MW00611717

# Curious About Cannabis®

# A Scientific Introduction to a Controversial Plant

# 3rd Edition

Curious About Cannabis®

A Scientific Introduction to a Controversial Plant

3rd Edition

Edited by Jason Wilson, MS with content contributions from

Kyle Boyar, Noelle Joy, PhD, Stanley Hagard, Matthew Gates, Sean Hula, Jonathan Mintle, Samuel Moore, Anthony Smith PhD and others

Published by Natural Learning Enterprises, LLC

Natural Learning Enterprises is a mission-driven science and philosophy education and media company dedicated to enhancing critical thinking skills and public scientific literacy about the natural world. Curious About Cannabis is just one of many learning initiatives managed by Natural Learning Enterprises. To learn more, visit www.NaturalEdu.com

ISBN 978-0-9985728-8-8

www.CACPodcast.com | www.CuriousAboutCannabisBook.com

Curious About Cannabis: A Scientific Introduction to a Controversial Plant

Cover image photos courtesy of Adobe Stock.

# Disclaimers

# ACKNOWLEDGEMENTS

Special thanks to my wife for tolerating the exorbitant amount of time that it took me to research and write this book. And thank you for inspiring me to press forward when I considered giving up – many, many times.

This book is certainly not just a result of the work that I put into it. It is built from the foundation that so many others have laid before. Immense thanks to the Cannabis and cannabinoid researchers that have been publishing their work and publicly sharing their data to help further our understanding of Cannabis, cannabinoids, and endocannabinoids. Many researchers chose to share their publications as open-source publications that allow for sharing figures and data in this book with attribution, which has allowed this book to present a lot of critical content for understanding Cannabis science including images and figures that would otherwise have not been shared. Thank you, thank you, thank you!

Special thanks to all the amazing contributors to the Curious About Cannabis Podcast which helped me restructure my thinking on many Cannabis science topics and informed many revisions that took place in this edition. Your contributions of your time and energy to publicly share your expertise with myself and our podcast listeners is immensely appreciated and respected. For a full list of CAC Podcast contributors, visit cacpodcast.com/contributors

Special thanks to the many science educators working in the Cannabis space that actively share Cannabis and cannabinoid science research findings and interpretations with the public. You have stimulated all manner of ideas in my head and many expansions and revisions in this edition would not have happened without your contributions to spreading awareness and education.

Special thanks to my various mentors throughout the years. You have gotten me to where I am now, and I hope my work brings honor to our time spent together.

Special thanks to those of you that contributed images for the book! They have made this edition far more interesting.

And finally, immense thanks to all our Curious About Cannabis supporters. Your support has allowed us to build something great in the Curious About Cannabis ecosystem.

Thank you, all. I appreciate you, and I love you.


Jason

# Adobe Stock License IDs for Photos

| | | |
|---|---|---|
| #465808679 | #462792402 | #307282946 |
| #175202496 | #512342699 | #71633411 |
| #272575233 | #321705542 | #211845638 |
| #281812433 | #165598422 | #411021795 |
| #22630083 | #70921206 | #452079133 |
| #79834136 | #457044315 | #203116960 |
| #300523079 | #211282703 | #401495876 |
| #393191765 | #326086350 | #194920456 |
| #210745174 | #208934481 | #195261151 |
| #240403341 | #246469302 | #194688317 |
| #159122183 | #207742631 | #264649706 |
| #519677216 | #177333267 | #264649101 |
| #191931836 | #483806672 | #263749937 |
| #182207670 | #132556980 | #133011448 |
| #53031854 | #320786832 | #85140549 |
| #402682611 | #5773410 | #357021250 |
| #488407223 | #378731372 | #290839138 |
| #487408968 | #405901264 | |
| #391873132 | #227927966 | |

# TABLE OF CONTENTS

# WAIT!

This book includes links to **multimedia elements** including relevant podcast episodes, educational videos, self-paced courses, quizzes and more via QR codes found throughout the text.

To get the most out of this book, including access to course content, sign up as a Curious About Cannabis member at **member.cacpodcast.com** and have your smartphone ready to scan QR codes (like the one below) featured throughout the book.

 Most smartphone cameras will automatically detect and read QR codes if the camera app is open. There are also many QR scanning apps available for free for both Android and iOS.

Photo Courtesy of Skylar Wendel

# Chapter 1:
## ARE YOU CURIOUS ABOUT CANNABIS?

*Marijuana. Hemp. Ganja. Bud. Reefer. Mary Jane. Hash Plant. Weed.*

"It's a plant that goes by many names...

Call it what you will - it's **Cannabis**. And it's got a lot of people curious..."

Cannabis not only has many names but also many uses such as food, fuel, fiber, medicine, recreation, spiritual sacrament, and more. The plant has been utilized by human civilizations for varying purposes for thousands of years, but until recently, there was little that was scientifically known about the plant affects the human body. What little that was known was often not generally available to the public due to taboos, social stigma, and regulatory prohibition. Despite the plant's vast utility, there may be no other plant on the planet that is as controversial as the Cannabis plant.

Cannabis prohibition around the world throughout the 19th, 20th and 21st centuries has greatly limited the research that has been possible to conduct on Cannabis thus far and, as a result, consumers, producers, and curious minds have had to rely on hearsay, pseudoscience, prohibitionist propaganda, and Cannabis culture lore to learn about this plant. It is my hope that this book may help the reader transcend potentially unreliable sources of information and begin developing a more mature perspective about the Cannabis plant, its potential risks and harms, as well as its potential benefits and opportunities – of which there are many.

Our journey to understand exactly how Cannabis works and how we may be able to treat various conditions is still in its adolescent, if not toddler, years. To illustrate how young the science of Cannabis is, consider the fact that although modern research into cannabinoids (the primary active compounds in Cannabis) began around the early 1900s, it was only in the late 1990s that the concept of the "endocannabinoid system", the human body's own cannabinoid-centered physiological system was described. It

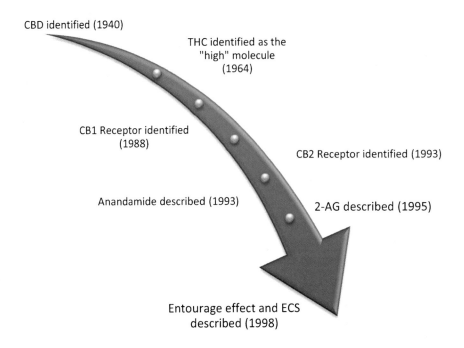

CBD identified (1940)

THC identified as the
"high" molecule
(1964)

CB1 Receptor identified
(1988)

CB2 Receptor identified (1993)

Anandamide described (1993)

2-AG described (1995)

Entourage effect and ECS
described (1998)

took nearly 100 years or more to recognize one of the most significant physiological systems in the human body. Since that discovery, we have had over 20 years to study the endocannabinoid system, which has led to incredible advances in our understanding of how the human body works.

Unfortunately, at the time of this writing, most health care workers are still unfamiliar with the term "endocannabinoid system" and medical science curricula either only briefly touch on the subject or ignore it altogether. In addition, most cannabinoid research that took place throughout the 1900s was largely focused on THC, only one of over 100 cannabinoids and hundreds of terpenoids found in the plant – not to mention the multitudes of other chemical compounds also found in Cannabis. We still have a long way to go toward understanding how Cannabis and cannabis compounds interact with the body – and that gives us plenty to be curious about!

You've probably picked up this book because you are curious about Cannabis, for one reason or another. Perhaps you are taking a Cannabis science course that uses this book as a reference text; perhaps you are interested in trying Cannabis for the first time and want to understand more about this controversial plant before you consume it; or maybe you or someone you know uses Cannabis to treat a medical condition and you want to better understand how Cannabis affects the body and human health.

Or moreover, maybe you are a dispensary worker, Cannabis cultivator, processor, or product manufacturer and you want to brush up on your Cannabis science knowledge to improve your business, product, or process. Whether you are a Cannabis novice or a well-seasoned Cannabis connoisseur, *Curious About Cannabis*® has something for you.

*Curious About Cannabis*® is intended to be a launching point for Cannabis education. The Curious About Cannabis ecosystem consists of far more than just this book, and I have made attempts to connect you with additional resources including videos, podcast episodes, and self-paced courses that are relevant to content you read. You can access this content using the QR codes that you will find distributed throughout the text. Just open your camera on your smartphone and scan a code to discover this additional content.

While this book covers a broad range of Cannabis science topics, it is by no means intended to be totally comprehensive – that would require several volumes. There are thousands of references to other reliable resource texts throughout this book to help fill in information that was chosen to be excluded. By the time you finish reviewing this text, try to answer the questions in the Cumulative Examination found in the Appendix to test your Cannabis science knowledge.

## ESSENTIAL LEARNING QUESTIONS

Use the following questions to help guide your journey toward learning more about Cannabis science using this text:

1. What is the difference between CBD and THC?
2. What are the therapeutic promises and limitations of Cannabis?
3. How have Cannabis medical claims arisen?
4. How is Cannabis consumed and how does it affect the body?
5. How long does it take for Cannabis to leave the body?
6. How do THC and CBD interact with other drugs/medications?
7. At what concentration does THC or CBD become toxic?
8. What adverse health effects might arise from Cannabis consumption?
9. What is the endocannabinoid system?
10. What is the endocannabinoidome?
11. What contaminants might be found in Cannabis products?
12. How is Cannabis tested for potency, pesticides, microbiology, residual solvents, and terpenes?
13. What sorts of challenges exist to interpreting the results of Cannabis research?
14. What are some of the environmental impacts of Cannabis cultivation?
15. How are endocannabinoids produced in the body and what roles do they serve?
16. What effects does Cannabis consumption have on driving?
17. What are synthetic cannabinoids?
18. What are semi-synthetic cannabinoids?
19. How does Cannabis use affect pre-existing mental health conditions?
20. Why is vaporization an often-preferred whole plant drug delivery system for Cannabis?
21. How do terpenes enhance skin penetration of drugs like cannabinoids?
22. What are the metabolic products of phytocannabinoids and endocannabinoids?
23. How does Cannabis use affect blood sugar and insulin levels in the body?
24. How are Cannabis extracts produced?
25. What variables affect the consistencies and textures of Cannabis extracts?

What else do you wonder about Cannabis? List some questions you have below!

_____

_____

_____

_____

_____

_____

Use the Notes section of this book to document answers to these and any other question you come up with. If you cannot find the information you need in this book, just use the references and resources listed in the appendices to find information from a variety of reputable books, articles, and websites.

Good luck on your journey exploring the science of Cannabis!

## P.S.

Find supplementary content that accompanies the content in this book by visiting the **Curious About Cannabis Virtual Campus**. Scan this QR code to jump into the Virtual Campus on your phone now!

Be on the lookout for other QR codes found throughout this book. Each one will connect you to additional content including videos, podcasts, courses and more!

**A FEW FEMALE CANNABIS PLANTS LOOK OUT INTO A NEARBY VALLEY**
PHOTO COURTESY OF SKYLAR WENDEL.

PHOTO COURTESY OF SKYLAR WENDEL

# Chapter 2:
## UNLEASH THE SCIENTIST WITHIN

*"You can Google Berberine and see what Berberine does in dozens of cell lines. But I think until you can really digest that host of data and think about it scientifically, it's not a good idea to make scientific conclusions or assumptions about any one of them."*

Anthony Smith, PhD
BTS #6 The Curious About Cannabis Podcast

**SCAN ME**

## Learning Questions

- What are some online resources for finding peer-reviewed Cannabis research articles?
- What are the various types of research that may be featured in a research article?
- What is the difference between statistical significance and clinical significance?

## YOU CAN BE A SCIENTIST

Whether you believe it or not, **you are a scientist**. Being a scientist has less to do about a career, but more to do with a state of mind. If you have ever wondered about something and sought to find an answer, you thought like a scientist. Thinking like a scientist simply involves developing questions and pursuing answers by collecting evidence through observations. Many children are *great* at thinking like scientists. Everything is new to them, and they are filled with curiosity and wonder. For many of us, that sense of curiosity and wonder fades as we grow older. But **it is not hard to start thinking like a scientist again!**

There is an activity you can try at home to try and get your mind in "science mode" again. Just pretend you just appeared where you are, and you have never experienced anything on Earth before. You are an alien from another planet. What sorts of questions would come to mind? What would you wonder about? Close your eyes and take a deep breath. Then **look around and complete the statement, "I wonder..."**

# STEPS OF THINKING LIKE A SCIENTIST

There are several steps we go through when we think like a scientist. The following should not necessarily be viewed as a linear step-by-step guide, because often we end up jumping around these steps as we acquire new information, develop new ideas, or ask new questions.

## Observation

Thinking like a scientist begins with taking the time to observe your environment around you. Let your mind wander to something that interests you.

## I Wonder...

Eventually, after observation you might wonder about something you have seen or experienced through another sense. This wonder turns into a question that can be tested. It is important that the question can be tested. *If it cannot be tested, it is outside of the realm of science.*

## Prediction

As you gather your observations, questions can develop into predictions that you can test. Scientists refer to these predictions as "hypotheses".

## Evidence Gathering

After you make your prediction, you can start to collect evidence that will assist in answering your question and testing your prediction.

## Modeling and Experimenting

You might then take your evidence and create models to synthesize the data into a form that can more easily be understood. You might also develop new experiments to test how something might work based on the models you have developed.

## Inferences and Conclusions

After you have collected your evidence and reviewed your information, you can then come to a conclusion about whether your prediction holds true. You might find that your prediction was right or wrong. You might decide you need more evidence before drawing a conclusion. Or perhaps you might learn that you do not have the proper resources to answer your question, in which you may need to get help from someone else.

## Sharing Information

Sharing information is crucial in science. If you do not have the resources to answer your question, there is probably someone else in the world that does. And in contrast, if you spend time experimenting and developing conclusions about a particular topic or idea, sharing that information can help others answer their own questions or perhaps ask better questions.

**Sometimes someone might criticize your conclusions or questions**. This should be welcomed! Science can be a lot of fun when we recognize that criticism can help us improve our thinking and make us better people for it. It makes us reevaluate our positions and potentially dive deeper into a concept to discover new and exciting ideas. Criticism is vital to the pursuit of knowledge.

# HOW TO SEARCH FOR RESEARCH ARTICLES

If you want to start to do your own science research, you need to know how to find reliable information. Peer-reviewed research journals are the best place to look for credible information on a topic. **Peer-reviewed journals** include **articles** written by experts in the field which are reviewed by peers that are also experts in the field. The peer-review committee submits changes and critiques on a proposed article which must be addressed before the article is published. This helps to ensure the quality of the articles published in the journal.

In this section, we will review a few different methods of finding peer-reviewed research articles online. You can use these methods to find papers listed in the resources section of the appendix or to find information about a topic that interests you.

# Types of Research

There are many different types of research study designs out there, with their own appropriate applications and limitations. Listed below are brief descriptions of some of the most common types of research studies you are likely to find when exploring Cannabis research papers:

- **Opinions**
  - Researchers and experts in various fields write opinion and editorial pieces occasionally for scholarly journals to weigh in on a topic of interest.
- **Case Reports**
  - Case reports or a case report series is simply a description of what one or more people experienced outside of a controlled setting.
- **Meta-Analysis**
  - A meta-analysis involves collecting data from across multiple studies and compiling them together to perform statistical analyses. Sometimes a meta-analysis may accompany a systematic review paper.
- **Literature Review/Systematic Review**
  - A review paper is exactly what it sounds like – a review of the available literature on a certain topic. These kinds of papers are great for getting introduced to a topic before diving into details. There are a lot of helpful review papers available for Cannabis research, many of which are referenced throughout this book! I often recommend that new learners start with Ethan Russo's review paper, *Taming THC* which is available free online.
- **Case Control Study**
  - A case-control study is unique in that it starts at the end, so to speak, and works backwards to determine the potential cause of an effect. This is done typically by comparing attributes between two populations, performing some basic interviews to determine behavior patterns, lifestyle choices, etc. and then the two populations are statistically evaluated.
- **Cross-Sectional Study**
  - A cross-sectional study is an observational study that looks at a population at a particular time or period of time.
- **Cohort Study/Prospective Observational Study**
  - A cohort study typically involves a group of individuals that exhibit a certain characteristic or feature some condition or treatment that are followed over time and compared to control groups that do not feature whatever characteristics, conditions, or treatments are being measured.
- *in vitro* **Pre-Clinical Study**
  - As mentioned previously, *in vitro* studies are petri-dish, or "test tube", experiments, typically involving cell cultures.
- **Randomized Control Trial**
  - RCTs are clinical trials that randomly assign participants to groups. If the RCT is blind, then the participants are unaware of what group they are assigned to. If the RCT is double-blind, then both the administrator of the study as well as the participants are unaware of who is in what

group. The double-blind, placebo controlled, randomized trial is often considered a gold standard for research because it does the best to remove human bias or influence from the results.

## WHERE CAN YOU FIND RESEARCH ARTICLES?

### GOOGLE SCHOLAR – SCHOLAR.GOOGLE.COM

Google scholar can be a great tool for beginning your search for reputable science papers. To begin, just navigate to http://scholar.google.com. There you will see a screen that looks very similar to the typical Google search screen.

There is an option here to either include patents in the search or not. Typically for searching for academic papers, you will not want this option checked.

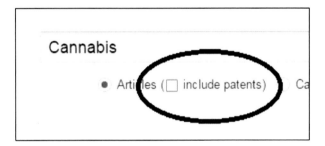

After performing your search, a list of results will appear:

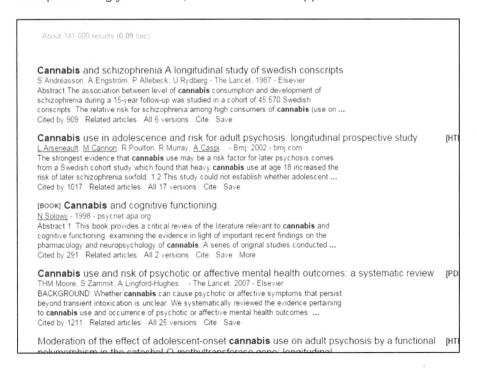

The PDF indicator lets you know that there is a PDF version of the document available online. Clicking the link will take you to the PDF where you can save and/or print the document.

Google Scholar also allows you to see "Related Articles." Clicking the Related Articles link will take you to a search results page with relevant articles listed.

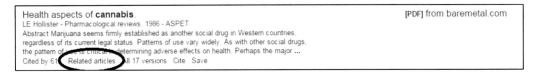

Google Scholar can be used to make collections of citations while you are performing research, so you can go back and review the various papers in your collection. It also allows you to see the various versions of the paper that have been found on the internet. It even tells you how many other papers have cited the paper you are reviewing.

## PubMed and PubChem

PubMed is an online library of biomedical research papers hosted by the US National Library of Medicine and the National Institutes of Health. Navigating to http://www.ncbi.nlm.nih.gov/pubmed will bring you to a page with a search bar at the top.

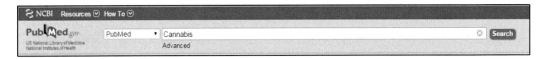

After performing a search, the following screen will appear. To narrow your search, use the options in the left sidebar. To limit the search results to only papers which are available in full text for free, choose "Free full text" under the "Text availability" sorting category. If you only want to view papers that are clinical trials, you can choose the Clinical Trial option under Article Types.

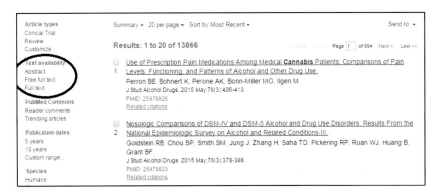

PubChem[1] is a database of chemicals that serves as a fantastic resource for gathering basic information about a compound. You can even search the PubChem database using molecular drawings. Once you find your compound of interest, you can learn about the compound's basic attributes including safety information, medical and industrial applications, patents and more.

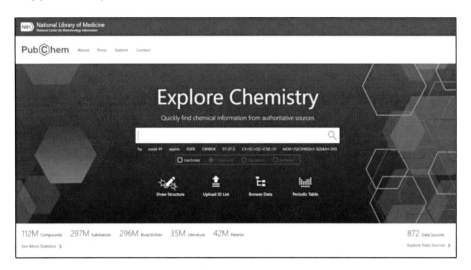

## SCIENCEDIRECT

Another great source for finding scientific research papers is the ScienceDirect database.[2] Navigating to http://www.sciencedirect.com will present a website with search options and a list of categories and subjects for browsing.

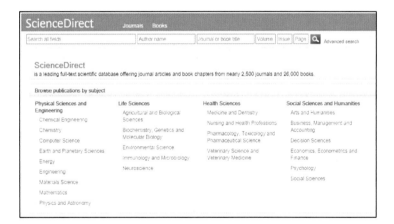

Performing a search leads to a screen very similar to the PubMed search screen. There are options to narrow your search on the left sidebar. You also have the ability to interact with multiple papers at once allowing you to buy, download, or save the citations of multiple papers simultaneously.

---

[1] https://pubchem.ncbi.nlm.nih.gov/
[2] www.sciencedirect.com

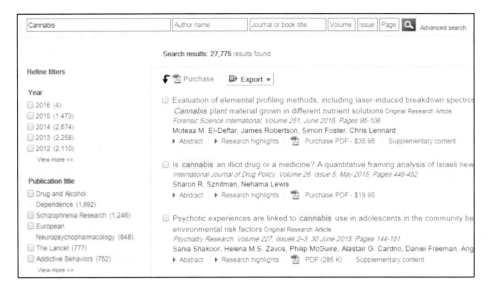

## RESEARCHGATE.NET AND ACADEMIA.EDU

If you happen to be affiliated with a school and have a ".edu" email address, you can sign up for ResearchGate.net[3] and Academia.edu[4] and gain access to free full text versions of research papers that are shared by the authors to the broader research community. When using ResearchGate, if a paper is not available, you often have the option of requesting the paper directly from the author.

## SCI-HUB

SciHub[5] is a digital repository of scientific publications, maintained by servers in various locations across the world, which provide users with access to almost any scientific paper, free of charge. All one needs to do is to search for a publication title, link, or DOI number and a PDF of the article will become available, if it is in SciHub's database.

While this is a very powerful resource that is available on the web, please note that some of the content on SciHub may be provided illegally, and anyone that downloads a pirated copy of a scientific publication could be breaking piracy laws, depending on where they are located. Because of the issue of piracy and the challenging nature of knowing whether an article on SciHub is being provided legally or not, SciHub cannot be recommended as a resource. If you choose to use SciHub, please understand that you do so at your own risk.

## HOW TO READ A RESEARCH PAPER

Reading a research paper can be very intimidating for anyone unaccustomed to the practice. A research paper comes in several primary components including title, abstract, introduction, methods, results, and discussion. There are various methods used to read and interpret research papers. The following method can be used to

---

[3] www.researchgate.com
[4] www.academia.edu
[5] Current mirror: https://www.sci-hub.se

quickly skim through papers to determine which papers are worth your time when you are trying to find out information about a specific topic:

1. Read the title and abstract to try and figure out what the point of the paper is and whether the paper is worth reading.
2. Read the introduction and determine the primary research question that the experiment is supposed to address as well as the researchers' prediction of the outcome of the research.
3. Look at the methods and results to determine if the experiment properly addressed the primary research question. What is the researcher or researchers finding(s)? What conclusions can you draw from the results? Were results statistically significant? Therapeutically/clinically significant?
4. Review the conclusion/discussion to find out what the researchers think their results mean. Do you agree with their conclusions? Does the data support their conclusions? What else needs to be known to draw further conclusions?

As you read through research papers, be prepared to look up definitions of unfamiliar terms. Research papers will also reference a variety of other research studies and articles, providing a wealth of resources to explore to gain a better understanding of the subject matter at hand.

---

## TRY THIS! CANNABIS RESEARCH ACTIVITY

Using the resources presented in this chapter, find three peer-reviewed research papers on any Cannabis science topic of your choosing. Document the titles, authors, sources, and a summary of each article.

---

# STATISTICAL VERSUS CLINICAL SIGNIFICANCE

The news media often throws around the word "significant" when referring to medical or other science research results without pointing out that scientists and mathematicians use the term "significant" quite differently than most of the public. It is important to understand significance from the point of view of a researcher to better comprehend results of research papers and understand what the results really mean in a practical sense. Researchers often talk about significance in one or two ways: **statistical significance** or **clinical significance**.

# STATISTICAL SIGNIFICANCE

**Statistical significance is a measure of the likelihood that an event is due to chance**. This value is represented as a **P value**. Research papers often list P values in the Results or Discussion sections. If you do not see the P value there, check for any tables that might be present in the paper.

As a rule of thumb, the lower the P value, the less likely the event was due to chance.

For instance, a recent study examining the effects of high potency Cannabis on white matter in the brain reported that high potency users of Cannabis exhibited higher Axial Diffusivity ($p = 0.004$) and higher Radial Diffusivity ($p = 0.04$) in the *corpus collosum* than low potency users or non-users. These p values mean that there's only a 0.4% and 4% chance respectively of these results being due to chance. These results would be considered *statistically significant*. The research did not evaluate whether this effect was *clinically significant*. And yet numerous media outlets reported on this research result touting that high potency Cannabis has a significant effect on brain matter.

# CLINICAL SIGNIFICANCE

Why is statistical significance not enough for clinicians to determine the usefulness of a research result?

The problem is that it is entirely possible for a result to be statistically significant but still fail to be of clinical significance or importance. For instance, a compound might be reported to provide statistically significant relief of pain or spasms, but if the compound only provides a small amount of relief, the result may not be considered clinically significant.

**Clinical significance is sometimes measured as a value called the Minimal Clinically Important Difference score (MCID).** The concept of MCID was first described in 1989 (Cook). It essentially refers to the smallest amount of improvement necessary for a treatment to be considered worthwhile. In his article *Clinimetrics Corner: The Minimal Clinically Important Change Score (MCID): A Necessary Pretense*, Chad Cook describes the development of this concept as such:

> *"...although statistically significant changes often occurred during use of instruments that measured change after intervention, in some cases the significant change had little clinical significance. Thus, their operational definition of a minimal clinically important difference was '...the smallest difference in score in the domain of interest which patients perceive as beneficial and which would mandate, in the absence of troublesome side effects and excessive cost, a change in the patient's management.'"*

Despite the introduction of the useful concept of MCID and other similar measures, these measures themselves have their own problems. Mostly, these measures rely heavily on reporting from patients, which can be laden with bias and error and often cannot be verified in an objective way. Another problem is that someone must define what a minimal clinically important value is. This usually ends up being the clinician.

## Reviewing and Interpreting Cannabis Research

When reviewing results from an experiment, there are some key things you can look for to determine the significance of the research results.

When reading the Results section of a Cannabis research paper, ask yourself these questions:

1) **What type of research was it?** Cell culture? Rodent? Observational? Clinical?

   There are a wide variety of types of research projects, each with unique applications and challenges. Identifying the type of research can help you decide how to proceed with evaluating the methods, results, and conclusion.

2) **What was administered?** THC? CBD? Whole plant extract? Vaporized Cannabis?

   It is rare that Cannabis research utilizes herbal Cannabis. Instead, it is common to find research which utilizes synthetic cannabinoids, isolated phytocannabinoids (THC, CBD), or formulated plant extracts. It is critical to understand exactly what was administered when evaluating the therapeutic or clinical significance of the result. Synthetic cannabinoid and isolated cannabinoid studies will not represent typical Cannabis use like studies that utilize herbal Cannabis or whole plant extracts, especially given what is now known about the entourage effect.

3) **What is the sample size?**

   An experiment's sample size will be listed as its $n$ value. The main thing to understand about sample size is that smaller sample sizes produce less reliable results that do not adequately represent larger sample sizes.

4) **How likely is the result due to chance?** What were the results compared to placebo? Has the study been replicated and if so, did the results agree or disagree with these results?

   Experimental results utilize $p$ values to indicate how likely the result is due to chance. $P$ values are typically found in the results or discussion section of the paper. The lower the $p$ value, the less likely the result is due to chance. If the value is 0.05 or less, it is generally considered statistically significant.

   If possible, search for similar experiments that have attempted to replicate the initial results, or, conversely, try to find out if the initial experiment is replicating any prior experiments and compare results. If the results agree, greater confidence can be established in the information.

5) **Is there sufficient data to suggest that the result is of clinical/therapeutic significance** or importance?

This is the hardest question to answer. Researchers can perform as many cell culture and rodent models of Cannabis and cannabinoid research all they want, but ultimately the data from these experiments never escapes a certain level of limitation in its scalability or practical applicability. It is not until research is conducted with humans, in clinical settings, with herbal cannabis and cannabis extracts, that experiments can produce results which can easily be said to be clinically significant or insignificant.

---

## Enduring Understandings

- There are many ways to find peer-reviewed research articles online.
- Care should always be taken to review the methods and results of a research article to determine if the discussion and conclusions of the article authors are consistent with the actual results.
- "in vitro" research is research performed in test tubes or petri dishes on isolated tissues, cells, or chemicals (like chemical receptors).
- "in vivo" research is research performed in animals, typically rodents, monkeys, dogs, or humans.
- The results of in vitro research or non-human in vivo research are not always directly scalable to humans and should be evaluated with caution.
- Statistical significance is a measure of the likelihood that a result is due to chance.
- Clinical significance is a measure of the likelihood that a treatment will provide therapeutic value.

# PART I: INTRODUCING THE CANNABIS PLANT

## Essential Questions to Consider

What is Cannabis?

What do the common colloquial terms for Cannabis products mean?

What is a Cannabis "strain"?

What are the various parts of the Cannabis plant?

What are trichomes and how many types of them are there?

How is Cannabis commonly propagated, harvested, and processed?

**PHOTO COURTESY OF SKYLAR WENDEL**

# Chapter 3:
## WHAT IS CANNABIS?

**Essential Questions**
- What is Cannabis?
- What products are made from Cannabis?
- What are the colloquial terms used to describe various Cannabis derived products?
- What are some technical terms that may be used as alternatives to colloquial Cannabis terminology?

*So, you're curious about Cannabis? Which Cannabis?*

**TOP PHOTO ADOBE STOCK # 320644853**
**BOTTOM PHOTOS COURTESY OF SKYLAR WENDEL**

As you should by now be well aware, **Cannabis is a plant**, and a complex one at that. It is critically important to acknowledge a fundamental truth about the Cannabis plant before we move forward. **Cannabis is not one single plant,** per se. As a plant, Cannabis can take many different forms, with very different chemical profiles, with different potential uses and applications. Cannabis grown for fiber is usually tall with minimal leaf or flower parts. Cannabis grown for resin can grow like tiny bushes or gian trees. The resin itself can feature a wide variety of chemicals that we will discuss later. The Cannabis plant can express itself in a wide variety of colors, too. Male Cannabis plants are different than female Cannabis plants (we will talk more about that later, too!)

So right from the beginning it is important that we clarify what we mean when we use the word "Cannabis." Beyond the plant itself, there are all manner of different products that can be made from Cannabis, which people may also refer to as simply "Cannabis" or "Cannabis products" but which are each also very unique.

For millennia, humans have utilized the Cannabis plant for various purposes ranging from food to medicine, fiber, and other applications. When we are talking about medical or adult-use Cannabis, we are generally talking about Cannabis that is being cultivated for its resin content, however it is important to remember that Cannabis can be cultivated for its other contributions like fiber and seed. The focus of this book will primarily be female Cannabis plants cultivated for their resin content.

It is the sticky **resin** produced around the flowers of female Cannabis plants (ideally seedless female, or "sinsemilla" Cannabis plants) that provide the characteristic effects that most people associate with Cannabis – euphoria, dry mouth, short term memory loss, appetite stimulation, etc. These sticky resins produced around the female flowers of the Cannabis plant contain hundreds, if not thousands, of different chemical compounds, which we will discuss in an upcoming series of chapters about Cannabis chemistry. The most dominant types of chemicals found in these resins are **cannabinoids** (like THC and CBD) and **terpenoids** (basically the essential oils of the plant).

Scientifically, Cannabis is often categorized into a few "types" – Type I, Type II and Type III are the most common.[6] Type I represents common THCA dominant Cannabis. This is what people typically think of as "marijuana". Type II Cannabis generally consists of a mix of THCA and CBDA. Type III plants are CBDA dominant (this would be what most people think of as "hemp"). There are two less common types. Type IV represents CBGA dominant plants and Type V represents Cannabis plants that do not produce detectable levels of cannabinoids.[7] As modern Cannabis breeding continues; we will likely see other Cannabis types added to this classification system over time.

---

[6] Small, E., Beckstead, H. Cannabinoid Phenotypes in Cannabis sativa. Nature 245, 147–148 (1973). https://doi.org/10.1038/245147a0

[7] Small, E., H. D. Beckstead, & Chan, A. (1975). The Evolution of Cannabinoid Phenotypes in Cannabis. Economic Botany, 29(3), 219–232. http://www.jstor.org/stable/4253607

*Flowering Cannabis Plant Photo Courtesy of Stanley Hagard*

| Cannabis Type | Description |
| --- | --- |
| Type I | THCA dominant |
| Type II | THCA:CBDA mix |
| Type III | CBDA dominant |
| Type IV | CBGA dominant (typically also featuring substantial concentrations of CBDA) |
| Type V | Cannabinoid free or cannabinoid deficient |

**FIGURE 1 CANNABIS TYPES BY CHEMICAL PROFILE**

Cannabis resins can be extracted, processed, and purified into a number of unique products that can have very different chemical profiles from one another, even if sourced from the same starting plant material. Ever more complexity – but it doesn't stop there.

There are a variety of different ways to get these resins or resin constituents into the body so that they can have effects. The most popular way is of course, smoking. But there are a lot of other ways to consume Cannabis, which we will discuss at length toward the end of the book. Cannabis can be consumed as pills, infused drinks, infused foods, topical creams, lip balms, nasal sprays, inhalers, suppositories, and more. Throughout this book we will discuss different issues associated with these various consumption methods, like unique contaminants you might expect to find in certain products over others, or how different types of products affect the body differently.

A TECHNICIAN STANDS BY A ROTARY EVAPORATOR AS SOLVENT IS REMOVED FROM A CANNABIS EXTRACT, PHOTO COURTESY OF ADOBE STOCK

# CANNABIS AND CANNABIS PRODUCT TERMINOLOGY

Deciphering the Vocabulary of the Cannabis Culture
Explore the content of this section in our online Learning Center by scanning the code!

If you are new to Cannabis and walk into any dispensary, you are likely to be overwhelmed by the variety of Cannabis products available. Cannabis can be found in many unique forms and formulations. On top of that, there are a plethora of words, phrases, and terms used colloquially to describe Cannabis and Cannabis products which can be very confusing to anyone that is new to Cannabis. In this section you will find a short breakdown of some of the most common colloquial Cannabis terms used in the Cannabis industry.

## CANNABIS STRAINS

In the Cannabis industry, different types of Cannabis are usually referred to as "strains." The recognized number of Cannabis strains in existence is highly disputed. The Cannabis-friendly website Leafly lists 6031 strains in their strains database at the time of this writing.[8] Although strain names are heavily used in commercial Cannabis activities and Cannabis culture, according to recent genetic research, strain names are unreliable and often do not adequately reflect genetic lineage.[9] Perform a bit of searching on the Connect[10] platform by Confident Cannabis, which allows you to explore chemical analysis data associated with a large dataset of Cannabis samples, and you will quickly find that strain names also do not correlate strongly with chemical profile. So, what gives?

These discrepancies could be for a variety of reasons. Strain names are sometimes accidentally mislabeled during cultivation, harvest, and processing. Sometimes strain names are purposefully mislabeled to enhance the value or marketability of a product.

Another reason strain names are unreliable is that it is common for strain names to follow both the sexual and asexual progeny (children) of the genetic progenitor (parent). When plants reproduce sexually by seed, genetic variation is introduced, and the progeny, or child plants, will not be true-to-type representations of their parent(s), yet they may be propagated under the same strain name as the parent. Alternatively, if a plant is reproduced asexually, as through cloning, the resulting child plant should be genetically similar to the parent, warranting an extension of the parent's strain name.

---

[8] www.leafly.com/strains
[9] Sawler J, Stout JM, Gardner KM, Hudson D, Vidmar J, et al. (2015) The Genetic Structure of Marijuana and Hemp. PLOS ONE 10(8): e0133292. https://doi.org/10.1371/journal.pone.0133292
[10] https://connect.confidentcannabis.com/

Some examples of strain names include:

| | | | | |
|---|---|---|---|---|
| "Blue Dream" | "Jack Herer" | "OG Kush" | "Sour Diesel" | "Cookies" |
| "Chocolope" | "Strawberry Cough" | "Super Silver Haze" | "Z7" | "Gorilla Glue" |
| "Trainwreck" | "Harlequin" | "Swiss Tsunami" | "Koala" | "Lemon Remedy" |
| "Vortex" | "Hash Plant" | "G13" | "CBD Therapy" | "Black Girl Magic OG" |
| "Zkittlez" | "Runtz" | "Moonshine Haze" | "Northern Lights" | "Buddha Cheese" |

A variety of biotechnology companies have begun work on sequencing the genomes of Cannabis to catalog different "strains" and better understand the relationships between them. In doing so they may be able to associate more specific genetic profiling data with strain names to make them more meaningful and reliable.

It should also be noted that the term "strain" as applied to Cannabis is generally not a scientific or technical term. As we will explore in the Cannabis Taxonomy chapter, many horticulturalists and botanists cannot agree on what the word "strain" means when applied to plants. Many researchers and cultivators of Cannabis now argue that the term "strain" should be retired in exchange for the term "cultivar", or in some contexts, "chemovar". We will be exploring these issues and arguments in later chapters. For now, just know that ultimately, when someone refers to a Cannabis "strain" they are more or less referring to a kind of brand or trade name.

# How Cannabis Products Make It To Market

**1 SOURCING GENETICS**

Cultivators must source Cannabis plant genetics in the form of seeds or clones to begin cultivating. Ideally cultivators source their seeds or clones from reputable breeders with strong stabilized genetic lines of plants.

**2 CULTIVATION**

Cannabis plants are cultivated either indoors or outdoors. Male Cannabis plants are culled while female plants are allowed to thrive as they produce cannabinoid-rich resin during their flowering cycle.

**3 DRYING AND CURING**

After harvest, Cannabis flowers are allowed to dry. Then they are stored, typically in air-tight containers, while they cure. Occasionally each batch will be "burped" to allow some of the air to exchange before resealing.

**4 PROCESSING**

After curing, the plant material is further processed to prepare it for its next step in the product life cycle. This can include additional trimming, decarboxylation, etc.

**5 EXTRACTION**

The resins in and around the Cannabis flowers is then extracted either through mechanical or chemical processes.

**6 REFINEMENT**

The resulting Cannabis extract is often refined to remove excess heavy fats and non-target chemical compounds.

**7 PRODUCT ASSEMBLY**

Once an extract has been made, it can be used as an ingredient in a finished product like an edible or topical.

**8 TESTING**

Whether the finished product is flower, an extract, or an infused product - it must be tested for potency and purity.

**9 DISPENSARY**

Upon receiving a satisfactory test result, the product may now make its way to store shelves.

# COMMON PRODUCTS OF THE CANNABIS PLANT

### FLOWERS, BUDS, NUGGETS AND NUGS

The term "**bud**" or "**nug**", short for "nugget", refers to a Cannabis inflorescence, or group of flowers. Usually this is in reference to dried, cured, and trimmed Cannabis flowers (see following image). The term "**flower**" is sometimes used as both a singular and plural term referring to collections of Cannabis inflorescences.

**DIFFERENT CANNABIS PLANTS CAN EXHIBIT UNIQUE COLORS AND FORMS**

### TRIM

"Trim" generally refers to the leaf material and small "buds" left behind after trimming a Cannabis inflorescence in preparation for retail sale. Trim contains cannabinoids and is often used to produce cannabinoid extracts or infused products.

### SUGAR LEAF

The term "sugar leaf" refers to leaf material that is densely covered in trichomes. "Sugar leaf" is often collected during the trimming process and used to produce cannabinoid extracts or pre-rolled Cannabis cigarettes.

### FAN LEAVES

Fan leaves are, in contrast to sugar leaves, large Cannabis leaves typically featuring 5 to 13 leaflets usually featuring little resin. These leaves are often cut off early when hanging harvested Cannabis plants to dry.

### SHAKE

"Shake" refers to bits of loose Cannabis leaves and flowers that fall off the buds and gather at the bottom of a container.

## CANNABIS EXTRACTS AND CONCENTRATES

Cannabis extracts and concentrates can take many different forms and consistencies. The term "dab" usually refers to a Cannabis concentrate. The term "dabbing" refers to the act of smoking a Cannabis concentrate (a dab will do you). **Dabbing** typically involves the use of a smoking device referred to as a "dab rig" which houses a receptacle that can withstand very high temperatures, often referred to as a "nail". The receptacle is heated with a torch until it is sufficiently hot. Then a small amount of Cannabis extract, or "dab", is touched to the hot surface, instantly burning, or vaporizing the product while the user inhales the resulting smoke or vapor.

These concentrated extract products come in a variety of forms and consistencies. The various consistencies of "dabs" has led to the development of unique terms to differentiate them such as "shatter", "taffy", "honey oil", "budder", and "wax" which are profiled in the following sections

Some of the variables that influence the consistency of a Cannabis extract include things like terpene content, as terpenes are often liquid at room temperature and can act as solvents for cannabinoids, as well as things like the concentration of cannabinoids that want to be solid at room temperature, like THCA or CBD. Additionally, the way that an extract is refined or handled can influence its texture or consistency. For instance, budder can be turned into badder by whipping it enough that it becomes aerated and fluffy. Additionally, extracts can be formulated, as with sauce or diamonds, where the ratio of crystallized cannabinoids to terpenes and liquid cannabinoids is altered to create a desired consistency.

The following is a chart that demonstrates the spectrum of Cannabis extract types, their consistencies, and their presumed chemical constituents. However, as with most things, there are exceptions to these rules, and formulated extracts like sauce and diamonds have been excluded from the chart to keep things simple. Sauce and diamonds would be examples of extracts that could have both high terpene content and high THCA or CBD content since the products are defined as crystallized cannabinoids soaked in a terpene rich liquid. Additionally, distillates can exhibit a wide range of consistencies, depending on chemical profile, but often it is the consistency of hot glue, which is why it has been placed in the middle of the chart.

| Dry/Wet | THCA or CBD Content | Terpene Content | Extract Type |
|---------|---------------------|-----------------|--------------|
| **Very Dry/Solid** | High | Low | |
| ↕ | ↕ | ↕ | Crystalline Isolate |
| | | | "Shatter" |
| | | | "Pull n Snap" |
| | | | Distillate (w/ terpenes) |
| | | | "Honey Oil" / "Hash Oil" |
| | | | Essential Oils |
| **Very Wet/Liquid** | Low | High | |

## KIEF AND HASH (DRY SIFT CONCENTRATES)

The term "**kief**" refers to mechanically sifted trichomes that have been separated from Cannabis flower and leaf tissue. This can be accomplished by simply tumbling Cannabis over a mesh screen placed above a collection receptacle. Sometimes the terms "kief" and "hash" are used interchangeably.

**KIEF**

**PRESSED HASH ROLLED INTO A "TEMPLE BALL"**

## BUBBLE HASH

**Bubble hash** is a form of hash produced by placing Cannabis flower in a series of mesh bags commonly referred to as "bubble bags" which are then submerged in ice water and agitated to encourage the resinous trichomes from the Cannabis flowers to break away and fall through the mesh screens where they separate by size. Larger mesh screens will collect plant particulates and allow the smaller trichome heads and stalks to slip through. The "purest" bubble hash is usually found in the lower mesh screens which typically contain only trichome heads with no stalks (the stalks are smaller than the heads and slip even further into smaller mesh screens).

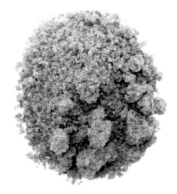

## ROSIN/ROSIN TECH

"**Rosin**" is a term referring to Cannabis extracts produced through a solvent-less heat pressing method. Cannabis material is placed within wax paper and then heated and squeezed to remove the oils from the plant material.

## HONEY OIL

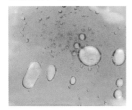

"**Honey oil**" is a term typically referring to hash oil that is light in color and runny at room temperature. The light color is generally thought to indicate purity, though this is not always the case. Honey oils tend to be rich in terpenes and cannabinoids like THC or CBDA which are more liquid at room temperature.

## TAFFY, SNAP, PULL 'N SNAP

"**Taffy**", "**Snap**", or "**Pull n Snap**" is a concentrate product with a consistency between that of shatter and oil. It is sticky, but still semi-solid, and will stretch apart like gum or taffy.

## SHATTER

Extracts called "**shatter**" have a semi-solid structure at room temperature. Shatter will usually easily break or shatter when handled. "Shatter" extracts typically have higher concentrations of either THCA or CBD, which tend to be more solid at room temperature, as opposed to THC or CBDA, which are more liquid at room temperature.

## Wax/Crumble

"**Wax**" or "**crumble**" has a light fluffy appearance at room temperature and is often orange to pale yellow in appearance. It is a "dry" extract which is brittle and crumbles when handled. Wax extracts tend to contain higher concentrations of either THCA or CBD, which tend to be primarily solid at room temperature.

## Sauce

"**Sauce**" is a hybrid product made from combining cannabinoid isolate or "diamonds" with essential oils.

Sauce is very flavorful because of the essential oils but also potent due to the crystalized cannabinoids that are mixed in heterogeneously.

## Distillate/Distty/Disty

A **distillate** is an extract that has undergone a distillation process, typically a "short path" distillation process, which is described in the Cannabis Extraction Technologies chapter. Distillate extracts are commonly referred to by the slang terms "disty" or "distty" among some circles of Cannabis extract producers.

## Diamonds/Diamond Oil

"**Diamonds**" is a relatively new term, generally referencing a product consisting of crystallized cannabinoids, soaked in essential oils, or terpenes. The THCA or CBD crystal somewhat resembles a diamond – hence the term "diamonds".

## Isolate/Zirconia

An "isolate" is a product that generally appears as a white, off-white, or slightly yellow powder or crystal which is thought to be >95% pure – generally either isolated THCA or isolated CBDA. Isolated cannabinoids are sometimes referred to as "zirconia", referencing their diamond-like appearance.

# CANNABIS TOPICALS

"Topicals" are products that are intended to be applied to the skin. Cannabis resins can be formulated into different topical products like balms, skin creams, and lotions.

## Balms

Balms are very firm topical products that are produced using high concentrations of heavy waxes. Balms do not feature water.

## Salves

Salves are soft solids at room temperature. They do not contain water and feature a heavy wax base, like balms. Salves often feature essential oils and other components which help to soften the product compared to a balm.

## Creams

Creams are products made by emulsifying oil and water together, featuring a greater concentration of oil to water.

## Lotions

Lotions typically feature water and oil emulsified together. Lotions usually contain a higher concentration of water to oil or wax.

# CANNABIS INFUSED EDIBLES

Cannabis infused foods are often referred to simply as "edibles". Common Cannabis edibles range from chocolates and gummies to sodas and hot sauces, and everything in between.

In 2021, the most common types of Cannabis edibles sold in California, Colorado, Michigan, Nevada, Oregon, and Washington were gummies, chocolate, caramels (and other chews/taffies), candy/gum, mints, cookies, and brownies.[11] Gummies were the most common Cannabis edible sold, with most packages (77.8%) containing a total of 100mg THC per package.

---

[11] https://mjbizdaily.com/led-by-gummies-edibles-keep-pace-with-growth-of-overall-us-marijuana-market/

# Cannabis Consumption Devices

### Joints and Pre-Rolls

A "joint" is a slang term referring to a Cannabis cigarette. Joints can be filtered or unfiltered, just like traditional tobacco cigarettes. Joints often contain somewhere between 0.5 to 1 gram of Cannabis, traditionally. As consumer products, joints are usually called "pre-rolls".

### Blunt

A "blunt" is a Cannabis cigarillo, also called a "'rillo", usually made by opening a tobacco cigarillo, discarding the tobacco contents, filling with Cannabis, and resealing the cigarillo. Blunts often contain anywhere from 0.75 to 1.5 grams of Cannabis, traditionally.

### Bong, Bubbler

A "bong" or "bubbler" is a smoking pipe that features a chamber that holds water which the smoke passes through before entering the user's body. It is often assumed that bongs, or water pipes, effectively filter Cannabis smoke, however research has brought that idea into question. Some studies indicate that bongs may expose users to more tar than using an unfiltered pipe or Cannabis cigarette.[12]

---

[12] Gieringer, D. 1996. Marijuana waterpipe and vaporizer study, MAPS Bull 6(3):59-66. Multidisciplinary Association for Psychedelic Studies, www.maps.org/news-letters/v06n3/06359mj1.html

## BOWL

The term "bowl" refers to a pipe's receptacle, which is generally bowl shaped. Cannabis smokers often use the phrase, "load a bowl" or "spark a bowl" to refer to engaging in the act of smoking Cannabis. A typical "bowl" usually holds somewhere between 0.25 to 0.5 grams of Cannabis.

## DAB RIG

A "dab rig" or "dab pipe" is a device specifically used for the smoking of concentrated Cannabis extracts, colloquially referred to as "dabs", as in, "a dab will do you." Dab rigs often feature significantly smaller receptacles compared to other

Cannabis smoking devices and are made of materials that can withstand the considerably higher temperatures often used to smoke "dabs". Some dab rigs feature electronic receptacles, called "e-nails" that heat up to programmed temperatures to allow for controlled vaporization or smoking.

Unlike a typical pipe, dab rig receptacles are heated *before* introducing the Cannabis product, allowing the product to vaporize or burn once it touches the hot surface.

# Vaporizer, Vapes, and Vape Pens

A **vaporizer**, or "**vape**", is a temperature-controlled device that is designed to heat Cannabis materials up to a point at which the chemicals in the plant will lightly volatize into a vapor stream, avoiding combustion of the plant material or extract and limiting exposure to tars and toxic compounds that would be found in the smoke. Some vaporizers are portable and referred to as "vape pens" or "electronic cigarettes".

## Other Terms and Concepts

### Sun Grown vs Indoor

When it comes to Cannabis flower, you will find it available in two separate categories – "sungrown" and indoor. "Sungrown" (often presented as one word) Cannabis is, as the term implies, Cannabis that has been grown outdoors under the light of the sun. Whereas "indoor" refers to Cannabis that has been grown indoors in an artificial environment under LED, HPS, Fluorescent or other types of lights. Generally indoor Cannabis is more uniform, and dense compared to sun grown Cannabis which tends to be a little more heterogeneous and less dense. In general, sun grown Cannabis is usually cheaper than indoor Cannabis because it costs much less to grow. However, if someone has severe environmental allergies to pollen and dust, sun grown Cannabis may carry more allergens and may be more likely to illicit an allergic reaction.

### Light Dep

"Light dep" is an abbreviated phrase referring to "light deprivation." Generally light dep cultivators grow Cannabis in greenhouses with retractable shades that can cover the top of the greenhouse – blocking out the light. This gives the grower the ability to send plants into flowering whenever they want by manipulating the plant's photoperiod – the amount of time that the plant receives light each day. This allows the grower to get multiple harvests per year from an outdoor crop.

### Live Resin vs Cured Resin

Live resin refers to Cannabis extracts produced from freshly harvested ("live") Cannabis material, which is typically frozen, commonly referred to as "fresh frozen", rather than dried, and then run through an extraction system. The result is an extract typically very high in monoterpenes compared to more traditional extracts produced from Cannabis materials that have already dried and volatized off some of their monoterpenes. Because of the high concentration of monoterpenes, live resins have a more pungent smell and is reported to have strong flavors during smoking or vaporizing.

The term "cured resin" simply refers to extracts produced from Cannabis biomass that was allowed to dry and cure in storage prior to extraction. While it is often claimed that it is possible to distinguish live resin extracts versus cured resin extracts by their color and fluidity, this is not always the case. While live resin extracts often feature brighter colors and a more fluid consistency, it is entirely possible to get a very similar outcome with cured biomass, depending on the extraction method.

### Nug Runs vs Trim Runs

If Cannabis buds, as opposed to leaf material, are used for producing Cannabis extracts, the extraction is considered a "nug run", referring to the use of "nugs", or inflorescences. An extraction that utilizes the trimmed off leaf material is referred to as a "trim run." It may be possible to obtain greater extraction yields using trim or "sugar leaf" due to the excess surface area available compared to dense inflorescences.

### Dank, Fire, Loud

The terms "dank", "fire", and "loud" are often used to refer to highly desirable or very **potent** Cannabis products. For instance, a consumer might comment, "That Afghan OG was super dank!" or "That Afghan OG was fire!", meaning that the Cannabis was potent and pleasurable. Potent Cannabis is often very aromatic, so someone might say, "Hey, that bud is loud!" meaning that the Cannabis smells very strongly and is presumed to be very potent.

### Decarb'ing/Activating Cannabinoids

The term "decarb'ing" is a shorthand term referring to the process of **decarboxylation**. Decarboxylation is the process of removing a carboxyl group from a molecule, often through exposure to heat or simply old age. All cannabinoids produced in Cannabis start off as cannabinoid acids, like THCA, before becoming decarboxylated and converting to their neutral forms, like THC. This process is often referred to as "activating cannabinoids".

### Pheno/Pheno Hunting

This is a shorthand term referring to the word "**phenotype**". The phenotype is the physical or morphological profile of an organism. This contrasts with genotype, which is the genetic profile of an organism, and the chemotype, which is the chemical profile of an organism. Breeders that cultivate many different plants of a strain by seed in search of varieties that exhibit desired characteristics are said to be "pheno hunting." Although it would be more correct to say they are both "pheno and chemo hunting".

### Terp(s)/Terp Juice

This is a shorthand term referencing **terpenes** and terpene products. Often this is a term used to bring attention to monoterpenoids present in Cannabis products, as these terpenes are more pungent and have stronger flavors than other heavier terpenoids.

The term "terp juice" refers to liquid lightweight terpenoids, usually in reference to particularly runny extracts like "diamonds" where the cannabinoids are not fully dissolved and well blended with the terpene fraction of the extract. "Terp juice" is also sometimes used more broadly to refer to essential oils or flavoring additives.

# ALTERNATIVES TO COMMON COLLOQUIAL CANNABIS TERMS

| Colloquial Term | Alternative Term | Description |
|---|---|---|
| **Banana(s)** | Anther | Pollen releasing structure of the male Cannabis plant, which somewhat resemble small bananas |
| **Blunt (large)** | Cannabis Cigar | |
| **Blunt (thin)** | Cannabis Cigarillo | |
| **Bong, Dab Rig** | Water Pipe | Pipe, often glass, featuring a chamber to hold water for purposes of smoke filtration |
| **Buds, Nugs, Flower** | Inflorescence(s) | Groups of Cannabis flowers |
| **Crystals, Sugar** | Trichomes | |
| **Dank, Fire** | Potent | Adjective describing desirable or potent Cannabis or cannabinoid products |
| **Decarb, Activating** | Decarboxylate | Applying heat to Cannabis products to convert cannabinoid acids (THCA, CBDA, etc) to neutral cannabinoids (THC, CBD, etc) |
| **Diamonds** | Crystalline THCA/CBD/etc | A pure cannabinoid crystal |
| **Distty, Disty** | Distillate | The resulting refined cannabinoid-rich extract after distillation |
| **Hairs** | Fused Stigma and Style | Part of the pistil that extends away from the plant to help guide pollen into the ovaries |
| **Joint** | Cannabis Cigarette | |
| **Loud** | Aromatic, Pungent | Reference to a strong odor often indicative of potency |
| **Oil, Dab, Wax, Rosin, etc** | Resin | Resinous secretions from the Cannabis plant that may be extracted and/or concentrated |
| **Pheno** | Phenotype | The physical attributes of an organism such as size, shape, color, etc. |
| **Raw Oil; Crude** | Oleoresin | A primary extract of plant essential oils and resins |
| **Strain** | Cultivar, Variety, Varietal, Form | A cultivated variety of the Cannabis plant, typically with a unique morphology or chemical profile |
| **Terp Juice** | Essential Oils, Terpenoid Solution | A solution comprised primarily of mono and sesquiterpenoids |
| **Terp(s)** | Terpenoid | |
| **Trim** | Trimmings | Whole or trimmed Cannabis leaves, separated from Cannabis flowers during harvest and post-harvest processing. |
| **Vac Purge** | Desolvate | Removing solvent or volatiles from a Cannabis extract using heat and a vacuum |
| **Zirconia** | Isolate | Crystalline cannabinoids resembling diamonds |

FIGURE 2: CANNABIS COLLOQUIAL TERMINOLOGY TRANSLATION GUIDE

# ARE YOU READY?

Let's stop and appreciate all this nuance for a moment.

Not only does Cannabis get complicated at the onset by the different forms and chemical profiles that the plant can exhibit – but also the way the plant is processed and the way that you choose to ingest Cannabis can change how it affects you.

But the complexity does not stop there. There is another piece to the puzzle – and that's your own biochemistry.

Once you ingest Cannabis, those active compounds start to do work within your body, largely at molecular targets in a critical physiological system called the endocannabinoid system, but also at other targets in other systems throughout the body. The endocannabinoid system is connected to nearly every function in the body, and as such it can influence many different things in the body. Research has shown that many disorders either result in or are caused by underlying endocannabinoid system derangements.

Toward the latter part of this book, we will explore some of the research around the endocannabinoid system and how Cannabis affects the body to try to unravel some of these complexities and make more sense of what Cannabis does to people.

If you are new to Cannabis, just covering these basics in this chapter might feel a little overwhelming. If you feel confused at this point, take some time to review this chapter again. After feeling comfortable with the basic concepts and terminology presented here, you will be well prepared to continue and dive into the details.

---

## Enduring Understandings

- Cannabis is a plant that can present itself in many forms, both physically and chemically.
- Female Cannabis plants produce resin that contains active constituents
- Cannabis resins can be consumed or administered in many ways. Resins can be consumed independently, or they can be extracted and used as an ingredient to produce infused products like edibles, topicals, transdermals, and other products.
- Cannabis products are primarily available as flower, extracts, edibles, sublinguals or topicals.
- There are a myriad of Cannabis extract products of different consistencies and formulations, each with unique colloquial names.
- There are many formal alternatives to most of the colloquial terms used to describe Cannabis and Cannabis products.
- Understanding the colloquial meanings behind commonly used Cannabis terms can help eliminate confusion for consumers, healthcare professionals and others that may be new to Cannabis.

# Chapter 4:
## CANNABIS TAXONOMY

"...We would all prefer simple nostrums to explain complex systems, but this is futile and even potentially dangerous in the context of a psychoactive drug such as Cannabis."

Ethan Russo, MD[13]

# Learning Questions

- How has Cannabis been classified throughout history?
- Where did Cannabis originate?
- How many species of Cannabis are there?
- What do the terms "sativa" and "indica" mean?
- How does Cannabis taxonomy affect consumers?

Explore the content of this chapter in our online Learning Center by scanning the code above!

What is in a name?

*Cannabis sativa. Cannabis indica. Cannabis ruderalis.*

For those readers already well versed in Cannabis lore, these names are often referred to as the three-definitive species of Cannabis. But the fact is, the taxonomy of Cannabis is not well understood or agreed upon among scientists. There has been a long-standing debate over the taxonomy of Cannabis ever since botanists and naturalists began working with the plant and confounded ever more by the chemists and geneticists working with it today. This chapter will explore the ways in which Cannabis has been named and categorized throughout history, and what modern science is telling us about the differences between Cannabis varieties.

. **Taxonomy** is a term which refers to the way that something is categorized and classified. In botany, plants are organized according to the following hierarchy: Kingdom, Class, Order Family, Genus, Species, Subspecies, Variety, Form

Botanical taxonomy utilizes a **binomial nomenclature**, or a "two-name system of naming," when categorizing and naming plants, which focuses on the plant's genus and species. For instance:

---

[13] Daniele Piomelli and Ethan B. Russo.Cannabis and Cannabinoid Research.Dec 2016.44-46. http://doi.org/10.1089/can.2015.29003.ebr

*Cannabis sativa*

> The first word refers to the **genus** of the organism and is always capitalized.
> The second word refers to the **species** of the organism and is lower case.
>> Subspecies, varieties, and forms are also written lower case.
>>> o   "ssp." = subspecies   "var." = variety or variant*   "f." = form

*varieties are only applicable to naturalized or wild-type Cannabis plants. Cultivated plants are subject to a different type of categorization that includes "cultivars" instead of true botanical varieties (more on that later).

The Cannabis genus belongs to the botanical family Cannabaceae, which also contains the genus Humulus, which are known as hops, commonly known as the plants used as bittering agents for beer. There are approximately 10 genera in the Cannabaceae as of the time of this writing.[14]

| Members of the Cannabaceae Family |
|---|
| Cannabis ("hemp", "marijuana") |
| Humulus (hops) |
| Aphananthe (evergreen trees in Madagascar, SE Asia, Mexico, Australia) |
| Celtis (hackberries) |
| Chaetachme (shrub/small tree, sometimes placed in Ulmaceae) |
| Gironniera (tropical trees) |
| Lozanella |
| Parasponia (small trees, sometimes placed in Ulmaceae) |
| Pteroceltis (blue sandalwood, indigenous to China) |
| Trema (evergreen trees, sometimes placed in Ulmaceae) |

## THE ORIGINS OF THE CANNABIS PLANT

The "original" wild ancestor of Cannabis has never been discovered, and likely no longer exists in much the same way that the original wild ancestors of many domesticated crops are no longer thought to exist.

So where did the Cannabis plant come from? This has been a difficult question to answer, but modern pollen research may provide the clues we need to retrace the spread of Cannabis throughout the world to pinpoint its origins. In 2018, McPartland et al published the results of genetic research of fossilized pollen from Cannabis and Humulus (hops).[15] They separated pollen based on the ecological environment under which they would have existed. Ancient Cannabis is associated with steppe environments, whereas ancient Humulus plants are associated with forested environments.

---

[14] Yang, M., van Velzen, R., Bakker, F.T., Sattarian, A., Li, D. and Yi, T. (2013), Molecular phylogenetics and character evolution of Cannabaceae. Taxon, 62: 473-485. doi.org/10.12705/623.9

[15] McPartland, J.M., Guy, G.W. & Hegman, W. Cannabis is indigenous to Europe and cultivation began during the Copper or Bronze age: a probabilistic synthesis of fossil pollen studies. Veget Hist Archaeobot 27, 635–648 (2018). https://doi.org/10.1007/s00334-018-0678-7

| Plant | Environment | Accompanying Plants |
|---|---|---|
| **Humulus lupus (hop)** | Forest | Alnus, Salix, Quercus, Robinia, Juglans |
| **Cannabis sativa** | Steppe (Grasslands) | Poaceae, *Artemisia*, Chenopodiaceae |

FIGURE 3: ANCIENT ENVIRONMENTS AND PLANTS ASSOCIATED WITH HUMULUS AND CANNABIS

Cannabis and Humulus are thought to have diverged approximately 28 million years ago.[16] The oldest Cannabis pollen that the researchers could identify was estimated to be approximately 19.6 million years ago from northwestern China.[17] Their results led them to posit that Cannabis may have been initially domesticated in Europe, near present-day Bulgaria and Romania, before it spread to Asia and Africa. Follow up research that was conducted after this initial pollen study showed that the origins of Cannabis likely extend back to the northeastern area of the Tibetan Plateau. It is thought that from the Tibetan Plateau, Cannabis traveled to Eastern Europe, where domestication of the Cannabis plant started to take hold, before moving to Eastern Asia and elsewhere.[18]

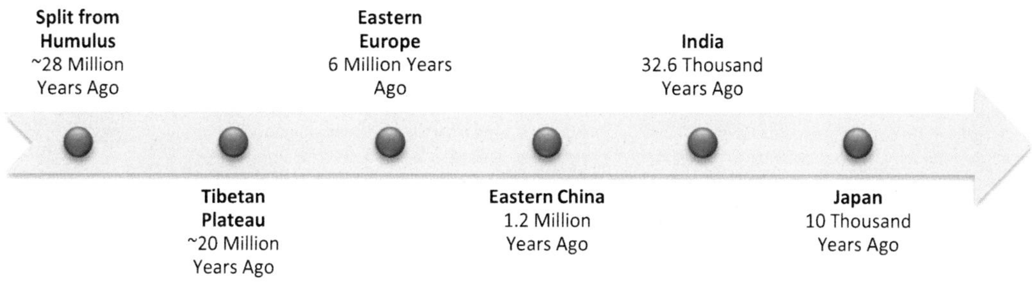

FIGURE 4: SPREAD OF CANNABIS ACROSS EUROPE AND ASIA

Cannabis wouldn't reach the Americas until more recently, in the last several hundred years. It is speculated that Cannabis may have reached South America as early as the 1500s, and North America within the 1800s.

---

[16] McPartland, J.M., Guy, G.W. & Hegman, W. Cannabis is indigenous to Europe and cultivation began during the Copper or Bronze age: a probabilistic synthesis of fossil pollen studies. Veget Hist Archaeobot 27, 635–648 (2018). https://doi.org/10.1007/s00334-018-0678-7

[17] McPartland, J.M., Guy, G.W. & Hegman, W. Cannabis is indigenous to Europe and cultivation began during the Copper or Bronze age: a probabilistic synthesis of fossil pollen studies. Veget Hist Archaeobot 27, 635–648 (2018). https://doi.org/10.1007/s00334-018-0678-7

[18] McPartland, J.M., Hegman, W. & Long, T. Cannabis in Asia: its center of origin and early cultivation, based on a synthesis of subfossil pollen and archaeobotanical studies. Veget Hist Archaeobot 28, 691–702 (2019). https://doi.org/10.1007/s00334-019-00731-8

# A Very Brief History of Cannabis Taxonomy

Cannabis was first formally classified by Carl, or Carolus, Linnaeus in 1753 in his *Species Planatarum*.[19] Linnaeus is responsible for formally applying the system of naming and categorizing organisms, like plants, that is still in use today. Linnaeus described only one species of Cannabis - *Cannabis sativa*. If you look at a listing for *Cannabis sativa*, it will usually read "*Cannabis sativa* L." The "L" refers to Linnaeus. The specimens that Linneaus used to characterize Cannabis were common forms of Cannabis cultivated throughout Europe, which today we would refer to as "hemp".

Jean-Baptiste Lamarck, a naturalist from the 18th and early 19th centuries who named well over 1600 distinct species in his lifetime, came along thirty years later and categorized a unique Cannabis plant with a sharp smell and intoxicating qualities as *Cannabis indica*.[20] Lamarck approached differentiating Cannabis types by looking at their different **morphologies,** or shapes and sizes, and their geographic ranges, while also considering their aromas and potency, or intoxicating qualities.[21] Lamarck categorized *Cannabis indica* as having more narrow leaflets than *Cannabis sativa*, which is opposite of how the terms are commonly used today. For Lamarck, *Cannabis indica* was any Cannabis plant with narrow leaflets from India (hence "indica") that were intoxicating.[22]

In 1929 Vavilov and Bukinich performed research on wild Cannabis populations in central Asia and Afghanistan.[23] They determined that there were two separate Cannabis species: *Cannabis sativa* and *Cannabis indica*. The wild variations of *Cannabis indica* were called *Cannabis indica* var. *kafiristanica*. The wild form of *Cannabis sativa* was called *Cannabis sativa* var. *spontanea*. The researchers felt that what was often called *Cannabis ruderalis* was in fact this *spontanea* variant. "Spontanea" was a term generally reserved to describe plants that had escaped cultivation.

---

[19] Linnaeus, C. 1753. *Species Plantarum* **2**: 1027. Salvius, Stockholm. [Facsimile edition, 1957–1959. Ray Society, London, U.K.]

[20] Lamarck, J.B. de., 1785. Encyclope´die me´thodique. Botanique. 1 part 2, Panckoucke, Paris, pp. 694–695.

[21] Hillig K. 2004. A chemotaxonomic analysis of terpenoid variation in Cannabis. Biochemical Systematics and Ecology. 32(10): 875-891. https://doi.org/10.1016/j.bse.2004.04.004

[22] Lamarck, J.B. de., 1785. Encyclope´die me´thodique. Botanique. 1 part 2, Panckoucke, Paris, pp. 694–695.

[23] Vavilov, N.I., Bukinich, D.D., 1929. Zemledel'cheskii Afghanistan. Trudy po Prikl. Bot. Gen. Sel. Suppl. 33, 380–382, ([Reissued 1959, Izdatel'stuo Akademii Nauk SSSR, Moskva-Leningrad]).

This sentiment would be echoed in 2004 when Karl Hillig published a paper that reported so few morphological differences were found between the so-called *Cannabis ruderalis* and the wild biotype of *Cannabis sativa* that Hillig was convinced of a two-species model for Cannabis: *Cannabis sativa* and *Cannabis indica*, with feral (wild) and cultivated varieties between each of them.[24]

In the book *Cannabis Evolution and Ethnobotany*, authors Robert Clarke and Mark Merlin explain that researcher Richard Schultes followed the work of Vavilov and Bukinich and worked to expand it, applying Lamarck's term *Cannabis indica* to a series of *Cannabis* varieties from both Afghanistan and India.[25] However, Lamarck's use of the term *Cannabis indica* was distinctively used to refer to varieties only from India, not Afghanistan. According to Clarke and Merlin, there was no evidence that Lamarck had even studied Afghan varieties of Cannabis. Schultes went on to describe *indica* varieties as Cannabis plants that were short and bushy, while *sativa* plants were characterized as being tall with wide spacing between branches – a model very similar to the colloquial "sativa" and "indica" model used in today's Cannabis culture.[26]

In 1973, Small and Beckstead broke Cannabis plants down into three different chemical phenotypes, or chemotypes.[27] These chemotypes were differentiated based on their ratios of delta-9 THC to CBD. They tried to average these ratios among plants to categorize them, but this made it impossible to distinguish the chemotype of an individual plant.[28]

In 1976 Small and Cronquist published a paper examining Cannabis taxonomy and claimed that *Cannabis indica* should be reduced to the status of subspecies, resulting in *Cannabis sativa* subsp. *sativa* and *Cannabis sativa* subsp. *indica*.[29] Then each of these was split into cultivated and wild varieties based on cannabinoid content of leaf tissues. In 1986, Robert Clarke visited the New York Botanical Garden herbarium to examine Small and Cronquist's Cannabis samples and found that varieties from Afghanistan were seemingly absent – revealing a problem with their proposed taxonomical system.[30] This problem would later be corrected in a revised taxonomy put forward by John McPartland and Ernest Small in 2020.[31]

---

[24] Hillig K. 2004. A chemotaxonomic analysis of terpenoid variation in Cannabis. Biochemical Systematics and Ecology. 32(10): 875-891. https://doi.org/10.1016/j.bse.2004.04.004

[25] Clarke, R. C., & Merlin, M. D. (2013). Cannabis: Evolution and Ethnobotany (1st ed.). University of California Press. http://www.jstor.org/stable/10.1525/j.ctt3fh2f8

[26] Schultes, R. E., Klein, W. M., Plowman, T., & Lockwood, T. E. (1974). CANNABIS: AN EXAMPLE OF TAXONOMIC NEGLECT. Botanical Museum Leaflets, Harvard University, 23(9), 337–367. http://www.jstor.org/stable/41762285

[27] Small, E., Beckstead, H.D., 1973b. Cannabinoid phenotypes in Cannabis sativa. Nature 245, 147–148.

[28] Small, E., Beckstead, H.D., 1973a. Common cannabinoid phenotypes in 350 stocks of Cannabis. Lloydia 36, 144–165.

[29] Small, E., Cronquist, A., 1976. A practical and natural taxonomy for Cannabis. Taxon 25, 405–435.

[30] Clarke, R. C., & Merlin, M. D. (2013). Cannabis: Evolution and Ethnobotany (1st ed.). University of California Press. http://www.jstor.org/stable/10.1525/j.ctt3fh2f8

[31] McPartland JM, Small E. A classification of endangered high-THC cannabis (Cannabis sativa subsp. indica) domesticates and their wild relatives. PhytoKeys. 2020 Apr 3;144:81-112. doi: 10.3897/phytokeys.144.46700. PMID: 32296283; PMCID: PMC7148385.

Other researchers disagreed with Small's approach. Emboden made the claim that the inebriant effect of a plant (i.e., THC content) cannot be a legitimate characteristic for determining taxonomic classification, thus the chemical levels of THC in the plant are completely irrelevant for Cannabis classification.[32]

Researchers looking again at morphological features of the Cannabis plant focused on the size of the leaflets between varieties. The researcher Loran Anderson would later refine Schultes' model in 1980 by stating that *sativa* plants had narrow leaflets, while *indica* plants had wife leaflets.[33] The work of Schultes and Anderson are what largely contributed to the colloquial nomenclature that is popular today – although Schultes and Anderson never intended these terms to be associated with plants of any particular chemical profile, which they stated explicitly. The idea that *sativa* and *indica* plants produce unique effects would come along later as the details of each of these different proposed taxonomical models would get confused in the minds of both lay people and researchers alike.

Along with cannabinoid-centric chemotype research, there is also taxonomical research now looking at how *terpenoid* variation might help reveal more information about how the Cannabis plant varieties should be categorized.[34] The process of examining the chemical profile of something for the purposes of taxonomical classification is called **chemotaxonomy**. The terpenoid variations among plants of known geographic origin, partnered with cannabinoid content and genetic information could help solidify the taxonomy of Cannabis.

Etienee de Meijer points out the deficits of categorizing Cannabis plants based on cannabinoid chemotypes in Chapter 2 of *Handbook of* Cannabis, *The Chemical Phenotypes (Chemotypes) of Cannabis* (2015):

> *"The great difficulty with such criteria is that [Cannabis plants] have, directly or indirectly, been subjected to human selection for ages. Furthermore, cannabinoid ratios are governed by simple genetic mechanisms and in segregating populations, or even in single plant progenies, morphologically similar plants can be found with strongly contrasting chemotypes. This makes the cannabinoid chemotype unsuitable as a taxonomic criterion."[35]   (Emphasis added)*

More recently attention has focused away from morphology and chemotypes, instead looking at the *genetics* of these varying plant types to look for **"restricted gene flow."** This means that researchers are trying to find any genetic markers that seem to belong solely to one type of Cannabis plant and not to others. Then, this might be a

---

[32] Emboden, W.A., 1981. The genus Cannabis and the correct use of taxonomic categories. J. Psychoactive Drugs 13, 15–21.

[33] Anderson, L. C. (1980). LEAF VARIATION AMONG CANNABIS SPECIES FROM A CONTROLLED GARDEN. Botanical Museum Leaflets, Harvard University, 28(1), 61–69. http://www.jstor.org/stable/41762825

[34] Hillig K. 2004. A chemotaxonomic analysis of terpenoid variation in Cannabis. Biochemical Systematics and Ecology. 32(10): 875-891. https://doi.org/10.1016/j.bse.2004.04.004

[35] De Meijer E. 2015. The Chemical Phenotypes (Chemotypes) of Cannabis. Handbook of Cannabis. Oxford University Press. Chapter 5. pp. 89-110.

means of at least differentiating the *varieties* of Cannabis plants and determining whether there may be distinct species or subspecies of Cannabis.

When using DNA evidence to support taxonomical changes, researchers also take the geographic origin of the plants into consideration, as this can help provide more information about how these genetic differences might have arisen. Knowing geographic origin can sometimes help resolve taxonomic disputes by giving researchers an idea of how various gene pools might have interacted with one another. The

> **Did You Know?**
>
> The term "**sativa**" means "cultivated".
>
> For example, the common cultivated oat is *Avena sativa*. Some researchers argue that all Cannabis is "sativa" because it has been cultivated for thousands of years, casting doubt that any true wild Cannabis plants exist anymore.

term **gene pool** refers to the "stock" of genes that are available in an organism's population. As different populations interact, the gene pools mix and change. If part of a gene pool becomes geographically isolated, gene flow is restricted, and the two pools may become substantially unique over time.

In 2014 John McPartland released details of research he and Dr. Geoffrey Guy undertook using "DNA barcoding" to determine if *Cannabis indica* and *sativa* were two distinct species. Their results revealed that they are actually one species, challenging his previous theories of a polytypic species model for Cannabis. The researchers claimed that the nomenclature of Cannabis varieties needed to be corrected so that what is currently traditionally being called "*sativa*" should instead be "*indica*", what is now called "*indica*" should be called "*afghanica*", and what is now called "*ruderalis*" should be called "*sativa*."[36]

McPartland described this new model as consisting of *Cannabis sativa* ssp. *indica*, *Cannabis sativa* ssp. *afghanica*, and *Cannabis sativa* ssp. *sativa*. The subspecies *indica* was characterized as being tall with spaced branching, containing much greater THC than CBD, and originating from India. Subspecies *afghanica* was characterized as being short, densely branched, containing more or roughly the same THC to CBD, and originating from Central Asia. Subspecies *sativa* was characterized as a mostly wild or ruderal species with a CBD content greater than THC content on average with variable morphology.

McPartland would later revise this proposed taxonomical model with the help of Ernest Small, where they posit that Cannabis truly only consists of one species, *Cannabis sativa*, with two subspecies, sativa and indica, and various varieties within those subspecies. In this revised model, all THC-rich Cannabis varieties fall under *Cannabis sativa ssp. indica*.[37]

---

[36] O'Shaughnessy's Online. 2014. McPartland's Correct(ed) Vernacular Nomenclature. http://www.beyondthc.com/mcpartlands-corrected-vernacular-nomenclature/

[37] McPartland JM, Small E. A classification of endangered high-THC cannabis (Cannabis sativa subsp. indica) domesticates and their wild relatives. PhytoKeys. 2020 Apr 3;144:81-112. doi: 10.3897/phytokeys.144.46700. PMID: 32296283; PMCID: PMC7148385.

A series of work conducted by Karl Hillig examining the genetic history of Cannabis seems to support a model similar to McPartland's proposal. Hillig's research revealed two primary gene pools in the *Cannabis sativa* lineage.[38] One gene pool seems to have started somewhere near Asia or Eastern Europe and consists of hemp type Cannabis landrace strains. The second primary gene pool includes both narrow and wide leaflet drug-type Cannabis varieties as well as a unique variety of hemp type Cannabis. This second gene pool extends from eastern Asia to southern Asia Africa, Latin America, Afghanistan, Pakistan, India, and Nepal. This data suggests that perhaps there are two genetically distinct Cannabis species or subspecies, but the narrow and wide leaflet varieties of THC-rich Cannabis are still the same species, as reflected by McPartland and Guy's DNA research. Instead, under Hillig's model, it would be hemp forms of Cannabis that fall under multiple species or subspecies.

Hillig's genetic variation research reveals two distinct gene pools of Cannabis. One gene pool (black arrows) seems to have spread from the Afghanistan region to Asia, Africa, Europe, and South America. This gene pool includes all drug type varieties of Cannabis as well as some hemp varieties of Cannabis. Meanwhile a separate gene pool (orange arrows) primarily consisting of unique hemp varieties spread to Eastern Europe and Western Asia.

## Examples of Monotypic Species Models of *Cannabis sativa*

| | |
|---|---|
| Kingdom | Plantae |
| Class | Magnoliopsida |
| Order | Rosales |
| Family | Cannabaceae |
| Genus | Cannabis |
| Species | sativa |
| Subspecies | sativa, indica |
| Varieties | sativa, indica, himalayensis, afghanica, asperrima |
| Commercial Hybrids | var. indica x var. afghanica, var. afghanica x var. indica |
| Cultivar epithets | 'GG #4', 'Koala', 'Moonshine Haze', etc. |

## Examples of Potential Polytypic Species Models of *Cannabis*

| | |
|---|---|
| Kingdom | Plantae |
| Class | Magnoliopsida |
| Order | Rosales |
| Family | Cannabaceae |
| Genus | Cannabis |
| Species | sativa, indica, ruderalis, etc. |
| Subspecies | sativa, indica, afghanica, ruderalis, spontanea, kafiristanica, etc. |
| Varieties | Perhaps distinctions between domesticated and wild-type versions of each subspecies? |
| Commercial Hybrids | ssp. sativa x ssp. indica, ssp. indica x ssp. ruderalis, ssp. sativa x ssp. ruderalis |
| Cultivar epithets | 'GG #4', 'Koala', 'Moonshine Haze', etc. |

---

[38] Hillig, K.W. Genetic evidence for speciation in *Cannabis* (Cannabaceae). *Genet Resour Crop Evol* **52**, 161–180 (2005). https://doi.org/10.1007/s10722-003-4452-y

# HOW MANY SPECIES OF CANNABIS ARE THERE?

The problem is not all scientists agree what a species of plant actually is. I know, that may sound weird. How could scientists not agree on something that seems so simple?

For biologists, "species" typically means anything that can mate and produce fertile offspring. However, geneticists and molecular biologists are challenging this definition after revealing diversity present among seemingly similar organisms once examined on a chemical or genetic level.

If we accept the typical biological definition of "species", then there is probably only one species of Cannabis, ultimately. Although Hillig revealed two gene pools in his research, it could be argued that this diversity is on a subspecies level, not the species level.

| Varying Definitions of "Species" | |
|---|---|
| **Biological Species** | Organisms that can interbreed, form viable offspring, and are reproductively isolated from other groups |
| **Ecological Species** | Organisms that can interbreed and are adapted to a particular set of resources in an environment |
| **Genetic/Phylogenetic Species** | Organisms comprising a unique gene pool, which can interbreed, and are genetically isolated from other gene pools. |

FIGURE 5: VARYING DEFINITIONS OF "SPECIES"

Although McPartland and Small presented a modern monotypic taxonomical model of Cannabis, there are modern polytypic, or multi-species, models that have been proposed as well. A recent polytypic model of Cannabis taxonomy was proposed in *Cannabis Evolution and Ethnobotany.* [39]The authors propose that there are at least two species of Cannabis, which came from a common ancestor which is either represented by some plants labeled *Cannabis ruderalis,* or plants that may no longer be in existence.

These two current species or subspecies, depending on how you define the term "species", would be *Cannabis sativa*, which represents a specific genetic pool of European hemp cultivars, and *Cannabis indica*, which represents all THC dominant "drug cultivars" as well as Asian broad leaf hemp cultivars.

Within the *indica* group, there are wide and narrow leaf varieties of THC-rich cultivars, with *Cannabis indica ssp. indica* representing narrow leaf THC-rich cultivars, and *Cannabis indica ssp. afghanica* representing broad leaf THC-rich cultivars. And among those varieties, there are feral varieties that have escaped cultivation and naturalized to their environments. This model is actually very close to the model proposed more recently by McPartland and Small, with the exception that McPartland

---

[39] Clarke, R. C., & Merlin, M. D. (2013). Cannabis: Evolution and Ethnobotany (1st ed.). University of California Press. http://www.jstor.org/stable/10.1525/j.ctt3fh2f8

and Small proposed a monotypic model and reduced all THC dominant cultivars to the ranks of varieties of the indica subspecies.

It appears more and more researchers are leaning toward embracing a monotypic model of Cannabis, as proposed by McPartland and Small, but there will likely always be camps of dissenters that provide compelling arguments for the idea that Cannabis consists of multiple species. This debate may be one that never ends.

Currently, the **Integrated Taxonomic Information System**, which provides authoritative information on plants, animals, fungi, and microbes of the world in partnership between ITIS-North America, Species 2000, and the Global Biodiversity Information Facility, recognizes only one species of Cannabis, *Cannabis sativa*.[40] *Cannabis sativa* is then broken down into two subspecies, *Cannabis sativa* ssp. *sativa* and *Cannabis sativa* ssp. *indica*. This is consistent with the taxonomical model proposed by McPartland and Small in 2020 and is likely to be the accepted model for botanists for the foreseeable future.

## A MODERN TAXONOMY FOR LANDRACE THC-RICH PLANTS

A "**landrace**" variety of Cannabis is one that has grown to be naturalized to its environment. Despite a popular misconception, "landrace strains" are *not* wild Cannabis varieties, but instead are naturalized varieties, adapted to their environment. It has been found that modern hybridized domesticate varieties of Cannabis can begin re-naturalizing and exhibiting wild-type characteristics in as few as 50 generations.[41] This is one reason why it is so difficult for researchers to determine whether any "wild" Cannabis plants exist. It is very challenging to distinguish between older landrace Cannabis varieties that are truly "wild-type" versus those that have recently escaped cultivation and re-naturalized.

In 2020, McPartland and Small published a paper that sought to formally categorize Cannabis into a new taxonomical model based on morphological, geographical, chemical, and genetic data.[42] Their focus was on THC-rich landrace cultivars of Cannabis and their hope was that a formal taxonomical system for these landrace plants will help researchers identify them in the field and contribute to preserving their genetic diversity before they are hybridized with other landraces or modern hybrid Cannabis varieties.

The following table summarizes their proposed taxonomical system for THC-rich landrace Cannabis varieties.

---

[40] https://www.itis.gov/

[41] McPartland, J. Cannabis: the plant, its evolution, and its genetics—with an emphasis on Italy. *Rend. Fis. Acc. Lincei* **31,** 939–948 (2020). https://doi.org/10.1007/s12210-020-00962-2

[42] McPartland JM, Small E. A classification of endangered high-THC cannabis (Cannabis sativa subsp. indica) domesticates and their wild relatives. PhytoKeys. 2020 Apr 3;144:81-112. doi: 10.3897/phytokeys.144.46700. PMID: 32296283; PMCID: PMC7148385.

| Cannabis sativa ssp. indica (All THC-rich Landrace Varieties) | | |
| --- | --- | --- |
| **var. indica** | Domesticated THC-rich varieties that are tall and widely branched, pleasant aroma, large seeds, THC/CBD ratio > 7 | South Asia; Colloquially commonly called "sativa" |
| **var. himalayensis** | Wild-type THC-rich varieties (THC/CBD ratio ~7) that are tall and widely branching, pleasant aroma, small seeds that easily drop | South Asia |
| **var. afghanica** | Domesticated THC-rich varieties that are short and bushy, skunky aroma, large seeds, THC/CBD ratio < 7 | Central Asia; Colloquially commonly called "indica" |
| **var. asperrima** | Wild-type THC-rich varieties (THC/CBD ratio <2) that are short and bushy, skunky aroma, small seeds that easily drop | Central Asia |

FIGURE 6: MODERN TAXONOMY FOR LANDRACE VARIETIES

It is interesting to note that the South Asian and Central Asian ecoregions for these landrace varieties converge somewhere around the borders of modern Pakistan and Afghanistan, resulting in a fascinating zone of diversity where all four of these varieties, as well as hybrids between them, may be found.

## WHAT IS A CANNABIS STRAIN? REALLY?

Beyond the indica/sativa debate, there is an ongoing debate bout Cannabis "strains". Are Cannabis "strains" all that different from one another? Or are they just brand names? Where does the idea of a Cannabis "strain" fit in Cannabis taxonomy?

The status of the term "strain" when applied to plants, especially Cannabis plants, is dubious. Generally, the term "strain" is used scientifically as a taxonomical level in microbiology for distinct types of bacteria, fungi, or viruses. For instance, genetically distinct strains of viruses, like the many variants of SARS-CoV-2, often form via mutations. These distinct strains are identified based on their genetic profile and can be tracked through DNA testing.

The term "strain" is not commonly applied in a formal sense in botany, though it does happen. Sometimes people assume that "strain" is a taxonomical rank somewhere below subspecies, however "strain" is not a taxonomical rank in botany.

When reviewing research databases like Elsevier or PubMed, you will struggle to find references to botanical strains beyond a handful of papers which focus on genetically modified and monitored plants like wheat and rice.

So, is "strain" a proper scientific term to refer to Cannabis "varieties?"

Something that complicates this issue is that formal botanical taxonomy does not quite apply to cultivated plants in the same way as it does to wild or naturalized plants. Once humans start manipulating plants to develop traits that we deem as interesting, it becomes very challenging to apply the same kind of hierarchical botanical taxonomical ranking structure that we would to wild plants. Instead, cultivated plants are classified according to a *cultonomic* scheme that focuses on traits that the culture (cult – on) deem important, rather than the traits that natural selection produced.

In the world of cultivated plants, there are several organizations that manage the way cultivated plants are named and categorized. The most relevant to the debate over the use of the word "strain" for Cannabis plants is the ICNCP – The International Code of Nomenclature for Cultivated Plants. The ICNCP is an international organization that works to standardize the way cultivated plants are named and categorized.

The International Code of Nomenclature for Cultivated Plants defines **strain** as:

*A confused term having several meanings; in cultivated plant nomenclature: often referring to a seed-raised cryptic variety.*[43]

Instead of using the word "strain" to describe unique types of Cannabis plants, some breeders and botanists suggest that the term "cultivar" should be used instead.

"**Cultivar**" is defined by the ICNCP as:

*An assemblage of plants that has been selected for a particular character or combination of characters and that is clearly distinct, uniform and stable in these characters and that when propagated by appropriate means retains those characters.*[44]

The problem here is that, while some commercial Cannabis plant genetics are stable and can be propagated consistently without losing their characteristics – others are not. It is fair to say simply that some Cannabis plants would qualify as some group of cultivars, while others would not. So, what about those plants that do not quite fit the cultivar definition set forth by the ICNCP? Should we use the term "strain" in those instances?

The ICNCP provides two solutions for us: "**cultivated plant**" or "**cultigen**"

*Deliberately selected plants that may have arisen by intentional or accidental hybridisation in cultivation, by selection from existing cultivated stocks, or from variants within wild populations that are maintained as recognizable entities solely by continued propagation.*[45]

This definition seems to fit all commercial Cannabis "varieties". These plants may be ephemeral – here today, gone tomorrow. While others may be stable and consistent. Those consistent genetic lines would be true "cultivars."

If we are to adhere to the definitions set forth by the ICNCP, it would appear that the best term to use to apply to commercial Cannabis "varieties" of unknown origin or stability in general would be "cultigen." If the plant line features "a particular character or combination of characters and that is clearly distinct, uniform and stable in

---

[43] International Code of Nomenclature for Cultivated Plants – Eighth Edition. Page 154
[44] International Code of Nomenclature for Cultivated Plants – Eighth Edition. Page 139
[45] International Code of Nomenclature for Cultivated Plants – Eighth Edition. Page 139

these characters and that when propagated by appropriate means retains those characters...", then it could be referred to as a "cultivar".

In this scheme, there seems little need for the word "strain." Given that it is widely acknowledged that the term "strain" has confused meanings when applied in botany, it would probably be best to do away with it entirely when discussing plants. However, not all scientists and taxonomists agree with this interpretation, and there are some that argue that the term "strain" should still be used to apply to Cannabis plants of an unknown background or origin, or Cannabis plants with unstable traits.

## THE CULTURAL NOMENCLATURE DEBUNKED

While researchers continue to try to categorize Cannabis, a "cultonomic" nomenclature, or culture-focused system of naming, of its own has already been established in the Cannabis culture which is due for revision. If you visit a Cannabis dispensary today, you are likely to be confronted with products labeled according to the traditional dichotomy of *sativa* vs. *indica* with unique physiological or psychoactive effects associated with each type. Many Cannabis dispensary technicians, also known as "budtenders", tend to advise consumers to use this system for identifying Cannabis products that will deliver the desired effects the consumer is looking for.

The term *Cannabis indica* is today often associated by enthusiasts with Cannabis plants featuring wide leaflets and a bushier appearance that supposedly produce "body heavy" or sedative effects whereas *Cannabis sativa* is associated with plants with thin leaflets and effects described as being more uplifting and energetic. Strains are often reported as falling along a spectrum of 100% indica to 100% sativa. A strain may be labeled as a "60% sativa/40% indica" variety, for instance, and would probably be said to be overall an uplifting variety with some pain-relieving qualities.

As mentioned in the previous chapter, strain names are not reliable indicators of genetic lineage or chemical profile. A plant's shape and size do not indicate its biochemistry. There is no such thing as a "60% sativa 40% indica hybrid" per se. Two Cannabis plants may look alike in every way and exhibit distinct cannabinoid and terpenoid profiles. Two Cannabis plants of the same strain cultivated in the same area can even end up exhibiting distinct chemical profiles. In addition, this traditional sativa/indica view assumes that the effects of Cannabis will always fall within a spectrum between only two states of being: sedation and stimulation. This characterization is an oversimplification of human experience and presents a false dichotomy.

While there *are* unique chemical differences between wide leaflet drug type varieties and narrow leaflet drug type varieties of Cannabis[46], there is little data supporting the idea that the biochemistry or even lineage of a plant can be assumed based on the morphology (size and shape) of the plant. The Cannabis plant is far more complex than the traditional view of "sativa vs. indica" supports and a new view is needed which embraces the available genetic and chemotaxonomic data and advises

---

[46] Hillig K. 2004. A chemotaxonomic analysis of terpenoid variation in Cannabis. Biochemical Systematics and Ecology. 32(10): 875-891. https://doi.org/10.1016/j.bse.2004.04.004

consumers to focus on the chemotype of a product, not the strain or indica/sativa indication.

In a 2016 interview published in the journal Cannabis and Cannabinoid Research, Cannabis and cannabinoid researcher Dr. Ethan Russo commented:

*"There are biochemically distinct strains of Cannabis, but the sativa/indica distinction as commonly applied in the lay literature is total nonsense and an exercise in futility. One cannot in any way currently guess the biochemical content of a given Cannabis plant based on its height, branching, or leaf morphology. The degree of interbreeding/hybridization is such that only a biochemical assay tells a potential consumer or scientist what is really in the plant. It is essential that future commerce allows complete and accurate cannabinoid and terpenoid profiles to be available...*

*...We would all prefer simple nostrums to explain complex systems, but this is futile and even potentially dangerous in the context of a psychoactive drug such as Cannabis. Once again, it is necessary to quantify the biochemical components of a given Cannabis strain and correlate these with the observed effects in real patients. Beyond the increasing number of CBD predominant strains in recent years, almost all Cannabis on the market has been from high-THC strains. The differences in observed effects in Cannabis are then due to their terpenoid content, which is rarely assayed, let alone reported to potential consumers."*[47]

In addition to focusing on chemical testing of Cannabis like cannabinoid and terpenoid testing, it has also been shown that organoleptic properties of Cannabis, like aroma, are significant characteristics to consider that affect outcomes.[48] Journaling can be a great way to keep track of what cannabinoid ratios, terpenoid profiles, and organoleptic characteristics your unique body responds to best.

## WHAT IS THE PROPER TAXONOMY FOR COMMERCIAL CANNABIS?

It is important to note that this taxonomical model that has been recently proposed by McPartland and Small for landrace Cannabis plants does not apply to commercial hybridized varieties of Cannabis like you would see in a medical or adult use Cannabis dispensary. Commercial Cannabis plants have been hybridized to the point that the major differences found in landrace varieties are largely no longer present.

Additionally, botanical taxonomy does not always neatly apply to domesticated crops. When we get into the world of horticulture, the categorization systems used are un-natural and generally focused on traits that humans deem interesting and have selected. This is quite different than taxonomy of wild plants which is focused on

---

[47] Piomelli Daniele and Russo Ethan B. Cannabis and Cannabinoid Research. January 2016, 1(1): 44-46. doi:10.1089/can.2015.29003.ebr.

[48] Plumb, J., Demirel, S., Sackett, J.L., Russo, E.B. and Wilson-Poe, A.R., 2022. The Nose Knows: Aroma, but Not THC Mediates the Subjective Effects of Smoked and Vaporized Cannabis Flower. Psychoactives, 1(2), pp.70-86. https://doi.org/10.3390/psychoactives1020008

*adapted* traits in the wild and is, more or less, a hierarchical system that follows traits brought about by natural selection, rather than artificial selection (for the most part).

The concept of the "**culton**" has been proposed as an alternative to the "**taxon**" concept used in botanical classification. Where a "taxon" is a particular taxonomic rank based on an evolutionary hierarchy, a "culton" would be any group of plants that share any group of traits that humans want to focus on – with little regard for concepts like genus, species, etc. In fact, once humans start artificially selecting and influencing plants, these taxonomic ranks sometimes completely break down. Some have even proposed that once we are discussing cultivars, the only taxonomic rank that matters is genus, and even then, plants can be so manipulated as to defy any recognized genus.[49]

However, if you still wanted to apply McPartland and Small's taxonomical model to commercial Cannabis, they have provided an easy way to think about it. Under this model, what Cannabis connoisseurs refer to as "Sativa" or "Indica" are hybrids between *Cannabis sativa ssp. indica var. indica* and *var. afghanica* with traits that lean toward the dominant traits of either the *var. indica* or *var. afghanica*.

| Colloquial Term | Suspected Hybridization | Description |
|---|---|---|
| **"Sativa"** | Cannabis sativa ssp. indica var. indica x var. afghanica | Hybrids of both domesticated THC-rich varieties, leaning toward var. indica traits over var. afghanica |
| **"Indica"** | Cannabis sativa ssp. indica var. afghanica x var. indica | Hybrids of both domesticated THC-rich varieties, leaning toward var. afghanica traits over var. indica |
| **"Ruderalis"** | Cannabis sativa ssp. sativa var. sativa x Cannabis sativa ssp. indica var. asperrima | Hybrids of domesticated hemp and a wild-type THC-rich variety from Central Asia |

FIGURE 7: DESCRIPTIONS OF SATIVA, INDICA, AND RUDERALIS HYBRIDIZATION

## CANNABIS TAXONOMY AND THE CONSUMER

How does all of this taxonomical debate affect the consumer?

Let's make one thing clear: all these debates about formal Cannabis taxonomy have little influence over the types of Cannabis found in the modern Cannabis industry, which is composed of intensely artificially selected and hybridized forms of Cannabis plants. The taxonomy debate is much more relevant for landrace cultivars and their wild-type forms which are reservoirs of genetic diversity that have not been touched (mostly) by modern intensive breeding. With a formal taxonomical model in place, botanists, breeders, seed collectors, and enthusiasts can ensure that underrepresented landrace genetics are collected and classified appropriately. But this doesn't really affect the common Cannabis *consumer* at all.

While researchers may continue to debate over details regarding Cannabis taxonomy, what modern researchers do agree on is that the different varieties of THC-rich Cannabis colloquially referred to as "indica" and "sativa" belong to a single species,

---

[49] Hetterscheid, W. L. A., & Brandenburg, W. A. (1995). Culton versus Taxon: Conceptual Issues in Cultivated Plant Systematics. *Taxon, 44*(2), 161–175. https://doi.org/10.2307/1222439

regardless of what we call that species, and there seem to be some chemotypical patterns between Cannabis plants of that species. Just as a single species of plant can exhibit a variety of shapes, colors, and sizes, a single species of plant can exhibit a variety of chemical profiles. Researchers also generally agree that hemp varieties display both narrow leaf and wide leaf varieties just like THC dominant "drug varieties". In addition, evidence has shown time and time again that strain names are often poorly correlated with genetic lineage or chemical profile, making their utility highly limited.

So, what does all this mean to a consumer or producer?

1. Recognize that the "indica" / "sativa" language used to describe THC-rich varieties of Cannabis is not scientifically supported and the terms are used inconsistently. Try to describe plants appropriately *without* these terms.
2. Recognize that "indica" / "sativa" labels are *not* reliable indicators of genetic lineage or chemical profile, just as strain names are not reliable indicators of genetic lineage or chemical profile.
3. Customers should focus on **chemotype**, especially CBD:THC ratios and terpenoid profiles, as well as **organoleptic characteristics** like aroma. Sometimes your nose knows best, and there is scientific evidence for it!
4. Keep an **experience journal** to track how different products, dosages, etc affect you. If you are worried about a medical condition, share this journal with a Cannabis-knowledgeable physician.

For more discussion on taxonomy, read *Cannabis Evolution and Ethnobotany* by Robert Clarke and Mark Merlin[50], the review article "Cannabis Systematics at the Levels of Family, Genus, and Species" by John McPartland[51] and the paper "A Classification of Endangered High-THC Cannabis (Cannabis sativa subsp. Indica) Domesticates and Their Wild Relatives" by John McPartland and Ernest Small.[52]

---

## Enduring Understandings

- Cannabis is currently thought to have originated from the Tibetan Plateau before it travelled to Eastern Europe where it began to be domesticated before making its way into Eastern Asia, South Asia, and Africa.
- Cannabis is currently considered by most researchers to consist of one species – *Cannabis sativa* – with various subspecies, varieties, and forms
- Cannabis "strains" should be thought of as cultivated varieties, or cultivars, in most cases. For Cannabis plants that do not have defined traits that can be reliably reproduced, they could be referred to as "cultigens" or simply "cultivated plants".
- Strain names and indica/sativa designations are not reliable in terms of genetic lineage or chemical profile.

---

[50] Clarke, R. C., & Merlin, M. D. (2013). Cannabis: Evolution and Ethnobotany (1st ed.). University of California Press. http://www.jstor.org/stable/10.1525/j.ctt3fh2f8

[51] McPartland J. 2018. Cannabis Systematics at the Levels of Family, Genus, and Species. Cannabis and Cannabinoid Research. Dec 2018. 203-212. https://doi.org/10.1089/can.2018.0039

[52] McPartland JM, Small E. A classification of endangered high-THC cannabis (Cannabis sativa subsp. indica) domesticates and their wild relatives. PhytoKeys. 2020 Apr 3;144:81-112. doi: https://doi.org/10.3897/phytokeys.144.46700 PMID: 32296283; PMCID: PMC7148385.

# Chapter 5:
## CANNABIS BOTANY AND HORTICULTURE

**SCAN ME**

## Learning Questions

- What are the various parts of the Cannabis plant?
- What are trichomes?
- What growing conditions do Cannabis plants prefer?
- How is Cannabis propagated?

### INTRODUCTION

The Cannabis plant can be a fascinating plant to cultivate, propagate, and observe. It displays dense groupings of highly irregular flower structures, bulbous trichomes, sharp serrated leaf edges, and can grow to be the size of a small tree within a single growing season (see photo).

To understand the basic biology of the Cannabis plant, it is important to cover a brief survey of general botany and soil science concepts. Cannabis horticulture deserves its own book and there are many adequate ones already in publication, so this chapter will only focus on broader botanical topics, rather than providing a "how-to" on growing Cannabis. The topics that will be covered in this chapter include general plant morphology, the components of the Cannabis plant, plant growth, plant reproduction and propagation, and basic soil science.

**FIGURE 1 AUTHOR HOLDING AN 8-9 FT BRANCH FROM A CANNABIS HARVEST**

### PLANT MORPHOLOGY

The plant kingdom is primarily broken up into two categories: **vascular and non-vascular plants**. The term "**vascular**" refers to whether the plant has a vascular system for pumping water and nutrients. The two pieces of the vascular system are the **phloem**, which transports nutrients, and **xylem**, which transports water. Nonvascular plants, like mosses or liverworts, are called **bryophytes**. Cannabis is a vascular plant.

Vascular plants are further broken down into more categories: **Seedless vascular plants, nonflowering plants, and flowering plants**. Ferns are an example of seedless vascular plants. They reproduce through spores rather than seeds. Plants that do have vascular systems but do not produce flowers are called **gymnosperms**. Conifers are examples of gymnosperms. Plants that produce flowers are called **angiosperms** (*angeion* = vessel; *sperma* = seed). Cannabis is an angiosperm.

There are a variety of different **morphologies**, or shapes, of flowering plants. The Cannabis plant is **dioecious**, meaning that it consists of two morphologically distinct male and female plants. The Cannabis plant typically does not pollinate and fertilize itself except under certain situations where the plant may become **hermaphroditic**, expressing both male and female reproductive structures, often due to environmental stress.

Instead, the male plant produces **staminate** flowers and pollen in its **stamen**, which consists of the **anther** and the **microsporangium** and **filament** (or "connective"). Staminate flowers are flowers only containing stamen, the male plant reproductive organs. Pollen is produced in the microsporangium and discharged from its anthers to begin their journey to a female Cannabis plant. The female plant produces **pistillate** flowers. Pistillate flowers are flowers only containing **pistils**, female plant reproductive organs. **Fertilization** and seed production occur if pollen successfully makes its way to the **ovary**.

In the plant kingdom, there are a variety of shapes and forms that flowers can take. Flowers can appear as single flowers or bundles of flowers called **inflorescences**. Female Cannabis flowers grow as a multiple branching inflorescence, called a **panicle**. Each branch of a panicle is called a **raceme**.

Each of the flowers of a female Cannabis plant contains a pistil, which consists of the stigma, style, and ovary. The **stigma** and **style** are fused to make up most of what is thought of as the "hairs" that extend from Cannabis flowers. The stigmas show up in pairs and are covered in **papillae** responsible for catching and guiding pollen or a pollen carrying insect into the **ovary**. The ovary is a swollen mass of tissue housed below the stigma and style, surrounded by the **calyx**.

There is debate among botanists and Cannabis enthusiasts about which tissues in the Cannabis flower are actually the calyx. Traditionally cultivators referred to the green tissue around the ovary as the calyx. More recently, however, there has been a push to refer to those green tissues as **bracts**. This is because there are small translucent tissues immediately surrounding the ovary which are often overlooked and, depending on one's perspective, could be referred to as either the corolla (these are the traditional petals of a regular flower), calyx, pseudocalyx, or the combined corolla and calyx, aka the **perianth**. If these translucent tissues around the ovary include the

**PANICLE INFLORESCENCE TYPE**

calyx, then an argument could be made that the green tissues surrounding the calyx should then be referred to as bracts.

To sort out this debate, let's refer to some well-established botanical definitions. According to the Jepson Manual, an authoritative botanical reference, a **bract** is defined as, *"1. Generally reduced, leaf- or scale-like structure subtending a branch, cone scale, inflorescence (infl bract), or sessile flower or pedicel (fl bract). 2. Generally reduced, leaf- or scale-like structure on a peduncle or scape that may or may not subtend another structure. (see bractlet)."*[53]

A **calyx** is defined as *"Collective term for sepals; outermost or lowermost whorl of flower parts, generally green and enclosing remainder of flower in bud. Sometimes indistinguishable from corolla."*[54]

Based on these definitions, it could be possible to refer to all the tissues that surround the ovary, including the translucent tissues immediately around the ovary, as well as the first set of green tissues that enclose the ovary and related tissues as a calyx. The term "calyx" need not refer to just *one* part of the flower. Alternatively, the bit of tissue surrounding the ovary could also be referred to as the **corolla**, pseudocorolla, or reduced corolla.

Additionally, the Jepson Manual definition of calyx indicates that calyces are "generally green and enclosing remainder of flower in bud." This seems to support the more traditional interpretation of Cannabis morphology. However, the definition of a bract is very broad and can refer to any bit of reduced leaf tissue that sits at the bottom of a flower, leaf, or branch. Additionally, because the calyx, as defined, can be indistinguishable from the corolla, it makes this issue even harder to agree on.

Because Cannabis flowers are irregular in their presentation, there may not be a clear answer to this semantic debate. If you decide to refer to the translucent tissues surrounding the ovary as a pseudocalyx or reduced corolla, then you could conceptually claim that the green tissues surrounding the ovary and the pseudocalyx are part of the true calyx. If you choose to refer to the translucent tissue around the ovary as including the calyx, thus making up a complete perianth, then – some would argue - you would be required to then refer to the next layer of tissues as bracts.

Female Cannabis plants are often harvested for their resin production which occurs during the **flowering stage of growth** in Fall. Once fertilization occurs, the plant puts less energy into producing resin, and puts energy into producing seeds. For this reason, Cannabis cultivators typically seek to grow "**sinsemilla**", or seedless, plants for maximum resin production. This resin contains high concentrations of cannabinoids and terpenes and is used for a variety of medical and recreational preparations. **Hemp** is a general term applied to low-THC varieties of Cannabis.

The Cannabis leaf is a **palmate** and **compound** leaf, meaning that the leaf shape is similar to that of a hand (palm) and consists of multiple distinct **leaflets**, sometimes referred to as "fingers." A Cannabis leaf can have anywhere between 3 to approximately 13 leaflets. The leaves are **serrated**, meaning that they feature a series of

---

[53] https://ucjeps.berkeley.edu/eflora/glossary.html
[54] https://ucjeps.berkeley.edu/eflora/glossary.html

notches, like the teeth of a saw, around the margins of all of the leaflets. Cannabis leaves have a unique **venation**, or arrangement of veins. The large prominent leaves of the Cannabis plant are referred to as **"fan leaves".** The leaves nearest the female inflorescence which are often covered in trichomes are referred to as **"sugar leaves"**.

*CANNABIS SATIVA* BOTANICAL DRAWING CIRCA 1900

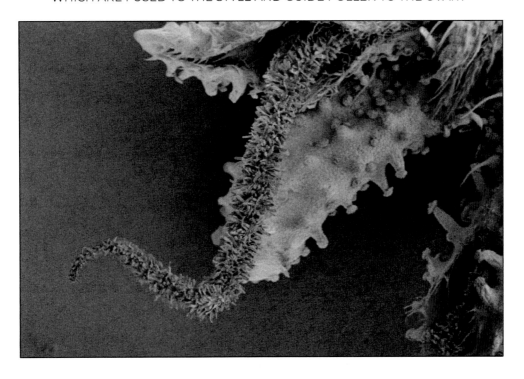

**STIGMAS FROM THE FUSED STIGMA AND STYLE ON A FEMALE CANNABIS FLOWER VIA SCANNING ELECTRON MICROSCOPY IMAGE COURTESY OF NOELLE JOY, PHD, COLORIZED BY JASON WILSON, MS**

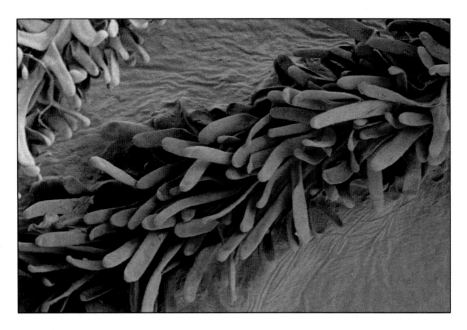

STIGMATIC PAPILLAE RESPONSIBLE FOR CATCHING POLLEN VIA SCANNING ELECTRON MICROSCOPY
IMAGE COURTESY OF NOELLE JOY, PHD, COLORIZED BY JASON WILSON, MS

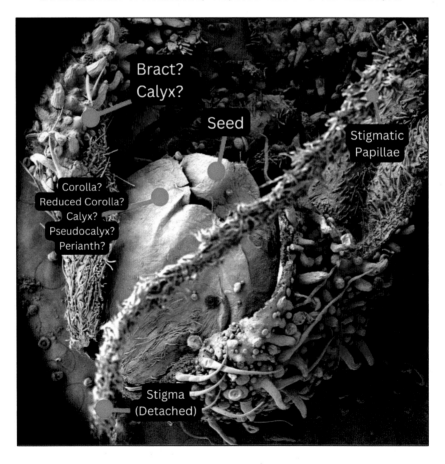

CANNABIS PISTIL WITH BRACTS OPEN TO REVEAL COROLLA/CALYX/PSEUDOCALYX AND IMMATURE SEED
VIA SCANNING ELECTRON MICROSCOPY
IMAGE COURTESY OF NOELLE JOY, PHD, COLORIZED BY JASON WILSON, MS

# TRY THIS! CANNABIS PLANT PRESSING

Traditionally, when botanists are researching plants, they create what are called **herbarium vouchers**, which feature a pressed sample of the plant as well as details about the plant and its growing environment. Whether you are studying Cannabis for fun or want to create your own Cannabis herbarium to help with your breeding or research projects – knowing how to press plants is an easy and valuable skill.

## Materials

For building the plant press
- Newspaper
- Cardboard
- Planks of wood (2x)
- Saw
- Utility straps (2x)

For collecting samples
- Cutting tools
- Permanent Marker

For creating the voucher
- Herbarium paper or alternative paper
- Adhesive
  - Hot glue recommended

## Building the Plant Press

1. Start off by determining how big you want your plant press to be. I recommend making it approximately two feet wide and three feet long, but this is completely subjective. In general, I recommend making the plant press to a size that can accommodate an entire newspaper page, folded.
2. Once you have determined your plant press size, cut your wooden boards to match your specified dimensions.
3. Cut pieces of cardboard that are the same size as the wooden boards. Start off with at least 10 pieces of cardboard.
4. Place one wooden board on the ground.
5. Stack all the cardboard pieces on top of the wooded board.
6. Place a stack of newspaper on top of the stack of cardboard.
7. Place the second wooden board on top of the newspaper.
8. Tighten a utility strap at either end of the plant press "sandwich"
9. Voila – you now have a plant press!
10. **Cheap Shortcut**: don't have the resources to make a true plant press? Just find a large, thick book that you can fit your cuttings in.

## Using the Plant Press

1. Collect a sample, whether it be part of a branch, a Cannabis inflorescence or just a single leaf, and place the sample within a folded piece of newspaper.
2. On the piece of newspaper, write the date, your initials, and any other important information, such as a cultivar name, in permanent marker.
3. Then place the folded newspaper containing the sample in between two of the pieces of cardboard.
4. Reassemble the plant press and tighten the utility straps as tight as possible.
5. Leave the sample undisturbed for several days or weeks until it has dried.

**Creating a Botanical Voucher**

1. Once the sample has been pressed and is dry, very carefully lift the sample from the newspaper and transfer to herbarium voucher paper or other media.
2. Use hot glue or some other adhesive to stick the sample to the paper.
3. Add any notes or other information that you may desire on the paper.

*Congratulations – you just made a botanical voucher with Cannabis!*

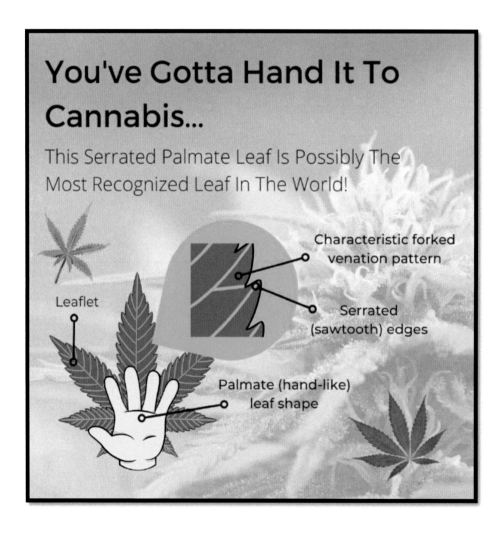

# CANNABIS MUTATIONS

Although the morphology of the Cannabis plant is so well recognized, there are several mutations that affect Cannabis plants that can render them looking quite different than we have described here. The following photos demonstrate some of the mutations that can be found among Cannabis plants.

*Mutation photos courtesy of Sean Hula of Flying Lion Research*

# TRICHOMES

Cannabis plants are one of many types of plants that produce **trichomes**. The word "trichome" is derived from the Greek word *trikhōma*, meaning "hair". Trichomes can aid plants in many ways such as trapping and disabling pests, providing insulation and protection from the elements, preventing water loss from plant tissue, or producing glandular trichomes full of chemicals that may attract pollinators or deter pests.

55

Aromatic compounds are sometimes produced in trichomes that attract predatory insects which may feed on pests. Sometimes these oils even aid in protecting the plant from bacterial and fungal diseases. The sticky glandular trichomes of Cannabis largely contain cannabinoids and terpenoids, the "active" compounds in Cannabis primarily responsible for its various physiological and psychological effects.

The Cannabis plant produces both **glandular** and **non-glandular trichomes**. Glandular trichomes feature a little ball, or head, often at the end of a stalk as seen in two of the images above. When a trichome features a glandular ball or head, it is called **capitate.** Cannabinoids and terpenoids are produced primarily in the glandular heads of trichomes. Non-glandular trichomes lack this head and resemble hairs. Trichomes can further be characterized by whether they have stalks or not. ***Capitate-sessile*** trichomes do not feature a stalk and look like droplets of dew on the plant. ***Capitate-stalked*** trichomes are shaped like the typical Cannabis trichome featuring both a stalk and head.

[55] Tanney CAS, Backer R, Geitmann A and Smith DL (2021) Cannabis Glandular Trichomes: A Cellular Metabolite Factory. Front. Plant Sci. 12:721986. doi: 10.3389/fpls.2021.721986 "Figure 1"

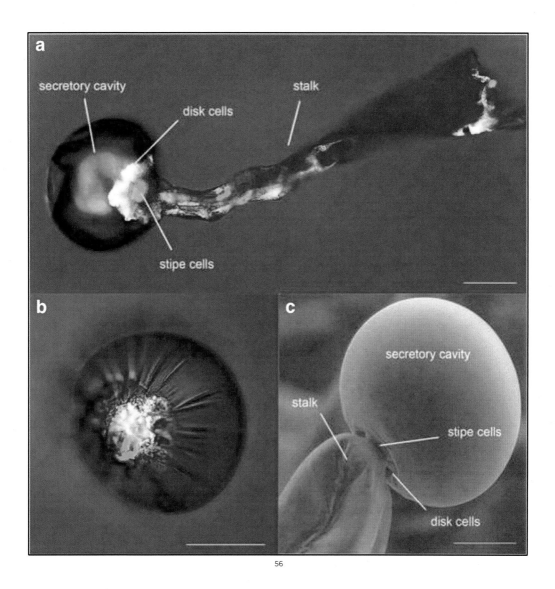

a
secretory cavity
disk cells
stalk
stipe cells

b

c
secretory cavity
stalk
stipe cells
disk cells

56

Cannabinoids and terpenoids are produced by a type of cell at the base of the glandular trichome "head" called disk cells. An organelle called a lipoplast is responsible for building lipid (fatty) molecules in cells, and in the context of glandular trichomes on the Cannabis plant, these lipoplasts help build cannabinoids and terpenoids. As cannabinoids and terpenoids are produced in the trichome "head", the secretory cavity fills up with oil, bound by the surrounding cuticle, which is made of a heavier wax that is strong and resistant to essential oils. However, if a trichome warms up enough, the cuticle can weaken causing the inner contents of the trichome to leak. This can be particularly important for producers of hash and rosin who generally want to work with trichomes that are in tact and feature weak necks for easy separation.

[56] Ebersbach, P., Stehle, F., Kayser, O. et al. Chemical fingerprinting of single glandular trichomes of Cannabis sativa by Coherent anti-Stokes Raman scattering (CARS) microscopy. BMC Plant Biol 18, 275 (2018). https://doi.org/10.1186/s12870-018-1481-4 (Fig. 3)

One particularly interesting aspect of Cannabis trichomes is that a Cannabis plant's chemistry will affect the shape, or morphology, of its trichomes! For instance, Cannabis plants that produce a lot of the cannabinoid, CBCA, exhibit mostly capitate-sessile, or stalk-less, trichomes. Cannabis plants with little to no cannabinoids produce headless trichomes. CBGA dominant plants produce exceptionally milky trichomes.[57]

| Common Types of Trichomes in Cannabis | |
|---|---|
| **Non-Glandular** | **Glandular** |
| (A) Unicellular Non-Glandular<br><br>These trichomes are the simplest trichomes, resembling small hairs with no other distinguishable features | (C) Capitate-Sessile<br><br>These trichomes appear as small spheres on the plant tissue, often said to resemble fish eggs. |
| (B) Cystolithic<br><br>These trichomes do not feature a "head" and resemble hairs with small knobs at their base | (D) Capitate-Stalked<br><br>These trichomes feature a stalk and "head" |
| | (E/F) Simple and Complex Bulbous<br><br>Bulbous trichomes are found throughout the plant but do not house cannabinoids. These trichomes produce an irregular glandular head on thin stalks. |

FIGURE 9: COMMON TYPES OF TRICHOMES IN CANNABIS

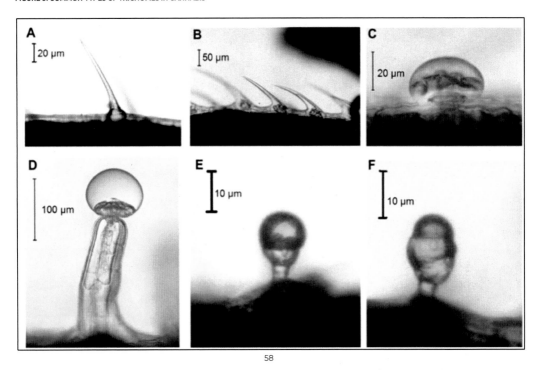

58

[57] De Meijer E. 2015. The Chemical Phenotypes (Chemotypes) of Cannabis. Handbook of Cannabis. Oxford University Press. Chapter 5. pp. 89-110.

[58] Andre CM, Hausman J-F and Guerriero G (2016) Cannabis sativa: The Plant of the Thousand and One Molecules. Front. Plant Sci. 7:19. doi: 10.3389/fpls.2016.00019 (Creative Commons Attribution License CC-BY)

Cannabis produces cannabinoids and terpenes in glandular trichomes which usually feature a stalk and a bulbous oily "head"

### Trichome Vocabulary

**Capitate** – forming a head

**Sessile** – lacking a stalk; attached at base

**GLANDULAR TRICHOME VIA SCANNING ELECTRON MICROSCOPY**
**IMAGE COURTESY OF NOELLE JOY, PHD**, COLORIZED BY JASON WILSON, MS

CURED TRICHOMES VIA SCANNING ELECTRON MICROSCOPY
IMAGE COURTESY OF NOELLE JOY, PHD, COLORIZED BY JASON WILSON, MS

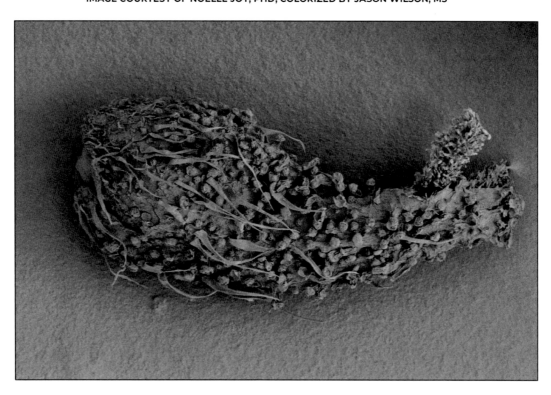

FEMALE CANNABIS FLOWER VIA SCANNING ELECTRON MICROSCOPY
IMAGE COURTESY OF NOELLE JOY, PHD, COLORIZED BY JASON WILSON, MS

GLANDULAR AND NON-GLANDULAR TRICHOMES ON A CANNABIS LEAF VIA SCANNING ELECTRON
MICROSCOPY
IMAGE COURTESY OF NOELLE JOY, PHD, COLORIZED BY JASON WILSON, MS

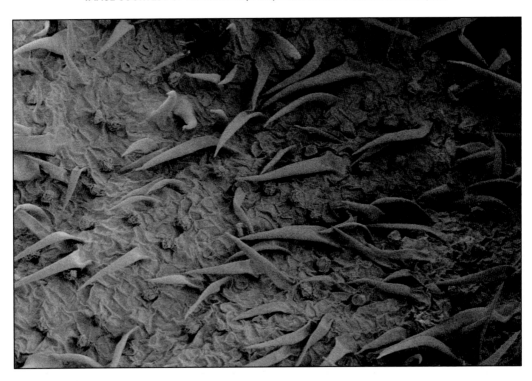

CAPITATE-SESSILE AND NON-GLANDULAR TRICHOMES ON FEMALE CANNABIS FLOWER VIA SCANNING
ELECTRON MICROSCOPY
IMAGE COURTESY OF NOELLE JOY, PHD, COLORIZED BY JASON WILSON, MS

Image courtesy of Skylar Wendel

# TRY THIS! SKETCH A TRICHOME

Have you ever looked at trichomes carefully up close? In this activity you will take what you have learned about trichomes and find at least two different types of trichomes on a Cannabis inflorescence and sketch them.

**Materials**

Resinous Cannabis inflorescence (Cannabis bud)

(If Cannabis is unavailable, any resinous plant will do)

Loupe, Magnifying Glass, or Microscope (40x or greater magnification recommended)

Pen or pencil (pencil recommended)

**Procedures**

1. First let's find a glandular trichome. Using a loupe, magnifying glass, or scope, find a glandular trichome in the form of a **capitate-stalked** trichome.
2. Sketch the capitate-stalked trichome below.
3. Are there any **capitate-sessile** trichomes around? If so, sketch and label one below in the "glandular trichomes" section.
4. Find a non-glandular trichome.
5. Sketch the non-glandular trichome below. Is it a **unicellular non-glandular** trichome or a **cystolithic** trichome?

| Glandular Trichome | Non-Glandular Trichome |
|---|---|
|  |  |

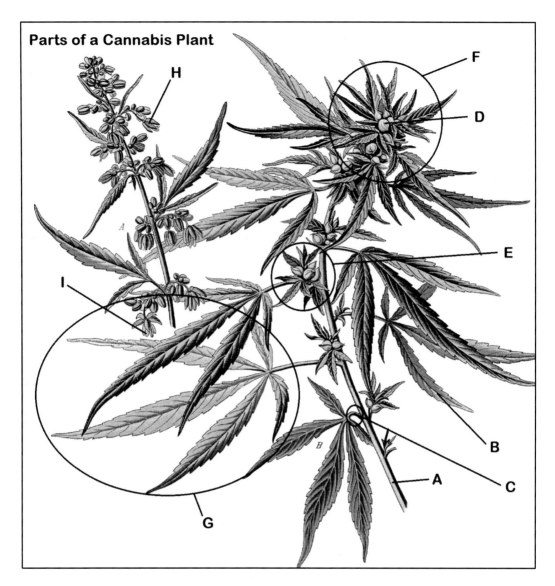

**Parts of a Cannabis Plant**

Match the following terms to the parts of the male and female Cannabis plants above.

1.___ Anther
2.___ Axillary Bud
3.___ Female Flower
4.___ Leaf
5.___ Leaflet
6.___ Male Flower
7.___ Petiole
8.___ Terminal Bud
9.___ Vegetative Shoot

# PLANT GROWTH

Plant growth begins at **germination**, when a seed receives enough water for growth. Cannabis seeds typically germinate within 15 days when regularly exposed to water.[59] The **embryo** of the seed uses the water while feeding on nutrition from the **endosperm** in the seed to begin new growth. A root with many root hairs is formed that exits the seed hull in search of more food and water. As the root makes its way into a substrate, like soil, and finds nutrients and more water, the **cotyledons**, or "seed leaves", emerge from within the seed and begin generating energy from sunlight through **photosynthesis**. Eventually **true leaves** appear, the cotyledons die off, and the plant begins to mature.

Photos courtesy of Cheryl Johnson

Plant growth occurs in regions of the plant called **meristems**. There are two different types of meristems, apical and lateral. The **apical meristem** regions are located at the tips of plant roots and shoots and are responsible for the elongation of plant parts while the **lateral meristem** regions are responsible for increasing the girth of plant parts. Plants require four things to grow: energy from the sun, carbon dioxide, water, and nutrients. When these conditions are satisfied, the meristematic regions actively grow.

Cannabis is an annual plant, meaning that it grows out its entire life cycle over the course of one year before developing seeds and dying. This is opposed to biennial or perennial plants which have lifecycles that span multiple years. The Cannabis lifecycle can be extended through a combination of **light deprivation** and **supplemental lighting** to keep the plant in a vegetative or flowering state.

Plants can be grown in a variety of ways through different growing media including **soil**, **hydroponic** solutions, and **aeroponic** solutions. Hydroponics involves growing a plant in a nutritive water solution. The plants rest in pots, filled with a non-nutritive medium like coco coir or rockwool, that are suspended over a reservoir that

---

[59] Cannabis Inflorescence Cannabis spp. Monograph. American Herbal Pharmacopoeia. 2013.

feeds the nutritive solution to the roots of the plant. In hydroponics, nutrient solutions should be between 5.2 and 5.8 pH.[60] Aeroponic systems expose roots to a nutritive solution as a vapor or mist, rather than submerging the roots.

**STOMATA ON CANNABIS FLOWER OPEN AND CLOSE TO TAKE IN CO2 AND RELEASE OXYGEN VIA SCANNING ELECTRON MICROSCOPY**
**IMAGE COURTESY OF NOELLE JOY, PHD, COLORIZED BY JASON WILSON, MS**

## CANNABIS ENDOPHYTES

All plants harbor micro-organisms within and around their tissues. These micro-organisms can alter how a plant uptakes nutrients, distributes water, defends itself against pests and more. These micro-organisms that live within the tissues of plants are called **endophytes**. Until recently, little was known about the populations of micro-organisms that live in and around the Cannabis plant. A 2020 review by Taghinasab and Jabaji organized much of the information that is currently known about the endophytes that are associated with Cannabis.[61] A summary of their findings is found below.

These micro-organisms can serve many different roles in the Cannabis plant. Some micro-organisms like *Bacillus*, *Pseudomonas*, *Pantoea*, *Serratia* and *Bipolaris* can promote growth in the plant. Many of these bacteria and fungi can attack plant pathogens under certain scenarios and may themselves act as pathogens in other scenarios. One of the exciting areas of future research for Cannabis lies in better

---

[60] Cannabis Inflorescence Cannabis spp. Monograph. American Herbal Pharmacopoeia. 2013.
[61] Taghinasab M, Jabaji S. 2020. Cannabis microbiome and the role of endophytes in modulating the production of secondary metabolites: an overview. Microorganisms. 8: 355
https://doi.org/10.3390/microorganisms8030355

understanding the roles that these micro-organisms may play in manipulating the production of secondary metabolites, like cannabinoids and terpenoids in Cannabis.

| Plant Part | Associated Micro-organisms | | |
|---|---|---|---|
| Inflorescence (Flowers, Buds) | Pantoea sp. Bacillus licheniformis | Mycobacterium sp. | Peniciillium copticola |
| Leaves | Bacillus sp. Pseudomonas sp. Aureobasidium sp. | Cochliobolus sp. Penicillium copticola | Alternaria sp. Aspergillus sp. |
| Petioles (Leaf Stems) | Acinetobacter sp. Agrobacterium sp. Bacillus sp. | Pseudomonas sp. Enterococcus sp. Aspergillus flavus | Alternaria sp. Cryptococcus sp. Penicillium copticola |
| Stems | Alternaria sp. Diaporthe sp. Schizophyllum sp. Thielavia sp. Curvularia sp. | Aspergillus flavus Aspergillus niger Aspergillus nidulans Penicillium citrinum Colletotrichum sp. | Penicillium Chrysogenum Phoma sp. Rhizopous sp. Cladosporium sp. |
| Roots | Proteobacteria: Rhizobiales Acinetobacter sp. | Chryseobacteirum sp. Enterobacter sp. | Microbacterium sp. Pseudomonas sp. Glomus sp. |
| Seeds | Pantoea sp. Bacillus sp. | Enterobacter sp. Brevibacterium sp. | Aureobasidium sp. Cladosporium sp. |

FIGURE 10: CANNABIS ENDOPHYTES

## PLANT REPRODUCTION

Angiosperms (flowering plants) reproduce either asexually or sexually. Some plants can reproduce asexually by producing clones of themselves from roots or vegetative material or by generating embryos *without* fertilization. Sexual reproduction occurs through a cycle of germination, vegetative growth, pollen production, dispersal, pollination, fertilization, and seed production. As mentioned previously, the components of the stamen produce **sperm** inside pollen while the ovary produces **eggs** in **embryo sacs**. When pollen is discharged it sometimes successfully meets a female flower's **stigma** and **style**. The pollen must then travel down the style and meet an embryo sac that contains an egg.

When the egg and sperm meet, **fertilization** occurs, and the production of the core contents of the future seed begin: **the endosperm, seed coat, and embryo**. The seed coat helps protect the embryo from harm. The embryo develops **cotyledons** in the seed, which are the first leaves of the plant that emerge from the seed. These leaves and petioles grow as they use up the nutrition of the **endosperm**. The endosperm is a bundle of nutritive material that provides just enough food to help the immature plant reach sunlight and produce roots.

In medical and recreational Cannabis production, seedless, or "**sinsemilla**", female flowers are desired, as these are more potent. When a Cannabis plant is pollinated, and the ovaries are fertilized, the plant begins producing seeds and the cannabinoid and terpenoid production is reduced. Male Cannabis plants are typically not allowed near female Cannabis plants being grown for resin production.

The following photographs on the next several pages depict Cannabis plants at varying stages of growth.

Cultivation photos courtesy of Samuel Moore.

**CANNABIS SEEDLINGS AND IMMATURE FEMALE PLANTS**

**IMMATURE FEMALE CANNABIS PLANTS,
APPROXIMATELY 2 MONTHS OLD**

**MATURING FEMALE CANNABIS PLANTS,
APPROXIMATELY 4 MONTHS OLD**

**MATURE FEMALE CANNABIS PLANTS ENTERING FLOWERING CYCLE, APPROXIMATELY 6 MONTHS OLD**

A CANNABIS FARMER RESTS BENEATH THE SHADE OF A FEMALE
CANNABIS PLANT, APPROXIMATELY 5-6 MONTHS OLD

FEMALE CANNABIS PLANTS NEARING PEAK FLOWERING MATURITY,
APPROXIMATELY 7-8 MONTHS OLD

**FEMALE CANNABIS PLANT AT FULL FLOWERING MATURITY, APPROXIMATELY 8 MONTHS OLD**

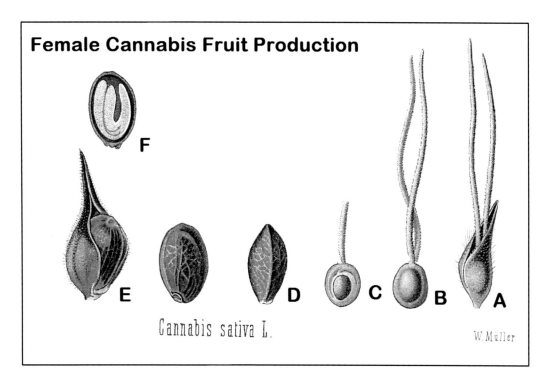

**Female Cannabis Fruit Production**

F

E

D

C

B

A

Cannabis sativa L.

W. Muller

Which of the following images represents the pistil (stigma, style, ovaries)? _____

What primary components make up the inside of a seed?

1. _____

2. _____

3. _____

What is the term used to describe the plant tissue seen in figures A and E, surrounding the ovary?

_____

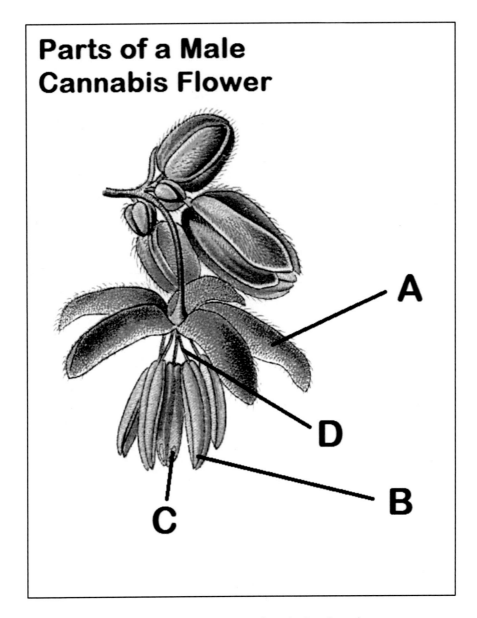

## Parts of a Male Cannabis Flower

Match the following terms to the labels above:

1._____ Anther

2._____ Calyx or Sepal

3._____ Filament

4._____ Microsporangium or Pollen

# PLANT PROPAGATION

Cannabis plants can be propagated a variety of ways. Plant **propagation** refers to how plants are perpetuated. Plants can typically be propagated via seed, cuttings, layering, grafting, and micropropagation. Each method has its advantages and disadvantages depending on what the grower desires.

## SEXUAL PROPAGATION: SEEDS

**Seed propagation** is a sexual form of propagation and usually involves farms that are totally dedicated to seed production. These farms keep crops far apart from other crops that might cross-pollinate with each other. Often bags are placed over the male flowers to collect their pollen and avoid airborne pollen. Pollen from one plant will be collected and manually introduced to female plants to breed and create hybrid plants, or "crosses."

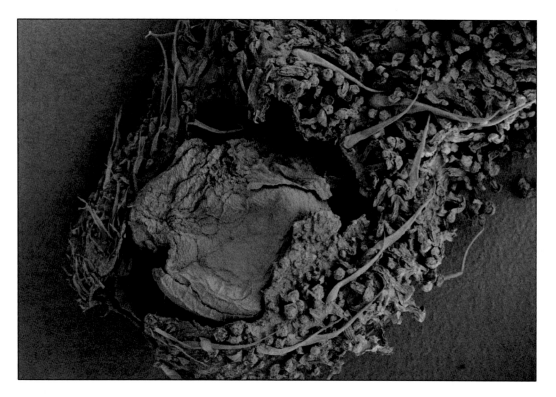

**IMMATURE SEED INSIDE OF A FEMALE CANNABIS FLOWER VIA SCANNING ELECTRON MICROSCOPY**
**IMAGE COURTESY OF NOELLE JOY, PHD, COLORIZED BY JASON WILSON, MS**

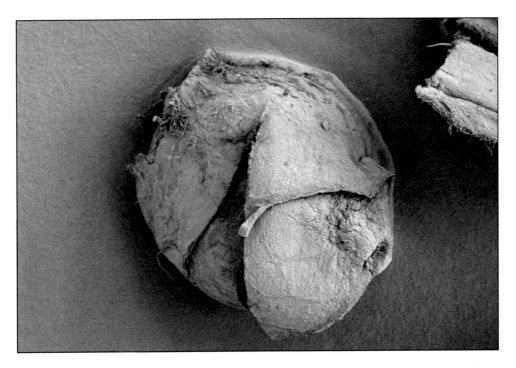

**CANNABIS SEED VIA SCANNING ELECTRON MICROSCOPY**
**IMAGE COURTESY OF NOELLE JOY, PHD, COLORIZED BY JASON WILSON, MS**

Photos courtesy of Cheryl Johnson

## Did You Know?

Cannabis seeds are highly nutritious, containing all the essential amino acids our bodies need but cannot produce on their own!

# TRY THIS! GERMINATING CANNABIS SEEDS

Want to see the magic of seed propagation yourself? Try germinating some seeds! This simple method is reliable and allows you to see all the changes happening in the seeds close up. Keep in mind that there are many ways to germinate seeds – this is just one simple way that allows for easy observation. Other methods that many people utilize include placing seeds in moistened peat pellets, placing seeds directly in water until germination, or even just directly sowing seeds into soil.

**DISCLAIMER**: Check your local laws before attempting this activity to avoid breaking any laws. Germinating Cannabis seeds may be illegal where you live. If you are in the United States, it is recommended to perform this activity with Cannabis seeds that are legally classified as hemp. Neither the author nor the publisher of Curious About Cannabis™ are responsible for any illegal activities performed, either intentionally or unintentionally.

## Materials

| | | |
|---|---|---|
| Cannabis Seeds | Paper Towel | Water |
| Ziplock Bag | Scope or Jeweler's Loupe | |

## Procedures

1. Moisten the paper towel and squeeze out excess water. The paper towel should be very moist, but not excessively dripping with water.
2. Place the seeds in the paper towel, leaving equal spacing between them.
3. Fold the paper towel over the seeds.
4. Place the folded paper towel into a plastic bag and seal approximately 80 to 90%. The bag should breathe a little, but overall should keep most of the moisture within the bag.
5. Place the plastic bag in a dark, warm area for 48 hours
6. Check the seeds for signs of germination. Use a scope or loupe to see the seeds up close.

Congratulations! You just germinated Cannabis seeds and began the process of life! What will you do now?

# ASEXUAL PROPAGATION: CLONING

**Cloning** involves propagating plants asexually either through **cuttings, layering, grafting**, or **micropropagation**. The **cutting** method of cloning involves cutting off a stem from a parent plant, introducing that stem to growth hormones that will stimulate root growth, and allowing the cutting to rest, heal, and grow in a well-maintained environment called a "rooting chamber" until it develops its own root system and can be transplanted.

**Layering** involves bending a branch of a plant down to the ground, covering it with soil, and coaxing it to produce roots before severing it from the parent plant. This only works with certain kinds of plants but rarely is used for Cannabis propagation. **Grafting** involves taking a vegetative shoot from one plant and connecting it to the root stock of another plant, fusing the two together into one plant. Grafting can be difficult and many times the two plants will not adopt each other. This is not a common propagation method for Cannabis.

All the previous mentioned methods of cloning have a major disadvantage in that they also propagate plant pathogens and other unfavorable traits. Clones from traditional propagation methods usually do not result in true clones and multiple cloning through generations can cause various mutations and genetic deviations. These drawbacks can be avoided using **micropropagation**. Micropropagation, through a process called **tissue culture,** involves harvesting meristem regions (regions of active growth) from the plant and growing clones from that tissue in sterile environments.

Typically, the apical bud is used for tissue culturing plants. All excess plant matter is removed, and the remaining bits of tissue are washed and transferred to a sterile nutritive growing medium. Once the plant develops in the sterile environment and develops a root system, it can be acclimated to the outdoor or indoor growing environment before finally becoming established in soil or another growing medium.

**Tissue culture** has some advantages over other methods of cloning. Tissue culture provides greater genetic stability between clones. It can produce high quantities of plants in a small area using very little starting material from a parent plant. A major disadvantage, as with all methods of asexual propagation, is that genetic diversity is reduced in the plant populations. If a disease or pest were to affect one plant, it would most likely affect all the plants. This can lead to total crop failure quickly. Genetic diversity through seed propagation is an effective way to minimize this effect.

Another disadvantage of micropropagation involves getting the clones acclimated to the outdoor environment. Because the plants are initially grown in very humid environments in containers, their **stomata**, or gas exchange pores, are not trained to close to hold water in the plant's tissues. Tissue culture plants must go through a delicate "hardening off" phase before fully transitioning to outdoor conditions.

# CANNABIS GROWING, HARVESTING, AND STORAGE

While Cannabis can thrive in a variety of conditions, it does seem to have some preferences. Cannabis reportedly grows best in soils that have a pH between 6.5 – 7.2 (neutral to alkaline) with a clay and loamy soil texture. The soil should be able to hold water while allowing excess water to drain. If growing hydroponically, the pH of the nutritive solution should be 5.2 to 6. Cannabis plants prefer approximately 18 hours of light (6-8 hours of darkness) during their vegetative growth phase. This is easily satisfied throughout the late spring and summer months outdoors in many areas throughout the world.

Cannabis typically begins to enter flowering when plants are exposed to approximately 12 hours of darkness. Cannabis plants that are "**autoflowering**" will proceed to flower regardless of light cycle (see section "Exceptions to the Rule: Autoflowering Cannabis" for more information).

In indoor growing, lights are automated to mimic the natural light cycle that would occur in Fall as the season transitions toward winter and the days get shorter. Actual harvest times can be optimized according to the desired chemical profile of the plant. Regularly monitoring of cannabinoids and terpenes can help optimize harvest to achieve desired chemical profiles. Optimal harvest times are sometimes determined by the browning and senescence of three quarters of the stigmas on the plant.[62]

*"Light absorption by chlorophyll A peaks at 430 nm in the blue band and 662nm in the red, and chlorophyll B peaks at 453 nm in the blue and 642 nm in the orange-red bands. Chlorophyll synthesis peaks at 435 nm and 445 nm in the blue spectrum and 640 and 675 nm in the red wavelengths."[63]*

Prior to cultivation, any soil or water used for growing Cannabis should be tested for pesticides and heavy metals to ensure the plant will not bioaccumulate these contaminants.

Seed cultivation usually begins between March and April in the northern hemisphere. It takes approximately eight weeks from seed for Cannabis plants to show their complete sexual characteristics so that males can be separated from females should pollination not be desired, as is the case in medicinal Cannabis flower production. The plant then takes approximately 6 to 8 months to reach full maturity before flowering.[64]

The cannabinoid content of the plant reaches its peak when flowers are in full bud and will typically maintain that peak for approximately two or three weeks. Both genetic and environmental conditions affect the concentration of active compounds in the plant resins. This may result in a greater diversity of chemical profiles present among plants cultivated outdoors than indoors.

When growing indoors, Cannabis growth and yield can sometimes be enhanced by increasing the ambient carbon dioxide in the room. While small increases in carbon dioxide do not stimulate photosynthesis or water use efficiency very much, nearly doubling the ambient carbon dioxide levels *does* have a significant effect,

---

[62] Cannabis Inflorescence Cannabis spp. Monograph. American Herbal Pharmacopoeia. 2013.
[63] Ed Rosenthal's Marijuana Grower's Handbook website; http://mjgrowers.com/book_what_light.htm
[64] Cannabis Inflorescence Cannabis spp. Monograph. American Herbal Pharmacopoeia. 2013.

although this effect may differ between cultivars. There is also scientific debate over whether these enhanced growth effects are long lasting or not.[65]

Generally, immature Cannabis plants can thrive in humid conditions (~75% humidity) but require lower humidity levels at maturity (~55-60% humidity), otherwise risking mold growth. According to the American Herbal Pharmacopeia, when drying, a humidity level of approximately 30% is ideal and drying should continue until the plant material is approximately 25% of its starting weight.[66] Seasoned Cannabis cultivators often report drying at humidity levels between 40-60% until stems snap cleanly.

CANNABIS HANGING TO DRY | PHOTOS COURTESY OF ADOBE STOCK

Cannabis must be stored properly to protect it from air and light, which lead to the degradation of cannabinoids, like THC. THCA steadily decarboxylates to THC during storage[67], however, one study showed that after one year of storage, approximately 90% of the original THC was still intact. Excessive handling of Cannabis material will expose trichomes to air and light, leading to oxidation and chemical degradation.[68] Cannabis

[65] Chandra, Suman; Lata, Hemant; Khan, Ikhlas A.; ElSohly, Mahmoud A. Photosynthetic response of Cannabis sativa L., an important medicinal plant, to elevated levels of CO2. Physiology and Molecular Biology of Plants. Vol. 17 (3). JUL 2011. 291-295 https://doi.org/10.1007%2Fs12298-011-0066-6

[66] Cannabis Inflorescence Cannabis spp. Monograph. American Herbal Pharmacopoeia. 2013.

[67] Cannabis Inflorescence Cannabis spp. Monograph. American Herbal Pharmacopoeia. 2013.

[68] Cannabis Inflorescence Cannabis spp. Monograph. American Herbal Pharmacopoeia. 2013.

can be stored at temperatures up to 20 degrees Celsius without causing significant changes to the THC content of the material.[69]

## SAFETY CONCERNS IN CULTIVATION OPERATIONS

Like any work environment, Cannabis cultivation, harvesting and processing comes with certain risks that are important to acknowledge. Throughout the plant's lifecycle, growers and workers can be exposed to pollen, dust, spores, and airborne micro-organisms. When the plants are flowering, they release a lot of volatile organic compounds into the air. As these VOCs oxidize, they become irritants. With repeated exposure, VOCs can cause sensitization of the airways and lungs to the point that even modest exposure can trigger adverse events including coughing, difficulty breathing, headaches, and dizziness. Exposures are worst when the plants are being handled, as during harvesting, bucking, and trimming.

While most people tolerate exposure to VOCs and other airborne contaminants with short-term acute exposure, long-term repeated exposure can cause serious adverse health effects and should be avoided. To minimize these risks, ensure that there is adequate ventilation and filtration in the work areas. Workers should be encouraged to wear masks to reduce their exposure.

*"Overall, we observed that exposures to respiratory hazards were highest in task zones where cannabis plants and material were manipulated by workers, including the trim, preroll, and the grow task areas."[70]*

## DON'T SUFFOCATE HYDROPONIC PLANTS!
### A NOTE ABOUT DISSOLVED OXYGEN

In order for plants to grow vigorously, they require oxygen, just like animals. In soil cultivation, plants have access to a lot of oxygen in the air and in spaces in the soil. In hydroponic cultivation systems, the primary source that plants receive oxygen is in water! Water contains varying levels of dissolved oxygen or DO. The temperature of the water will determine how much DO can be contained in the water. In general, water temperature should be around 70°F to support high levels of dissolved oxygen!

In hydroponic cultivation, it is important to monitor the temperature and dissolved oxygen levels of the growing solution to ensure plant roots do not suffocate in the water!

---

[69] Cannabis Inflorescence Cannabis spp. Monograph. American Herbal Pharmacopoeia. 2013.
[70] Silvey B, Seto E, Gipe A, Ghodsian N, Simpson CD. Occupational Exposure to Particulate Matter and Volatile Organic Compounds in Two Indoor Cannabis Production Facilities. Ann Work Expo Health. 2020 Aug 6;64(7):715-727. https://doi.org10.1093/annweh/wxaa067

## Glandular Trichome Sketching

Can you recall the differences between the different **glandular trichomes** produced by Cannabis?

Phytocannabinoids are produced in **glandular trichomes**. Glandular trichomes can be broken down into two further categories: _____-_____ and _____-_____.

(HINT: head and/or neck?)

Use the space below to sketch these two different types of trichomes.

# EXCEPTIONS TO THE RULE: AUTOFLOWERING CANNABIS PLANTS

Not all Cannabis plants follow the basic rule of requiring certain photoperiods to trigger vegetative growth versus flowering. There are a variety of Cannabis plants called "autoflowering" plants, which, as their name suggests, will automatically flower with age, regardless of photoperiod. As of the time of this writing, many famous THC dominant Cannabis strains have now been crossed with autoflowering plants to produce autoflowering versions of well-known strains like "White Widow", "Blueberry", "Gorilla Glue", "Bruce Banner", "Northern Lights", and "Sour Diesel".

As Cannabis decriminalization and legalization continues to spread across the world, it is likely that autoflowering Cannabis plants will be the varieties that the average person grows in their home, because they can grow in smaller containers, do not require as much attention, and can produce substantial yields of resinous flowers in a short period of time. Autoflowering Cannabis plants can sometimes be grown from seed to harvest in a matter of 2.5 months or less.

At the time of this writing, breeders are actively crossing autoflowering varieties into other lineages, imparting some of the desirable qualities of autoflowering varieties while still maintaining fairly long growth periods, leading to larger plants and larger yields.

"PURPLE PUNCH" AUTOFLOWER CANNABIS PLANT, ADOBE STOCK #512342699

# FOR THE LOVE OF SOIL

Cannabis prefers neutral to alkaline clay and loamy soils. To understand how to obtain the perfect soil type for Cannabis, we must first discuss how soils are categorized. Soil is a mixture of broken down rock and organic matter. A combination of humus, mineral fragments, plant residues, and clay form what we normally think of as soil.

| The Primary Mineral Components of Soil | |
|---|---|
| Particle | Particle Size |
| Sand | 2 - 0.02mm |
| Silt | 0.02 - 0.002mm |
| Clay | <0.002 mm |

Soils contain three major classes of minerals including: sand, silt, and clay. The ratios of sand to silt to clay determine what soil type is present. A **soil ternary diagram** can be used to calculate your soil type and texture.

**FIGURE 2: SOIL TERNARY DIAGRAM**

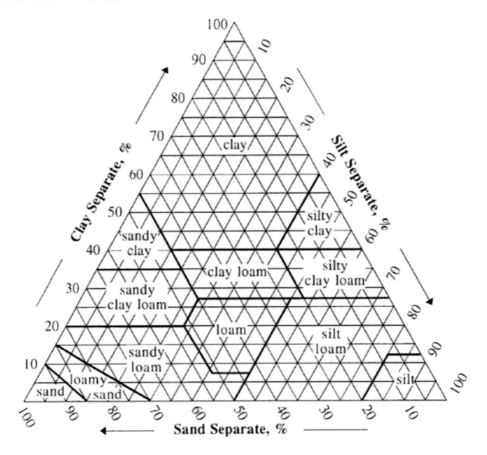

# Try This! Soil Texture Activity

Are you interested in trying to learn what the texture of your soil is? Here is a simple activity to help you determine your soil texture using a soil ternary diagram. You will need a quart jar, soil, water, a dispersing agent like table salt or Calgon, and a ruler.

**Materials**

Quart Jar     Soil          Water          Dispersing Agent          Ruler
                                           (table salt or Calgon)

**Procedures**

Fill the quart jar with one inch of dry soil.

Fill the jar 2/3 full of water.

Add one teaspoon of salt or Calgon.

Vigorously shake the jar.

Let the contents settle for several days.

Use the ruler to measure the depth of each layer.

Convert the measurements into ratios of sand:silt:clay.

Use a **soil ternary diagram** to determine your soil texture type! If you don't want to use a soil ternary diagram manually, you can also use the Soil Texture Calculator on the USDA NRCS website by visiting https://www.nrcs.usda.gov/wps/portal/nrcs/main/soils/survey/tools/

## SOIL CHEMISTRY

As mentioned earlier, Cannabis prefers an alkaline clay or loamy soil. But what does it mean for a soil to be alkaline? The term alkaline is referring to the pH of the soil, which may be influenced by several factors. The chemistry of soil primarily involves several major parts: the colloidal particles found in clay, the parent rock compounds like sand and silt, the organic matter, and water.

Before we talk about soil pH, we should first talk about soil colloids, which are tiny particles found most often in the clay portion of soil. More specifically, colloids are particles that remain suspended in solution. Colloidal particles carry an electrical charge, and because of this electrical charge, ions (charged elements or molecules) are held very tightly against the surface of the colloids with other ions gathered around them in a less tightly bound ionic "cloud". This helps to keep chemicals in place for a while. Because of this buffering effect, clay soils are packed with nutrients. It is also this buffering effect that causes colloids to have a profound influence on the pH of the soil.

The **pH** refers to the alkalinity or acidity of the soil, which is determined by the concentration of negative and positively charged hydrogen ions, in the form of H+ and OH-. In water, these ions are expressed as hydronium ($H_3O^+$) and hydroxide ($OH^-$) ions.

pH is measured on a scale of 0 to 14 with 0 being very acidic and equivalent to battery acid and 14 being very alkaline (basic), the equivalent of bleach. A neutral pH is 7. **Cannabis prefers neutral (7 pH) to alkaline soils**. With a soil and water pH near neutral, the maximum number of nutrients become available to the plant. Outside of 6.5 to 7.5 pH, minerals start to become unavailable and "locked out" from the plant's roots – even if they are present in the soil.

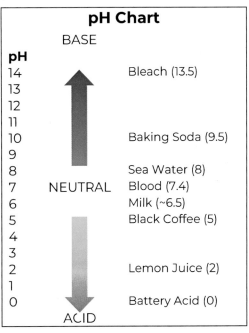

**pH Chart**

BASE

| pH | |
|---|---|
| 14 | Bleach (13.5) |
| 13 | |
| 12 | |
| 11 | |
| 10 | Baking Soda (9.5) |
| 9 | |
| 8 | Sea Water (8) |
| 7 NEUTRAL | Blood (7.4) |
| 6 | Milk (~6.5) |
| 5 | Black Coffee (5) |
| 4 | |
| 3 | |
| 2 | Lemon Juice (2) |
| 1 | |
| 0 | Battery Acid (0) |

ACID

Clay soils attract positively charged ions, like H+ ions. This can lead to an accumulation of positively charged hydrogen ions in a soil, causing a change in pH.

pH affects a compound's solubility in water, which affects the chemical forms that various nutrients may take in the soil. Take Phosphorous for example. At a pH of 1, Phosphorous is generally found in the form of $H_3PO_4$. At a pH of 5 it is usually $H_2PO^-_4$. At a pH of 9 it becomes $HPO^{2-}_4$. Finally, at a pH of 14 Phosphorous is found primarily as $PO^{3-}_4$. These changes are due to the changes in availability of positively charged hydrogen ions. Nutrient availability charts can easily be found online detailing the pH levels at which certain nutrients become available or unavailable to a plant.

If a pH is low and soil is very acidic, the solubility of heavy metals in water is enhanced, leading to higher metal accumulations in plants. This is especially relevant for Cannabis plants because they appear to be supreme nutrient accumulators, though much more research is needed on the subject. Cannabis plants have been shown to accumulate heavy metals from soil into every tissue of the plant.[71]

Phosphorous is typically found in the soil as an **anion**, meaning it is negatively charged. Since colloidal particles are usually also negatively charged, the **phosphorous and colloidal particles repel each other and phosphorous is prone to leaching** out of the area.

## WATER AND SOIL

Soils do more for plants than just provide a reservoir of nutrients for growth. Soil also affects a plant's ability to receive water. Different textures of soils have varying **water holding capacities**. The water holding capacity is defined as the soil's ability to retain water for periods of time. This is all dependent on the size of the particles in the soil. If you were to pour water into a cup of sand, which consists of relatively large particles, the water would pass through quickly due to the larger spaces between particles.

If you were to pour water into a cup of clay, which are very small particles, the water would pass through slowly and saturate the clay, eventually being held tightly in place as a mud ball. A plant's roots and soil are in a constant battle for water, and it all has to do with **water tension** and **available water**. A plant root is always "pulling" at water. The soil texture affects how strongly the soil holds on to water, resisting the plant's pull. When soil is saturated with water, there is low tension and the water in the soil is easy for the roots to suck up.

| Available Soil Moisture Holding Capacity for Different Soil Textures ||
|---|---|
| **Soil Texture** | **Inches of Water/Foot of Soil** |
| Coarse Sand/gravel | 0.2 to 0.7 |
| Sand | 0.5 to 1.1 |
| Loamy Sand | 0.7 to 1.4 |
| Sandy Loam | 1.3 to 1.8 |
| Clay Loam and Silty Clay Loam | 1.7 to 2.5 |
| Silty Clay and Clay | 1.6 to 2.2 |

FIGURE 12: SOIL MOISTURE HOLDING CAPACITIES[72]

As the soil starts to dry, though, the tension increases, and the soil starts to hang ever tighter to the water that is present. The point at which water is present in the soil but unavailable to plant roots is called the **permanent wilting point**. This is one reason why some plants struggle in a heavy clay soil. The clay hangs on to a lot of water, potentially drowning or rotting the roots, while at the same time maintaining high tension and holding tightly to the water so the roots cannot easily draw in water to help the plant grow. Plants can be in deserts even if they are surrounded by water!

---

[71] Linger, P, Mussig, J, Fischer, H, Kobert, J. 2002. Industrial hemp (Cannabis sativa L.) growing on heavy metal contaminated soil: fibre quality and phytoremediation potential. Industrial Crops and Products. 16:33-42 https://doi.org/10.1016/S0926-6690(02)00005-5

[72] "Soild, Water and Plant Characteristics important to Irrigation" by T. Scherer, D. Franzen, L. Cihacek, NDSU Extension Service, AE1675, 2017; https://www.ag.ndsu.edu/publications/crops/soil-water-and-plant-characteristics-important-to-irrigation/

## RECOMMENDED RESOURCE: THE WEB SOIL SURVEY

If you live in the United States, there is a great soil information resource available online provided by the US Natural Resources Conservation Service to help you find out more information about the soil and geology of your area. This tool is called The Web Soil Survey and the information can be a great resource when designing a garden or farm.[73]

For more information about soil dynamics, check out the **Soil Biology Primer**, authored by Elaine Ingham, Andrew Moldenke, Clive Edwards and available **free** through the USDA NRCS.[74] I also recommend the "Teaming with..." series from Jeff Lowenfels including Teaming with Microbes, Teaming with Nutrients, Teaming with Fungi and Teaming with Bacteria.[75]

---

### Enduring Understandings

- Cannabis is a dioecious plant, meaning that it has distinct male and female forms, although sometimes, usually under stress, Cannabis can appear as monoecious, with both male and female reproductive parts on one plant.
- Cannabis flowers form in groups called inflorescences.
- The Cannabis plant produces various types of trichomes, including glandular and non-glandular varieties.
- Cannabinoids are produced in capitate-stalked and capitate-sessile glandular trichomes.
- Cannabis plants typically don't produce flowers until they experience at least 12 hours of darkness at a time each day, unless they are autoflowering varieties of Cannabis.
- Cannabis plants are commonly propagated either sexually, through seeds, or asexually through cloning, usually through cuttings or tissue culture.
- Cannabis prefers neutral to alkaline clay and loamy soils.

---

---

[73] http://websoilsurvey.sc.egov.usda.gov/App/HomePage.htm

[74] http://www.nrcs.usda.gov/wps/portal/nrcs/main/soils/health/biology

[75] https://www.jefflowenfels.com/

# Try This! Water Availability Activity

Here is a quick activity you can do at home to easily demonstrate the concepts of water tension, water availability, and permanent wilting point.

## Materials

Water        Dry Sponge

## Procedures

1. First, obtain a dry sponge. Imagine that the dry sponge represents dry soil.
2. Now soak the sponge in water. This represents rain or irrigation. The sponge now represents a **water saturated soil**.
3. Turn the sponge vertically and let water pour out, but do not squeeze the sponge. The dripping water represents run-off as well as water available to plants.
4. Now squeeze the sponge, releasing more water. This represents the pull exerted by a plant root as the plant pulls in more water away from the soil as it "drinks".
5. Finally, ring the sponge out completely so that no more water drips out when you squeeze it. When you feel the sponge, you should be able to feel that it is wet, but no water will drip out of the sponge. This represents the **_permanent wilting point_**. This represents water that, though present in the soil, would be totally unavailable to plants because the soil is exerting a greater pull on the water than the plant roots. At this point, the plant may as well be growing in a desert!

# Chapter 6:
## Cannabis Pests and Pathogens

## Learning Questions

- What insects negatively impact the growth of Cannabis plants?
- What pathogenic fungi affect Cannabis plants?
- What bacteria and viruses can infect Cannabis plants?

### Insect Pests

Cannabis is affected by many common garden pests, most notably: aphids, russet mites, broad mites, white flies, spider mites, thrips, fungus gnats, and, in flowering Cannabis, caterpillars. Different pests attack various parts of the plant. Fungus gnats reside in the soil and roots. As such, fungus gnats can typically be combated by ensuring that soil dries out in between watering. White fly larvae may start in soil and adults move on to feeding on leaf and stem tissue. Microscopic pests, like broad mites, can use other pests like white flies to travel and spread among plants.

A mature Cannabis plant infested with russet mites.
Although the mites do not kill the plant, the flower and resin yield will suffer.

# Aphids

There are several types of aphids that are well-known to cause problems for Cannabis cultivators, the two primary ones being the Cannabis aphid (*Phorodon cannabis*) and the Rice Root Aphid (*Rhopalosiphum rufiabdominalis*).[76]

Aphids feed on the plant's nutrients contained in its phloem. When enough aphids come around, they can cause significant damage to a plant by depriving it of its own nutrients, usually resulting in wilting, weak growth, leaf discoloration and other signs of plant stress.

PHOTO COURTESTY OF MATTHEW GATES, ZENTHANOL.COM

Aphids leave behind a sticky substance called honeydew which can appear as shiny droplets on the leaf surface. They also leave behind castings as they shed their exoskeleton. If you suspect that you have an aphid infestation, check for signs of honeydew and castings for confirmation.

Generally, aphid infestations must be managed early by preventing a large number of aphids from getting on a plant. This is typically done through the use of sticky fly traps, pheromone repellant, or bug zappers.

There are a number of predatory bugs that feed on aphids, including green and brown lacewings, ladybugs, hover flies, midges, damselflies, soldier beetles, and more.[77]

PHOTO COURTESTY OF MATTHEW GATES, ZENTHANOL.COM

---

[76] Lagos-Kutz, D., Potter, B., DiFonzo, C., Russell, H. and Hartman, G.L. (2018), Two Aphid Species, Phorodon cannabis and Rhopalosiphum rufiabdominale, Identified as Potential Pests on Industrial Hemp, Cannabis sativa L., in the US Midwest. Crop, Forage & Turfgrass Management, 4: 1-3 180032. https://doi.org/10.2134/cftm2018.04.0032
[77] https://hyg.ipm.illinois.edu/pastpest/200107a.html

# Fungus Gnats

Fungus gnats are a very annoying, yet less damaging pest that growers often must combat when cultivating Cannabis. A fungus gnat infestation often starts due to humid and moist conditions in the grow environment. Soil that is too wet or filled with too much organic material will attract fungus gnats who will then lay eggs in the soil.

A fungus gnat infestation is usually easy to detect because hordes of fungus gnats will come flying out of infested soils when moving or bumping plants in the grow room.

Sticky traps can be an easy and cheap way to quickly reduce a fungus gnat population, however ultimately the cultivation environment must be kept clean, free from any decomposing debris, and relatively dry to prevent attracting fungus gnats. Additionally, it is important to be mindful of the amount of organic matter that is added to soil mixes. As organic matter decomposes, it attracts animals that want to feed on decomposers.

## WHITE FLIES

The greenhouse whitefly (*Trialeurodes vaporariorum*) is another pest that on its own seems to be more of a nuisance than a real concern. However white flies often serve as vectors for smaller, harder to combat pests to make their way into your garden. Whiteflies are 1-2mm in length. They lay their eggs on the underside of leaves like many other insect pests. They feed on the plant's phloem sap and excrete honeydew, like aphids.

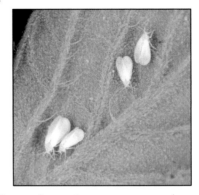

The predatory mite *Amblyseius swirskii* has been shown to prey on greenhouse whiteflies, however research has shown that it is crucial that the predatory mites be present *before* the white fly infestation begins in order to successfully control their population.[78] This highlights the need to be proactive in controlling for pests before they become a problem.

## THRIPS

Thrips are very small slender insects that, like many other pests of Cannabis, use their mouths to pierce the tissues of the Cannabis plant and suck out the nutritive juices. Thrips can reproduce asexually, making them particularly resilient. Thrips can also be vectors for plant diseases, such as pathogenic bacteria, fungi, or viruses.[79] [80]

PHOTO COURTESTY OF MATTHEW GATES, ZENTHANOL.COM

The juvenile thrips are pale and translucent, becoming darker and opaquer with age. In their young stages they do not have wings but develop them as adults. The two primary species of thrips found to affect Cannabis are Onion Thrips (*Thrips tabaci*) and Flower Thrips (*Frankliniella schultzei*). The predator insects *Amblyseius cucumeris* and *Amblyseius swirskii* have been reported to be effective for thrips control.[81]

[78] Mortazavi, N., Fathipour, Y., & Talebi, A. (2019). The efficiency of Amblyseius swirskii in control of Tetranychus urticae and Trialeurodes vaporariorum is affected by various factors. Bulletin of Entomological Research, 109(3), 365-375. https://doi.org/0.1017/S0007485318000640

[79] Jones, D.R. Plant Viruses Transmitted by Thrips. Eur J Plant Pathol 113, 119–157 (2005). https://doi.org/10.1007/s10658-005-2334-1

[80] Blake, J. (1988). MITES AND THRIPS AS BACTERIAL AND FUNGAL VECTORS BETWEEN PLANT TISSUE CULTURES. Acta Hortic. 225, 163-166 DOI: 10.17660/ActaHortic.1988.225.17 https://doi.org/10.17660/ActaHortic.1988.225.17

[81] Dalir, S., Hajiqanbar, H., Fathipour, Y. and Khanamani, M. (2021), A comprehensive picture of foraging strategies of Neoseiulus cucumeris and Amblyseius swirskii on western flower thrips. Pest Manag Sci, 77: 5418-5429. https://doi.org/10.1002/ps.6581

# SPIDER MITES

The two-spotted spider mite (*Tetranychus urticae*) is notorious for devastating indoor Cannabis grows, as one small infestation can quickly bloom to a frustrating and devastating loss. Spider mites are very small, only about 1/50th of an inch long.[82]

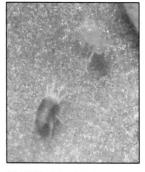

Spider mite infestations are pretty easy to identify due to their characteristic webs that take over an entire terminal bud on the plant, as seen in the image below.

Spider mites thrive in hot, dry environments, which is typical of Cannabis cultivation environments. If the temperature of a grow environment surpasses 90°F (32.2°C) for an extended length of time, spider mites can very quickly

PHOTO COURTESTY OF MATTHEW GATES, ZENTHANOL.COM

explode in numbers within a week or two. They feed on the nutrients found in the underside of leaves – often hiding from detection until they begin spinning webs. Typically, infested plants must be eliminated from the grow area to prevent spread, and all other plants in the area are treated with beneficial predatory mites like *A. andersoni, N. californicus, P. persimilis.* or *A. swirskii.*

To check for spider mites that may be hiding under your plant leaves, you can take a piece of paper, hold it under the leaves, and then shake the leaves to see if any spider mites fall on to the piece of paper. This also makes it easy to collect specimens for proper identification.

PHOTO COURTESTY OF MATTHEW GATES, ZENTHANOL.COM

---

[82] https://extension.umn.edu/yard-and-garden-insects/spider-mites

# RUSSET MITES

The hemp russet mite (*Aculops cannabicola*) are quite small, ranging in size from 160 to 210 microns, just bigger than the size of a human hair![83] Russet mite infections cause a characteristic leaf curling and yellowing in affected plants. Russet mites are hard to see with the naked eye until there are a lot of them gathered together, at which point they often resemble sawdust on the leaves.

The predatory mite *Amblysieus andersoni* feeds on russet mites and may be an effective tool for controlling Russet mites in indoor settings (it is hard to control the behavior of predator bugs outdoors!).

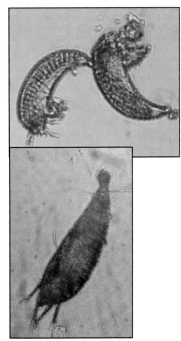

LEAF PHOTOS COURTESTY OF MATTHEW GATES, ZENTHANOL.COM

RUSSET MITE MICROSCOPY PHOTOS BY JASON WILSON, MS

---

[83] https://content.ces.ncsu.edu/hemp-russet-mite-in-industrial-hemp

# BROAD MITES

Broad mites (*Polyphagotarsonemus latus*) are even smaller than russet mites, if you can believe it. Broad mites are less than half the size of a spider mite – no larger than 0.2mm.[84] Similar to russet mites, broad mite infestations can cause a plant's leaves to curl, twist and yellow. Typically, growth is stunted in affected plants and crop yields are sacrificed.

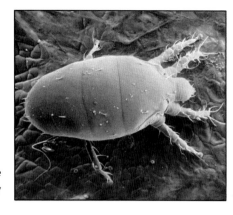

The life cycle of a broad mite is very short, running its course in only 1 to 2 weeks. The female lays approximate 4 female eggs for every 1 male egg, leading to very rapid growth in the mite population. Broad mites move to other plants by hitching a ride on other insects like aphids or white flies.

The predatory mite *Amblyseius cucumeris* is known to feed on broad mites and may be an effective biological control.[85]

# CATERPILLARS

One of the saddest days for a Cannabis cultivator is when they step into their field to check on their plants, and the find their precious buds completely decimated by caterpillars. Caterpillars feed on plant tissues and resins, eating their way into a dense bud and consuming it from the inside out, all while releasing its waste around the Cannabis flowers. This often promotes other problems like fungal or bacterial infections and can cause a cultivator to have to sacrifice their plants only weeks from harvest.

There are a variety of insects whose larvae will feed on Cannabis. One of the most well-known is the Hemp Borer, or Hemp Moth (*Grapholita delineana*). When the moth is in its adolescent stage, it will bore its way into the stem of a Cannabis plant and feed on the plant, working its way along the stem until it grows into its adult moth

---

[84] https://www.tnstate.edu/extension/documents/Broad%20Mites%20-%20TSUNRC%20Fact%20Sheet-1.pdf
[85] https://extension.psu.edu/broad-mites-an-example-of-using-biocontrols-for-management

form. Another common Cannabis caterpillar pest is the Beet Armyworm (*Spodoptera exigua*) which feeds more on leaves, traditionally, rather than flowers.[86]

Generally, caterpillars must be removed by hand or vacuum, as it is not recommended to apply any chemical treatments to Cannabis while it is flowering. Because caterpillars generally become a problem close to harvest, predatory insects are often not an effective control strategy. Prevention can be effective by eliminating excess debris like leaves and stems that might attract opportunistic caterpillars.

## PATHOGENIC FUNGI

There are many different fungi which may attack the Cannabis plant at varying stages of growth. The most common type of pathogenic fungus that attacks Cannabis is *Botrytis cinerea*, or gray mold.[87] Gray mold is a very common type of pathogenic fungus that attacks diverse types of plants. In fiber type, hemp plants, gray mold tends to attack the stem and cause cankers which girdle the stem and kill off everything above the canker.

In drug type varieties of Cannabis, gray mold tends to attack the dense inflorescences, or buds. Dense buds will retain a lot of moisture which presents a perfect environment for molds to grow and take over the plant material. When a group of Cannabis flowers is infected with Botrytis, the fan leaves will turn yellow and die off, followed by a darkening of the fused stigmas and styles that extend from the calyx of each flower. Eventually the inflorescence will become covered in mold. Cannabis cultivars from arid regions, like Afghanistan, are exceptionally susceptible to mold.

Some fungi attack young Cannabis plants early, causing a condition called "damping off". There are a variety of genera of fungi that cause damping off including *Pythium*, *Rhizoctonia*, *Botrytis*, *Macrophomina*, and *Fusarium*. Another condition that can kill off a plant is "root rot". This occurs when the plant's roots have been saturated with water for too long, leading to a fungal infection of the roots. It is important to allow soil to dry between watering to avoid root rot. When growing Cannabis in containers, it is important to ensure that the container is big enough to allow the plant's root system to extend and grow without becoming bound in the container.

Powdery mildew is another common fungal pathogen common to Cannabis and many other plants. Powdery mildew is often caused by high humidity levels or excess watering. There are several species of powdery mildew fungi including *Leveillula taurica*, *Oidiopsis taurica*, and *Sphaerotheca macularis*.

## PATHOGENIC BACTERIA

There are four primary species of pathogenic bacteria that afflict Cannabis plants. They include bacterial blight caused by *Pseudomonas syringae* pv. *cannabina*; crown gall caused by *Agrobacterium tumefaciens*; bacterial wilt caused by *Erwinia tracheiphila*; and xanthomonas leaf spot caused by *Xanthomonas campestris* pv.

---

[86] https://webdoc.agsci.colostate.edu/hempinsects/PDFs/Beet%20armyworm%20with%20photos.pdf
[87] McPartland, J.M. 1996. Cannabis pests. Journal of the International Hemp Association 3(2): 49, 52-55. http://www.internationalhempassociation.org/jiha/iha03201.html

*cannabis.* Of these four pathogenic bacteria, *Pseudomonas syringae* is the most common bacterial pathogen of Cannabis.[88]

## Pathogenic Viruses

There are several different viruses that may attack Cannabis. Although viruses rarely kill Cannabis plants, they can drastically reduce yield and growth vigor. Once a virus has infected a plant, they are essentially impossible to get rid of. Sometimes viruses may even infect pollen or seeds, effectively passing the virus on to the plant's progeny. Some of the most common viruses that are thought to affect Cannabis are the Cannabis cryptic Virus (CanCV), hemp streak virus (HSV) and hemp mosaic virus (HMV).

| Examples of Viruses Known or Presumed to Affect Cannabis | |
|---|---|
| VIRUS NAME | SYMPTOMS |
| Beet Curly Top Virus (BCTV) | Stunted growth, yellowing leaves; Newly developed leaves narrower and pale green with slight sideways curl |
| Cannabis Cryptic Virus (CanCV) | Asymptomatic; transmitted through seeds, but not contact |
| Hemp Streak Virus (HSV) | Leaves turn pale green, followed by yellow streaks developing from veins |
| Hemp Mosaic Virus (HMV) | Discoloration, leaf mottling, stunted growth |
| Hop Latent Viroid (HLVd) | Brittle stems, horizontal growth, reduced flower mass, reduced trichome mass; can be transmitted through seeds |

Another virus affecting Cannabis that was recently identified and characterized is the Hop Latent Viroid (HLVd), which caused a series of symptoms in Cannabis including "brittle stems, an outwardly horizontal plant structure and reduced flower mass and trichomes", although hops plants infected with HLVd often exhibit no symptoms.[89] The symptoms presented in infected Cannabis plants are often referred to colloquially as "dudding". One of the most recent viruses to be found to infect Cannabis plants is the Beet Curly Top Virus (BCTV), reported in Cannabis for the first time in 2019.[90]

Insects may carry viruses from one plant to another as they feed. Symptoms of viral infections of Cannabis often include discoloring and curling of leaves. Despite numerous reports by cultivators for decades, Tobacco Mosaic Virus (TMV) has not been

---

[88] McPartland, J. M., 1996. A review of Cannabis diseases. Journal of the International Hemp Association 3(1): 19-23. https://druglibrary.org/olsen/hemp/iha/iha03111.html

[89] Bektas A, Hardwick KM, Waterman K, Kristof J. 2019. The occurrence of hop latent viroid in Cannabis sativa with symptoms of Cannabis stunting disease in California. Plant Disease. https://doi.org/10.1094/PDIS-03-19-0459-PDN

[90] Giladi Y, Hadad L, Luria N, Cranshaw W, Lachman O. 2019. First Report of Beet Curly Top Virus Infecting Cannabis sativa L., in Western Colorado. Plant Disease. American Phytopathological Society. https://doi.org/10.1094/PDIS-08-19-1656-PDN

identified on Cannabis in any peer-reviewed published scientific literature, though some private companies claim to have identified it.

## PLANT DISEASE VS MALNUTRITION VS ENVIRONMENTAL STRESS

The symptoms of disease in plants can often resemble the symptoms of nutrient deficiency or stress response. It is important to properly diagnose symptoms to determine the severity of the condition and take appropriate action. Symptoms such as discoloration, leaf spotting, and leaf curling could be indicative of one of many different problems including pest infestation, disease, or nutrient imbalance.

To learn more about Cannabis plant pathogens, I recommend:
*Hemp Diseases and Pests: Management and Biological Control* by John McPartland, Robert Clarke, and DP Watson (2000) and *Marijuana Horticulture: The Indoor/Outdoor Medical Grower's Bible* by Jorge Cervantes.

To learn more about Cannabis pests and integrated pest management, I recommend checking out the educational content produced by Matthew Gates of Zenthanol Consulting.[91] His YouTube channel[92] is full of free educational content that dives deep into the physiology and ecology of Cannabis pests and beneficial insects.

---

### Enduring Understandings

- Common insect pests affecting Cannabis are aphids, spider mites, whiteflies, russet mites, broad mites, fungus gnats, and caterpillars.
- Common fungal pests affecting Cannabis include those responsible for gray mold, powdery mildew, and root rot.
- Viruses in Cannabis plants can be difficult to recognize and identify definitively.
- Some viruses thought to affect Cannabis plants are things like Cannabis Cryptic Virus, Hop Latent Virus, Curly Beet Top Virus, Hemp Streak Virus, and Hemp Mosaic Virus.
- When pathogens affect a Cannabis plant, the symptoms can sometimes mimic nutrient deficiencies, and cultivators must take care to rule out nutrient deficiencies when having a difficult time identifying why a plant is exhibiting problematic symptoms.

---

[91] https://zenthanol.com/index.html
[92] https://www.youtube.com/user/Zenthanol

# Chapter 7:
## CANNABIS CONTAMINANTS

SCAN ME

### Learning Questions

- What makes something toxic?
- What contaminants are commonly found in Cannabis or Cannabis products?
- What are the major classes of pesticides and how do they differ in their modes of action?
- What additives are sometimes found in Cannabis products?

## WHAT IS A TOXIN?

> *"Alle Dinge sind Gift und nichts ist ohne Gift, allein die Dosis macht es, dass ein Ding kein Gift ist."*
>
> *"All things are poison, and nothing is without poison; only the dose makes a thing not a poison."*
>
> Paracelsus

**Paracelsus** (1493 – 1541) was one of the original founders of toxicology and studied a variety of subjects including physiology, botany, alchemy, and astrology. He has become popular for coining the above phrase, which is often shortened to "The dose makes the poison." It is important to keep this phrase in mind any time the subject of poisons, toxins, or contaminants is at hand. Something's toxicity is relative and depends on the length of time or frequency of exposure, the dose or level of exposure, and the nuances of an organism's individual biochemistry. Water is toxic if consumed in too large of an amount in too short amount of a time, no matter how healthy you are!

When studying toxins, it is important to do research about both acute and chronic exposure health effects at various dosages to get an idea of how a compound might affect the body. Some pesticides, for instance, are relatively nontoxic at low dose acute exposures, whereas the same compounds might lead to neurotoxicity with increased exposure for prolonged periods of time. Some things, like mycotoxins, can be either acutely or chronically toxic depending on a person's immune system.

# FUNGI

**Molds, mildews, and yeasts** are all fungi. **Molds** are multicellular and produce strands of hyphae, giving them a fuzzy stringy appearance. **Yeasts** are unicellular and reproduce through "budding," creating a smooth appearance. They can cause a variety of negative health effects when ingested such as sinus infections, coughing, headaches, sneezing, and allergic reactions. Usually when a Cannabis product is smoked, the heat kills much of the microorganisms and spores present in the material, although it is still possible for viable spores to pass into the smoke and be inhaled into the lungs.

## ASPERGILLOSIS

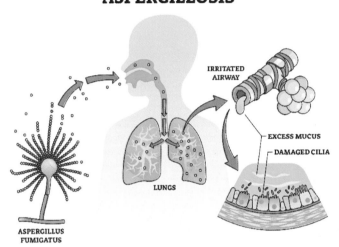

Some fungi are polyphenic and can change between different fungal forms such as mold or yeast. One example of this type of fungus is *Candida albicans*, the fungus responsible for the typical yeast infection in humans as well as Thrush, a fungal condition affecting the tongue, mouth, and throat. Chronic Cannabis consumers might house higher populations of *C. albicans* than acute or abstinent users of Cannabis.[93]

Some spores of fungi can cause illness in humans. The spores of certain species of *Aspergillus*, like *Aspergillus niger* and *Aspergillus fumigatus,* can enter the lungs and grow into a mass in the lungs which can cause internal bleeding and become fatal. This condition is called **Aspergillosis**. There is a recorded death due to Aspergillosis associated with Cannabis use by an immunocompromised 34-year-old man.[94] More recent literature demonstrates this is not limited to the immunocompromised.[95]

---

[93] Darling MR, Arendorf TM, Coldrey NA. 1990. Effect of cannabis use on oral candidal carriage. J Oral Pathol Med. 19(7):319-321. https://doi.org/10.1111/j.1600-0714.1990.tb00852.x

[94] Hamadeh, R, Adehali, A, Locsley, RM, York MK. 1988. Fatal Aspergillosis associated with smoking contaminated marijuana, in a marrow transplant recipient. Chest. 94(2):432-433 https://doi.org/10.1378/chest.94.2.432

[95] Stone T, Henkle J, Prakash V. 2019. Pulmonary mucormycosis associated with medical marijuana use. Respiratory Medicine Case Reports 26:176–179. https://doi.org/10.1016/j. rmcr.2019.01.008

Additionally, there are other microorganisms that can cause respiratory illness such as *Mucor* that have been shown to infect the lungs.[96]

| Examples of Aspergillosis Causing Fungi |
|---|
| *Aspergillus flavus* |
| *Aspergillus fumigatus* |
| *Aspergillus nidulans* |
| *Aspergillus niger* |
| *Aspergillus terreus* |

FIGURE 13: EXAMPLES OF ASPERGILLOSIS-CAUSING SPECIES OF ASPERGILLUS

# MYCOTOXINS

**Mycotoxins** are the toxic byproducts of some types of fungi. You could think of them as a mold's personalized pesticide. Mycotoxins are quite persistent and will remain on a material after the mold that produced it has died. A sample may appear clean in any other way, or perhaps the material was sterilized, but it could still contain dangerous levels of mycotoxins. Some mycotoxins are highly carcinogenic and can be dangerous even when smoked.

Aflatoxin is an example of one of these dangerous mycotoxins. Aflatoxin is produced primarily by the mold *Aspergillus flavus* and is not only highly carcinogenic but is produced in copious amounts. Aflatoxin has been linked to liver cancer.[97] Another common type of mycotoxin is Ochratoxin, such as Ochratoxin A. Ochratoxin A can cause substantial damage to the brain and is classified as "potentially carcinogenic" by the International Agency for Research on Cancer (IARC).[98] There are a variety of other types of mold that are commonly detected in Cannabis flowers that can also produce mycotoxins, like Penicillium and Cladosporium.

It is important to understand that when we talk about mycotoxins, we are often actually referring to groups of compounds. Each type of mycotoxin has a myriad of variations. For instance, of the Aflatoxins there is Aflatoxin B1, B2, G1, G2, M1, M2, AFL, and Q1. Of the Ochratoxins there is Ochratoxin A, B, C, and TA.

Perhaps just as important although not commonly referenced are the Fusarium toxins. Among the most toxic and prevalent fusaria) toxins are the following: zearalenone, fumonisins, moniliformin and trichothecenes (T-2/HT-2 toxin, deoxynivalenol, diacetoxyscirpenol, nivalenol).[99] Although testing for these compounds is not mandated as with the aflatoxins and ochratoxins, there (is evidence to suggest that these toxins are found in cannabis extracts.[100]

---

[96] Stone T, Henkle J, Prakash V. 2019. Pulmonary mucormycosis associated with medical marijuana use. Respiratory Medicine Case Reports 26:176–179. https://doi.org/10.1016/j. rmcr.2019.01.008
[97] Bhatnagar-Mathur P, Sunkara S, Bhatnagar-Panwar M, Waliyar F, Sharma KK. Biotechnological advances for combating Aspergillus flavus and aflatoxin contamination in crops. Plant Sci. 2015 May;234:119-32. https://doi.org/10.1016/j.plantsci.2015.02.009 Epub 2015 Feb 25. PMID: 25804815.
[98] https://www.iarc.who.int/news-events/mycotoxin-exposure-and-human-cancer-risk-a-systematic-review-of-epidemiological-studies/
[99] Nesic K, Ivanovic S, Nesic V. Fusarial toxins: secondary metabolites of Fusarium fungi. Rev Environ Contam Toxicol. 2014;228:101-20. https://doi.org/10.1007/978-3-319-01619-1_5
[100] Maguire W, et al. 2018. Survey of mycotoxin residues in Oregon cannabis crops by LC-MS/MS [Conference Poster]. Cannabis Science Conference, Portland, OR, 2018.

# BACTERIA

There are a wide variety of potential pathogenic bacteria that could be found on Cannabis. Primarily, the bacteria that are generally considered of most concern are shiga toxin-producing strains of *E. coli, Salmonella,* and certain species and strains of *Pseudomonas. E coli* and *Salmonella* are bacteria that share the same biological family, Enterobacteriaceae, and exposure to certain species of each can lead to gastrointestinal disease, like food poisoning.

Shiga toxin is the toxin responsible for causing dysentery, for instance. Salmonella is commonly associated with food poisonings. While the source of *E. coli* and *Salmonella* outbreaks is usually thought to be meats and egg products, more attention has recently been brought to plant products like ready to eat herbs as a threat for Salmonella contamination.[101] Typically, *E. coli* and/or *Salmonella* contaminations in Cannabis occur during post-harvest handling.

*Pseudomonas* is in a family unto itself, separate from *E. coli* or *Salmonella*, but certain species of *Pseudomonas*, namely *P. aeruginosa*, can cause significant infections in the body and can quickly adapt to resist antibiotic drugs. Like E. coli and Salmonella, Pseudomonas can also be found in the environment, and many species and strains of the bacteria are not actually harmful. Rather, it is a small group of particular species and strains that infect the body or produce bacterial endotoxins, causing someone to feel sick.

Ruchlemer et al (2015) found that Cannabis can be plasma sterilized to ensure the absence of microbiological contaminants while only decreasing the potency of THC by approximately 12.6 percent, which in the study resulted in a potency reduction of approximately two percentage points.[102] The Cannabis can then be vaporized using a temperature controlled herbal vaporizer to deliver the drug to the body more safely. Of course, the question remains, *how are the multitude of chemical constituents of Cannabis other than THC affected by sterilization techniques?*

## BACTERIAL ENDOTOXINS

Endotoxins are toxic compounds that are embedded in the cell membranes of certain kinds of bacteria. When the cell is disturbed or destroyed, the toxins are released into the surrounding environment. In the human body endotoxins typically initiate a response from the immune system leading to inflammation. In rare cases the inflammation can become so bad that the individual enters septic shock and can be fatal.

---

[101] Zweifel C, Stephan R. 2011. Spices and herbs as source of Salmonella-related foodborne diseases. Food Research International. 45:765-769.

[102] Ruchlemer R, Amit-Kohn M, Raveh D, Hanuš L. Inhaled medicinal cannabis and the immunocompromised patient. Support Care Cancer. 2015 Mar;23(3):819-22. https://doi.org/10.1007/s00520-014-2429-3 Epub 2014 Sep 13. PMID: 25216851.

# AGROCHEMICALS

Agrochemicals like pesticides or herbicides are primarily used to control insect damage and fungal contamination of crops, or to suppress the growth of undesirable, or "weedy", plants. However, some agrochemicals, like fertilizers or plant hormones, may be used to manipulate the growth of a plant or the resin yield of a Cannabis crop.

Many pesticides are active by disrupting the central nervous system in animals, rendering them paralyzed and eventually killing them. As a potential or current Cannabis consumer, you may be wondering, "Okay, sure pesticides may be found in Cannabis, but will those pesticides actually pass through into the smoke?" The answer is yes. Pesticides have been recovered in Cannabis smoke.[103] Extended exposure to some of these compounds can result in serious health effects in humans.

| Common Agrochemicals Found in Cannabis Products ||
|--------------------------|--------------------------|
| Malathion | Myclobutanil |
| Carbaryl | Imidacloprid |
| Propoxur | Abamectin |
| Bifenthrin | Bifenazate |
| Permethrin | Azadirachtin |
| Piperonyl Butoxide | Spinosad |
| Paclobutrazol | Pyrethrin I and II |

FIGURE 14: COMMON AGROCHEMICALS FOUND IN CANNABIS

## COMMON CLASSES OF PESTICIDES

| Pesticide Class | Description | Examples |
|-----------------|-------------|----------|
| **Pyrethroids** | Derived from pyrethrum | Allethrin, Bifenthrin, Permethrin |
| **Carbamates** | Derived from carbamic acid | Carbofuran, Carbaryl, Methomyl |
| **Organochlorides** | Organic compounds containing chlorine | DDT, Aldrin, Chlordane, Lindane |
| **Organophosphates** | Organic compounds containing phosphorous | Diazinon, Malathion, Chlorpyrifos, Parathion, Diazinon, Isofenphos |

### PYRETHROIDS

Pyrethroids are insecticides that mimic natural pyrethrins in some flowers like chrysanthemums. These chemicals are toxic to many organisms that feed and support many food chains like pollinators and aquatic organisms. Cyanide can be found in some Pyrethroids leading to health risks with repeated exposure. Exposure to some pyrethroids has been linked to an increased risk of prostate cancer.[104]

Pyrethroid Examples: Allethrin, Bifenthrin, permethrin

---

[103] Sullivan N, Sytze E, Raber JC. 2013. Determination of Pesticide Residues in Cannabis Smoke. Journal of Toxicology. Vol 2013. Article ID 378168 https://doi.org/10.1155/2013/378168

[104] Alavanja MCR, Samanic C, Dosemeci M, Lubin J, Tarone R, et al. 2003. Use of agricultural pesticides and prostate cancer risk in the Agricultural Health Study Cohort. Am. J. Epidemiol. 157:1-13 https://doi.org/10.1093/aje/kwg040

## CARBAMATES

Carbamates, like organophosphates, can disrupt the nervous systems of animals. High-level exposure can lead to central nervous system damage, nausea, vomiting, muscle weakness, changes in heart rate, convulsions, and coma.[105] Chronic exposure to carbamates has also been linked to an increased risk for Parkinson's Disease.[106]

Carbamate Examples: Carbofuran, carbaryl, methomyl

## ORGANOCHLORIDES (ORGANOCHLORINES)

Organochlorides, or organochlorines, include pesticides like DDT, the pesticide that was the subject of Rachel Carson's famous writing, *Silent Spring,* which breathed new life into the environmental movement in the 1960s.[107]

These chemicals cling to tissue for very long periods of time, giving these pesticides a high potential to accumulate in water supplies and organisms for long periods of time after exposure to the chemical has ended. Some organochlorides exhibit very serious negative health effects, particularly in individuals with compromised immune systems. Organochlorines have been linked to non-Hodgkin's lymphoma and neurotoxicity[108] [109] [110]

Organochlorine Examples: DDT, Aldrin, chlordane, lindane

## ORGANOPHOSPHATES

Organophosphates, like Carbamates, can disrupt the nervous systems of animals, causing central nervous system damage. Organophosphates can be carcinogenic. Although organophosphates can be highly toxic, they do not last in the environment very long, breaking down quickly when exposed to air and light.

Both organophosphates and organochlorides have been linked to Non-Hodgkin's lymphoma.[111] Organophosphates and carbamates have both been linked to chronic lymphocytic leukemia.[112] Organophosphate exposure can also lead to a condition called organophosphate-induced delayed polyneuropathy (OPIDP), which is

---

[105] Alavanja MCR, Hoppin J, Kamel F. 2004. Health Effects of Chronic Pesticide Exposure: Cancer and Neurotoxicity. Annu. Rev. Public Health. 25:155-97 https://doi.org/10.1146/annurev.publhealth.25.101802.123020

[106] Seidler A, Hellenbrand W, Robra BP, Vieregge P, Nischan P, et al. 1996. Possible environmental, occupational, and other etiologic factors for Parkinson's disease: a case-control study in Germany. Neurology 46: 1257-84 https://doi.org/10.1212/wnl.46.5.1275

[107] http://www.rachelcarson.org/SilentSpring.aspx

[108] Blair A, Zahm SH. 1991. Cancer among farmers. Occup. Med. 3:335-54 https://doi.org/10.5271/sjweh.2208

[109] Blair A, Zahm SH. 1995. Agricultural exposures and cancer. Environ. Health Perspect. 103:205-8

[110] Keifer M, Mahurin R. 1997. Chronic neurologic effects of pesticide overexposure. Occup. Med. 12:291-304 https://doi.org/10.1289/ehp.95103s8205

[111] Blair A, Zahm SH. 1991. Cancer among farmers. Occup. Med. 3:335-54 https://doi.org/10.5271/sjweh.2208

[112] Nanni O, Amadori D, Lugaresi C, Falcini F, Scarpi E, et al. 1996. Chronic lymphoctic leukemias and non-Hodgkin's lymphoma by histological type in farming animal breeding workers: a population case-control study based on a priori exposure matrices. Occup. Environ. Med. 53:652-57

a condition consisting of muscle cramps, lethargy, changes to the senses, and possibly paralysis.[113]

Organophosphate Examples: diazinon, malathion, chlorpyrifos, parathion, diazinon, isofenphos

## OTHER AGROCHEMICALS IN CANNABIS

Some fungicides, like **myclobutanil**, can disrupt hormone signaling in organisms. This prevents fungi from producing a critical steroid needed to build their cell walls. In humans, chronic exposure to these types of fungicides can disrupt the endocrine system causing hormonal problems in the human such as high or low levels of various estrogens.

**Spinosad** is a commonly used organic pesticide which is toxic to pollinators and other small organisms. **Pyrethrum**, an organic pesticide containing pyrethrins I and II extracted from chrysanthemum flowers, is moderately to highly toxic to many other organisms than insect pests.[114] [115] There is little known about the level of toxicity that pyrethrins exhibit in humans. **Abamectin** is an acaricide, or miticide. Abamectin is a compound synthesized from a particular bacterium and exhibits broad toxicity toward many kinds of organisms including fish and mammals.[116] **Bifenazate** is another pesticide compound commonly found in Cannabis products. Bifenazate is used to treat mites. Bifenazate is not approved for food crop use, so *there are no required chronic toxicity studies available,* meaning that it is not known what health effects repeated exposure to bifenazate would cause. Acute exposure toxicity studies show that it exhibits fairly low toxicity in humans but exhibits moderate or high toxicity in aquatic animals, honeybees, and earthworms.[117]

**Fumigants** are sometimes used to sterilize grow rooms, drying rooms, storage rooms, and even soils and plants. Fumigants often contain various pesticides like Pyrethroids and organophosphates. Residues of these pesticides can hang around for prolonged periods of time if used in an enclosed space, potentially leading to contamination if plant material is brought into the area too soon. These fumigants often also contain synergistic compounds to enhance the effects of the pesticide such as piperonyl butoxide (PBO). PBO has been found to be nearly ubiquitous among Cannabis products, being found in approximately 60% of samples according to the results presented in a white paper published by the Cannabis Safety Institute.[118] PBO is not only added to pyrethroid products, but also to a variety of pyrethrin and carbamate products.

Certain **plant growth regulators** (PGRs) like paclobutrazol or daminozide, which are only approved for use on ornamental plants, *not* food crops meant for consumption, find their way into Cannabis plants. PGRs are typically used in indoor hydroponic growing to enhance Cannabis flower density and are sometimes unlisted

---

[113] Alavanja MCR, Hoppin J, Kamel F. 2004. Health Effects of Chronic Pesticide Exposure: Cancer and Neurotoxicity. Annu. Rev. Public Health. 25:155-97
https://doi.org/10.1146/annurev.publhealth.25.101802.123020
[114] http://sitem.herts.ac.uk/aeru/ppdb/en/
[115] http://sitem.herts.ac.uk/aeru/bpdb/index.htm
[116] http://sitem.herts.ac.uk/aeru/bpdb/Reports/8.htm
[117] http://sitem.herts.ac.uk/aeru/ppdb/en/Reports/76.htm
[118] Voelker R, Holmes M. 2014. Pesticide Use on Cannabis. Cannabis Safety Institute white paper publication. https://cdn.technologynetworks.com/tn/Resources/pdf/pesticide-use-on-cannabis.pdf

ingredients in various products. These compounds have been banned for use on food crops by the EPA since 1989 due to proposed cancer and cytotoxicity (cell damage) risks to humans.

## THINKING CRITICALLY ABOUT PESTICIDE TOXICITY

It is important to take a moment to point out that exposure rates and dose are critical variables when determining how toxic something is. Many pesticides are not thought to be harmful in acute exposures at low dosages. However, if someone is exposed to pesticides frequently at low dosages, it could become a problem. Likewise, if someone is exposed to pesticides one time, but at a high dose, it could be a problem. The dose and frequency of exposure make the poison, in this case.

When determining how to think about pesticide exposure, one would have to examine the toxicology information for each pesticide individually, and identify the risks associated with both acute and chronic exposure, and at what dosages that exposure becomes dangerous. When handling any agrochemical, it is important to wear appropriate personal protective equipment to shield the eyes, ears, airways, and skin from exposure. For consumers, it is generally best to be cautious and discerning of the Cannabis they are purchasing. Generally, consumers should only purchase Cannabis that has been tested to be free of major pesticides of concern, though this is not always possible, particularly in regions that have not yet legalized medical or adult use Cannabis.

## PESTICIDE PERSISTENCE AND MOBILITY

There are many other distinct types of pesticides with varying degrees of toxicity and persistence. Most pesticides act by either suppressing or overexciting an animal's central nervous system. Because of this, chronic exposure to some pesticides can result in neurological damage.

**Persistence** is a compound's ability to resist breaking down in the environment. Persistence is measured using half-life. A **half-life** is the amount of time it takes for half of the original amount of a compound to break down. Organochlorine pesticides like DDT are highly persistent (DDT can have a half-life of 2 – 15 years in some cases![119]) and can remain in soil and water for a very long time. Other pesticides like Pyrethroids and Carbamates are typically *not* persistent.

Persistence in soil is directly influenced by a compounds soil adsorption coefficient and its half-life. The **soil adsorption coefficient** is a number which represents how likely the compound is to become mobile, leaching away from the application area. The smaller the soil adsorption coefficient, the more likely a compound is to become mobile. A compound's soil adsorption coefficient and half-life can help you get an idea of how persistent a compound might be. If a compound has a low soil adsorption coefficient and a high half-life, the compound is likely to migrate out and contaminate surrounding water and soil without breaking down for an extended period of time.

---

[119] https://www.atsdr.cdc.gov/toxguides/toxguide-35.pdf

# MODES OF ACTION:
## CONTACT VS. SYSTEMIC VS. TRANSLAMINAR PESTICIDES

Not all pesticides affect plants equally or act the same way to kill insects. The way in which pesticides behave can influence whether pesticide residues may be present on harvested Cannabis. Generally, pesticides can be broken down into three primary modes of action – contact, systemic, and translaminar.

Contact pesticides are pesticides which kill insects upon contact. A common household example would be wasp spray. The pesticides in wasp spray will only kill a wasp if the spray contacts the wasp. Likewise, some pesticides applied to plants are only affective if they make direct contact with pests. Contact pesticides are often applied thoroughly on the undersides and tops of leaves to ensure thorough coverage and contact with pests. Some examples of common contact pesticides used in Cannabis cultivation are carbaryl, bifenthrin, pyrethrins, and bifenazate.

| Common Pesticides by Mode of Action | | |
|---|---|---|
| Contact Pesticides (Kill on Contact) | Translaminar Pesticides (Soak into Tissues) | Systemic Pesticides (Accumulate) |
| Carbaryl | Spinosad | Azadirachtin |
| Bifenthrin | Abamectin | Imidacloprid |
| Pyrethrins | Acephate | Myclobutanil |
| Bifenazate | Chlorfenapyr | |

FIGURE 15: PESTICIDES BY MODE OF ACTION

Systemic pesticides work by circulating through the inside of the plant throughout its vascular tissues. Over time, pesticides concentrate into tissues throughout the plant, killing pests that consume the plant material. **Systemic pesticides can linger for a very long time, in some cases months after application.** Examples of commonly used systemic pesticides in Cannabis cultivation include azadirachtin, imidacloprid, and myclobutanil.

Another type of pesticide, which lingers in plants for a long time, but acts more like a contact pesticide, are translaminar pesticides. These are pesticides which will soak through leaf and stem tissues to form small pockets of pesticide within the plant tissue. If an insect feeds on the plant material or attempts to drink water from plant tissues, the insect will contact the pesticide and potentially die. Because these pesticides can become trapped in leaf tissue, they can be present long after application. It is important that Cannabis treated with translaminar pesticides be very thoroughly trimmed to remove any potential contaminated leaf material. Examples of translaminar pesticides commonly used in Cannabis cultivation include spinosad, abamectin, acephate, and chlorfenapyr.

## ENVIRONMENTAL IMPACT OF RESIDUAL PESTICIDES

Many pesticides are toxic to pollinators, aquatic organisms, and other critical components of the interconnected systems that keep natural processes and ecosystems functioning as we know them. If these organisms are negatively impacted, over time the entire system of which they are a part will feel the effects of their decline in some way. This presents environmental concern depending on the sites of pesticide contamination and the persistence of the particular contaminant.

Neonicotinoid pesticides have been in the press over recent years as a possible culprit for Colony Collapse Disorder among some bee populations. Pollinators are necessary for many types of food and seed production. Without pollination, food crops and many flowering plants would not reproduce and would steadily decline in number. Eventually humans and many other organisms would struggle to survive. Although some plants can rely on wind-assisted pollination, most plants also require assistance from animals, like insects, to ensure pollination occurs.

Aquatic organisms like microinvertebrates help recycle nutrients in water systems, boosting dissolved oxygen levels, making it easier for fish and other organisms to breathe, and keeping the water clean. As aquatic organism populations fall, water quality suffers, sometimes leading to microbiological pathogen contaminations which can ultimately poison animals (including humans) that drink the water. When biodiversity in a water system drops, other organisms begin to dominate, like algae. When algal blooms occur, oxygen in the water is reduced, making it even harder for other organisms to live. Light is prevented from reaching other plants that grow in the water which provide food to other organisms. A cascading effect is initiated which slowly reduces the biodiversity, and ultimately the quality, of the water system.

Nearly all pesticides, including those derived from natural sources like azadirachtin, are often moderately to highly toxic to soil organisms that are responsible for nutrient cycling in the soil, maintaining bacterial and fungal populations, while also sometimes serving as predators for potential pests. The environmental impacts of pesticide use can be minimized through integrated pest management, proper planning, and if necessary to apply pesticides, utilizing light and direct applications. It should be noted that **some cultivators have learned how to avoid using pesticides or synthetic fertilizers altogether in turn for a cultivation system involving no tilling of the soil, strategic interplanting of other plant species, and integrated pest management with success.**

*To learn more about pesticide persistence, human health effects, and potential environmental effects, I recommend visiting the Pesticide Properties Database[120] and Biopesticides Properties Database[121] websites.*

# RESIDUAL SOLVENTS

## "Solvent" Is A Scary Word – But It Shouldn't Be

Solvents are liquids that can dissolve other liquids or solids. There are many things which act as solvents that we often do not think of as solvents – like water, vegetable oils, or essential oils (terpenoids). Flavonoids dissolve in water. Cannabinoids and terpenoids dissolve in fats and oils like vegetable oil. Essential oils can dissolve rubber!

---

[120] http://sitem.herts.ac.uk/aeru/ppdb/en/
[121] http://sitem.herts.ac.uk/aeru/bpdb/index.htm

Some solvents are more aggressive and dangerous than others. Ethanol is a common solvent used to produce Cannabis extracts which humans can ingest acutely in low doses without much adverse effect. However, methanol, which is just one carbon smaller than ethanol, can cause blindness when consumed even in small quantities.

Some common examples of solvents used in Cannabis extractions are butane, propane, hexane, ethanol, isopropanol, and carbon dioxide. Traces of many of these solvents can be left behind during the production process (apart from carbon dioxide, generally). Depending on the purity of the solvent, there could also be a variety of industrial contaminants present in the solvent itself which can find their way into the extract or finished product.

Organic solvents can also be found in the environment such as in the air or water, particularly in industrial areas, which can end up being absorbed into the plant or into the air systems of product manufacturing buildings – potentially making their way into products. However, the simple present of solvents in a product is not necessarily cause for alarm. It is important to understand which solvents are particularly dangerous and what concentrations humans can be exposed to before suffering adverse reactions.

The toxicity of solvents is classified among three classes. Class 1 represents compounds which have been shown to be carcinogenic, damaging to the nervous system, or otherwise highly toxic. Benzene is a Class 1 solvent and is highly toxic. Class 2 represents compounds which have not been shown to be extremely toxic upon light exposure but may be dangerous with repeated exposure or direct ingestion. Compounds like hexane and methanol are Class 2 solvents. Class 3 solvents are compounds which have relatively low toxic potential, like ethanol, butane, and propane.

## Solvent Toxicity Classes

| CLASS 1 – DANGER! HIGH TOXICITY |
| --- |
| Compounds which have been shown to be carcinogenic, damaging to the nervous system, or otherwise highly toxic. Example: Benzene |
| **CLASS 2 – MODERATE TOXICITY** |
| Compounds which have not been shown to be extremely toxic upon light exposure but may be dangerous with repeated exposure or direct ingestion. Examples: Hexane, Methanol |
| **CLASS 3 – LOW TOXICITY** |
| Compounds with a relatively low toxic potential. Examples: Ethanol, Butane, Propane |

FIGURE 16: SOLVENT TOXICITY CLASSES

# OTHER CHEMICAL CONTAMINANTS

Most pesticides and many commercial solvents have varying amounts of other chemicals present besides the target chemicals which can carry over into natural products. One common example is **piperonyl butoxide**, a synergist agent added to many pesticides to keep them from breaking down quickly, thus making them more effective. Lower purity grades of solvents (<99% purity) may have a variety of other compounds present in them. Commercial laboratories testing for residual solvents in Cannabis products may be able to assist in uncovering hidden industrial contaminants in solvents.

It is also possible to get chemical contaminants in a Cannabis product if the product is not manufactured appropriately with adequate quality controls. For instance, if a manufacturer is synthesizing a particular cannabinoid, like delta-8-THC, from another cannabinoid, like CBD, it is very easy to produce a lot of non-target compounds in the process which may be difficult or impossible to identify. Some of these compounds may be miscellaneous cannabinoids or terpenoids that may be fairly innocuous, but some could be much more toxic, like benzene or various aldehyde compounds. These unintended chemical byproducts which are not present in the plant material must be considered contaminants or additives and should be treated as such.

# HEAVY METALS

Cannabis is a great nutrient accumulator. Cannabis is so good at drawing things out of the ground that it can be used to help remove toxic metals out of a contaminated soil. Depending on where and how Cannabis is being grown, it is possible for Cannabis to absorb elevated levels of metals. Certain pesticides contain heavy metals that can become concentrated with repeated applications.

Cannabis accumulates heavy metals in all plant parts, although newer research indicates that the highest concentration of metals typically accumulates in the roots.[122] In some cases, it can concentrate nickel as much as 63 ppm in leaves, 33 ppm in seeds, and 7 ppm in fibers.[123] These metals can become distributed throughout food chains that involve Cannabis. Heavy metals can accumulate in the body leading to health risks after constant exposure.

In addition to heavy metal contaminant exposure coming from the plant itself, heavy metals from contact surfaces and storage containers can also contaminate Cannabis products, like Cannabis extracts and tinctures, with heavy metals. For instance, heavy metals have been found in vaporizer components used in common Cannabis vaporizer pens.[124] Furthermore, early research on this subject demonstrates that these heavy metals are capable of leaching from contaminated vaporizer hardware into the extract. In 2019, Boyar et al. demonstrated that lead (Pb) exceeding action levels in CA was found in cannabis extracts after being exposed to contaminated hardware over the course of two months.[125] The work of Boyar was expanded upon by

---

[122] Galic M, Percin A, Zgorelec Z, Kisic I. 2019. Evaluation of heavy metals accumulation potential of hemp (Cannabis sativa L.). Journal of Central European Agriculture. 20(2): 700 – 711. https://doi.org/10.5513/JCEA01/20.2.2201

[123] Linger, P, Mussig, J, Fischer, H, Kobert, J. 2002. Industrial hemp (Cannabis sativa L.) growing on heavy metal contaminated soil: fibre quality and phytoremediation potential. Industrial Crops and Products. 16:33-42 https://doi.org/10.1016/S0926-6690(02)00005-5

[124] https://cacpodcast.com/bts-06-anthony-smith-phd-on-cannabis-contaminants-cannabis-testing-and-molecular-biology/

[125] *viva voce*

McDaniel et al. in 2021 using a larger panel of heavy metals and found chromium (Cr), nickel (Ni), and copper (Cu) were the primary contaminats found in cannabis vaporizer cartridges. This finidng makes sense considering many of the heating elements found in cannabis vaporizer cartridges are composed of nichrome wire.[126]

It is very important for product manufacturers to conduct chemical compatibility tests on their materials prior to releasing products into the market to ensure that they are not leaching chemicals, like metals, from their equipment or storage containers into an otherwise clean Cannabis product.

Additionally heavy metals contamination can come from contaminated growth media. When I spoke with pharmacognosy researcher and molecular biologist Dr. Anthony Smith in season one of The Curious About Cannabis™ Podcast, he explained that, from his own experience testing Cannabis product samples for metals, some growers are finding high levels of metals in their immature plants due to contaminated rock wool.[127]

## ADDITIVES IN INHALABLE CANNABIS PRODUCTS

As novel Cannabis products are developed, the issue of additives in Cannabis products become a growing concern. This is of particular concern in inhalable products, like "vape pens" because toxins that are inhaled can damage the lungs and enter the bloodstream without first being broken down by the liver as they would normally be if consumed orally.

In 2019, a series of lung infections and deaths attributed to vaping were identified, resulting in over 2000 injuries and 40 deaths nationwide.[128] The phenomenon was called E-cigarette or Vaping Product Use-Associated Lung Injury, or EVALI. After testing tissue samples of affected individuals, the Centers for Disease Control (CDC) announced that they had identified an additive that was consistent in all the samples tested.[129] The additive that was identified was tocopherol acetate, or Vitamin E acetate.

Another contaminant that was later identified in some of these vaping solutions was a compound called Squalane, which is a derivative of a compound called Squalene which is known to cause lipoid pneumonia and other lung complications.[130] Vitamin E acetate and Squalane were being added to Cannabis oils, as well as nicotine oils for electronic cigarettes, as a thickening agent and a cheaper alternative to Vitamin E to reduce lung irritation and coughing. The consequence was that these thickeners

---

[126] McDaniel C, Mallampati SR, Wise A. Metals in Cannabis Vaporizer Aerosols: Sources, Possible Mechanisms, and Exposure Profiles. Chem Res Toxicol. 2021 Nov 15;34(11):2331-2342. https://doi.org/10.1021/acs.chemrestox.1c00230

[127] https://cacpodcast.com/bts-06-anthony-smith-phd-on-cannabis-contaminants-cannabis-testing-and-molecular-biology/

[128] https://www.cdc.gov/tobacco/basic_information/e-cigarettes/severe-lung-disease.html

[129] https://www.cdc.gov/mmwr/volumes/68/wr/mm6847e1.htm

[130] Duffy B, Li L, Lu S, Durocher L, Dittmar M, Delaney-Baldwin E, Panawennage D, LeMaster D, Navarette K, Spink D. 2020. Analysis of cannabinoid-containing fluids in illicit vaping cartridges recovered from pulmonary injury patients: identification of vitamin E acetate as a major diluent. Toxics. 8(1):8. https://doi.org/10.3390/toxics8010008

could not be properly removed from the lungs after vaping, and the substance coated the lungs, making it difficult for the lungs to keep up with normal functioning.

Additionally, many Cannabis products are starting to be formulated with the additions of many different flavoring compounds and diluents. While many of these compounds, like common plant-derived terpenoids, have been used traditionally in foods and topicals for many years, these compounds have not been traditionally ingested through smoking or vaping – which means there is not a lot of health or safety information regarding the use of these compounds in this manner.

Foreign materials which are known to be hazardous to inhale, such as pine rosin, are being used to dilute Cannabis extracts.[131] This pine rosin adulterant seems to primarily show up in "shatter" extracts and are now referred to as "fake shatter". The consequences of smoking pine rosin can be very similar to the symptoms seen in EVALI patients. At the time that the study identifying pine rosin in Cannabis extracts was published, EVALI patient tissues had not been tested for some of the chemical markers of pine rosin.

It would be naïve to think that this adulteration is limited to illicit Cannabis markets. Even in states that require Cannabis quality testing, labs cannot identify adulterants that they are not prepared to look for. For instance, now that pine rosin is a known adulterant in Cannabis extracts, laboratories can develop assays that look for some of the unique chemicals found in pine rosin, such as abietic acid, palustric acid, pimaric acid, communic acid, and pimarol.[132]

In the United States, the FDA has begun compiling a list of harmful or potentially harmful compounds (HPHCs) in tobacco products, which can help serve as a guide to Cannabis producers on what additives to definitely avoid using in products. In 2019, the FDA submitted to add several more compounds to the current list of HPHCs in response to unique compounds found in vaping devices and electronic nicotine delivery systems (ENDS).[133]

| Proposed Additions to the FDA's List of HPHCs | | |
|---|---|---|
| Acetic Acid | Ethyl Acetate | Isobutyl Acetate |
| Acetoin | Ethyl Acetoacetate | Methyl Acetate |
| Acetyl Propionyl | Ethylene Glycol | n-butanol |
| Benzyl Acetate | Furfural | Propionic Acid |
| Butyraldehyde | Glycerol | Propylene Glycol |
| Diacetyl | Glycidol | |
| Diethylene Glycol | Isoamyl Acetate | |

Figure 17: Proposed Additions to FDA List of Harmful Compounds

---

[131] Meehan-Atrash J, Strongin RM. 2020. Pine rosin identified as a toxic cannabis extract adulterant. Forensic Science International. 312: 110301. https://doi.org/10.1016/j.forsciint.2020.110301

[132] Meehan-Atrash J, Strongin RM. 2020. Pine rosin identified as a toxic cannabis extract adulterant. Forensic Science International. 312: 110301. https://doi.org/10.1016/j.forsciint.2020.110301
[133] https://www.federalregister.gov/documents/2019/08/05/2019-16658/harmful-and-potentially-harmful-constituents-in-tobacco-products-established-list-proposed-additions

## Additives Found in Cannabis Extracts

| | | | |
|---|---|---|---|
| **Propylene Glycol (PG)** | May irritate lungs in high doses; Formaldehyde is a degradation product; Turns into propylene oxide when burned, which is carcinogenic | **Squalane and Squalene** | Squalene can cause lipoid pneumonia when inhaled and is sometimes found as a contaminant in squalane. |
| **Vegetable Glycerin (VG)** | May irritate lungs in high doses; Formaldehyde is a degradation product | **Tocopherol (Vitamin E)** | May impair lung function |
| **Terpenoids** | May irritate lungs and cause inflammation in high concentrations, particularly if the terpenoids are oxidized | **Tocopherol Acetate (Vitamin E Acetate)** | May impair lung function |
| **Medium Chain Triglycerides (MCT Oil)** | May impair lung function and cause inflammation | **Pine Rosin** | More common in "shatter"; can cause severe lung dysfunction |

FIGURE 18: COMMON ADDITIVES FOUND IN CANNABIS EXTRACTS

## Enduring Understandings

- Something's toxicity is relative to the dose and rate of exposure ("the dose makes the poison").
- Some of the common contaminants found in Cannabis include fungi, like molds, mycotoxins, bacteria, pesticides, and metals.
- Common contaminants found in Cannabis extracts include mycotoxins, pesticides, metals, and residual solvents.
- Common contaminants found in finished Cannabis infused products typically include bacteria, like *E. coli*, *Salmonella*, or *Pseudomonas*.
- Various additives may also be found in Cannabis products, like propylene glycol, tocopherol acetate (vitamin E acetate), or squalene.
- More recently, pine rosin has been identified as an adulterant in Cannabis extracts, and primarily in "shatter" extracts

# Pop Quiz!

What is the primary source of bacterial contamination of Cannabis?


Mycotoxins can pass into side stream smoke during Cannabis smoking.

TRUE          FALSE


In what parts of the Cannabis plant do metals accumulate?

 a)  Roots
 b)  Roots and Shoots
 c)  Leaves
 d)  All plant parts
 e)  No plant parts


Describe the concepts of pesticide persistence and mobility.



List at least four additives that may be found in Cannabis extracts.

Answers: Post-harvest handling; True; D; Persistence relates to half life, mobility relates to the likelihood a compound will move – usually related to affinity for water; see additives table on previous page

142

# Chapter 8:
## CANNABIS GENETICS

**SCAN ME**

## Learning Questions

- What is the difference between filial generations (F1, F2, etc) of Cannabis plants?
- How do genes determine how cannabinoids and terpenoids are produced in the Cannabis plant?
- How are feminized seeds produced?

This chapter is meant to provide a basic introduction to plant genetics and how genetics influence attributes in the Cannabis plant, such as cannabinoid production. However, this chapter barely scrapes the surface of the depth of this highly nuanced topic. Genetics is a complicated topic in just about any context. In the context of Cannabis and cannabinoid science, it is especially complicated. This is compounded by the fact that researchers keep learning more and more about the Cannabis genome and the mechanisms responsible for cannabinoid and terpenoid production in the plant. Let's start with some basics.

### WHAT ARE GENES?

All living organisms contain **DNA** in the nucleus of all their cells which contain **genes**. A gene is a bit of DNA that codes for one or more **proteins** in an organism. A protein is a broad term used to describe a molecular machine that does some sort of work in an organism. So basically, genes are the codes embedded in DNA which tell a cell what chemical machines to build and when to build them. These chemical machines then go on to form tissues, organelles, organs, and organisms!

By examining an organism's genes, it can be possible to determine characteristics of the organism as well as potential characteristics of an organism's offspring such as sex, disease susceptibility, paternity and more.

To examine and better understand the genes of various organisms, scientists have begun to map the **genomes** of organisms of interest. A genome is simply the complete (or mostly complete) genetic code of an organism. It is a map of all the genes of an organism.

The Human Genome Project[134], the world's largest collaborative scientific effort which was conceived in the late 1980s and completed by the early 2000s, was an attempt to map the entire human genome to better understand and treat diseases. This was an immense project. Genetic variation among individuals meant that it was not enough to just map all the genetic information of one individual, but rather the project required a very large sample size to map the differing genetic variations that

---

[134] https://www.genome.gov/human-genome-project

may be present in the human population. One problem that arose from this project was that clinicians discovered that seeing the genetic code of a human is not very helpful if you don't understand how to interpret it. Mapping a genome is only one piece of a bigger puzzle to understanding how to utilize genetic information in a meaningful way.

Today, a new effort is underway to conduct much the same sort of genome mapping, but with Cannabis. There are a variety of groups throughout the world and the US which are attempting to catalog the genetic information of as many strains of Cannabis as possible as an attempt to better understand the plant, develop plants with very specific chemical and physical profiles, secure strain data for protection against patenting, and more.

## GENETIC INHERITANCE AND HYBRIDIZATION

Organisms change over time in response to various selection pressures, whether it be natural selection or artificial selection. **Natural selection** is the concept of genetic traits being influenced by the natural environment over time. **Artificial selection** is the concept of genetic traits being influenced by other means, like human manipulation through domestication and breeding. Some scientists argue that artificial selection is really a misnomer since humans are very much inescapably a part of nature, but alas...

Cannabis genetics have been influenced both naturally and artificially for thousands of years as the plant has coevolved with humans. Cannabis cultivators have been working diligently for thousands of years to breed different Cannabis varieties for different desirable characteristics such as resin yield, fiber quality, or seed crop. Because Cannabis has been coevolving alongside humans for so long, the plant has undergone a massive amount of hybridization, or mixing, between varieties. The result is that there is now a seemingly endless array of Cannabis varieties to satisfy most any desire.

However, this sense of diversity is somewhat of an illusion because intensive hybridization and artificial selection ultimately results in a loss of "native" genes that served functions or produced traits which were not selected for. In ecological science, there is a predictable model by which we can see how intensive hybridization leads to losses in a genome, which may ultimately set up future offspring to be less adaptable to ecological conditions, leading to a potential extinction event. It is for this reason that it is critical that native organisms, or in the case of Cannabis, naturalized "landrace" cultivars, be preserved.

We are already experiencing intensive hybridization of Cannabis varieties across the planet. Even landrace cultivars are largely contaminated, having been intentionally or unintentionally crossed with other landrace varieties.[135] Let's assume all these landrace varieties were now extinct, and all that exists are the cannabinoid resin-rich cultivars currently present in the commercial Cannabis market. Through the intensive hybridization and selection for resin-rich production, perhaps a handful of

---

[135] McPartland JM, Small E. 2020. A classification of endangered high-THC cannabis (Cannabis sativa subsp. Indica) domesticates and their wild relatives. PhytoKeys. 144:81-112. https://doi.org/10.3897/phytokeys.144.46700

genes which once belonged to the ancient landrace varieties from which the plant descended was lost in the process.

In this scenario, what would happen if some previously unnoticed viral disease started wiping out commercial Cannabis crops across the world? The landrace cultivars that were naturally resistant to the virus would have had those very genes that were lost in the commercial Cannabis varieties due to intensive breeding for cannabinoids and terpenes. If the purer landrace varieties were still accessible, they could be crossed once again into the modern commercial Cannabis gene pool to give plants the resistance and adaptability needed to survive. However, in this worst-case scenario those landrace varieties would *not* be available, and the only hope would be to rely on external controls like pesticides or invasive genetic modification. And with those external controls come other considerations, like consumer health and safety.

This is a very simple thought experiment, but it demonstrates the risks to an organism's population if distinct varieties are allowed to hybridize without any preservation of the native genome. You might be asking, "How does someone preserve a genome?" The answer is simple – seeds. Seed banks have been established for many native and non-native plants to ensure that, should we ever need access to a genome from the past, whether for research purposes, restoration, or breeding – it is available. Another way that genomes are preserved is by tissue culturing plants, creating a callus which can be turned into a synthetic seed. Tissue culturing allows a genetically identical copy of a plant to be preserved for future reference, rather than the offspring as in seed collection.

Genetic breeding affects the predictability of inherited traits of child Cannabis plants from parent Cannabis plants. The first hybrid generation of an organism is referred to as the F1, or first **filial**, generation. This generation of organisms will contain genes from both parents and, thus, will display mixed dominant traits of each. For example, mules are F1 hybrids of horses and donkeys; peppermint is an F1 hybrid of watermint and spearmint. Generally, F1 organisms will end up being consistent if the same parent organisms are used for crossing/breeding. This means that you will always end up with a mule if you breed a horse and donkey; likewise, if you cross a watermint and spearmint, you will always end up with peppermint. These characteristics generally make F1 organisms more desirable for professional breeders or nurseries – they are predictable.

F2 organisms, the offspring of two F1 parents, can exhibit a wide variety of phenotypes due to the advanced genetic mixing that has occurred between the different hybrids. This leads to F2 plants expressing both dominant and recessive traits. Because of the high variability of F2 organisms, these organisms are generally less desired by professional breeders because they are unpredictable. Over time a breeder may continue to breed out more filial generations, selecting plants with desirable and/or consistent traits at each level until eventually they reach a stabilized inbred line (IBL) that performs like an F1 generation plant would, in the sense that its progeny tend to maintain the selected traits.

Alternatively, a breeder may decide to backcross a plant, where a plant with desirable traits is crossed with its parent, producing progeny that theoretically will more strongly retain whatever desired traits that they each had that the breeder selected. This is sometimes a way of stabilizing a cultivar faster.

Additionally, breeders will sometimes "self" a plant, where the plant is stressed to induce hermaphroditic traits – producing both male and female flowers. The breeder will then ensure that the plant pollinates itself and produces seed. That seed will then be used to breed new plants. This process is often performed when trying to produce "feminized" seeds as we will discuss later in the chapter.

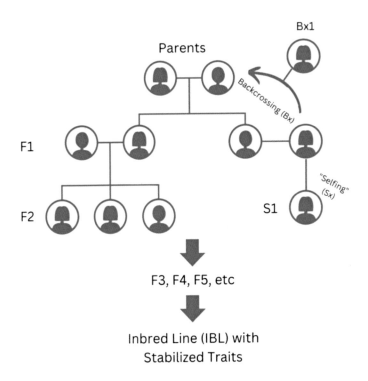

Review the differences between genotypes, phenotypes, and chemotypes on the following figure.

| Genotype | Phenotype | Chemotype |
|---|---|---|
| Genetic characteristics of an organism | Physical characteristics of an organism (what you see, feel, etc) | Chemical characteristics of an organism (chemical phenotype) |
| Controlled by genetic transcription | Controlled by genes and environment | Controlled by genes and environment |
| Examples: $B_T$ alleles present in DNA of Cannabis plant, promoting THCA production | Examples: plant's size, shape, color, etc | Examples: THC/CBD ratio, terpene profile |

FIGURE 19: GENOTYPE VS PHENOTYPE VS CHEMOTYPE

## Cannabinoid and Terpenoid Biosynthesis in Cannabis

To understand the genetics behind cannabinoid and terpenoid production, we must first talk about the chemical pathways involved in producing cannabinoids and terpenoids in the Cannabis plant. There are elaborate series of chemical pathways that lead to the formation of terpenes and cannabinoids in Cannabis, and not all these pathways are well understood. Monoterpenoids, sesquiterpenoids, the olivetolic acid-based cannabinoids (CBGA, THCA, CBDA, CBCA), and the divarinic acid based cannabinoids (CBGVA, THCVA, CBDVA, CBCVA), all stem from a common chemical pathway, called the deoxyxylulose synthetic pathway. This pathway begins with the combination of **DMAPP** (Dimethylallyl pyrophosphate/diphosphate) and **IPP** (Isopentenyl pyrophosphate/diphosphate) to form geranyl-pyrophosphate, or **GPP**.

**Geranyl-pyrophosphate** then either binds with olivetolic acid or divarinic acid to form the unique pathways toward the various phytocannabinoids.[136] [137] If GPP binds with **olivetolic acid**, the synthetic pathway leads toward CBGA which can then be synthesized into either THCA, CBDA, or CBCA. If GPP binds with **divarinic acid**, the pathway leads toward THCV, CBDV, etc.[138]

Through a particular enzymatic process, GPP could instead transition toward other terpenoids, like the monoterpenoids or sesquiterpenoids. If GPP does not acquire any extra isoprene units, it might encounter an enzyme which rearranges the GPP molecule into what we now know as the monoterpene limonene. If GPP *does* acquire an extra isoprene unit and then encounters certain enzymes, it might be transformed into a sesquiterpenoid.

Note that decarboxylated cannabinoids like THC, CBD, THCV, etc are not actually synthesized by Cannabis. Instead, the plant synthesizes cannabinoid acids such as THCA, CBDA, THCVA, etc.

## Why Does Cannabis Produce Terpenoids and Cannabinoids?

Terpenoids are hypothesized to serve a variety of functions in the Cannabis plant, but no one really knows exactly why the Cannabis plant produces the compounds that it does. Some primary functions of terpenoids are thought to be: **protection from desiccation (drying), insect predation, and UV radiation**. Since cannabinoids are oily, they can serve as good barriers to water loss in surrounding plant tissues.[139] In THC chemotype Cannabis plants, THC concentration tends to increase with increased UV-B radiation, potentially producing a protective effect for the plant. This effect does not exist for other cannabinoids like CBD, lending a particular evolutionary advantage to THC dominant Cannabis plants in higher elevation areas.[140] The

---

[136] Fellermeier M, Eisenreich W, Bacher A, Zenk MH. Biosynthesis of cannabinoids. Incorporation experiments with (13)C-labeled glucoses. Eur J Biochem. 2001;268:1596–1604. https://doi.org/10.1046/j.1432-1033.2001.02030.x

[137] De Meijer E. 2015. The Chemical Phenotypes (Chemotypes) of Cannabis. Handbook of Cannabis. Oxford University Press. Chapter 5. pp. 89-110.

[138] Russo EB. 2011. Taming THC: potential Cannabis synergy and phytocannabinoid-terpenoid entourage effects. Br J of Pharmacol 163:1344-1364. https://doi.org/10.1111/j.1476-5381.2011.01238.x

[139] https://www.druglibrary.org/olsen/hemp/iha/iha01201.html

[140] https://www.druglibrary.org/olsen/hemp/iha/iha01201.html

cannabinoid acids present in growing Cannabis have demonstrated insecticidal properties that could discourage insect predation.

Ethan Russo points out that the Cannabis plant expresses a "phytochemical polymorphism", meaning that the plant produces varying concentrations of terpenoids in varying parts of the plant.[141] For instance, the bottom portion of the plant typically produces higher concentrations of bitter sesquiterpenoids that discourage herbivory from grazing animals.[142] [143] [144] Plants typically produce excess terpenes in response to environmental stresses to attract predatory insects and repel herbivorous insect predators. Terpene concentrations are influenced by poor soil nutrition as well, as one research project demonstrated that terpene concentrations were higher in plants that experienced reduced nitrogen prior to harvest.[145]

In Michael Pollan's book turned PBS documentary, *Botany of Desire*[146] [147], Pollan remarks on how smells and intoxication effects have influenced humans to help the plant spread its geographical reach, reproduce, and express itself in countless physical and chemical varieties. By artificially selecting plant varieties based on how they meet various human desires such as intoxication, smell, and taste, humans have drastically affected the evolution of the Cannabis plant and have bred out a huge variety of cannabinoid and terpene profiles.

[141] Russo EB. 2011. Taming THC: potential Cannabis synergy and phytocannabinoid-terpenoid entourage effects. Br J of Pharmacol 163:1344-1364. https://doi.org/10.1111/j.1476-5381.2011.01238.x
[142] Russo EB. 2011. Taming THC: potential Cannabis synergy and phytocannabinoid-terpenoid entourage effects. Br J of Pharmacol 163:1344-1364. https://doi.org/10.1111/j.1476-5381.2011.01238.x
[143] Franz C, Novak J. Sources of essential oils. In: Baser KHC, Buchbauer G, editors. Handbook of Essential Oils: Science, Technology, and Applications. Boca Raton, FL: CRC Press; 2010. pp. 39–82.
[144] Nerio LS, Olivero-Verbel J, Stashenko E. Repellent activity of essential oils: a review. Bioresour Technol. 2010;101:372–378. https://doi.org/10.1016/j.biortech.2009.07.048
[145] Potter D. Growth and morphology of medicinal cannabis. In: Guy GW, Whittle BA, Robson P, editors. Medicinal Uses of Cannabis and Cannabinoids. London: Pharmaceutical Press; 2004. pp. 17–54.
[146] https://michaelpollan.com/books/the-botany-of-desire/
[147] https://shop.pbs.org/WA8682.html

# Cannabinoid Biosynthetic Pathway in Cannabis

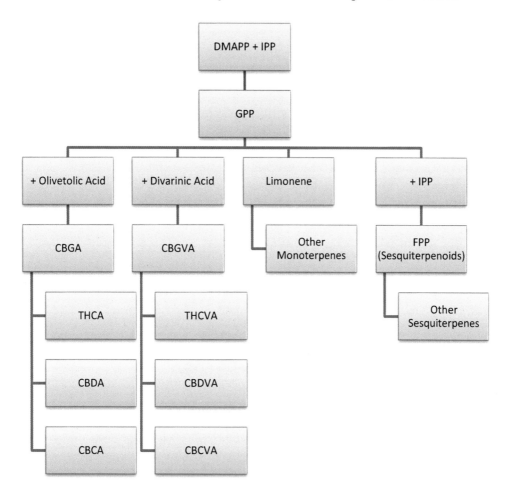

**FIGURE 20: DEOXYXYLULOSE PATHWAY FOR CANNABINOID AND TERPENOID SYNTHESIS**[148] [149] [150]

| | | | |
|---|---|---|---|
| DMAPP | Dimethylallyl pyrophosphate | CBDA | Cannabidiolic acid |
| IPP | Isopentenyl pyrophosphate | CBCA | Cannabichromenic acid |
| GPP | Geranyl pyrophosphate | CBGVA | Cannabigerivarinic acid |
| FPP | Farnesyl pyrophosphate | THCVA | Tetrahydrocannabivarinic acid |
| CBGA | Cannabigerolic Acid | CBDVA | Cannabidivarinic acid |
| THCA | Delta-9-tetrahydrocannabinolic acid | CBCVA | Cannabichromivarinic acid |

[148] Russo EB. 2011. Taming THC: potential Cannabis synergy and phytocannabinoid-terpenoid entourage effects. Br J of Pharmacol 163:1344-1364. https://doi.org/10.1111/j.1476-5381.2011.01238.x

[149] De Meijer E. 2015. The Chemical Phenotypes (Chemotypes) of Cannabis. Handbook of Cannabis. Oxford University Press. Chapter 5. pp. 89-110.

[150] Fellermeier M, Eisenreich W, Bacher A, Zenk MH. Biosynthesis of cannabinoids. Incorporation experiments with (13)C-labeled glucoses. Eur J Biochem. 2001 Mar;268(6):1596-604. doi: 10.1046/j.1432-1033.2001.02030.x. PMID: 11248677. https://doi.org/10.1046/j.1432-1033.2001.02030.x

# CANNABINOID GENES

So far, researchers are under the assumption that there are three primary dominant cannabinoid phenotypes present in Cannabis: THC dominant, CBD dominant, and CBG dominant. To be more accurate in accounting for carboxylic acids, it would be THCA dominant, CBDA dominant, and CBGA dominant. Among these dominant cannabinoid phenotypes there are intermediaries, forming a spectrum of possible phenotypes. Other chemotypes have been identified and/or developed such as the CBCA dominant chemotype, but these are considered rare, for now.

The ratios of cannabinoids in the Cannabis plant are primarily controlled by genetics and generally affected little by the environment, though little is understood about potential epigenetic effects in Cannabis. However, the *concentrations* of compounds in Cannabis can be influenced heavily by the environment.

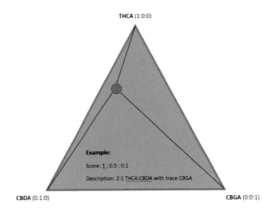

FIGURE 21: VISUALIZATION OF THCA:CBDA:CBGA CHEMOTYPE SPECTRUM

Cannabis is naturally a **diploid** organism with each Cannabis plant containing two (di-) separate sets of genes (-ploid), one from each parent. However modern breeding has produced **tetraploid** Cannabis plants, containing two sets of genes from each parent, which have then been bred with diploid plants to produce **triploid** Cannabis plants containing two sets of genes from one parent and one set of genes from another parent.[151]

These genes are present as tightly wound bunches of DNA that are coiled into structures called chromosomes. Cannabis plants contain 20 chromosomes total – 10 from each parent. Throughout these chromosomes are certain sections, or **loci** (locations), responsible for providing genetic instructions for building particular proteins, like an enzyme responsible for making THCA, for example. The different variations of a gene at a single location on a chromosome are called **alleles**.

In many cases, some alleles are considered "dominant", while others are considered "recessive". When different alleles for a genetic trait are mixed in a progeny, the dominant alleles will be expressed unless two recessive alleles are paired together. In the case of THC and CBD production in Cannabis, the associated alleles for THC and

---

[151] https://oregoncbdseeds.com/triploids/

CBD production are "codominant", meaning that the presence of one does not override the other. If the $B_D$ allele (C$\underline{BD}$ allele at the "B" locus) is present, the plant will produce CBD. If the $B_T$ allele ($\underline{T}$HC allele at the "B" locus) is present, the plant will produce THC. If both the $B_D$ and $B_T$ allele are present, the plant will produce a mix of CBD and THC.

A variety of genetic models describing cannabinoid production exist. One proposed mechanism consists of four genetic loci on Cannabis chromosomes that affect the cannabinoid chemotype of a Cannabis plant.

### Proposed Genetic Loci Associated with Cannabinoid Production in Cannabis[152]

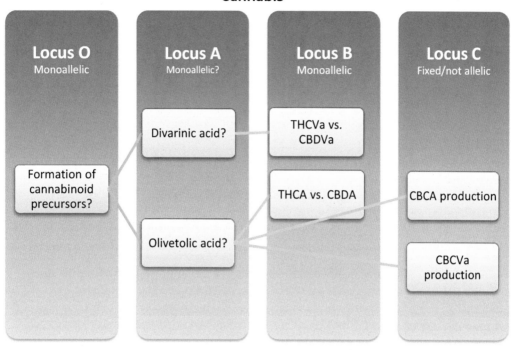

| Locus | Traits Affected | Notes |
|---|---|---|
| **Locus O** | Will cannabinoid precursors be formed? | Resorcinolic acids are either formed or not formed, leading to the production of geranylpyrophosphate (GPP), one of the primary precursors for cannabinoids. |
| **Locus A** | How much olivetolic acid and divarinic acid will be made? | These alleles are thought to control production of divarinic and olivetolic acid, or somehow control how GPP joins with either DA or OA to produce CBGA or CBGVA. |
| **Locus B** | How efficiently will CBGA/CBGVA convert to THCA/THCVA, CBDA/CBDVA, etc? | $B_T$ alleles control THCA production, $B_D$ alleles control CBDA production. $B_T/B_T$ = high THC plant. $B_D/B_D$ = high CBD plant. $B_D/B_T$ plants responsible for intermediate THC:CBD ratio chemotypes. Mutant alleles ($B_0$) produce excess CBGA or CBGVA in the plant |
| **Locus C** | CBCA production? | Fixed, not allelic |

FIGURE 22: GENETIC LOCI FOR CBGA, CBCA, AND THCA CANNABINOID PRODUCTION IN CANNABIS

[152] de Meijer E. 2015. The Chemical Phenotypes (Chemotypes) of Cannabis. Chapter Five. Handbook of Cannabis. Oxford University Press. 89-110

One thing that is very interesting about the genetics that control cannabinoid production, is that a Cannabis lineage could be bred to eliminate the THCA synthase gene, which would mean that, in theory, the THCA synthase *enzyme* should not be produced in the plant, and thus THCA itself should not be produced in the plant - and yet the plant could still produce trace amounts of THCA. This is because, simply put, genes are not perfect. They behave in different ways depending on a variety of factors. It may be possible for the CBDA synthase gene, for instance, to occasionally build THCA synthase enzymes instead of CBDA synthase enzymes.[153]

Additionally, genes that control for traits like cannabinoid expression, may also be associated with other characteristics like pathogen resistance.[154] Breeding that is targeted at specific cannabinoids could potentially end up breeding out pathogen resistance, putting the crop at greater risk of attack or infection (remember that worst-case example we went through earlier about preserving landrace varieties of Cannabis?).

**Do cannabinoid genes show up in other plants?** Yes!

A 2019 study published results from a search researchers performed to hunt for CBDAS and THCAS in other organisms. They found that "both cannabinoid synthases seem to be widely distributed in the plant kingdom." The mulberry plant Morus notabilis was found to contain genes that were most similar to Cannabis' CBDAS or THCAS. The researchers reported that they did not find any genetic sequences in fungi or bacteria that matched that of CBDAS or THCAS, though sequences were found in *Tramates versicolor* (Turkey Tail Mushrooms) and *Aspergillus saccharolyticus* that were similar to THCAS.[155]

Cannabinoid synthase genes are most closely related to **Berberine Bridge Enzyme (BBE)** genes, which are responsible for the production of many secondary metabolites in plants in the form of alkaloids. It may be that at some point in evolutionary history, cannabinoid synthase genes evolved from BBEs – or vice versa.

## TERPENOID GENES

Terpene production in plants is made possible because of enzymes called terpene synthases, or TPS. Terpene synthase genes, or TPS genes, control the production of these critical enzymes. When terpenoids are being produced in the Cannabis plant, they are formed from a common precursor shared with cannabinoids – geranyl pyrophosphate. Only, instead of pairing with olivetolic acid or divarinic acid to form CBGA or CBGVA – terpene synthases can change geranyl pyrophosphate into any

---

[153] McKernan KJ, Helbert Y, Kane LT, Ebling H, Zhang L, Liu B, Eaton Z, McLaughlin S, Kingan S, Baybayan P, Concepcion G, Jordan M, Riva A, Barbazuk W, Harkins T. 2020. Sequence and Annotation of 42 Cannabis Genomes Reveals Extensive Copy Number Variation in Cannabinoid Synthesis and Pathogen Resistance Genes. bioRxiv. Pre-print. Published January 05, 2020.
[154] McKernan KJ, Helbert Y, Kane LT, Ebling H, Zhang L, Liu B, Eaton Z, McLaughlin S, Kingan S, Baybayan P, Concepcion G, Jordan M, Riva A, Barbazuk W, Harkins T. 2020. Sequence and Annotation of 42 Cannabis Genomes Reveals Extensive Copy Number Variation in Cannabinoid Synthesis and Pathogen Resistance Genes. bioRxiv. Pre-print. Published January 05, 2020.
[155] Aryal, N., Orellana, D.F. & Bouie, J. Distribution of cannabinoid synthase genes in non-Cannabis organisms. J Cannabis Res 1, 8 (2019). https://doi.org/10.1186/s42238-019-0008-7

number of monoterpenoids, or it can bring in other compounds like isopentenyl pyrophosphate, which provides enough isoprene units to form larger terpenoids like sesquiterpenoids.

There are various subfamilies of TPS genes – names TPS-a, TPS-b, and TPS-g. TPS-a genes are typically associated with sesquiterpenoid production. TPS-b genes are typically associated with monoterpenoid production, although it has been shown that these genes can sometimes also contribute to the production of sesquiterpenoids. TPS-g genes form certain acyclic monoterpenoids.

Research into understanding the genes behind terpene synthase production is still relatively early. Currently 30 unique TPS genes have been characterized, isolated from only 14 cultivars. This highlights the immense research opportunity available to understand how terpene profiles vary on a genetic level between cultivars. In a recent 2020 study, one TPS gene, CsTPS9, which is responsible for producing the enzyme that produces beta-caryophyllene and alpha-humulene, was found in all of the cultivars studied.[156] This study also verified that the TPS genes in Cannabis are very similar to those found in hops (*Humulus lupulus*) and much of the terpenoid diversity we see in Cannabis today is likely a result of "relatively recent multiplications of a few ancestral CsTPSs." When examining the variation of terpenoid profiles between cultivars of different and identical names, they found that **"…there was as much variation among plants that were named as the same cultivar as there was variation between plants that were labeled as different cultivars."** [157]

| TPS Gene Subfamily | Description |
|---|---|
| TPS-a | Mostly sesquiterpenoids |
| TPS-b | Mostly monoterpenoids, but also contributes to sesquiterpenoid production |
| TPS-g | Acyclic monoterpenoids |

## EPIGENETICS AND FEMINIZED SEEDS

The genetic story of an organism does not end at its conception when its parents' genetic information mixes to produce the offspring's DNA. Genetics are not entirely determined but also influenced throughout the life of the organism. Environmental conditions can affect how cells read genes and what genes are turned on and off. This means that a cell's ability to perform its function in a tissue, organelle, or organ can become altered or compromised at various times throughout its life based on environmental stress or other factors. The study of how DNA is altered through response to environmental factors rather than direct DNA manipulation is called

[156] Booth JK, Yuen MMS, Jancsik S, Madilao L, Page J, Bohlmann J. 2020. Terpene synthases and terpene variation in Cannabis sativa. Plant Physiology. doi: 10.1104/pp.20.00593
[157] Booth JK, Yuen MMS, Jancsik S, Madilao L, Page J, Bohlmann J. 2020. Terpene synthases and terpene variation in Cannabis sativa. Plant Physiology. doi: 10.1104/pp.20.00593

**epigenetics**. Epigenetic factors affecting Cannabis are not well understood at this time but are the target of genomic research currently being done with Cannabis.

An example of epigenetic effects in Cannabis can be found in "feminized seeds". An otherwise female Cannabis plant can undergo environmental stresses which can cause the plant's genes to signal the production of different sexual hormones, leading to the production of male sexual structures, potentially causing self-fertilization. Hermaphroditism is at the heart of developing "feminized seeds." **"Feminized seeds"** are seeds which have been developed to produce approximately 80 - 98%+ female plants upon germination, on average. This is contrasted with the roughly 50% chance of getting a female from non-feminized seeds. Generally feminized seeds are marketed as an advantage for cultivators because it takes some of the guesswork out of the process of growing for resin production and results in a greater number of desired plants while using less seeds, and thus less money – in theory.

The process of producing feminized seeds is fairly straightforward. A female Cannabis plant is first stressed, sometimes using exposure to colloidal silver or other stressors, to exhibit hermaphroditic tendencies. Once the stressed female plant produces male flowers and pollen, the pollen is collected and distributed to other female plants of the same variety which have not been stressed. The pollen then fertilizes the female plants to produce seeds. The resulting seeds often have a higher potential of growing into female seeds.

Unfortunately, it is often the case that these resulting seeds often produce plants which are more sensitive to environmental stress and may become hermaphrodites more easily than other plants grown from traditional seeds.  It should be noted that there are other ways to produce feminized seeds other than the method mentioned in this example. Modern breeding practices are utilizing DNA and RNA analytical technology to understand genetic changes in plants, allowing for the production of seeds that tend to produce females which cannot produce seed or male pollen should they revert to hermaphroditism.[158]

---

## Enduring Understandings

- The Cannabis plant is diploid, and its DNA consists of 20 chromosomes (10 pairs)
- A filial generation is a generation of plants produced through hybridization.
- Cannabinoids and terpenes are produced in Cannabis through a biosynthetic pathway called the deoxyxylulose pathway.
- Cannabinoid ratios are genetically controlled by cannabinoid synthase genes.
- Cannabinoid synthase genes can be promiscuous, sometimes producing other cannabinoid synthases than expected. For instance, CBCA and CBDA synthase genes can also produce THCA synthase under certain conditions.
- Cannabinoid genetics can be affected by the environment.
- Terpenoid production is moderated by terpene synthase (TPS) genes

---

[158] https://oregoncbdseeds.com/triploids/

# Chapter 9:
## HEMP

SCAN ME

### Learning Questions

- How has the term "hemp" been used throughout history?
- What is the difference between "hemp" and "marijuana"?
- What are some of the ways in which Cannabis can be used industrially?

## WHAT IS HEMP?

Cannabis plants that are low in the intoxicating component THC are often referred to as "hemp". The word "hemp" has been used to refer to all kinds of plants, not just Cannabis. In Ernest Small and David Marcus' paper *Hemp: A New Crop with New Uses for North America*, they point out that "the term has been applied to dozens of species representing at least 22 genera, often prominent fiber crops."[159] By that reasoning, it would seem apt to say that **"hemp" is a generic term referring to any plant that serves as a particularly good fiber crop**, and *Cannabis sativa* certainly fits that bill.

Cannabis that is labeled as hemp is often used for a wide variety of things ranging from fiber and fuel to food, medicine and more. The fiber from Cannabis makes very durable roping and paper. It can also be pressed into composite boards and used like traditional composite wood. Cannabis "hemp" seeds can be found in many birdseed mixes as well as breakfast cereals. One way that Cannabis may have spread throughout the world is through seed distribution as humans brought the nutritious food with them when travelling. Hemp can even be used as a source of carbon sheets used for supercapacitors to store and move electricity!

DURING WORLD WAR II, US FARMERS WERE ENCOURAGED TO GROW HEMP WITH INCENTIVES IN THE FORM OF "SPECIAL TAX STAMPS" TO PRODUCE IT, AS SEEN ABOVE.

Traditionally "industrial hemp" is thought of as varieties of Cannabis that are suitable for fiber, but today the term hemp has everything to do with its chemical profile rather than its intended use. Instead of THC, hemp plants often have much higher levels of a different cannabinoid - cannabidiol (CBD). CBD is extracted from

---

[159] Small, E., Marcus, D., Janick, J., & Whipkey, A. (2002). Hemp: a new crop with new uses for North America.

hemp type Cannabis to produce CBD-based products like tinctures, topicals, and dietary supplements. Additionally, at the time of this writing, hemp farmers are also starting to grow hemp crops featuring resin rich in Cannabigerol, or CBG.

**Today, hemp is legally defined in most places as a *Cannabis sativa* plant with trace levels of delta-9 tetrahydrocannabinol (THC), often at 0.3% or lower concentration by weight** depending on the country or state. At the time of this writing in the United States, the THC in hemp is legally defined as THC "post-decarboxylation", meaning the total theoretical concentration of THC after THCA has decarboxylated. This has confused many hemp farmers operating under the assumption or misinterpretation that THC is defined as delta-9-THC alone. The practical impact that this definition has is substantial – as it makes it much more challenging to cultivate cannabinoid rich resin Cannabis crops while staying within the legally allowed concentration of THC.

The actual text of the United States Agricultural Improvement Act of 2018[160] aka the 2018 Farm Bill states on section 297B "State and Tribal Plans" that *"A State or Tribal plan…shall only be required to include… a procedure for testing, using **post-decarboxylation** or other similarly reliable methods, delta-9 tetrahydrocannabinol concentration levels of hemp produced in the State or territory of the Indian tribe…"*

Because the text of this bill requires all states to report the amount of THC after decarboxylation, it de facto defines "THC" as what many would call "Total THC" (a combination of THC and THCA, corrected by a decarboxylation factor of 0.877 – more on that later!).

## "Hemp" vs. "Marijuana"

Hemp and marijuana are ultimately the same species of plant – *Cannabis sativa*. The difference between hemp and marijuana is their chemical profile, and arguably also their intended use.

Hemp type varieties of Cannabis are typically defined as having low concentrations of THC and high concentrations of CBDA or CBGA, whereas "marijuana" varieties of Cannabis are typically characterized as having high concentrations of THC and low concentrations of other cannabinoids.

However, this distinction has gotten very blurred as breeders have begun focusing on cultivating Cannabis varieties that contain a wide spectrum of THC to CBD ratios, as well as CBG dominant varieties. As the value of other non-THC and non-CBD cannabinoids, like CBG, CBC, THCV, and CBDV, increases, breeders will likely focus on teasing out those other cannabinoid constituents to add to the immense variety and complexity of Cannabis chemical profiles.

Some argue that the difference between hemp and marijuana primary lies in the plant's intended use. Hemp is traditionally used for industrial purposes, whereas "marijuana" is typically used for recreational or medical purposes. But this distinction is

---

[160] https://www.congress.gov/115/plaws/publ334/PLAW-115publ334.pdf

also becoming blurred as many people have begun using hemp for medical purposes, due to the CBD and/or CBG content, and "marijuana" for industrial purposes.

Perhaps the entire dichotomy between hemp and marijuana is obsolete. After all, they are both the same plant, presenting itself in a variety of forms that can be used for a wide variety of purposes. This highlights this persistent issue surrounding Cannabis regarding how Cannabis varieties are classified. It seems inevitable that a new nomenclature will evolve as Cannabis decriminalization and legalization continues in areas throughout the world.

## CASHING IN ON CBD?

*"We talk about hemp being this crop that can save the world. Well, CBD probably isn't that crop..."*[161]

Samuel Moore, Hemp Farmer
The Curious About Cannabis Podcast
Behind-the-Scenes (BTS) Episode #21

There is no question that currently the hemp industry is primarily focused on one thing: Cannabidiol, or as it is better known - CBD.

The CBD industry began growing substantially in 2017, with roots as far back as the early 2010s. In 2019, when the Farm Bill was passed in the United States, hemp became federally legal, under certain conditions and guidelines.[162] Companies rushed to cash in on the now legal hemp commodity. Many companies interpreted the Farm Bill as having not only legalized hemp, but also CBD. However, the truth was a bit more complicated.

Technically, in the United States, CBD is a "drug" because it has undergone clinical trials and been subject to drug approval, in the form of the pharmaceutical Epidiolex[163], produced by GW Pharmaceuticals[164]. While the DEA has de-scheduled Epidiolex, CBD remains a scheduled drug. To make things more confusing, The Farm Bill makes all cannabinoids and other plant compounds from hemp legal, to a limited extent. CBD is perfectly legal to possess, if derived from hemp, but once you try to feed it to people, things get tricky.

Because CBD is considered a drug, it cannot be added to foods or cosmetics unless the FDA assigns it a status called GRAS, Generally Recognized As Safe.[165] Until the FDA undertakes the project of assigning GRAS status to CBD or other cannabinoids

[161] https://cacpodcast.com/bts-21-samuel-moore-of-hillside-hemp-oregon-on-sustainable-farming-seed-sourcing-cbd/
[162] https://www.congress.gov/115/plaws/publ334/PLAW-115publ334.pdf
[163] https://www.epidiolex.com
[164] https://www.jazzpharma.com
[165] https://www.fda.gov/food/food-ingredients-packaging/generally-recognized-safe-gras

or Cannabinoids that may become pharmaceuticals, the only option companies have to legally add CBD to foods is by achieving "self-affirmed GRAS status."

In this process, a company must assemble an independent group of scientists to oversee the required testing needed to prove that a product is safe. It can cost upwards of a million dollars or more to complete and usually takes a year or more to complete. The Food, Drugs, and Cosmetics Act (FD&C) provides the policy on this issue in the United States which the Food and Drug Administration (FDA) must enforce.

As of the time of this writing, there have been no indications that Congress intends on changing the FD&C Act to accommodate the CBD industry. However, this has not stopped the CBD industry from rapidly growing and establishing a foothold in the consciousnesses of consumers while regulators determine the appropriate action to take.

## EVALUATING HEMP COMPANIES AND PRODUCTS

There is a plethora of hemp-derived cannabinoid products on the market as of the time of this writing. Due to an immature industry and a lack of regulatory guidance, these products exhibit a wide spectrum of quality, leaving consumers confused about how to evaluate these products to make informed decisions. In this section I will share some of the questions that go through my mind whenever I am evaluating a hemp-derived cannabinoid product (or really any Cannabis product or dietary supplement).

### DOES THE COMPANY FOLLOW GOOD MANUFACTURING PRACTICES (cGMPs)?

Good manufacturing practices, or GMPs, are industry standards that manufacturers are required to follow to ensure the quality of the products that they manufacture. GMP requires that companies evaluate their component ingredient suppliers, test ingredients to ensure they are of a known potency and purity, keep work areas, equipment, and utensils clean, ensure personnel wear protective equipment to combat contamination, and more.

In the US, the FDA sets basic requirements for how different types of products must be manufactured to ensure that the product is protected from contamination and that consumer health and safety is protected. The FDA has GMP rules for foods (21 CFR 110/117)[166] [167], dietary supplements (21 CFR 111)[168], pharmaceuticals (21 CFR 210/211)[169], and cosmetics (21 CFR 700)[170].

Internationally, there are various GMP standards, such as the Pharmaceutical Inspection Co-operation Scheme (PIC/S)[171] GMP standard, or the International Council for Harmonisation of Technical Requirements for Pharmaceuticals for Human Use (ICH)[172]. For food products, there is the international standard ISO 22000[173] which

---

[166] https://www.ecfr.gov/current/title-21/chapter-I/subchapter-B/part-110
[167] https://www.ecfr.gov/current/title-21/chapter-I/subchapter-B/part-117
[168] https://www.ecfr.gov/current/title-21/chapter-I/subchapter-B/part-111
[169] https://www.ecfr.gov/current/title-21/chapter-I/subchapter-C/part-210
[170] https://www.ecfr.gov/current/title-21/chapter-I/subchapter-G/part-700
[171] https://picscheme.org/en/picscheme
[172] https://www.ich.org/
[173] https://www.iso.org/iso-22000-food-safety-management.html

provides guidance on how to maintain a food safety management system to ensure the quality of food products. In general, compliance with ISO 22000 ensures basic compliance with the US FDA's Food Safety Modernization Act requirements.

### How does the company manage product quality?

Companies must utilize effective quality management systems to ensure their operations produce intended results, that regulatory requirements are met, and that the company is continuously improving. An effective quality management system produces traceable records which prove to any third parties that policies and procedures are being followed and executed as intended. The quality system also provides structure for key processes that ensure products are of a high quality. This usually includes processes like supplier evaluations, ingredient testing and inspection, environmental controls, production controls, product testing, product inspections, and production records reviews.

Product
Specifications

Supplier and Ingredient
Evaluation

Equipment
Validation

Process Validation

Product Manufacturing
Controls

Product Testing
and Inspection

Records Review

FIGURE 23: EXAMPLES OF QUALITY CONTROL STEPS IN PRODUCT MANUFACTURING

Under an effective quality management system, materials must be held in quarantine until they are approved for use and finished products must not be released for distribution until they have been tested and inspected.

### Does the company make medical claims?

Always be wary of bold medical claims about products that have not undergone any clinical trials to back up the claims. Currently the FDA does not permit any medical claims about hemp-derived cannabinoids to be made by any producers about hemp-based products, without written approval from the FDA. This is not to say that all medical claims about cannabinoids like CBD are deceptive or wrong. It is true that CBD, for instance, has therapeutic applications, under certain conditions, for certain medical conditions, for some people. If a company makes therapeutic claims about their product, ask for evidence. If they cannot provide evidence, the best approach is skepticism.

One thing to be wary of regarding medical claims is the use of references to research literature. Often companies may not make direct medical claims about their products but may share research articles about the medical benefits of an ingredient in their product, such as CBD. Often what happens is the reader is misled into believing that the research results of a study somehow represent the company's product – which is not necessarily the case.

## WHAT IS THE SOURCE OF CBD, CBG, CBN, ETC?

CBD can come from a variety of sources. It is well-known now that CBD can be sourced from the Cannabis plant. CBD can also be produced in "bioreactors" which consist of micro-organisms like yeasts or bacteria that can produce target compounds. Additionally, CBD can be produced in a laboratory through chemical reactions. Some companies produce CBD synthetically using a compound called olivetol sourced from lichen and other natural sources.

But even within the world of hemp-derived cannabinoids, there are many different types of extracts, each with different chemical characteristics and levels of phytochemical diversity. It is first important to understand how the extract was produced. What was the quality of hemp material used for extraction? Were only female flowers extracted, or were whole plants ground down and extracted? How refined was the extract before it was used in the product? There is a big difference between the chemistry of a crude alcohol extract versus a highly refined cannabinoid distillate. If a product says that it is "broad spectrum" or "full spectrum", what does the company mean by those terms?

## WHAT IS THE CANNABINOID POTENCY?

Always determine the potency of a product before consuming it. Recently I was in a store and came across a CBD product that featured in bold typeface across the label: "1000 mg". I immediately thought to myself, "1000 mg of what?". Of course, I knew that the manufacturer intended for me to assume it referred to CBD, but I found it suspicious that it did not specifically say what compound the 1000 mg statement referred to. Upon review of the ingredients, I found that the product contained "1000 mg of hemp". That left me more confused. Do they mean hemp flower? Hemp extract? If so, what kind of extract?

This experience highlights some of the critical problems with hemp product marketing, at least at the time of this writing. Always determine the potency of a product before consuming it. If you cannot determine the potency of a product through the product's label, do not purchase or consume that product. However, even if you figure out the potency of a CBD product, how do you know you can trust the potency claim?

## WHAT IS THE QUALITY OF THE OTHER INGREDIENTS IN THE PRODUCT?

When evaluating hemp cannabinoid products, or any Cannabis product, it is important to understand what the other ingredients are in the product, and what the quality of those ingredients might be. For instance, many ingestible CBD products are made with MCT oil, as an alternative to ethanolic (alcohol) tinctures. But MCT oil can be sourced from a variety of sources, including palm, coconut, and dairy products. Some MCT oils are standardized, and some are not, meaning that some MCT oils have other chemicals in them other than the primary medium chain triglycerides, whereas standardized MCT oils only contain defined concentrations of medium chain triglycerides and nothing else.

Some MCT oils are made from mixed sources, whereas other are sourced only from a single source. It is important to note that palm sourced MCT oil is currently under criticism for exacerbating environmental decline and wildlife species loss in areas where the palm is cultivated. It is generally recommended to source MCT oil from coconut sources only to minimize the negative environmental impacts of MCT oil production.

Additionally, ethanol can be produced from a variety of sources, such as grape, corn, sugarcane, barley, and many other plants. The cultivation of these different crops has different environmental impacts.

It is also important to understand whether there may be other ingredients in a Cannabis product that may affect the way that the CBD or other Cannabis ingredient may interact with the body. A product that contains a variety of other medicinal plant ingredients may exhibit markedly different effects than a product whose primary ingredient is only Cannabis extract.

When evaluating a Cannabis product manufacturer, it is important to understand what quality control measures the company is taking to evaluate the quality of their additional ingredients, especially if ingredients are being sourced from other countries that may have different quality standards and regulations. In general, component ingredients of Cannabis products should be tested for identity, potency, and purity before being used in a product. Although component ingredients typically come with associated test results, demonstrating the identity, potency, and purity of the ingredient – manufacturers must establish rationale for trusting those supplied test results. To do this, they must submit component ingredients for verification testing routinely so that they can have confidence that the test results received with a product are accurate. This is required under US FDA GMP rules, although many Cannabis manufacturers, as of the time of this writing, are not compliant with these rules.

### Has the finished product been tested for potency & purity?

Once a CBD or hemp product has been manufactured, it needs to be tested by an accredited third-party laboratory to ensure that the product has a known potency and is free from contaminants. This allows the manufacturer to back up their safety claims about the product.

Notice that I say that products need to be tested by *an accredited third-party* laboratory. It is generally not enough for a company to test their own products using their in-house testing laboratory. This presents opportunity to cast doubt on the integrity and reliability of the data. By having a third-party laboratory that is accredited for the scope of testing being performed on the product, the company is demonstrating that their claims are trustworthy and backed by someone that has no financial interest in their company or product.

# THE FUTURE OF HEMP

It is likely that hemp regulations across the world are going to continue to evolve in response to the demands of farmers, product manufacturers, and consumers. As it becomes easier for producers and researchers to work with hemp, novel uses of the plant and its chemical constituents will likely be identified.

## Did You Know?

Hemp seed oil contains an excellent ratio of Omega 3 and Omega 6 fatty acids! According to Callaway (2004), "The omega 6 to omega 3 ratio in hempseed oil is normally between 2:1 to 3:1, which is considered optimum for human health."

For instance, some researchers are looking at how to use hemp as a source for the cannabinoid cannabigerol (CBG) which might have some therapeutic use as a cannabinoid intoxication reliever among other applications.[174] In other words, it might have the potential to alleviate a particularly stressful "high" in a Cannabis consumer – perhaps more effectively than CBD.

Indeed, as of 2018, CBG dominant varieties of hemp began significantly appearing in the hemp market. Unless there is some legal impediment, it is likely that Cannabis breeding will focus on teasing out as many cannabinoids and terpenoids as possible within the limitations of the plant's genes, and perhaps even outside of those limits as genetically modified Cannabis becomes more common. Along with the popularity of hemp-derived CBG, there is also a growing demand for other hemp-derived cannabinoids like CBN, CBDV, CBC, and delta-8-THC.

One issue facing hemp's use in other industrial applications such as in construction materials or fiber, is that the value of a hemp crop per acre can be orders of magnitude greater if cultivating the crop for cannabinoid-rich resin yield. Until the market matures and it makes financial sense for farmers to cultivate hemp varieties for other uses, it is likely that hemp farming will remain focused on resin-rich varieties for the foreseeable future.

For more information about hemp including a history of the use of hemp in the United States, I recommend the book, ***The Emperor Wears No Clothes*** by Jack Herer.[175]

---

[174] de Meijer, E.P.M., Hammond, K.M. The inheritance of chemical phenotype in Cannabis sativa L. (II): Cannabigerol predominant plants. Euphytica 145, 189–198 (2005). https://doi.org/10.1007/s10681-005-1164-8
[175] https://commons.wikimedia.org/wiki/File:Jack_Herer_-_The_Emperor_Wears_No_Clothes.pdf

## Enduring Understandings

- The term "hemp" has been applied to many fiber crops throughout history.
- Today, "hemp" is thought to primarily refer to varieties of Cannabis which contain less than 0.3% THC.
- "Hemp" and "marijuana" are the same species of plant – *Cannabis sativa*.
- Hemp varieties of Cannabis can be used industrially for a wide variety of purposes including food, fiber, biofuel, building materials, animal feed, and more.
- Most hemp today is grown for CBD-rich resin production to supply the CBD product market.

# PART II: THE CHEMISTRY OF CANNABIS

## Essential Questions

What are the primary chemical compounds found in Cannabis?

What are cannabinoids?

What are terpenoids?

What are synthetic and semi-synthetic cannabinoids?

# Chapter 10:
## CANNABIS CHEMISTRY INTRODUCTION

### Learning Questions

- What is chemical polarity? Are cannabinoids polar or nonpolar?
- What is a chemical functional group?
- What are some common chemical functional groups that are likely to show up in Cannabis compounds?
- What chemical compounds are found in the Cannabis plant?

## INTRODUCTION TO KEY CHEMISTRY CONCEPTS

In some of the upcoming chapters we will be exploring the chemistry of the Cannabis plant. However, before diving into the chemistry of Cannabis, it is important to brush up on some basic chemistry terms and concepts like chemical polarity and functional groups. If you are already familiar with these terms, you might like to skip ahead to the next chapter.

### CHEMICAL POLARITY

Oil and water do not mix. The reason for this is chemical polarity. **Polarity is a description of how the bonds in a molecule are sharing electrons.** Even further, it refers to whether electrons are shared equally between atoms. Electrons carry a negative charge. If there are unpaired electrons present, a negative charge is present. If all electrons are paired up, no electrical charge is generated. If an electron is removed, a positive charge is generated. This is the core principle of polarity.

**If the electrons in the bond are equally shared, the molecule is considered nonpolar.** Nonpolar compounds are typically made of lots of carbons and hydrogens. Propane, which is made of 3 carbons and 5 hydrogens, is nonpolar. An example of a nonpolar compound would be vegetable oil. Nonpolar compounds are considered **hydrophobic** because they do not dissolve in water. They are, however, **lipophilic** because they dissolve easily in lipids, fats, and oils.

**If the electrons in the bond are shared unequally, the molecule is considered polar.** An example of a polar compound is water. Polar compounds are **hydrophilic**, meaning they dissolve in water. Polar compounds are **lipophobic** meaning they do not dissolve in lipids.

| Polarity | Hydro- | Lipo- | Description | Examples |
|---|---|---|---|---|
| **Polar** | Hydrophilic | Lipophobic | Dissolve in water; Oxygen, nitrogen, etc often present | Water, Caffeine, Flavonoids |
| **Nonpolar** | Hydrophobic | Lipophilic | Dissolve in lipids; Primarily made of hydrogen and carbon | Cannabinoids, Terpenes, Vegetable Oil |

If a polar compound like water and a nonpolar compound like oil are mixed, the two substances will eventually separate and form two layers due to the nonpolar compound's hydrophobic characteristic and the polar compound's lipophobic characteristic which repel each other.

There is a third category of polarity called a hybrid. This usually occurs in larger molecules where one side of the molecule is more polar while another side is more nonpolar, allowing it to have an affinity for both polar and nonpolar compounds. Many compounds exhibit hybrid polarity to some level. Additionally, polarity can be manipulated by things like temperature and pH.

**Cannabinoids and terpenes in Cannabis are nonpolar**. Because of this, cannabinoids and terpenes mix well with other nonpolar compounds like oils and fats. **Organic solvents** like butane and propane are also nonpolar, which is why they are used in Cannabis extract production (the term "**organic**" refers to compounds with carbon in them). The polarity of Cannabis compounds also explains why cannabinoids tend to cling to fatty tissues in the body.

### READING CHEMICAL DIAGRAMS

There are a variety of ways to draw a molecule. The two most common methods are shown in the following figure. These are line diagrams that represent the same compound, butane. The first diagram has every atom labeled with lines showing the bonds between each atom.

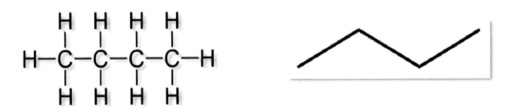

*Both of these diagrams represent butane, C4H10*

In the second diagram, the carbon and hydrogen atoms are not drawn but implied. This is common in diagrams of *organic* compounds. **Organic compounds contain carbon.** Each end of a line in these diagrams represents a carbon atom and each carbon atom is implied to be surrounded by hydrogen unless otherwise noted. Each end of a line represents a carbon atom. If there is a line above one of these lines, it represents a double bond.

As for the inorganic parts of a molecule, the bonds are represented by small lines connecting one element to another. If there are two lines, then it represents a double bond. If it has a "-" next to an atom, that means that it gained an electron, and thus has a *negative* charge (because electrons are negatively charged). If it has a "+" next to an atom, it lost an electron (which is negatively charged) and has become *positively* charged.

### CHEMICAL FUNCTIONAL GROUPS

Functional groups are molecules that attach to compounds and give them certain characteristics. For instance, **-OH is an alcohol** functional group. Any compound with an –OH group attached is considered an alcohol and will have the "–ol" suffix. The functional group that is responsible for the behavior or cannabinoid acids is **–COOH, or the carboxylic acid functional group**. As the compound is exposed to heat, the -COOH functional group pops off in a process called decarboxylation, leaving behind the neutral cannabinoid.

There are many different functional groups and each one changes the behavior of the molecule it is attached to in some way. When reading a functional group diagram, the "R" refers to the rest of the molecule that the group is attached to.

### NUMBERING CARBONS IN A MOLECULE

You may notice that many chemicals, including the formal name for THC, delta-9-tetrahydrocannabinol, feature a number within the name. This number typically represents the location of a significant functional group or bond. The way that the carbon atoms in a molecule are numbered starts with finding the longest carbon chain in the molecule. This is referred to as the "parent chain". The next step involves identifying the "highest priority" functional group in the molecule. This ultimately dictates where you start numbering, because the highest priority functional group must have the smallest number in the carbon numbering sequence.

There are tables of functional group priorities[176] that you can look up that explain which functional groups are considered higher priority than others for the purposes of numbering carbons and naming molecules. Once the highest priority functional group has been identified, you start counting carbons, one by one, following the longest path of the carbon chain. If there is a bond or functional group somewhere along that chain, you would indicate that in the chemical name by using a number that represents the location of the carbon atom where

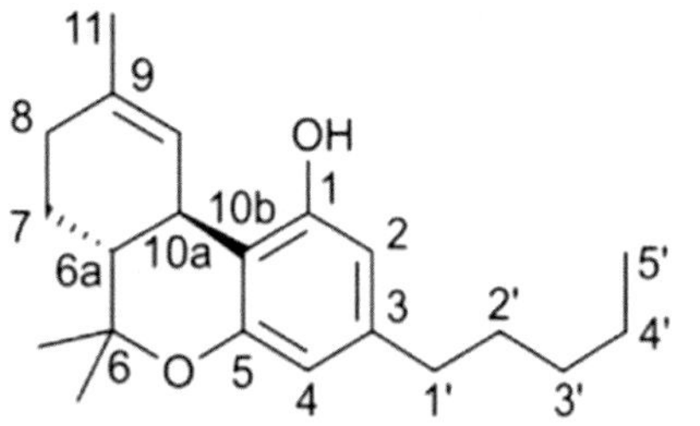

**FIGURE 3 THC MOLECULE WITH CARBON NUMBERING**

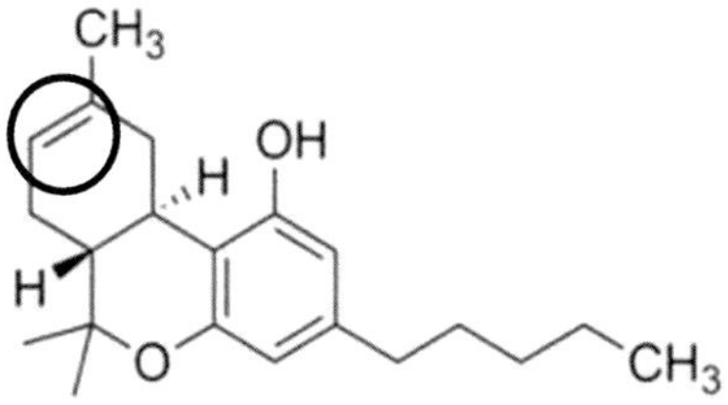

the bond or functional group is located. For instance, the "9" in delta-9-THC represents the location of a double bond within a carbon ring. The difference between delta-8-THC vs delta-9-THC lies in the location of the double bond.

**DELTA-8-THC**

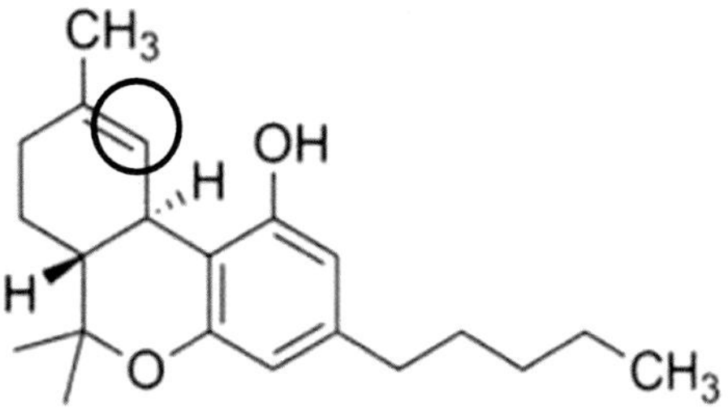

**DELTA-9-THC**

---

[176] https://www.masterorganicchemistry.com/2011/02/14/table-of-functional-group-priorities-for-nomenclature/

## Examples of Common Functional Groups

| Functional Group | Description | Example |
|---|---|---|
| **Carboxylic Acid** | Carbon featuring a double bonded oxygen and a hydroxyl group<br><br>R-COOH | 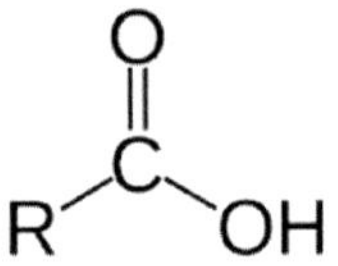 |
| **Alcohol (Hydroxyl)** | Simple bonded oxygen and hydrogen (-OH)<br><br>R-OH | 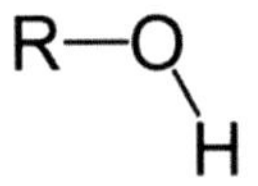 |
| **Ester** | Results when a hydroxyl (-OH) group is replaced with an oxygen attached to another organic molecule – often derived from carboxylic acids and alcohols. | 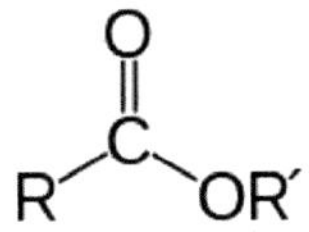 |
| **Ketone** | Double bonded oxygen connecting two organic molecules<br><br>R – C (=O) - R<br><br>Acetone is a simple ketone 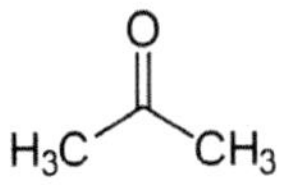<br><br> | 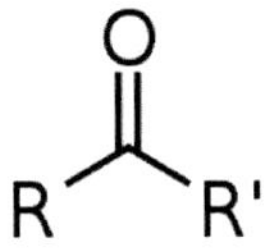 |
| **Aldehyde** | Carbon with a single bonded hydrogen and a double bonded oxygen<br><br>R – C (= O) - H | 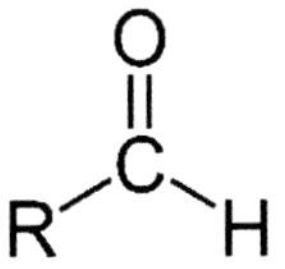 |
| **Phenyl** | Aromatic ring with a functional group.<br><br>**Phenols** are phenyls bonded to a hydroxyl group (-OH) | 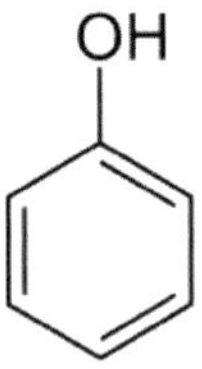 |

FIGURE 25: EXAMPLES OF COMMON FUNCTIONAL GROUPS

# OVERVIEW OF CANNABIS CHEMICAL CONSTITUENTS

Over 550 compounds have been described in the Cannabis plant and approximately 200 more in Cannabis smoke.[177] Among these compounds, there are over 150 **phytocannabinoids** that have been identified in Cannabis[178] [179] [180], and over 200 **phytoterpenoids** have been identified.[181] [182] [183] [184] [185] [186] [187] [188]

Cannabis also consists of over twenty different **flavonoids**.[189] It is estimated that Cannabis leaves consist of approximately 1% flavonoids.[190] There are also other compounds in Cannabis like glycoproteins and alkaloids, with relatively unknown pharmacological effects. Cannabis also contains various carotenoids, which are orange-yellow pigment compounds, and vitamin K.[191]

Some of these compounds are either **phenolic** or **polyphenolic** compounds. A **phenol** is a series of carbons in an aromatic ring with an –OH group attached, making it

---

[177] McPartland JM, Russo EB. 2001b. Cannabis and Cannabis extracts: greater than the sum of their parts? J Cannabis Therap 1: 103–132.

[178] Citti, C., Linciano, P., Russo, F. et al. A novel phytocannabinoid isolated from Cannabis sativa L. with an in vivo cannabimimetic activity higher than Δ⁹-tetrahydrocannabinol: Δ⁹-Tetrahydrocannabiphorol. Sci Rep 9, 20335 (2019). https://doi.org/10.1038/s41598-019-56785-1

[179] Hanuš LO, Meyer SM, Muñoz E, Taglialatela-Scafati O, Appendino G. Phytocannabinoids: a unified critical inventory. Nat Prod Rep. 2016 Nov 23;33(12):1357-1392. https://doi.org10.1039/c6np00074f PMID: 27722705.

[180] Citti C, Linciano P, Panseri S, Vezzalini F, Forni F, Vandelli MA, Cannazza G. Cannabinoid Profiling of Hemp Seed Oil by Liquid Chromatography Coupled to High-Resolution Mass Spectrometry. Front Plant Sci. 2019 Feb 13;10:120. https://doi.org/10.3389/fpls.2019.00120 PMID: 30815007; PMCID: PMC6381057.

[181] Hendriks H, Malingré TM, Batterman S, Bos R (1975). Mono- and sesqui-terpene hydrocarbons of the eseential oil of Cannabis *sativa*. Phytochem 14: 814–815. https://doi.org/10.1016/0031-9422%2875%2983045-7

[182] Hendriks H, Malingré TM, Batterman S, Bos R (1977). Alkanes of the essential oil of Cannabis *sativa*. Phytochem 16: 719–721. https://doi.org/10.1016/S0031-9422(00)89239-0

[183] Malingre T, Hendriks H, Batterman S, Bos R, Visser J (1975). The essential oil of Cannabis sativa. Planta Med 28: 56–61. https://doi.org/10.1055/s-0028-1097829

[184] Davalos SD, Fournier G, Boucher F, Paris M (1977). [Contribution to the study of Mexican marihuana. Preliminary studies: cannabinoids and essential oil (author's transl)]. J Pharm Belg 32:89–99.

[185] Ross SA, ElSohly MA. 1996. The volatile oil composition of fresh and air-dried buds of Cannabis sativa. J Nat Prod 59: 49–51. https://doi.org/10.1021/np960004a

[186] Mediavilla V, Steinemann S. 1997. Essential oil of Cannabis *sativa* L. strains. J Intl Hemp Assoc 4: 82–84. http://www.internationalhempassociation.org/jiha/jiha4208.html

[187] Rothschild M, Bergstrom G, Wangberg S-A. 2005. Cannabis *sativa*: volatile compounds from pollen and entire male and female plants of two variants, Northern Lights and Hawaian Indica. Bot J Linn Soc 147: 387–397. https://doi.org/10.1111/j.1095-8339.2005.00417.x

[188] Brenneisen R. 2007. Chemistry and analysis of phytocannabinoids and other Cannabis constituents. In: Elsohly M (ed.). Marijuana and the Cannabinoids. Humana Press: Totowa, NY, pp. 17–49.

[189] Turner, C.E., M.A. Elsohly, and E.G. Boeren. 1980. Constituents of Cannabis *sativa* L. XVII. A review of the natural constituents. *J Nat Prod* 43:169-304.

[190] Paris, R.R., E. Henri, and M. Paris. 1976. Sur les c-flavonoïdes du Cannabis *sativa* L. *Plantes Médicinales et Phytothérapie* 10:144-54.

[191] Brenneisen R. 2007. Chemistry and analysis of phytocannabinoids and other Cannabis constituents. In: Elsohly M (ed.). Marijuana and the Cannabinoids. Humana Press: Totowa, NY, pp. 17–49.

essentially an "aromatic alcohol." A **polyphenol** is simply a compound that is made of multiple phenol groups.

| Notable Cannabis Chemical Constituents | |
|---|---|
| **Aldehydes** | Benzaldehyde, Decanal, Heptanal, Octanal, Hexanal, Isobutyraldehyde |
| **Alkaloids** | Cannabisativine, annhydrocannabisativine found in Cannabis roots[192] |
| **Cannabinoids** | >150 described in Cannabis; found in trichomes of Cannabis |
| **Esters** | Hexyl acetate, linalyl acetate, methyl anthranilate |
| **Flavonoids** | ~20 described in Cannabis; pigment compounds in Cannabis leaf tissues |
| **Glycoproteins (sugar proteins)** | Galactose, xylose, glucose, mannose, arabinose, rhamnose, galacturonic acid from Cannabis leaves[193] |
| **Ketones** | 2-methyl-4-heptanone, 2-methyl-3-heptanone, methylisohexenyl ketone, 1-chloroacetophenone |
| **Phenanthrenes** | |
| **Spirans** | Cannabispirketal, $\alpha$-cannabispiranol 4'-O-$\beta$-D-glucopyranose |
| **Sterols** | Campesterene, Stigmasterol, Beta-Sitosterol |
| **Stilbenoids** | Denbinobin, Canniprene |
| **Terpenoids** | >200 described in Cannabis; primary essential oil fraction of Cannabis; triterpenoids found in Cannabis roots |
| **Thiols** | 3-methyl-2-butene-1-thiol |
| **Vitamins** | Vitamin K; Vitamin E found in seeds |
| **Lignanamides** | Cannabisin A; found in Cannabis seeds[194] |

FIGURE 26: NOTABLE CANNABIS CHEMICAL CONSTITUENTS

[192] Turner CE, Hsu MH, Knapp JE, Schiff PL Jr, Slatkin DJ. Isolation of cannabisativine, an alkaloid, from Cannabis sativa L. root. J Pharm Sci. 1976 Jul;65(7):1084-5. https://doi.org/10.1002/jps.2600650736

[193] Hillestad A, Wold JK, Paulsen BS. Structural studies of water-soluble glycoproteins from Cannabis sativa L. Carbohydr Res. 1977 Aug;57:135-44. https://doi.org/10.1016/s0008-6215(00)81926-6

[194] Sakakibara I, Ikeya Y, Hayashi K, Okada M, Maruno M. Three acyclic bis-phenylpropane lignanamides from fruits of Cannabis sativa. Phytochemistry. 1995 Mar;38(4):1003-7. https://doi.org/10.1016/0031-9422(94)00773-m

# Enduring Understandings

- When the electrons in a molecule are equally shared, the molecule is considered nonpolar. Nonpolar compounds typically contain primarily only carbon and hydrogen and are often not soluble in water (i.e., vegetable oils, cannabinoids, etc)

- When the electrons in a molecule are not equally shared, the molecule is considered polar. Polar compounds typically contain elements like oxygen, nitrogen, etc and are often soluble in water. (i.e., caffeine, flavonoids)

- Functional groups affect the behavior of a molecule.

- Numbers in a chemical name indicate the location of a significant chemical bond or functional group.

- Numbering carbons begins with identifying the parent chain, then identifying the functional group of highest priority before numbering each carbon along the parent chain.

- To date, Cannabis is thought to produce well over 500 chemicals, and it is likely that the plant produces thousands of chemical compounds.

- Over 200 unique compounds have been identified in Cannabis smoke.

- Some of the most common chemical compounds found in Cannabis include cannabinoids, terpenoids, flavonoids, esters, sterols, alkaloids, glycoproteins, and vitamins.

# Chapter 11:
## CANNABINOIDS INTRODUCTION

## Learning Questions

- How many cannabinoids have been identified in Cannabis?
- How are cannabinoids and terpenoids related?
- What is decarboxylation?
- What are some of the common cannabinoids found in the Cannabis plant?
- What are some of the common degradation products of phytocannabinoids?
- What are some of the common metabolites of phytocannabinoids?

### INTRODUCTION TO CANNABINOIDS

Many of the most sought-after chemical compounds in Cannabis, including CBD and THC, are phytocannabinoids, or "plant cannabinoids". At the time of this writing, there are approximately 550 chemical compounds that have been identified in Cannabis so far. Of these chemical compounds, approximately 150 are cannabinoids. Currently the most sophisticated commercial Cannabis testing laboratories in the United States test for approximately 10 – 15 different cannabinoids. To say that we still have a long way to go in understanding the chemistry of commercial Cannabis is an understatement.

Cannabinoids are **terpenophenolic** (terpene + phenol group) meroterpenoid (terpene-like) compounds produced in secretory cells in glandular trichomes primarily in unfertilized female flowers, often referred to as "sinsemilla", or "seedless" Cannabis flowers.  The ratios of primary cannabinoids such as THCA and CBDA are predetermined genetically. However, the environment significantly influences the concentrations of cannabinoids present as well as what cannabinoid degradation products may be present in the plant resins.

What does it mean for cannabinoids to be "meroterpenoids"? Are cannabinoids terpenes? Well, sort of. Terpenoids are **isoprenoids**, meaning that they are compounds made of variously arranged isoprene units. An isoprene is a simple five carbon compound with two double bonds, as pictured here.

**ISOPRENE UNIT**

**PHENOL STRUCTURE**

Remember that cannabinoids are considered terpenophenolic compounds, meaning that they are terpenoids featuring a phenol group...

Isoprene Units (Terpenoid)   +   Phenol   =   Terpenophenolic Compound

...but cannabinoids are also sometimes thought of as **polyketide terpenoids**. This is because cannabinoids are formed through the combination of a geranyl pyrophosphate, which lends two isoprene units (a simple monoterpene), and olivetolic acid, which lends a polyketide structure with a carbon tail. Polyketides are compounds that feature alternating oxygen bonds. Although olivetolic acid features many oxygens in its structure, making it a more obvious polyketide compound, only two of those oxygens remain when it is bound with the remaining isoprene units of geranyl pyrophosphate.

OLIVETOLIC ACID            GERANYL PYROPHOSPHATE (GPP)

Cannabinoids are synthesized through a chemical pathway called the deoxyxylulose pathway.[195] This pathway is responsible for both the production of cannabinoids as well as mono and sesquiterpenoids. And for each cannabinoid found in the Cannabis plant, there are minor variations and degradation products that form an entire class of compounds. For instance, there are at least 18 or more compounds that belong to the "delta-9 THC type" chemical class.[196]

## DECARBOXYLATION

THCA                    HEAT                    THC

In the plant, Cannabinoids are typically found in their carboxylic acid forms. Carboxylic acid cannabinoids, like THCA, are cannabinoids that have a carbon dioxide, or $CO_2$, group attached to it. When the molecule is heated up or receives enough energy, the $CO_2$ group breaks off, leaving behind the "neutral cannabinoid", such as THC. The process of heating a carboxylic acid so that a carboxyl group breaks off the molecule is called **decarboxylation**. For example, CBGA is a cannabinoid acid that the

[195] Russo EB. 2011. Taming THC: potential Cannabis synergy and phytocannabinoid-terpenoid entourage effects. Br J of Pharmacol 163:1344-1364. https://doi.org/10.1111/j.1476-5381.2011.01238.x
[196] Pertwee RG. 2015. Handbook of Cannabis. Oxford University Press.

plant can synthesize into THCA, CBDA, or CBCA which could then be heated to leave behind THC, CBD, and CBC. Alternatively, CBGA could be decarboxylated to CBG.

Cannabinoid acids have not been shown to be psychoactive or intoxicating, although there is some evidence supporting a variety of pharmacological effects. Cannabinoid acids can exhibit anti-inflammatory behavior.[197] [198] There is also evidence that THCA and CBDA can act as anti-vomiting agents.[199] [200] [201] There is even evidence that some of the cannabinoid acids can inhibit prostate cancer cell growth *in vivo* and *in vitro*.[202]

Despite common assumption, cannabinoids are not unique to the Cannabis plant, but have been found in a variety of other organisms. As cannabinoids are researched further, it is likely that our definition of what constitutes a cannabinoid will expand, encompassing more compounds. For instance, the terpenoid beta-caryophyllene is now considered to be a cannabinoid because it interacts with cannabinoid chemical receptors in the body.[203] Beta-caryophyllene is an essential oil component found in a wide array of plants including vegetables like corn![204] [205]

## TRUE OR FALSE?

Cannabinoids are polar compounds and mix easily with water.

Circle One:     TRUE          FALSE

---

[197] Starks, Michael (1990). Marijuana Chemistry: Genetics, Processing, Potency. Ronin Publishing

[198] Ruhaak LR, Felth J, Karlsson PC, Rafter JJ, Verpoorte R, Bohlin L. 2011. Evaluation of the cyclooxygenase inhibiting effects of six major cannabinoids isolated from Cannabis sativa. Biological and Pharmaceutical Bulletin 34 (5): 774–778 https://doi.org/10.1248/bpb.34.774

[199] Moldzio R, Pacher T, Krewenka C, Kranner B, Novak J, Duvigneau JC, Rausch WD. 2012. Effects of cannabinoids Δ(9)-tetrahydrocannabinol, Δ(9)-tetrahydrocannabinolic acid and cannabidiol in MPP(+) affected murine mesencephalic cultures. Phytomedicine 19(8-9): 819–24 https://doi.org/10.1016/j.phymed.2012.04.002

[200] Bolognini D, Rock EM, Cluny NL, Cascio MG, Limebeer CL, Duncan M, Stott CG, Javid FA, Parker LA, Pertwee RG. 2013. Cannabidiolic acid prevents vomiting in *Suncus murinus* and nausea-induced behavior in rats by enhancing 5-HT1A receptor activation. Br J Phar. 168(6):1456-1470. https://doi.org/10.1111/bph.12043

[201] Rock EM, Kopstick RL, Limebeer CL, Parker LA. 2013. Tetrahydrocannabinolic acid reduces nausea-induced conditioned gaping in rats and vomiting in Suncus murinus. Br J Pharmacol. 170(3):641-648 https://doi.org/10.1111/bph.12316

[202] De Petrocellis L, Ligresti A., Moriello A.S., Iappelli M., Verde R., Stott C.G., Cristino L., Orlando P., and Di Marzo V. 2013. Non-THC cannabinoids inhibit prostate carcinoma growth in vitro and in vivo: pro-apoptotic effects and underlying mechanisms. British Journal of Pharmacology 168 (1): 79–10 https://doi.org/10.1111/j.1476-5381.2012.02027.x

[203] Gertsch J, Leonti M, Raduner S, Racz I, Chen JZ, Xie XQ, Altmann KH, Karsak M, Zimmer A. Beta-caryophyllene is a dietary cannabinoid. Proc Natl Acad Sci U S A. 2008 Jul 1;105(26):9099-104. https://doi.org/10.1073/pnas.0803601105 Epub 2008 Jun 23. PMID: 18574142; PMCID: PMC2449371.

[204] Smith WE, Shivaji R, Williams WP, Luthe DS, Sandoya GV, Smith CL, Sparks DL, Brown AE. A maize line resistant to herbivory constitutively releases (E) -beta-caryophyllene. J Econ Entomol. 2012 Feb;105(1):120-8. https://doi.org/10.1603/ec11107 PMID: 22420263.

[205] Köllner TG, Held M, Lenk C, Hiltpold I, Turlings TC, Gershenzon J, Degenhardt J. A maize (E)-beta-caryophyllene synthase implicated in indirect defense responses against herbivores is not expressed in most American maize varieties. Plant Cell. 2008 Feb;20(2):482-94. https://doi.org/10.1105/tpc.107.051672 Epub 2008 Feb 22. PMID: 18296628; PMCID: PMC2276456.

# Delta-9-Tetrahydrocannabinol (THC)

THC is the primary **psychoactive** and intoxicating component of Cannabis. Its carboxylic acid form, THCA, is the most common cannabinoid found in Cannabis. THC has been reported as being an effective **painkiller** and **muscle relaxant**.[206] THC has been shown to act as a **bronchodilator**, decreasing resistance in the airways and increasing airflow into the lungs.[207] THC has also been reported as having 20x the **anti-inflammatory** power of aspirin and twice the anti-inflammatory power of hydrocortisone.[208]

THCA, the acidic precursor of THC, has exhibited a number of therapeutic effects as well, including anti-inflammatory[209] and cytoprotective effects. Although THCA exhibits very little activity at CB1 or CB2 receptors (the research is a bit muddied due to natural THCA decarboxylation in samples), THCA has been found to be an agonist of PPARγ receptors.

| Members of the Delta-9 THC Type Chemical Class | Degradation Products of THC | Examples of THC Metabolites |
|---|---|---|
| THC acid A | Cannabinol (CBN) | 11-OH-THC |
| THC acid B | Delta-8 THC | 11-COOH-THC |
| THCA-C4 | Delta-10 THC | |
| THC-C4 | | |
| Delta-9 Tetrahydrocannabiorcolic Acid | | |
| Delta-9 Tetrahydrocannabiorcol | | |

[206] Pacher P, Batkai S, Kunos G (2006). The endocannabinoid system as an emerging target of pharmacotherapy. Pharmacol Rev 58: 389–462.

[207] Williams SJ, Hartley JP, Graham JD. 1976. Bronchodilator effect of delta1-tetrahydrocannabinol administered by aerosol of asthmatic patients. Thorax 31: 720–723.

[208] Evans FJ (1991). Cannabinoids: the separation of central from peripheral effects on a structural basis. Planta Med 57: S60–S67.

[209] Carmona-Hidalgo B, González-Mariscal I, García-Martín A, Prados ME, Ruiz-Pino F, Appendino G, Tena-Sempere M, Muñoz E. Δ9-Tetrahydrocannabinolic Acid markedly alleviates liver fibrosis and inflammation in mice. Phytomedicine. 2021 Jan;81:153426. https://doi.org/10.1016/j.phymed.2020.153426 Epub 2020 Nov 30. PMID: 33341026.

# Delta-9-Tetrahydrocannabivarin (THCV)

The divarinic cannabinoids, or propyl chain cannabinoids, such as THCV and CBDV feature shorter carbon tails extending from the phenol group in the molecule as seen above. **THCV** is psychoactive and potentially intoxicating at certain dosages, but less so than delta-9 THC, although the effects come on more quickly.[210][211] THCV can **suppresses the appetite at certain dosages.**[212][213] In rodent models, THCV showed **anticonvulsant** effects as well.[214]

# Delta-8-Tetrahydrocannabivarin (D8-THCV)

**Delta-8-THCV** is molecular equivalent to THCV except that the double bond has been relocated from the 9 position to the 8 position.

At the time of this writing, little is known regarding the pharmacology or potential applications of delta-8-THCV.

---

[210] Hollister LE. Structure-activity relationships in man of cannabis constituents, and homologs and metabolites of delta9-tetrahydrocannabinol. Pharmacology. 1974;11(1):3-11. https://doi.org/10.1159/000136462

[211] Gill EW, Paton WD, Pertwee RG. Preliminary experiments on the chemistry and pharmacology of cannabis. Nature. 1970 Oct 10;228(5267):134-6. https://doi.org/10.1038/228134a0

[212] Wargent, E., Zaibi, M., Silvestri, C. et al. The cannabinoid Δ9-tetrahydrocannabivarin (THCV) ameliorates insulin sensitivity in two mouse models of obesity. Nutr & Diabetes 3, e68 (2013). https://doi.org/10.1038/nutd.2013.9

[213] Riedel G, Fadda P, McKillop-Smith S, Pertwee RG, Platt B, Robinson L. Synthetic and plant-derived cannabinoid receptor antagonists show hypophagic properties in fasted and non-fasted mice. Br J Pharmacol. 2009 Apr;156(7):1154-66. https://doi.org/10.1111/j.1476-5381.2008.00107.x

[214] Hill AJ, Weston SE, Jones NA, Smith I, Bevan SA, Williamson EM, Stephens GJ, Williams CM, Whalley BJ. Δ9-Tetrahydrocannabivarin suppresses in vitro epileptiform and in vivo seizure activity in adult rats. Epilepsia. 2010 Aug;51(8):1522-32. https://doi.org/10.1111/j.1528-1167.2010.02523.x

## DELTA-9-TETRAHYDROCANNABUTOL (THCB, THC-C4)

**THCB** is a version of THC that features one less carbon in the carbon tail of the molecule compared to THC. THCB has exhibited similar potency as THC in cannabinoid receptor binding assays. THCB is also known as delta-9-THC-C4.

## DELTA-9-TETRAHYDROCANNABIPHOROL (THCP, THC-C7)

**THCP** is a version of THC that features a couple of extra carbon atoms in the molecule's carbon tail, which in turn makes THCP exhibit an affinity for CB1 receptors that is 30 times that of THC! While it is unclear exactly how this difference relates to differences in psychoactivity, the discovery of THCP and other similar cannabinoids, has helped researchers better understand how the molecular structure of a cannabinoid correlates with cannabinoid receptor activity, which may in turn help researchers develop tools for predicting how a cannabinoid may interact with cannabinoid receptors.

In addition to its enhanced activity at CB1 receptors, THCP is five to ten times more active at CB2 receptors compared to THC. THCP may appear in concentrations as high as 5% in refined ethanol extracts of Cannabis. (Citti et al, 2019)

## 3-Octyl-Delta-9-Tetrahydrocannabinol
## (Tetrahydrocannabiocytyl aka THCjd)

Also known as THC$_{JD}$, 3-octyl-delta-9-THC is a delta-9-THC molecule with an 8 carbon (octyl) chain off the primary THC moiety, rather than a five-chain carbon tail as is found in the traditional THC molecule. Extending the length of this carbon chain seems to make the molecule more potent at CB1 receptors.[215]

## 3-Octyl-Delta-8-Tetrahydrocannabinol (JWH 138)

3-octyl-delta-8-THC, or delta-8-THC-C8, is simply a delta-8-THC molecule with an 8 carbon (octyl) chain off the primary THC structure. As with the delta-9 octyl THC, extending the length of this carbon chain seems to make the molecule more potent at CB1 receptors.[216] Sometimes delta-8-THC-C8 is referred to as THC$_{JD}$ – often conflating the isomers together – making it unclear which chemicals are actually present in "THC$_{JD}$" products.

---

[215] Martin BR, Jefferson R, Winckler R, Wiley JL, Huffman JW, Crocker PJ, Saha B, Razdan RK. Manipulation of the tetrahydrocannabinol side chain delineates agonists, partial agonists, and antagonists. J Pharmacol Exp Ther. 1999 Sep;290(3):1065-79. PMID: 10454479.

[216] Martin BR, Jefferson R, Winckler R, Wiley JL, Huffman JW, Crocker PJ, Saha B, Razdan RK. Manipulation of the tetrahydrocannabinol side chain delineates agonists, partial agonists, and antagonists. J Pharmacol Exp Ther. 1999 Sep;290(3):1065-79. PMID: 10454479.

# Cannabidiol (CBD)

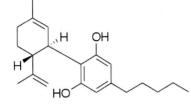

**In its carboxylic acid form, CBDA** is the second most common cannabinoid in medical Cannabis and is the most common cannabinoid present in fibre hemp Cannabis plants (Russo, 2011). CBD has a unique ability to **reduce the effects of THC** by quieting the CB1 receptor while THC is binding to it.[217]

CBD has been shown to display a wide variety of medicinally beneficial effects in animal and *in vitro* models. CBD has been reported to exhibit **anti-anxiety and anticonvulsant effects** as well as the ability to **reduce acne bacteria.**[218] [219] [220] 33 or more metabolites of CBD have been identified, very few have been thoroughly characterized.

| Examples of Other Members of the CBD Type Chemical Class | Examples of Degradation Products of CBD | Examples of CBD Metabolites |
|---|---|---|
| CBDM | Cannabinodiol (CBND) | 7-OH-CBD |
| CBD-C1 | Delta-9-Tetrahydrocannabinol (d9-THC) and derivatives may form under acidic conditions | 7-COOH-CBD |
| CBDV Acid | | Cannabielsoin (CBE) |
| CBDP | | |
| Cannabimovone | | |
| CBD-C4 (aka CBDB) | | |
| CBDV | | |

---

[217] Thomas A, Baillie GL, Phillips AM, Razdan RK, Ross RA, Pertwee RG (2007). Cannabidiol displays unexpectedly high potency as an antagonist of CB1 and CB2 receptor agonists in vitro. Br J Pharmacol 150: 613–623.

[218] Russo EB, Burnett A, Hall B, Parker KK. 2005. Agonistic properties of cannabidiol at 5-HT-1a receptors. Neurochem Res 30: 1037–1043.

[219] Jones NA, Hill AJ, Smith I, Bevan SA, Williams CM, Whalley BJ, Stephens GJ. Cannabidiol displays antiepileptiform and antiseizure properties in vitro and in vivo. J Pharmacol Exp Ther. 2010 Feb;332(2):569-77. https://doi.org/10.1124/jpet.109.159145  Epub 2009 Nov 11. PMID: 19906779; PMCID: PMC2819831.

[220] Biro T, Olah A, Toth BI, Czifra G, Zouboulis CC, Paus R. 2009. Cannabidiol as a novel anti-acne agent? Cannabidiol inhibits lipid synthesis and induces cell death in human sebaceous gland-derived sebocytes. Proceedings 19th Annual Conference on the Cannabinoids. International Cannabinoid Research Society: Pheasant Run, St. Charles, IL, p. 28.

## Cannabidivarin (CBDV)

**CBDV** has become a compound of interest lately due to its anticonvulsant effects both observed in animal models and *in vitro* (Hill et al, 2013; Amada et al, 2013).[221] [222] CBDV is currently being studied in human clinical trials for the treatment of epilepsy under the name **GWP42006**.[223]

## Cannabidibutol (CBDB, CBD-C4)

**CBDB** is a version of CBD that features one less carbon in the carbon tail of the molecule compared to CBD. CBDB has been discovered as an impurity in CBD extracts of hemp.[224] CBDB is also known as CBD-C4. Like CBD, it does not have significant affinity for CB1 or CB2 receptors.

## Cannabidiphorol (CBDP, CBD-C7)

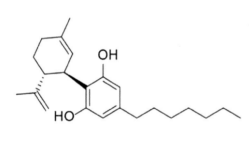

Like THCP, **CBDP** is a version of CBD featuring an extra-long carbon tail. At the time of this writing, very little is known about CBDP, and no chemical receptor binding assays or pharmacological data was available. In 2021, Salbini et al reported that CBDP and CBDB cause damage to breast cancer cells through a mechanism that can be manipulated by inhibiting enzymes that typically degrade endocannabinoids.[225]

[221] Hill TDM, Cascio M-G, Romano B, Duncan M, Pertwee RG, Williams CM, Whalley BJ, Hill AJ. 2013. Cannabidivarin-rich cannabis extracts are anticonvulsant in mouse and rat via a CB1 receptor-independent mechanism. Br J Phar. 170:679-692. https://doi.org/10.1111/bph.12321

[222] Amada N, Yamasaki Y, Williams CM, Whalley BJ. 2013. Cannabidivarin (CBDV) suppresses pentylenetetrazole (PTZ)-induced increases in epilepsy-related gene expression. PeerJ. 1:e214. https://doi.org/10.7717/peerj.214 eCollection 2013.

[223] Brodie MJ, Czapinski P, Pazdera L, Sander JW, Toledo M, Napoles M, Sahebkar F, Schreiber A; GWEP1330 Study Group. A Phase 2 Randomized Controlled Trial of the Efficacy and Safety of Cannabidivarin as Add-on Therapy in Participants with Inadequately Controlled Focal Seizures. Cannabis Cannabinoid Res. 2021 Dec;6(6):528-536. https://doi.org/10.1089/can.2020.0075

[224] Linciano P, Citti C, Luongo L, Belardo C, Maione S, Vandelli MA, Forni F, Gigli G, Laganà A, Montone CM, Cannazza G. Isolation of a High-Affinity Cannabinoid for the Human CB1 Receptor from a Medicinal Cannabis sativa Variety: Δ9-Tetrahydrocannabutol, the Butyl Homologue of Δ9-Tetrahydrocannabinol. J Nat Prod. 2020 Jan 24;83(1):88-98. https://doi.org/10.1021/acs.jnatprod.9b00876

[225] Salbini M, Quarta A, Russo F, Giudetti AM, Citti C, Cannazza G, Gigli G, Vergara D, Gaballo A. Oxidative Stress and Multi-Organel Damage Induced by Two Novel Phytocannabinoids, CBDB and CBDP, in Breast Cancer Cells. Molecules. 2021 Sep 14;26(18):5576. https://doi.org/10.3390/molecules26185576

# CANNABIGEROL (CBG)

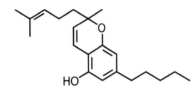

**Cannabigerol** is often referred to as the "parent" phytocannabinoid because CBGA goes on to synthesize into THCA, CBDA, and CBCA. CBG has been shown to be an anti-fungal, antidepressant, and painkiller.[226] [227] CBG has also been indicated as a potential treatment for skin conditions, glaucoma, sex hormonal dysregulations, eating disorders, irritable bowel syndromes and bone disease.[228]

| Examples of Other Members of the CBG Type Chemical Class: ||
| --- | --- |
| CBG Acid | CBG-C5 |
| Cannabigerolic Acid Monomethyl Ether (CBGAM) | Cannabigerol Monomethyl Ether (CBGM) |
| CBGV Acid | CBGV |

# CANNABICHROMENE (CBC)

**CBC** exhibits potential to **reduce THC intoxication**, like CBD.[229] It has also displayed **anti-inflammatory**[230] and **painkilling** properties.[231] CBC has been shown to produce powerful **antidepressant** effects in rodent models.[232] CBC is also a noted **antifungal** and **antibiotic**.[233]

| Examples of Other Members of the CBC Type Chemical Class || Example Degradation Product of CBC |
| --- | --- | --- |
| CBC Acid | CBC-C3 | Cannabicyclol (CBL) |
| CBCV Acid | CBCV | |

[226] Cascio MG, Gauson LA, Stevenson LA, Ross RA, Pertwee RG. Evidence that the plant cannabinoid cannabigerol is a highly potent alpha2-adrenoceptor agonist and moderately potent 5HT1A receptor antagonist. Br J Pharmacol. 2010 Jan;159(1):129-41. https://doi.org/10.1111/j.1476-5381.2009.00515.x

[227] Eisohly HN, Turner CE, Clark AM, Eisohly MA. Synthesis and antimicrobial activities of certain cannabichromene and cannabigerol related compounds. J Pharm Sci. 1982 Dec;71(12):1319-23. https://doi.org/10.1002/jps.2600711204

[228] Deiana S. 2017. Potential Medical Uses of Cannabigerol: A Brief Overview. Handbook of Cannabis and Related Pathologies. Chapter 99. Academic Press. Pages 958-967. https://doi.org/10.1016/B978-0-12-800756-3.00115-0

[229] Hatoum NS, Davis WM, Elsohly MA, Turner CE. 1981. Cannabichromene and delta-9-tetrahydrocannabinol: Interactions relative to lethality, hypothermia and hexobarbital hypnosis. Gen Pharmacol. 12(5):357-362. https://doi.org/10.1016/0306-3623(81)90090-2

[230] Wirth PW, Watson ES, ElSohly M, Turner CE, Murphy JC (1980). Anti-inflammatory properties of cannabichromene. Life Sci 26: 1991–1995. https://doi.org/10.1016/0024-3205(80)90631-1

[231] Davis WM, Hatoum NS (1983). Neurobehavioral actions of cannabichromene and interactions with delta 9-tetrahydrocannabinol. Gen Pharmacol 14: 247–252. https://doi.org/10.1016/0306-3623(83)90004-6

[232] Deyo R, Musty R (2003). A cannabichromene (CBC) extract alters behavioral despair on the mouse tail suspension test of depression. Proceedings 2003 Symposium on the Cannabinoids. International Cannabinoid Research Society: Cornwall, ON, p. 146.

[233] ElSohly HN, Turner CE, Clark AM, ElSohly MA (1982). Synthesis and antimicrobial activities of certain cannabichromene and cannabigerol related compounds. J Pharm Sci 71: 1319–1323. https://doi.org/10.1002/jps.2600711204

# Cannabicitran (CBT/CBcT)

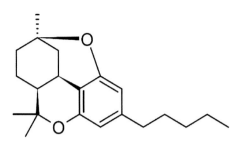

**Cannabicitran** was originally identified in the 1970s in Lebanesh hash.[234] CBT has been shown to be a modest inhibitor of acetylcholinesterase (AChE) and butyrylcholinesterase (BChE), possibly having a stimulating effect on the nervous system.[235] The general pharmacokinetics and potential therapeutic applications of CBT have not been thoroughly investigated at the time of this writing.

# Cannabimovone (CBM)

**Cannabimovone** is a cannabinoid that was discovered in 2010 from hemp.[236] It is an interesting cannabinoid because, unlike many other cannabinoids, it is polar, due to the abundance of oxygen in the molecule. CBM has not demonstrated much affinity for CB1 or CB2 receptors, but has demonstrated mild affinity for TRPV1 receptors, similar to CBD's activity. CBM has also been demonstrated as an agonist of PPARγ receptors *in silico*.[237]

---

[234] Bercht, C.L., Lousberg, R.J.C., Küppers, F.J. and Salemink, C.A., 1974. Cannabicitran: A new naturally occurring tetracyclic diether from lebanese Cannabis sativa. Phytochemistry, 13(3), pp.619-621.

[235] Puopolo T, Liu C, Ma H, Seeram NP. Inhibitory Effects of Cannabinoids on Acetylcholinesterase and Butyrylcholinesterase Enzyme Activities. Med Cannabis Cannabinoids. 2022 Apr 19;5(1):85-94. https://doi.org/10.1159/000524086  PMID: 35702400; PMCID: PMC9149358.

[236] Taglialatela-Scafati, O., Pagani, A., Scala, F., De Petrocellis, L., Di Marzo, V., Grassi, G. and Appendino, G. (2010), Cannabimovone, a Cannabinoid with a Rearranged Terpenoid Skeleton from Hemp. Eur. J. Org. Chem., 2010: 2067-2072. https://doi.org/10.1002/ejoc.200901464

[237] Iannotti FA, De Maio F, Panza E, Appendino G, Taglialatela-Scafati O, De Petrocellis L, Amodeo P, Vitale RM. Identification and Characterization of Cannabimovone, a Cannabinoid from Cannabis sativa, as a Novel PPAR γ Agonist via a Combined Computational and Functional Study. Molecules. 2020 Mar 3;25(5):1119. https://doi.org/10.3390/molecules25051119

# What Happens to Cannabis as it Ages?

Over time, the chemical compounds in Cannabis change as they react to things like heat, oxygen, and light. Terpenoids are often most impacted by degradation over time. Pure monoterpenes quickly oxidize, forming terpenoid alcohols. For instance, Myrcene oxidizes to become other terpenoids like geraniol or linalool. In addition, terpenes are more volatile than cannabinoids, leaving behind heavier sesquiterpenes and cannabinoids. As a result, the smell of the Cannabis changes.

Cannabinoids do not tend to volatize out of Cannabis, but they do react to heat and light to form various degradation products. Little is known about the pharmacological activity of many of these photodegradation and oxidation products. When compounds are ingested, they change again. If consumed orally, compounds will be changed into metabolic products in the liver and gut. While some information is known about THC metabolites, little is known about other metabolites.

| Starting Compound | Decarboxylation Product | | |
|---|---|---|---|
| THCA | THC | | **Degradation Product(s)** |
| | | | CBN |
| | | | Delta-8 THC |
| | | | **Metabolic Product(s)** |
| | | | 11-OH-THC |
| | | | 11-nor-9-COOH-THC |
| CBDA | CBD | | **Degradation Product(s)** |
| | | | CBND, CBE |
| | | | **Metabolic Product(s)** |
| | | | 7-OH-CBD |
| | | | 7-COOH-CBD |
| CBCA | CBC | | **Degradation Product(s)** |
| | | | CBL |
| | | | **Metabolic Product(s)** |
| | | | Hydroxylated Metabolites |
| THCVA | THCV | | **Degradation Product(s)** |
| | | | CBV |
| | | | Delta-8 THCV |
| | | | **Metabolic Product(s)** |
| | | | 11-OH-THCV |
| | | | 11-nor-9-COOH-THCV |
| CBDVA | CBDV | | **Degradation Product(s)** |
| | | | CBV |
| | | | **Metabolic Product(s)** |
| | | | 11-OH-CBDV |
| | | | 11-nor-9-COOH-CBDV |

FIGURE 27: METABOLIC PRODUCTS OF PHYTOCANNABINOIDS

# Common Cannabinoid Degradation Products

## Delta-8-Tetrahydrocannabinol (D8-THC)

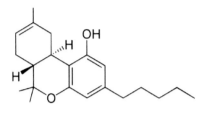

**Delta-8 THC** is almost the same as delta-9 THC, structurally, except that the location of a double bong has changed. It is psychoactive and intoxicating but less so than delta-9 THC.[238] In a study focusing on children ages 2 – 13 undergoing chemotherapy treatments, delta-8 THC displayed no psychoactive effects in the children and effectively **reduced nausea** at the doses administered of 18mg per square meter of body surface area.[239]

## Cannabinol (CBN)

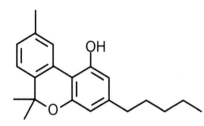

**CBN is a breakdown product of THC** and is commonly found in higher quantities in older Cannabis samples.[240] It has been indicated as a **sedative** and seems to only be active in the presence of THC.[241] CBN, like CBD, has also demonstrated **anticonvulsant** effects.[242] And, like THC, it has demonstrated **anti-inflammatory** effects.[243]

Examples of other members of the CBN Type Chemical Class:

| | | |
|---|---|---|
| CBN Acid | CBN-C3 | CBN-C4 |
| Cannabiorcol | Cannabinol Methyl Ether | CBN-C2 |

---

[238] Hollister LE (1974). Structure-activity relationships in man of Cannabis constituents, and homologs and metabolites of delta9-tetrahydrocannabinol. Pharmacol 11: 3–11. https://doi.org/10.1159/000136462

[239] Abrahamov, A., and R. Mechoulam. 1995. An efficient new cannabinoid antiemetic in pediatric oncology. Life Sci 56(23-24):2097-102. https://doi.org/10.1016/0024-3205(95)00194-b

[240] Merzouki A, Mesa JM. 2002. Concerning kif, a Cannabis sativa L. preparation smoked in the Rif mountains of northern Morocco. J Ethnopharmacol 81: 403–406. https://doi.org/10.1016/s0378-8741(02)00119-8

[241] Musty RE, Karniol IG, Shirikawa I, Takahashi RN, Knobel E (1976). Interactions of delta-9-tetrahydrocannabinol and cannabinol in man. In: Braude

[242] Turner, C.E., M.A. Elsohly, and E.G. Boeren. 1980. Constituents of Cannabis sativa L. XVII. A review of the natural constituents. J Nat Prod 43:169-304.

[243] Evans FJ (1991). Cannabinoids: the separation of central from peripheral effects on a structural basis. Planta Med 57: S60–S67. https://pubmed.ncbi.nlm.nih.gov/1659702/

## CANNABIVARIN (CBV)

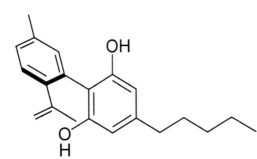

**Cannabivarin**, or **CBV**, is an oxidation product of THCV, much like CBN is an oxidation product of THC. It was originally identified in hashish in the 1970s.[244] Any pharmacological effects are currently unknown.

## CANNABINODIOL (CBND)

**CBND** is the result of the photochemical transformation of cannabinol (CBN) and cannabidiol (CBD). Any pharmacological effects are unknown.[245]

## CANNABICYCLOL (CBL)

**CBL** is the result of the photochemical transformation of cannabichromene (CBC) and is more commonly found in hashish.[246] **Cannabicyclolic acid** (CBLA) results from the irradiation of CBCA. There is no pharmacological information available.

---

[244] Merkus FW. Cannabivarin and tetrahydrocannabivarin, two new constituents of hashish. Nature. 1971 Aug 20;232(5312):579-80. https://doi.org/10.1038/232579a0

[245] ElSohly MA, Slade D. 2005. Chemical constituents of marijuana: the complex mixture of natural cannabinoids. Life Sciences. 78:539-548.

[246] Crombie L, Ponsford R, Shani A, Yagnitinsky B, Mechoulam R. Hashish components. Photochemical production of cannabicyclol from cannabichromene. Tetrahedron Lett. 1968 Nov;(55):5771-2. https://doi.org/10.1016/s0040-4039(00)76346-5

# CANNABINOQUINOIDS

QUINONE STRUCTURE

CANNABIDIOLQUINONE (CBDQ, AKA HU-331)

Once cannabinoids have been decarboxylated they can degrade into a class of compounds called **cannabinoquinoids**, which are compounds that contain the structure of quinone, containing two double bonded oxygens on an aromatic ring. All phenolic compounds are sensitive to this kind of degradation. Little is currently known about the pharmacological activity of many cannabinoquinoids, but cannabinoquinoids have been used to produce semi-synthetic cannabinoid drugs, like the semi-synthetic form of cannabidiolquinone, or CBDQ, called VCE-004.8. Cannabinoquinoids may be responsible for some of the colors present in Cannabis extracts, such as deep red colors.[247]

---

[247] Caprioglio D, Mattoteia D, Pollastro F, Negri R, Lopatriello A, Chianese G, Minassi A, Collado JA, Munoz E, Taglialatela-Scafati O, Appendino G. 2020. The Oxidation of Phytocannabinoids to Cannabinoquinoids. J. Nat. Prod. Pre-Print. Published April 21, 2020. https://doi.org/10.1021/acs.jnatprod.9b01284

# Common Cannabinoid Metabolites

## 11-Hydroxy-THC

**11-Hydroxy-THC** is not actually a phytocannabinoid but is a highly potent psychoactive primary metabolite of the phytocannabinoid THC, produced in the liver after ingestion.[248] It is the compound primarily responsible for the unique effects attributed to Cannabis infused edibles. 11-Hydroxy-THC is thought to be 4x as potent as THC.

## 11-nor-9-carboxy-THC
## (THC-COOH; 11-COOH-THC)

**11-COOH-THC** is a *secondary metabolite* of THC formed in the liver through the oxidation of 11-OH-THC. This compound is not psychoactive but has a long half-life, making it the target of urinalysis drug tests to identify Cannabis use. This compound has the ability to reduce the effects of THC by antagonizing cannabinoid receptors.[249] It may exhibit some anti-inflammatory and analgesic effects.[250] Some researchers speculate that THC might be a **pro-drug** for 11-COOH-THC.[251]

---

[248] Johnson JR, Jennison TA, Peat MA, Foltz RL (1984). "Stability of delta 9-tetrahydrocannabinol (THC), 11-hydroxy-THC, and 11-nor-9-carboxy-THC in blood and plasma". Journal of analytical toxicology 8 (5): 202–4. https://doi.org/10.1093/jat/8.5.202

[249] Burstein SH, Hunter SA, Latham V, Renzulli L. 1986. Prostaglandins and cannabis. XVI. Antagonism of delta-1-tetrahydrocannabinol action by its metabolites. Biochem Pharmacol.35(15):2553-2558. https://doi.org/10.1016/0006-2952(86)90053-5

[250] Burstein SH, Hull K, Hunter SA, Latham V. 1988. Cannabinoids and pain responses: a possible role for prostaglandins. FASEB J. 2(14):3022-3026. https://doi.org/10.1096/fasebj.2.14.2846397

[251] Ujvary I, Grotenhermen F. 2014. 11-nor-9-carboxy-delta-9-tetrahydrocannbinol – a ubiquitous yet underresearched cannabinoid. A review of the literature. Cannabinoids. 9(1):1-8.

# 7-OH-CBD and 7-COOH-CBD

Little is known about the metabolites of CBD. There are over 100 metabolites of CBD that have been identified among different animals, but the two most well-known are 7-OH-CBD and 7-COOH-CBD.[252] 7-OH-CBD inhibits FAAH, the enzyme that breaks down anandamide, although 7-COOH-CBD does not exhibit this activity.

# Cannabielsoin (CBE)

**Cannabielsoin is a metabolite of cannabidiol (CBD)** formed in the liver after oral ingestion of CBD.[253] There is currently little pharmacological information available about cannabielsoin. Cannabielsoin may reduce intraocular pressure.[254]

[252] Ujváry I, Hanuš L. Human Metabolites of Cannabidiol: A Review on Their Formation, Biological Activity, and Relevance in Therapy. Cannabis Cannabinoid Res. 2016 Mar 1;1(1):90-101. https://doi.org/10.1089/can.2015.0012

[253] Yamamoto I, Gohda H, Narimatsu S, Watanabe K, Yoshimura H. 1991. Cannabielsoin as a new metabolite of cannabidiol in mammals. Pharmacol Biochem Behav. 40(3):541-546. https://doi.org/10.1016/0091-3057(91)90360-e

[254] Ujváry I, Hanuš L. Human Metabolites of Cannabidiol: A Review on Their Formation, Biological Activity, and Relevance in Therapy. Cannabis Cannabinoid Res. 2016 Mar 1;1(1):90-101. https://doi.org/10.1089/can.2015.0012

## CYCLO-CBG

**Cyclo-CBG**, or 2-Methyl-2-(4-methyl-3-penten-1-yl)-7-pentyl-3,5-chromanediol, is a bioactive metabolite of CBG formed primarily from CYP2J2, CYP3A4, CYP2D6, CYP2C8, and CYP2C9 isoforms. Cyclo-CBG has demonstrated anti-inflammatory effects in vitro.[255]

## 11-OH-CBN, 8-OH-CBN

The metabolites of the cannabinoid Cannabinol are not very well studied, although there are a handful of in vitro metabolite studies that have examined CBN's common degradation products. Two of the primary metabolites of CBN are 11-OH-CBN and 8-OH-CBN.[256] Very little is known about the pharmacology of these CBN metabolites, presenting an area ripe for research as the cannabinoid grows in popularity.

## 11-OH-THCV, THCV-11-OIC ACID

The metabolites of divarinic cannabinoids like THCV and CBDV are not well studied, although the metabolites 11-hydroxy-THCV (or 11-OH-THCV) and delta-9-THCV-11-oic Acid have been identified. Additionally, there are likely other THCV derivatives that are formed during metabolism such as 8a-OH-THCV and 8b-OH-THCV.[257] Likewise, there are certainly comparable metabolites of CBDV present after metabolism as well.

---

[255] Roy P, Dennis DG, Eschbach MD, Anand SD, Xu F, Maturano J, Hellman J, Sarlah D, Das A. Metabolites of Cannabigerol Generated by Human Cytochrome P450s Are Bioactive. Biochemistry. 2022 Nov 1;61(21):2398-2408. https://doi.org/10.1021/acs.biochem.2c00383

[256] Watanabe, K., Yamaori, S., Funahashi, T. et al. 8-Hydroxycannabinol: a new metabolite of cannabinol formed by human hepatic microsomes. Forensic Toxicol 24, 80–82 (2006). https://doi.org/10.1007/s11419-006-0016-0

[257] Tinto F, Villano R, Kostrzewa M, Ligresti A, Straker H, Manzo E. Synthesis of the Major Mammalian Metabolites of THCV. J Nat Prod. 2020 Jul 24;83(7):2060-2065. https://doi.org/10.1021/acs.jnatprod.9b00831

## Enduring Understandings

- Cannabis produces well over 100 cannabinoids.
- Cannabinoids produced by a plant are called "phytocannabinoids".
- Cannabinoids like THC or CBD are initially produced in the Cannabis plant as cannabinoid acids, like THCA or CBDA, which feature a carboxylic acid functional group.
- The process of removing the carboxylic acid functional group from a cannabinoid acid is called decarboxylation and is often achieved by applying heat to Cannabis.
- Many of the degradation and metabolic products of cannabinoids are not well understood.

# Chapter 12:
## MORE ON CANNABIDIOL (CBD)

> **Learning Questions**
> - What is CBD and how is it different than THC?
> - How has CBD been studied throughout history?
> - How does CBD affect the body?
> - What contraindications and safety issues are associated with CBD?

### CBD vs. THC

Cannabidiol (CBD)          Delta-9-Tetrahydrocannabinol (THC)

CBD is markedly different than THC, although they look similar. To start, CBD does not cause intoxicating or euphoric effects like THC does.[258] This feature has gotten the attention of a lot of people, ranging from medical researchers looking to unlock the therapeutic potential of Cannabis without the risk of abuse to consumers interested in Cannabis but not looking to get high. Although CBD is not intoxicating, it *is* psychoactive, meaning that it elicits effects on neurons. This is a common misunderstanding about CBD.

CBD also affects the body in very different ways. While THC is a partial agonist, or stimulator, of CB1 and CB2 receptors in the body, CBD barely has any affinity for these chemical receptors at all. Instead, CBD stimulates the production of the endocannabinoid Anandamide, which then stimulates CB1 and CB2 receptors. In this way, CBD could be thought of as encouraging the body to do what it does naturally, stimulating the ECS indirectly, while THC could be seen as hijacking the endocannabinoid system and stimulating it directly. Additionally, CBD interacts with a host of other receptor types in the body, including serotonin, adenosine, transient receptor potential ion channels, PPAR-gamma receptors, and miscellaneous g-protein coupled receptors.

---

[258] Russo EB. 2011. Taming THC: potential Cannabis synergy and phytocannabinoid-terpenoid entourage effects. Br J of Pharmacol 163:1344-1364. https://doi.org/10.1111/j.1476-5381.2011.01238.x

# A Brief History of CBD Science

The story of CBD goes back thousands of years – as cultures across time have used non-psychoactive varieties of Cannabis for different uses. But the most relevant part of CBD's story really starts in 1940, when researchers Roger Adams, Madison Hunt and JH Clark published a report indicating the structure of a compound that they extracted and isolated from wild hemp in Minnesota.[259] These researchers named this compound, Cannabidiol, or CBD as it would become commonly known. CBD was only the second cannabinoid found in Cannabis at the time, the first reportedly being Cannabinol, or CBN – a degradation product of THC. However later it would be discovered that what researchers reported as CBN in the late 1800s and early 1900s was likely THC.[260]

In 1944 it was discovered that the effects of barbiturates could be extended if administered with CBD, but not with CBN or THC.[261] Their answer to why CBD had this effect would come almost 30 years later.

For a moment in 1963, scientists in Israel would shine light on CBD once again, before announcing their discovery of THC as the intoxicating components of Cannabis – a year later in 1964.[262] CBD would become a bit more ignored once again until around the 1970s and 80s when research into CBD really began to pick up steam.

In 1972 it would be discovered that CBD inhibited certain enzymes in the body, which affects how the body metabolizes certain foods and drugs.[263] This helped begin to complete the puzzle that stemmed from the barbiturate study three decades prior. In 1981 researchers were able to demonstrate anticonvulsant effects in humans – indicating that it might be an effective treatment for certain forms of epilepsy and spasticity.[264]  In 1982 CBD was found to exhibit anti-anxiety effects, which would later be reconfirmed in 1993.[265] [266] In 1995 it was discovered that CBD improves symptoms of

---

[259] Adams R, Hunt M, Clark JH. 1940. Structure of Cannabidiol, a Product Isolated from the Marihuana Extract of Minnesota Wild Hemp. I. J. Am. Chem. Soc. 62(1): 196-200. https://doi.org/10.1021/ja01858a058

[260] Scialdone, M. *viva voce*

[261] Loewe S. 1944. Studies on the pharmacology of marihuana The Marihuana Problems in the City of New Yorked. The Mayor's Committee on Marihuana. pp. 149–212.Lancaster, PA: The Jaques Cattell Press

[262] Mechoulam R, Shvo Y. Hashish. I. The structure of cannabidiol. Tetrahedron. 1963 Dec;19(12):2073-8. https://doi.org/10.1016/0040-4020(63)85022-x

[263] Paton WD, Pertwee RG. Effect of cannabis and certain of its constituents on pentobarbitone sleeping time and phenazone metabolism. Br J Pharmacol. 1972 Feb;44(2):250-61. https://pubmed.ncbi.nlm.nih.gov/4668592/

[264] Carlini EA and Cunha JM. 1981. Hypnotic and antiepileptic effects of cannabidiol. Journal of Clinical Pharmacology. 21: 417S–427S. https://doi.org/10.1002/j.1552-4604.1981.tb02622.x

[265] Zuardi AW, Shirawaka I, Finkelfarb E, Karniol IG. 1982. Action of cannabidiol on the anxiety and other effects produced by delta 9-THC in normal subjects. Psychopharmacology. 76: 245–250. https://doi.org/10.1007/bf00432554

[266] Zuardi AW, Cosme RA, Graeff FG, Guimaraes FS. 1993. Effects of ipsapirone and cannabidiol on human experimental anxiety. Journal of Psychopharmacology. 7: 82–88. https://doi.org/10.1177/026988119300700112

psychosis.[267] In 1998 the United States government filed a patent on the antioxidant and neuroprotective effects of CBD, as well as THC, which expired in 2019.[268]

The 2000s would become the decade of elucidating the activity of CBD. In 2001, researchers began to finally understand more about how CBD actually works in the body by revealing that CBD targets non-cannabinoid receptors in the body, stimulates the production of at least one endocannabinoid, Anandamide, and inhibits an enzyme responsible for breaking down Anandamide, effectively allowing it to linger in the body longer.[269]

In 2002 researchers would confirm that CBD exhibits anti-nausea effects, which had already been reported as far back as the 1800s when systematic Cannabis research really began to take shape.[270] In 2004 it was discovered that at certain dosages CBD can increase wakefulness and counteract THC induced sedation.[271] So if you are feeling sleepy after using THC-rich Cannabis, a little bit of CBD might wake you back up! However, CBD exhibits what is known as biphasic activity, meaning it acts differently in low doses versus high doses. At high doses, CBD can be sedating.[272]

In 2005 it was discovered that CBD interacts with certain serotonin receptors in the body.[273] In 2006 researchers would go on to discover that CBD also enhances adenosine receptor signaling, which is associated with heart health, blood pressure, and body temperature regulation.[274] It was also in 2006 that researchers discovered that CBD could kill breast cancer cells – bringing significant attention to the compound as a potential anti-cancer drug.[275]

In 2007 researchers began to understand why CBD reduced the effects of THC in some of their prior research. It turns out that CBD changes the shape and activity of CB1 receptors, even though it does not exhibit much affinity for them directly.[276] In this

[267] Zuardi AW, Morais SL, Guimarães FS, Mechoulam R. Antipsychotic effect of cannabidiol. J Clin Psychiatry. 1995 Oct;56(10):485-6.

[268] https://patents.google.com/patent/US6630507B1/en (Patent #: US6630507B1)

[269] Bisogno T, Hanus L, De Petrocellis L, Tchilibon S, Ponde DE, Brandi I, Moriello AS, Davis JB, Mechoulam R, Di Marzo V. Molecular targets for cannabidiol and its synthetic analogues: effect on vanilloid VR1 receptors and on the cellular uptake and enzymatic hydrolysis of anandamide. Br J Pharmacol. 2001 Oct;134(4):845-52. https://doi.org/10.1038/sj.bjp.0704327

[270] Parker LA, Mechoulam R, Schlievert C. Cannabidiol, a non-psychoactive component of cannabis and its synthetic dimethylheptyl homolog suppress nausea in an experimental model with rats. Neuroreport. 2002 Apr 16;13(5):567-70. https://doi.org/10.1097/00001756-200204160-00006

[271] Nicholson AN, Turner C, Stone BM, Robson PJ. Effect of Delta-9-tetrahydrocannabinol and cannabidiol on nocturnal sleep and early-morning behavior in young adults. J Clin Psychopharmacol. 2004 Jun;24(3):305-13. https://doi.org/10.1097/01.jcp.0000125688.05091.8f

[272] Zuardi AW, Cosme RA, Graeff FG, Guimaraes FS. 1993. Effects of ipsapirone and cannabidiol on human experimental anxiety. Journal of Psychopharmacology. 7: 82–88. https://doi.org/10.1177/026988119300700112

[273] Russo EB, Burnett A, Hall B, Parker KK. 2005. Agonistic properties of cannabidiol at 5-HT-1a receptors. Neurochem Res 30: 1037–1043. https://doi.org/10.1007/s11064-005-6978-1

[274] Carrier EJ, Auchampach JA, Hillard CJ. Inhibition of an equilibrium nucleoside transporter by cannabidiol: a mechanism of cannabinoid immunosuppression. Proc Natl Acad Sci U S A. 2006 May 16;103(20):7895-900. https://doi.org/10.1073/pnas.0511232103

[275] Ligresti A, Moriello AS, Starowicz K, Matias I, Pisanti S, De Petrocellis L, Laezza C, Portella G, Bifulco M, Di Marzo V. Antitumor activity of plant cannabinoids with emphasis on the effect of cannabidiol on human breast carcinoma. J Pharmacol Exp Ther. 2006 Sep;318(3):1375-87. https://doi.org/10.1124/jpet.106.105247

[276] Thomas A, Baillie GL, Phillips AM, Razdan RK, Ross RA, Pertwee RG (2007). Cannabidiol displays unexpectedly high potency as an antagonist of CB1 and CB2 receptor agonists in vitro. Br J Pharmacol 150: 613–623. https://doi.org/10.1038/sj.bjp.0707133

way, it changes the way that THC binds to the CB1 receptor, modulating its activity. This kind of activity is called allosteric modulation, and CBD is considered an allosteric modulator of the CB1 receptor. This is why CBD can reduce the high associated with THC – it essentially deforms the CB1 receptor so that THC cannot stimulate the receptor as well as it normally would.

In 2008 it was discovered that CBD was a potent antibiotic against MRSA – a powerful infection that is commonly picked up in hospitals and often resists treatment.[277] In 2012 researchers discovered that CBD may be as effective as standard antipsychotics.[278] In 2014 it was discovered that CBD might be able to effectively treat acne in the skin by reducing inflammation, fighting bacteria on the skin, and changing the way that the skin produces oil.[279]

## Is CBD Safe?

In general CBD has been demonstrated to be a very safe compound when consumed in oral dosages less than 1500mg/day.[280] At high dosages above 15-20mg of CBD per kg of body weight per day, liver damage could begin to occur, although it is uncommon for most consumers to encounter dosages this high.[281] The most common adverse effects of CBD that have been demonstrated in clinical trials are lethargy, gastrointestinal upset, and changes to appetite.[282] It should be noted that some of these side effects may be attributable to other drugs taken at the same time as CBD during these clinical trials.

The biggest safety issue related to CBD is how it interacts with other drugs. CBD inhibits the activity of cytochrome p450 enzymes in the liver which are responsible for breaking down all sorts of medications. This effect is often referred to as the "grapefruit effect" because grapefruits are notorious for causing drug interactions through suppression of liver enzymes. The effect is so common that many medications now feature "grapefruit warnings" on them.

By taking CBD with other medications, the risk for adverse effects associated with elevated levels of other medications may increase. This risk is even more serious if someone is using a CBD product that has been manipulated in a way that enhances CBD's bioavailability and absorption in the body, such as through pico- or nano-

---

[277] Appendino G, Gibbons S, Giana A, Pagani A, Grassi G, Stavri M, Smith E, Rahman MM. Antibacterial cannabinoids from Cannabis sativa: a structure-activity study. J Nat Prod. 2008 Aug;71(8):1427-30. https://doi.org/10.1021/np8002673
[278] Leweke FM, Piomelli D, Pahlisch F, Muhl D, Gerth CW, Hoyer C, Klosterkötter J, Hellmich M, Koethe D. Cannabidiol enhances anandamide signaling and alleviates psychotic symptoms of schizophrenia. Transl Psychiatry. 2012 Mar 20;2(3):e94. https://doi.org/10.1038/tp.2012.15
[279] Oláh A, Tóth BI, Borbíró I, Sugawara K, Szöllõsi AG, Czifra G, Pál B, Ambrus L, Kloepper J, Camera E, Ludovici M, Picardo M, Voets T, Zouboulis CC, Paus R, Bíró T. Cannabidiol exerts sebostatic and antiinflammatory effects on human sebocytes. J Clin Invest. 2014 Sep;124(9):3713-24. https://doi.org/10.1172/JCI64628
[280] https://www.accessdata.fda.gov/drugsatfda_docs/label/2018/210365lbl.pdf
[281] Ewing LE, Skinner CM, Quick CM, Kennon-McGill S, McGill MR, Walker LA, ElSohly MA, Gurley BJ, Koturbash I. Hepatotoxicity of a Cannabidiol-Rich Cannabis Extract in the Mouse Model. Molecules. 2019 Apr 30;24(9):1694. https://doi.org/10.3390/molecules24091694
[282] Iffland K and Grotenhermen F. 2017. An Update on Safety and Side Effects of Cannabidiol: A Review of Clinical Data and Relevant Animal Studies. Cannabis and Cannabinoid Research. Vol. 2.1. http://doi.org/10.1089/can.2016.0034

emulsification, where the CBD oil is split into droplets the size of picometers or nanometers before being surrounded by a water-loving, or hydrophilic, shell. This keeps the oil droplets from coming back together when in an aqueous solution, thus increasing surface area and allowing the body to process more of the CBD, faster.

There was a recent report of a fatality associated with the use of nano-emulsified CBD.[283] The patient had been using CBD products with no problems for some time before she suddenly developed Stevens Johnson syndrome after trying a liposomal CBD product. Her skin began breaking out in severe rashes before starting to peel off. The reaction was a side effect of one of the medications, meloxicam, that the patient was taking at the time, although the patient had tolerated Meloxicam well. It is possible that, due to the enhanced bioavailability of CBD in the emulsified product, levels of the patient's medications were elevated to dangerous levels. However, at the time of this writing, the exact cause of the reaction could not be determined.

This kind of incident, regardless of whether it was definitively caused by CBD-drug interactions or not, highlights the need for consumers to be aware of the potential serious adverse reactions that can happen when CBD is mixed with other medications. It also highlights the need for doctors and other health care professionals to be educated on the liver enzyme altering effects of CBD. In general, one should always consult with a licensed healthcare professional that is educated in cannabinoids prior to mixing CBD or any other cannabinoid therapy with other medications.

---

# Enduring Understandings

- CBD is not intoxicating, but it *is* psychoactive, meaning that it has effects on neurons in the brain.
- CBD was first isolated and characterized in 1940.
- Most relevant CBD research kicked off in the 1970s and 1980s.
- CBD's mechanisms of action began to be understood in the early 2000s but are still not properly understood.
- CBD has demonstrated a host of potential therapeutic applications in pre-clinical research, but more clinical research is needed to understand how to utilize CBD as a medicine more effectively.
- CBD is generally safe and well tolerated by most people at dosages up to 1500mg per day, however CBD can interact with medications and possibly contribute to serious, potentially life-threatening, drug interactions due to the way CBD can inhibit certain enzymes in the liver that would normally break down common drugs.

---

[283] Yin HY, Hadjokas N, Mirchia K, Swan R, Alpert S. Commercial Cannabinoid Oil-Induced Stevens-Johnson Syndrome. Case Rep Ophthalmol Med. 2020 Feb 19;2020:6760272. https://doi.org/10.1155/2020/6760272

# Chapter 13:
## MORE ON CANNABIGEROL (CBG)

## Learning Questions

- What is CBG?
- How is CBG produced in Cannabis?
- Why are hemp cultivators turning to CBG over CBD?
- How does CBG affect the body?
- What are the potential therapeutic applications of CBG?

### Hemp Farmers Are Hyped On CBG

When the 2018 US Farm Bill passed in the USA, there was a lot of excitement around the future of CBD and CBD products. Many farmers, new and old, rushed to get CBD-rich resin producing Cannabis plants into the ground, sourcing genetics from all manner of suppliers. When the first harvest came around and the USDA started issuing their cannabinoid test results for hemp, many farmers were faced with a devastating surprise – "hot" hemp.

"Hot" hemp is hemp that tests over the legal threshold for THC. Hemp goes "hot" for several reasons. Sometimes farmers source unstable seeds or unreliable cuttings that do not produce the intended chemotype. Other times it is because a farm waits to have their field tested too late in the growth cycle, resulting in higher concentrations of cannabinoids than would otherwise be measured. But ultimately, the struggle comes down to genetics.

The gene responsible for making CBDA, also produces THCA. The CBDA synthase gene is considered "promiscuous" or "leaky". Even if a farmer got genetics that did not include a single THCA synthase gene, THCA would still be produced by the plant through the CBDA synthase gene. Partner this fact with the fact that the .3% THC limit currently applied to hemp in the United States is an arbitrary limit based on outdated information from the 1970s, and we have a serious problem for hemp farmers that want to grow hemp for resin content. How do you get a reliable hemp crop for resin that will not go "hot"?

The answer is (somewhat) in CBGA! Because CBGA is a precursor to CBDA and THCA, a CBGA abundant Cannabis plant will have substantially lower levels of trace THCA compared to CBDA abundant plants. Because of this shift toward CBGA abundant hemp plants that reduce the farmer's risk, consumers are seeing more CBG and CBGA containing products on store shelves.

### WHERE DOES CBG COME FROM?

The Cannabis plant initially synthesizes CBG in its acidic form, like it does all other phytocannabinoids. When cannabigerolic acid (CBGA) is heated up, it decarboxylates – releasing a carboxylic acid functional group in the form of carbon dioxide – and is transformed to cannabigerol (CBG).

CBGA → HEAT → CBG

Depending on the genetics of the plant, various synthase enzymes like CBDA or THCA synthase can take CBGA and transform it to THCA, CBDA, or CBCA.

## How Does CBG Work?

Like many other cannabinoids, CBG is active at many different chemical receptors in the body. At the time of this writing, CBG is known to interact with both CB1 and CB2 receptors – though the exact mechanisms of action are unclear. Some studies have been published that report CBG as a CB1 agonist whereas others contradict this claim. CBG is also known to interact with TRPV1, TRPV2, TRPV3, TRPV4, TRPM8 and TRPA1 ion channels. It is also a serotonin 5-HT1A antagonist and an a2 adrenergic receptor agonist. CBG's activities at adrenergic receptors is notable considering CBG can be active at sub-nanomolar concentrations in the blood.

| Receptor Target | CBG Activity | Notes |
|---|---|---|
| CB1 | Partial Agonist? / Protean Agonist | CNS modulator |
| CB2 | Partial Agonist | Immune functioning, neuron functioning/growth |
| PPARy | Agonist | Insulin resistance, metabolism, bone growth |
| Alpha-2 Adrenergic | Agonist | Presynaptic receptor; Inhibition of norepinephrine, increased glucagon release, enhanced insulin activity |
| TRPV1 | Agonist | Capsaicin receptor; Temperature sensing, pain, and heat sensing |
| TRPV2 | Agonist | Cardiovascular function, neuron development |
| TRPV3 | Agonist | Temperature sensing, wound healing, itch, pain |
| TRPV4 | Agonist | Immune function, bone growth, neuron growth |
| TRPA1 | Agonist | Pain, itch, cold sensing |
| TRPM8 | Antagonist | Menthol receptor; temperature sensing, detection of cold |
| 5-HT1A | Antagonist | Cardiovascular function, hormone regulation, mood |
| COX1 / COX2 | Antagonist | Inflammation |

Alpha 2 adrenergic receptors are primarily associated with cardiovascular health and blood pressure. Stimulation of these receptors can lead to vasoconstriction and a reduction in blood pressure. CBG is currently the only known cannabinoid to act as an agonist on adrenergic receptors.[284] If someone is taking heart medications regularly, they may need to exercise caution when using CBG.

CBG is considered a competitive inhibitor of anandamide metabolism, as it has a greater affinity for CYP2J2 and other CYP isoforms compared to Anandamide as well as many other phytocannabinoids.[285]

## ACTIVE METABOLITES OF CBG

It turns out that not only is CBG therapeutically active in the body, but its metabolites, like cyclo-CBG, may also have therapeutic activity. CBG is primarily metabolized by the CYP2J2 isoform to produce a range of byproducts that are yet to be adequately investigated. A 2022 study investigating the activity of CBG metabolites reported:

*"These investigations revealed that cyclo-CBG, a recently isolated phytocannabinoid, is the major metabolite that is rapidly formed by selected human cytochrome P450s (CYP2J2, CYP3A4, CYP2D6, CYP2C8, and CYP2C9)...Importantly, we found out that CBG and its oxidized CBG metabolites reduced inflammation in BV2 microglial cells stimulated with LPS. Overall...we showcase that CBG is rapidly metabolized by human P450s to form oxidized metabolites that are bioactive."[286]*

Time will tell how other CBG metabolites may influence human physiology and what therapeutic role they may have to play.

## THERAPEUTIC POTENTIAL OF CBG

At the time of this writing evidence exists indicating that CBG may have several significant therapeutic applications – including, but not limited to, neuroprotection/neuromodulation, gastrointestinal disease, metabolic syndrome, and antimicrobial applications.[287]

### CBG AND NEUROPROTECTION

In 2015 Valdeolivas et al reported that CBG can help prevent striatal neuron death in the brain while reducing critical markers of inflammation, ultimately

[284] Cascio MG, Gauson LA, Stevenson LA, Ross RA, and Pertwee RG (2010) Evidence that the plant cannabinoid cannabigerol is a highly potent alpha2-adrenoceptor agonist and moderately potent 5HT1A receptor antagonist. Br J Pharmacol 159:129–141. https://doi.org/10.1111/j.1476-5381.2009.00515.x

[285] Fabrizio Calapai, Luigi Cardia, Emanuela Esposito, Ilaria Ammendolia, Cristina Mondello, Roberto Lo Giudice, Sebastiano Gangemi, Gioacchino Calapai, Carmen Mannucci, "Pharmacological Aspects and Biological Effects of Cannabigerol and Its Synthetic Derivatives", Evidence-Based Complementary and Alternative Medicine, vol. 2022, Article ID 3336516, 14 pages, 2022. https://doi.org/10.1155/2022/3336516

[286] Roy P, Dennis DG, Eschbach MD, Anand SD, Xu F, Maturano J, Hellman J, Sarlah D, Das A. Metabolites of Cannabigerol Generated by Human Cytochrome P450s Are Bioactive. Biochemistry. 2022 Nov 1;61(21):2398-2408. https://doi.org/0.1021/acs.biochem.2c00383

[287] Nachnani R, Raup-Konsavage WM, Vrana KE. The Pharmacological Case for Cannabigerol. J Pharmacol Exp Ther. 2021 Feb;376(2):204-212. https://doi.org10.1124/jpet.120.000340

improving motor coordination and activity.[288] In 2020, Echeverry et al reported that in vitro CBG exhibits neuroprotective effects through the 5HT1A receptors.[289] [290]

## CBG and Gastrointestinal Health

CBG has been shown to help increase tissue recovery in the colon *in vitro*.[291] In a 2020 rodent study, CBG reduced colon inflammation substantially, while CBD did not.[292] It has also been reported that CBG can interrupt the anti-nausea effects of CBD and possibly other cannabinoids.[293] [294]

## CBG and Metabolic Syndromes

Metabolic syndrome is characterized by insulin resistance, obesity, hypertension, high levels of low-density lipoprotein, and reduced levels of high-density lipoprotein. Traditionally, adrenoceptor agonists and PPARa/y agonists have been targeted to treat metabolic syndrome by lowering blood pressure and treating insulin resistance. Because CBG is an adrenoceptor agonist and PPAR agonist, it seems to fit the bill as a solid candidate for the treatment of metabolic syndrome, though no clinical research has yet been performed to further examine CBG's potential in this realm.[295]

## Antimicrobial Activity of CBG

CBG is one of the most potent cannabinoids that acts against antibiotic resistant strains of *Staphylococcus aureus*.[296] In a 2020 study, CBG reduced the colony forming units of Staph in mice at the same strength as vancomycin.[297] CBG may also be an effective antimicrobial agent against gram negative bacteria like E. coli and

---

[288] Valdeolivas S, Navarrete C, Cantarero I, Bellido ML, Muñoz E, and Sagredo O (2015) Neuroprotective properties of cannabigerol in Huntington's disease: studies in R6/2 mice and 3-nitropropionate-lesioned mice. Neurotherapeutics 12:185–199. https://doi.org/10.1007/s13311-014-0304-z

[289] Echeverry C, Prunell G, Narbondo C, de Medina VS, Nadal X, Reyes-Parada M, and Scorza C (2020) A Comparative in vitro study of the neuroprotective effect induced by cannabidiol, cannabigerol, and their respective acid forms: relevance of the 5-HT. Neurotox Res. https://doi.org10.1007/s12640-020-00277-y

[290] Nachnani R, Raup-Konsavage WM, Vrana KE. The Pharmacological Case for Cannabigerol. J Pharmacol Exp Ther. 2021 Feb;376(2):204-212. https://doi.org10.1124/jpet.120.000340

[291] Borrelli F, Fasolino I, Romano B, Capasso R, Maiello F, Coppola D, Orlando P, Battista G, Pagano E, Di Marzo V, et al. (2013) Beneficial effect of the nonpsychotropic plant cannabinoid cannabigerol on experimental inflammatory bowel disease. Biochem Pharmacol 85:1306–1316 https://doi.org/10.1016/j.bcp.2013.01.017

[292] Pagano E, Iannotti FA, Piscitelli F, Romano B, Lucariello G, Venneri T, Di Marzo V, Izzo AA, and Borrelli F (2020) Efficacy of combined therapy with fish oil and phytocannabinoids in murine intestinal inflammation. Phytother Res. https://doi.org10.1002/ptr.6831

[293] Rock EM, Goodwin JM, Limebeer CL, Breuer A, Pertwee RG, Mechoulam R, and Parker LA (2011) Interaction between non-psychotropic cannabinoids in marihuana: effect of cannabigerol (CBG) on the anti-nausea or anti-emetic effects of cannabidiol (CBD) in rats and shrews. Psychopharmacology (Berl) 215:505–512. https://doi.org/10.1007/s00213-010-2157-4

[294] Nachnani R, Raup-Konsavage WM, Vrana KE. The Pharmacological Case for Cannabigerol. J Pharmacol Exp Ther. 2021 Feb;376(2):204-212. https://doi.org10.1124/jpet.120.000340

[295] Nachnani R, Raup-Konsavage WM, Vrana KE. The Pharmacological Case for Cannabigerol. J Pharmacol Exp Ther. 2021 Feb;376(2):204-212. https://doi.org10.1124/jpet.120.000340

[296] Appendino G, Gibbons S, Giana A, Pagani A, Grassi G, Stavri M, Smith E, and Rahman MM (2008) Antibacterial cannabinoids from Cannabis sativa: a structure-activity study. J Nat Prod 71:1427–1430. https://doi.org/10.1021/np8002673

[297] Farha MA, El-Halfawy OM, Gale RT, MacNair CR, Carfrae LA, Zhang X, Jentsch NG, Magolan J, and Brown ED (2020) Uncovering the hidden antibiotic potential of cannabis. ACS Infect Dis 6:338–346. https://doi.org/10.1021/acsinfecdis.9b00419

Pseudomonas if administered with an adjuvant drug that can help break the bacterial membranes which are challenging for cannabinoids to pass through on their own.[298] CBG's antimicrobial activity seems to be due, in part, to its ability to inhibit enoyl acyl carrier protein reductase (InhA), disrupting fatty acid synthesis in the bacteria.[299] [300]

## OTHER ACTIVITIES OF CBG

In addition to the previously mentioned applications of CBG, CBG exhibits significant anti-inflammatory and antitumoral properties, like other cannabinoids. It has been suggested that CBG may be a candidate for adjuvant therapy for glioblastoma, a type of brain cancer.[301] Because of CBG's effects on the cardiovascular system, as well as its effects on CB1 and 5HT1A, CBG may have applications as an anxiolytic, or anti-anxiety agent. There is also some evidence that CBG may reduce intraocular pressure through non-CB1 or CB2 receptor mechanisms. CBG has also been studied for its potential anti-acne effects and anti-psoriatic effects based on its ability to reduce the expression of keratin, involucrin and transglutaminase genes in skin cells.[302] We are still in the early stages of beginning to research and understand how CBG works and how it compares to cannabinoids we better understand like THC or CBD.

# IS CBG SAFE?

In general, cannabigerol seems to be just as safe as other phytocannabinoids like CBD or THC. The primary concern regarding potential adverse effects relate to potential interactions with other medications. As mentioned previously, anyone taking medications that lower blood pressure should be particularly careful with using CBG. Additionally, anyone utilizing cannabinoids for their antiemetic (anti-nausea) effects should avoid formulations that include CBG. While CBG exhibits antiemetic effects alone, it seems to undo those effects from other cannabinoids.

---

[298] Farha MA, El-Halfawy OM, Gale RT, MacNair CR, Carfrae LA, Zhang X, Jentsch NG, Magolan J, and Brown ED (2020) Uncovering the hidden antibiotic potential of cannabis. ACS Infect Dis 6:338–346. https://doi.org/10.1021/acsinfecdis.9b00419

[299] Pinzi L, Lherbet C, Baltas M, Pellati F, and Rastelli G (2019) In silico repositioning of cannabigerol as a novel inhibitor of the enoyl Acyl Carrier Protein (ACP) reductase (InhA). Molecules 24:2567. https://doi.org/10.3390/molecules24142567

[300] Nachnani R, Raup-Konsavage WM, Vrana KE. The Pharmacological Case for Cannabigerol. J Pharmacol Exp Ther. 2021 Feb;376(2):204-212. https://doi.org10.1124/jpet.120.000340

[301] Lah TT, Novak M, Pena Almidon MA, Marinelli O, Žvar Baškovič B, Majc B, Mlinar M, Bošnjak R, Breznik B, Zomer R, Nabissi M. Cannabigerol Is a Potential Therapeutic Agent in a Novel Combined Therapy for Glioblastoma. Cells. 2021 Feb 5;10(2):340. https://doi.org/10.3390/cells10020340/

[302] Fabrizio Calapai, Luigi Cardia, Emanuela Esposito, Ilaria Ammendolia, Cristina Mondello, Roberto Lo Giudice, Sebastiano Gangemi, Gioacchino Calapai, Carmen Mannucci, "Pharmacological Aspects and Biological Effects of Cannabigerol and Its Synthetic Derivatives", Evidence-Based Complementary and Alternative Medicine, vol. 2022, Article ID 3336516, 14 pages, 2022. https://doi.org/10.1155/2022/3336516

# Enduring Understandings

- Cannabigerol, or CBG, is the decarboxylated form of CBGA, the chemical precursor to THCA, CBDA and CBCA.
- Because CBGA is a precursor to THCA, CBGA dominant hemp cultivars have exceptionally low trace concentrations of THCA compared to CBDA dominant cultivars.
- CBG's effects on the body are not as well understood as CBD or THC
- CBG seems to interact with many different receptors including CB1, CB2, the TRPVs, a-2 adrenergic receptors, PPARa/y, 5HT1A and possibly others.
- CBG's effects on a-2 adrenergic receptors is very potent, at nanomolar and sub-nanomolar concentrations. This causes reduced heart rate, sedation, and other cardiovascular effects. At high doses, CBG can have hypertensive effects.
- There is pre-clinical evidence indicating that CBG may be effective at helping treat neuroinflammation, gastrointestinal disease, metabolic disorders, and bacterial infections.

# Chapter 14:
## CANNABIS TERPENOIDS

**Learning Questions**

- What are terpenes?
- How do terpene concentrations change over time after Cannabis has been harvested?
- What are the most common terpenes found in Cannabis?

## INTRODUCTION

Terpenes are essential oil components of plants and other organisms, imparting some of their aromas and flavors, and at one time were considered the fifth element alongside earth, wind, water, and fire.[303] **Terpenoids** make up the largest group of plant chemicals consisting of approximately twenty thousand terpenes that have currently been scientifically described.

There are several different classifications of terpenes based on the size of the molecule. **Monoterpenoids** and **Sesquiterpenoids** are the most common types of terpenoids encountered. Monoterpenoids are very simple terpenoids consisting of two isoprene units and a molecular formula of $C_{10}H_{16}$. Sesquiterpenoids contain three isoprene units and maintain a molecular formula of $C_{15}H_{24}$, making them heavier and less volatile. Cannabinoids are considered **meroterpenoids**, a term used for compounds that contain partial terpenoid structures.

| Terpenoid Classification | Number of Carbon Atoms | Common Examples in Cannabis |
|---|---|---|
| Monoterpenoid | 10 | Myrcene, Limonene, Linalool |
| Sesquiterpenoid | 15 | Beta-Caryophyllene, Humulene |
| Diterpenoid | 20 | Phytol |
| Triterpenoid | 30 | Friedelin, Epifriedelanol |

FIGURE 28: TERPENE CLASSIFICATIONS

The terpenes of Cannabis have largely already been discovered and researched in other plants, although the diversity and density of these compounds in Cannabis varieties are only recently being explored. Monoterpenoids are highly volatile due to their very simple structure and dissipate quite a bit after the drying of Cannabis.[304] [305]

---

[303] Russo EB. Taming THC: potential cannabis synergy and phytocannabinoid-terpenoid entourage effects. Br J Pharmacol. 2011 Aug;163(7):1344-64. https://doi.org/10.1111/j.1476-5381.2011.01238.x

[304] Turner, C.E., M.A. Elsohly, and E.G. Boeren. 1980. Constituents of Cannabis sativa L. XVII. A review of the natural constituents. J Nat Prod 43:169-304.

[305] Ross SA, ElSohly MA. 1996. The volatile oil composition of fresh and air-dried buds of Cannabis sativa. J Nat Prod 59: 49–51. https://doi.org/10.1021/np960004a

Terpenes undergo a lot of changes from the time a Cannabis plant is harvested to the time the material makes its way to a user. One research study found that if not kept in an air-tight container, 31% of terpenes were lost in Cannabis material after 1 week of drying at room temperature; 44.8% of terpenes were lost in material that was dried for 1 week and then stored in a paper bag for 1 month; 55.2% of terpenes were lost in material that had been dried at room temperature for 1 week and then stored in a paper bag for 3 months.[306]

The concentration of monoterpenes in this study went from being 92.48% of the terpene fraction in fresh Cannabis, to 85.54% in material that had been dried for 1 week at room temperature. It dropped further to 67.60% in material that was stored for 3 months in a paper bag.

This results in a greater proportion of sesquiterpenoids, with beta-caryophyllene usually being the most dominant. Sesquiterpene concentration can increase approximately six times the original content over three months of storage. Contrary to cannabinoid yield, phytoterpenoid yield occurs best in soils with reduced fertility.[307]

Many terpenes oxidize into a variety of other terpenes during aging while other terpenes quickly volatize off from the plant material, making test results difficult to meaningfully interpret. Oxidized terpenes include things like linalool, geraniol, and terpinol. The non-oxidized terpenes, or terpenes lacking any oxygen atoms, are often referred to as "true terpenes". Examples of true terpenes include limonene, myrcene, and terpinolene.

The high degree of volatility and variability of terpenes makes them a sort of moving target for Cannabis testing labs. For instance, the true terpene myrcene can oxidize and turn into linalool. When a testing lab finds linalool in a sample, is it because linalool was present or did the lab improperly store the sample, causing oxidation and degradation of myrcene and other true terpenes, resulting in a greater proportion of sesquiterpenes and oxygen containing terpenes?

Recent research has focused on whether terpenes might be responsible for some of the reported effects of Cannabis and whether these compounds might have synergistic effects with cannabinoids. Animal studies seem to support this idea of the "entourage effect".[308]

Most terpenes are not very acutely toxic if ingested directly in small amounts but can act as respiratory irritants when inhaled. There is little toxicity information available about persistent long-term exposure to terpene compounds when inhaled. **There is currently little or no research on the health effects of directly smoking**

[306] https://herbal-ahp.org/online-ordering-cannabis-inflorescence-qc-monograph/
[307] Langenheim JH (1994). Higher plant terpenoids: a phytocentric overview of their ecological roles. J Chem Ecol 20: 1223–1279.  https://doi.org/10.1007/bf02059809
[308] Buchbauer G, Jirovetz L, Jäger W, Plank C, Dietrich H. Fragrance compounds and essential oils with sedative effects upon inhalation. J Pharm Sci. 1993 Jun;82(6):660-4. https://doi.org/10.1002/jps.2600820623

**large concentrations of terpenes, as are found in some terpene enriched Cannabis extracts.**

Terpenes interact with molecules in the air such as $NO_3$, OH, and others to form oxidative products. These secondary organic aerosols can cause lung irritation and gastrointestinal problems. There have been no studies on mammalian health effects of chronic exposures to elevated levels of secondary organic aerosols from terpene oxidation products that would be found in Cannabis or Cannabis products.

### AVERAGE CONCENTRATION RANGES OF COMMON TERPENOIDS IN CANNABIS FLOWERS

| Compound | % Content |
|---|---|
| a-Pinene | 0.1 – 0.75 |
| b-Myrcene | 0.1 - 2.0 |
| d-Limonene | 0.1 – 1.5 |
| Terpinolene | 0.1 – 1.25 |
| Linalool | 0.1 – 0.5 |
| b-Caryophyllene | 0.1 – 1.5 |

FIGURE 29: AVERAGE TERPENOID CONCENTRATIONS IN CANNABIS

Data Source: *viva voce* Kenevir Research, Oregon, USA, 2015

**Note**: According to Cannabis researcher, Dr. Ethan Russo, terpenoid concentrations of 0.05% or greater are of pharmacological interest.[309]

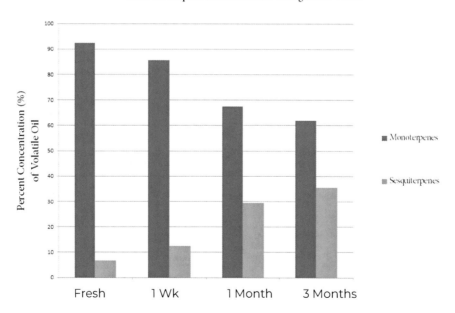

FIGURE 30: HOW DO TERPENE CONCENTRATIONS CHANGE OVER TIME?[310]

---

[309] Russo EB. Taming THC: potential cannabis synergy and phytocannabinoid-terpenoid entourage effects. Br J Pharmacol. 2011 Aug;163(7):1344-64. https://doi.org/10.1111/j.1476-5381.2011.01238.x
[310] Ross SA, ElSohly MA. 1996. The volatile oil composition of fresh and air-dried buds of Cannabis sativa. J Nat Prod 59: 49–51. https://doi.org/10.1021/np960004a

## WHICH TERPENE? A NOTE ABOUT CHIRALITY

There is a glaring problem facing Cannabis terpenoid data, currently – and that is that most analytical laboratories performing Cannabis testing do not test for something call enantiomers. Enantiomers are molecules that have the same exact chemical structure but are mirror opposites of one another – like your left hand and right hand. They are built the same, with the same components, and they look the same – only they are mirror opposites of one another. Enantiomers are examples of a concept called chirality. Chirality is property that describes asymmetry in something, and in chemistry a set of compounds are chiral if they are the same structure but cannot be superposed upon one another no matter what way the molecule is manipulated.

The implications for not understanding the enantiomers of Cannabis compounds are quite significant. Although enantiomers may seem to be essentially the same molecule, the way they interact with chemical receptors in the body, and thus the physiological effects they promote, can be very different.

Because the enantiomers of Cannabis terpenoids are not well understood, and the data provided by Cannabis testing labs is largely inadequate, often improperly validating the identification of specific terpenoid enantiomers, I stress caution when attempting to interpret terpene results of Cannabis products. This issue also highlights one of several reasons why terpene profiles are unreliable for predicting the effects a Cannabis product may have on a consumer.

## DO TERPENOIDS DETERMINE EFFECTS?

There is a prevailing notion throughout the Cannabis community that terpenoids produce unique effects among Cannabis varieties. This then often leads people to jump to the conclusion that if they study the effects of individual terpenes, and then recognize the dominant terpenes in a Cannabis product, that they might be able to predict how the Cannabis product with affect them. This is a problematic idea for several reasons.

First, there is the issue around enantiomers that we just covered. When a lab reports limonene concentration in Cannabis, is that d-Limonene, or l-Limonene? When a lab reports linalool, is that S-linalool or R-linalool? Evidence suggests that this really matters in terms of therapeutic activity.

Next there is the problem that terpenoids have been shown to elicit different effects depending on the context in which they are administered. This is tied into the concept of "set and setting." Set and setting describes the physical environmental and psychological mindset involved in the administration of a drug. Going back to research around linalool, it has been shown that different enantiomers of linalool perform differently when administered under different circumstances. While linalool might be calming in one environment, it might precipitate feelings of irritation in another setting.[311]

---

[311] Hoferl M, Krist S, Buchbauer G. 2006. Chirality influences the effects of linalool on physiological parameters of stress. Planta Med. 72(13): 1188-1192. https://doi.org/10.1055/s-2006-947202

Finally, the effect of a medication or drug is not just dependent on the chemistry of that product, but also the physiology and psychology of the consumer. The chemistry is just one piece of a bigger puzzle. Even if you know the chemistry of a product, and the psychological component (set and setting) are controlled, there is still the fact that different people feature different biochemistry that influences how that product will behave in the body once consumed. To make things even more complicated, your biochemistry is not static. Drugs affect the body differently depending on the time of day, your age, your diet, and many other factors.

Despite these nuances, there are many companies – both well intentioned and not – that try to capitalize on a narrative that someone can learn what Cannabis varieties are best for different conditions by understanding the terpene content of the plant or cannabinoid product. The "science" offered for this approach is generally based on research around isolated terpenoids, and often without references to specific enantiomers. The ironic thing about this approach is that it ignores the concept of the "entourage effect" which informs us that compounds may produce unique activities that are greater than the sum of their parts. Given that we already acknowledge the entourage effect and its importance in the therapeutic activity of Cannabis, why would someone assume that the activity of an isolated terpenoid will produce a certain effect when it is administered in the presence of hundreds of other terpenoids and cannabinoids?

To summarize the point, terpenoids certainly contribute to the effects elicited by Cannabis. But it is currently impossible to determine to what degree these effects occur, and what meaningful conclusions we can draw from knowing the concentrations of terpenoids in a Cannabis product. Even if we had a perfect understanding of the chemistry of a Cannabis product, which we certainly do not, we would still have difficulty predicting the effects that a Cannabis product will have. A Cannabis product that has a lot of linalool in it is not necessarily going to help with sleep. In fact, it could have the opposite effect in certain situations. A Cannabis variety dominant in terpinolene or limonene is not necessarily going to cause excitability or give someone energy, as is often commonly thought.

The picture is much more complex, and we must be careful not to let our minds oversimplify the dynamics involved. It is okay to admit that we do not yet properly understand how terpenoids influence the effects of Cannabis, and there is a lot of research needed to begin to tackle that question.

# Cannabis Monoterpenoids

## (10 Carbons)

### Ocimene

cis-$\beta$-Ocimene

trans-$\beta$-Ocimene

**Ocimene** is typically associated with some of the rarer fruity aromas and tastes of Cannabis, as is found in the famous Cannabis cultivar "Strawberry Cough". This terpene has a sweet aroma and is frequently used in perfumes. Interestingly enough, cis-Beta-Ocimene is used industrially as a protective film for flexible electronics.[312] Ocimene has been shown to have antimicrobial properties, as many monoterpenoids do.[313] [314]

### Beta-Myrcene

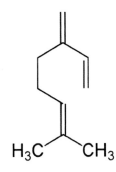

**Beta-myrcene** is commonly found in fresh Cannabis, as well as hops (*Humulus lupus*) and exhibits anti-inflammatory effects.[315] It has also been shown to fight cancer caused by the mycotoxin, aflatoxin.[316]

Myrcene is found in hops and acts as a sedative.[317] In rodent studies, myrcene has been demonstrated to act as a muscle relaxant. It has been speculated that myrcene's sedative and muscle relaxant properties combined with other terpenoids might be responsible for the "couch lock" effect.[318]

[312] Bazaka, K., Destefani, R. & Jacob, M. Plant-derived cis-$\beta$-ocimene as a precursor for biocompatible, transparent, thermally-stable dielectric and encapsulating layers for organic electronics. Sci Rep 6, 38571 (2016). https://doi.org/10.1038/srep38571

[313] Thakre, A. , Mulange, S. , Kodgire, S. , Zore, G. and Karuppayil, S. (2016) Effects of Cinnamaldehyde, Ocimene, Camphene, Curcumin and Farnesene on Candida albicans. Advances in Microbiology, 6, 627-643. https://doi.org/10.4236/aim.2016.69062

[314] Novak, J., Zitterl-Eglseer, K., Deans, S.G. and Franz, C.M. (2001), Essential oils of different cultivars of Cannabis sativa L. and their antimicrobial activity. Flavour Fragr. J., 16: 259-262. https://doi.org/10.1002/ffj.993

[315] Lorenzetti BB, Souza GE, Sarti SJ, Santos Filho D, Ferreira SH (1991). Myrcene mimics the peripheral analgesic activity of lemongrass tea. J Ethnopharmacol 34: 43–48. https://doi.org/10.1016/0378-8741(91)90187-i

[316] De Oliveira AC, Ribeiro-Pinto LF, Paumgartten JR (1997). In vitro inhibition of CYP2B1 monooxygenase by beta-myrcene and other monoterpenoid compounds. Toxicol Lett 92: 39–46. https://doi.org/10.1016/s0378-4274(97)00034-9

[317] Bisset NG, Wichtl M 2004. Herbal Drugs and Phytopharmaceuticals: A Handbook for Practice on A Scientific Basis, 3rd edn. Medpharm Scientific Publishers: Stuttgart; CRC

[318] Russo EB. Taming THC: potential cannabis synergy and phytocannabinoid-terpenoid entourage effects. Br J Pharmacol. 2011 Aug;163(7):1344-64. https://doi.org/10.1111/j.1476-5381.2011.01238.x

# LIMONENE

**Limonene** is a terpene that is common to citrus fruits and is the second most common terpenoid in nature.[319] Studies suggest it to have significant anti-anxiety effects.[320] [321] Throughout history, lemons have been thought of as an antidote to Cannabis intoxication or hang over.[322]

Limonene has also exhibited potent antioxidant effects.[323] Some data suggests that it might also be a treatment of gastro-esophageal reflux.[324]

Although it's called "Limon"-ene, it actually smells like oranges, though the enantiomer l-limonene is reported to have a more piney scent compared to the dominant citrus scent of d-limonene (enantiomers matter!).

# TERPINOLENE

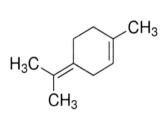

One research group found that the concentration of **a-terpinolene** was a key distinguisher between Cannabis varieties from two different geographical regions.[325] It is described as having a woody, citrusy, and piney odor. The odor is also said to resemble lilac.

Terpinolene has demonstrated **antioxidant** and **sedative** properties in recent studies.[326] [327]

Terpinolene has also been cited as an effective skin penetration enhancer for trans-dermal drug delivery.[328]

[319] Noma Y, Asakawa Y (2010). Biotransformation of monoterpenoids by microorganisms, insects, and mammals. In: Baser KHC, Buchbauer G (eds). Handbook of Essential Oils: Science, Technology, and Applications. CRC Press: Boca Raton, FL, pp. 585–736.

[320] Carvalho-Freitas MI, Costa M (2002). Anxiolytic and sedative effects of extracts and essential oil from Citrus aurantium L. Biol Pharm Bull 25: 1629–1633. https://doi.org/10.1248/bpb.25.1629

[321] Pultrini Ade M, Galindo LA, Costa M (2006). Effects of the essential oil from Citrus aurantium L. in experimental anxiety models in mice. Life Sci 78: 1720–1725. https://doi.org/10.1016/j.lfs.2005.08.004

[322] Christison A (1851). On the natural history, action, and uses of Indian hemp. Monthly J Med Sci Edinburgh, Scotland 13: 26–45. 117-121. https://www.ncbi.nlm.nih.gov/pmc/articles/PMC5891280/

[323] Choi HS, Song HS, Ukeda H, Sawamura M (2000). Radical-scavenging activities of citrus essential oils and their components: detection using 1,1-diphenyl-2-picrylhydrazyl. J Agric Food Chem 48: 4156–4161. https://doi.org/10.1021/jf000227d

[324] Harris B (2010). Phytotherapeutic uses of essential oils. In: Baser KHC, Buchbauer G (eds). Handbook of Essential Oils: Science, Technology, and Applications. CRC Press: Boca Raton, FL, pp. 315–352.

[325] Novak J, Zitterl-Eglseer K, Deans SG, Franz CM. 2001. Essential oils of different cultivars of Cannabis sativa L. and their microbioal activity. Flavour and Fragrance Journal. 16(4):259-262. https://doi.org/10.3390/molecules25204631

[326] Turkez H, Aydın E, Geyikoglu F, Cetin D. Genotoxic and oxidative damage potentials in human lymphocytes after exposure to terpinolene in vitro. Cytotechnology. 2015 May;67(3):409-18. https://doi.org/10.1007/s10616-014-9698-z

[327] Ito K, Ito M. The sedative effect of inhaled terpinolene in mice and its structure-activity relationships. J Nat Med. 2013 Oct;67(4):833-7. https://doi.org/10.1007/s11418-012-0732-1

[328] Aqil M, Ahad A, Sultana Y, Ali A. 2007. Status of terpenes as skin penetration enhancers. Drug Disc Today. 12:1061-1067. https://doi.org/10.1016/j.drudis.2007.09.001

# PINENE

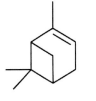

## Alpha-Pinene

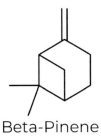

## Beta-Pinene

**alpha-Pinene** and **beta-pinene** are the most widely encountered terpenes in nature.[329] They can be found in conifers and many other plant essential oils, seemingly performing an insect-repellent role in the plants.[330]

The pinenes exhibit anti-inflammatory activity[331], elicit bronchodilation in humans at low exposure levels[332], and act as broad-spectrum antibiotics.[333] They can also aid memory, possibly offsetting some of the memory loss effects of THC.[334]

## ALPHA-THUJENE

**Alpha-thujene** is an often under recognized monoterpenoid found in Cannabis which has been found to be unique enough among certain Cannabis varieties that it could be used for chemotaxonomical purposes. It is a primary component of the essential oil of Boswellia (Indian Frankincense) and in high concentrations, alpha-thujene may exhibit anti-inflammatory and antimicrobial properties.[335] [336]

---

[329] Noma Y, Asakawa Y (2010). Biotransformation of monoterpenoids by microorganisms, insects, and mammals. In: Baser KHC, Buchbauer G (eds). Handbook of Essential Oils: Science, Technology, and Applications. CRC Press: Boca Raton, FL, pp. 585–736.

[330] Nerio LS, Olivero-Verbel J, Stashenko E. Repellent activity of essential oils: a review. Bioresour Technol. 2010 Jan;101(1):372-8. https://doi.org/10.1016/j.biortech.2009.07.048

[331] Gil ML, Jimenez J, Ocete MA, Zarzuelo A, Cabo MM (1989). Comparative study of different essential oils of Bupleurum gibraltaricum Lamarck. Pharmazie 44: 284–287. https://pubmed.ncbi.nlm.nih.gov/2772005/

[332] Falk AA, Hagberg MT, Lof AE, Wigaeus-Hjelm EM, Wang ZP (1990). Uptake, distribution and elimination of alpha-pinene in man after exposure by inhalation. Scand J Work Environ Health 16: 372–378. https://doi.org/10.5271/sjweh.1771

[333] Nissen L, Zatta A, Stefanini I, Grandi S, Sgorbati B, Biavati B et al. (2010). Characterization and antimicrobial activity of essential oils of industrial hemp varieties (Cannabis sativa L.). Fitoterapia 81: 413–419. https://doi.org/10.1016/j.fitote.2009.11.010

[334] Perry NS, Houghton PJ, Theobald A, Jenner P, Perry EK (2000). In-vitro inhibition of human erythrocyte acetylcholinesterase by salvia lavandulaefolia essential oil and constituent terpenes. J Pharm Pharmacol 52: 895–902. https://doi.org/10.1211/0022357001774598

[335] Mothana RAA, Hasson SS, Schultze W, Mowitz A, Lindequist U. 2011. Phytochemical composition and in vitro antimicrobial and antioxidant activities of essential oils of three endemic Soqotraen Boswellia species. Food Chemistry. 126(3): 1149-1154. https://doi.org/10.1016/j.foodchem.2012.07.084

[336] Siddiqui MZ. 2011. Boswellia Serrata, a Potential Antiinflammatory Agent: An Overview. Indian J Pharm Sci. 73(3): 255-261. https://doi.org/10.4103/0250-474x.93507

# ALPHA-TERPINEOL

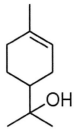

**Terpineol** is a monoterpene found in Cannabis which exhibits some affinity for CB1 and CB2 receptors, making it a non-traditional cannabinoid of sorts, along with other terpenes like beta-caryophyllene and humulene.[337] Alpha-terpineol has a pleasant aroma and is often used in perfumes. It is commonly sourced in nature, as well as being manufactured using alpha-pinene as a precursor. Terpineol is said to have a piney lilac aroma.

# ALPHA-PHELLANDRENE

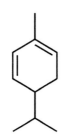

**a-phellandrene** is a constituent commonly found in eucalyptus oils and has a citrusy, peppery aroma. Phellandrene has been traditionally associated with "sativa" Cannabis strains, presumed to provide a more stimulating experience.[338]

# LINALOOL

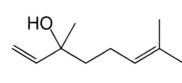

**Delta-Linalool** is a monoterpene that is common in lavender.[339] In rodent models, linalool has been shown to act as a sedative when inhaled.[340][341] It is thought to be a compound responsible for healing burns with reduced scarring.[342] It has been shown to have anesthetic effects like procaine and menthol.[343] It has also demonstrated anticonvulsant activity.[344]

[337] Mehmedic Z, Radwan MM, Wanas AS, Khan IA, Cutler SJ, ElSohly MA. 2014. In vitro binding affinity to human cb1 and cb2 receptors and antimicrobial activity of volatile oil from high potency Cannabis sativa. Planta medica. 80(10) https://doi.org/10.1055/s-0034-1382491

[338] Casano, S., Grassi, G., Martini, V., & Michelozzi, M. (2011). VARIATIONS IN TERPENE PROFILES OF DIFFERENT STRAINS OF CANNABIS SATIVA L. Acta Horticulturae, (925), 115–121. https://doi.org/10.17660/actahortic.2011.925.15

[339] Białoń M, Krzyśko-Łupicka T, Nowakowska-Bogdan E, Wieczorek PP. Chemical Composition of Two Different Lavender Essential Oils and Their Effect on Facial Skin Microbiota. Molecules. 2019 Sep 8;24(18):3270. https://doi.org/10.3390/molecules24183270

[340] Buchbauer G, Jirovetz L, Jager W, Dietrich H, Plank C. 1991. Aromatherapy: evidence for sedative effects of the essential oil of lavender after inhalation. Z Naturforsch [C] 46: 1067–1072. https://doi.org/10.1515/znc-1991-11-1223

[341] Jirovetz L, Buchbauer G, Jager W, Woidich A, Nikiforov A (1992). Analysis of fragrance compounds in blood samples of mice by gas chromatography, mass spectrometry, GC/FTIR and GC/AES after inhalation of sandalwood oil. Biomed Chromatogr 6: 133–134. https://doi.org/10.1002/bmc.1130060307

[342] Gattefosse R-M (1993). Gatefosse's Aromatherapy. C.W. Daniel: Essex, MD.

[343] Ghelardini C, Galeotti N, Salvatore G, Mazzanti G (1999). Local anaesthetic activity of the essential oil of Lavandula angustifolia. Planta Med 65: 700–703. https://doi.org/10.1055/s-1999-14045

[344] Ismail M (2006). Central properties and chemcial composition of Ocimum basilicum essential oil. Pharm Biol 44: 619–626. https://doi.org/10.1080/13880200600897544

## EUCALYPTOL (CINEOL, CINEOLE, CAJEPUTOL)

**Eucalyptol** has demonstrated anti-inflammatory effects in asthma patients.[345] As the name implies, this compound is a dominate compound in eucalyptus oil and smells strongly of eucalyptus. It is an ingredient in many types of mouthwash and cough medicines.

## BORNEOL

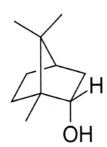

**Borneol** is a terpene derivative found in Cannabis and many other plants, which exhibits a piney-woody odor. This compound has been utilized in traditional Chinese herbal medicine for many years to help other therapeutic agents reach the central nervous system. It is now known that borneol has a unique ability to open the blood brain barrier, allowing greater concentrations of drugs to enter the brain.[346]

---

## TRY THIS! TERPENE AROMA SKETCHING

As you learn about each terpenoid in Cannabis, draw something that represents the aroma associated with each compound to help you remember what that compound smells like! For instance, for eucalyptol, you could draw a eucalyptus leaf. For beta-caryophyllene you could draw a pepper shaker. Get creative and have fun with it!

---

[345] Juergens UR, Dethlefsen U, Steinkamp G, Gillissen A, Repges R, Vetter H. 2003. Anti-Inflammatory activity of 1.8-cineol (Eucalyptol) in bronchial asthma: a double-blind placebo-controlled trial. Respir Med. 97(3):250-256. https://doi.org/10.1053/rmed.2003.1432

[346] Yu B, Ruan M, Dong X, Yu Y, Cheng H. The mechanism of the opening of the blood-brain barrier by borneol: a pharmacodynamics and pharmacokinetics combination study. J Ethnopharmacol. 2013 Dec 12;150(3):1096-108. https://pubmed.ncbi.nlm.nih.gov/24432371/

# CANNABIS SESQUITERPENOIDS

## (15 Carbons)

### ALPHA-CARYOPHYLLENE / HUMULENE

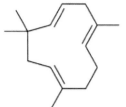

**Humulene** is a terpene commonly found in hops and has some affinity for CB1 and CB2 receptors, making it a non-traditional cannabinoid, in some sense.[347] It has been shown to exhibit anti-cancer activity which is enhanced with the combination of beta-caryophyllene.[348] Humulene has been demonstrated to show anti-inflammatory effects.[349]

### BETA-CARYOPHYLLENE

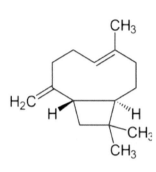

**beta-Caryophyllene** is usually the most common sesquiterpenoid found in Cannabis samples.[350] The Cannabis plant uses this terpene to attract predatory lacewings which feed on Cannabis pests.[351] It is the predominant terpenoid in Cannabis extracts or other products that have been decarboxylated under heat for long periods of time.

Beta-Caryophyllene is an anti-inflammatory[352], gastric cytoprotective[353], and is a full CB2 agonist[354] (Gertsch *et al.*, 2008). Because of its affinity for a cannabinoid receptor, it is now considered a "dietary cannabinoid" by some researchers. Beta-caryophyllene has a spicy, clove-like odor.

[347] Mehmedic Z, Radwan MM, Wanas AS, Khan IA, Cutler SJ, ElSohly MA. 2014. In vitro binding affinity to human cb1 and cb2 receptors and antimicrobial activity of volatile oil from high potency Cannabis sativa. Planta medica. 80(10) https://doi.org/10.1055/s-0034-1382491

[348] Legault J, A Pichette. (2010) Potentiating effect of B-caryophyllene on anticancer activity of a-humulene, isocaryophyllene and paclitaxel. J Parm and Pharmacol. 59:1643-1647 https://doi.org/10.1211/jpp.59.12.0005

[349] Fernandes ES, Passos GF, Medeiros R, da Cunha FM, Ferreira J, Campos MM, Pianowski LF, Calixto JB. (2007) Anti-inflammatory effects of compounds alpha-humulene and (-)-trans-caryophyllene isolated from the essential oil of Cordia verbenacea. Eur J Pharmacol. 569(3):228-236. https://doi.org/10.1016/j.ejphar.2007.04.059

[350] Mediavilla V, Steinemann S. 1997. Essential oil of Cannabis sativa L. strains. J Intl Hemp Assoc 4: 82–84. http://www.internationalhempassociation.org/jiha/jiha4208.html

[351] Langenheim JH (1994). Higher plant terpenoids: a phytocentric overview of their ecological roles. J Chem Ecol 20: 1223–1279.

[352] Basile AC, Sertie JA, Freitas PC, Zanini AC. 1988. Anti-inflammatory activity of oleoresin from Brazilian Copaifera. J Ethnopharmacol 22: 101–109. https://doi.org/10.1016/0378-8741(88)90235-8

[353] Tambe Y, Tsujiuchi H, Honda G, Ikeshiro Y, Tanaka S (1996). Gastric cytoprotection of the non-steroidal anti-inflammatory sesquiterpene, beta-caryophyllene. Planta Med 62: 469–470. https://doi.org/10.1055/s-2006-957942

[354] Gertsch J, Leonti M, Raduner S, Racz I, Chen JZ, Xie XQ et al. (2008). Beta-caryophyllene is a dietary cannabinoid. Proc Natl Acad Sci USA 105: 9099–9104. https://doi.org/10.1073/pnas.0803601105

## TRANS-Β-FARNESENE

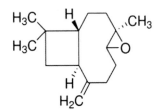

**Trans-beta-farnesene** is a scent compound that acts as an aphid repellent. This terpene has been found to be correlated with narrow leaflet drug varieties of Cannabis, conventionally referred to as "Cannabis sativa".[355] It is described as having a sweet woody odor.

## CARYOPHYLLENE OXIDE

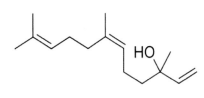

**Caryophyllene oxide** is commonly found in lemon balm and eucalyptus.[356] It seems to exhibit insecticidal, anti-feedant, and antifungal properties for plant defense.[357] [358] It is also the component in Cannabis responsible for identification by drug sniffing dogs.[359]

## NEROLIDOL

**Nerolidol** is a low-level compound in citrus peels. It acts as a skin penetration enhancer[360] as well as an antifungal[361]. There is evidence that Nerolidol has the ability to control parasites and malaria (Lopes et al., 1999; Goulart et al., 2004).[362] [363]

[355] Hillig, K. W. (2004). A chemotaxonomic analysis of terpenoid variation in Cannabis. Biochemical systematics and ecology, 32(10), 875-891. https://doi.org/10.1016/j.bse.2004.04.004

[356] Farag RS, Shalaby AS, El-Baroty GA, Ibrahim NA, Ali MA, Hassan EM (2004). Chemical and biological evaluation of the essential oils of different Melaleuca species. Phytother Res 18: 30–35. https://doi.org/10.1002/ptr.1348

[357] Bettarini F, Borgonovi GE, Fiorani T, Gagliardi I, Caprioli V, Massardo P et al. 1993. Antiparasitic compounds from East African plants: isolation and biological activtiry of anonaine, matricarianol, canthin-6-one, and caryophyllene oxide. Insect Sci Appl 14: 93–99. https://doi.org/10.1017/S174275840001345X

[358] Langenheim JH (1994). Higher plant terpenoids: a phytocentric overview of their ecological roles. J Chem Ecol 20: 1223–1279. https://doi.org/10.1007/bf02059809

[359] Stahl E, Kunde R 1973. Die Leitsubstanzen der Haschisch-Suchhunde. Kriminalistik: Z Gesamte Kriminal Wiss Prax 27: 385–389.

[360] Cornwell PA, Barry BW (1994). Sesquiterpene components of volatile oils as skin penetration enhancers for the hydrophilic permeant 5-fluorouracil. J Pharm Pharmacol 46: 261–269. https://doi.org/10.1111/j.2042-7158.1994.tb03791.x

[361] Langenheim JH (1994). Higher plant terpenoids: a phytocentric overview of their ecological roles. J Chem Ecol 20: 1223–1279. https://doi.org/10.1007/bf02059809

[362] Lopes NP, Kato MJ, Andrade EH, Maia JG, Yoshida M, Planchart AR et al. (1999). Antimalarial use of volatile oil from leaves of Virola surinamensis (Rol.) Warb. by Waiapi Amazon Indians. J Ethnopharmacol 67: 313–319. https://doi.org/10.1016/s0378-8741(99)00072-0

[363] Rodrigues Goulart H, Kimura EA, Peres VJ, Couto AS, Aquino Duarte FA, Katzin AM (2004). Terpenes arrest parasite development and inhibit biosynthesis of isoprenoids in Plasmodium

# BISABOLOL

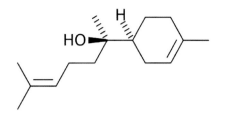

**Bisabolol** is a sesquiterpenoid most commonly found in Chamomile flowers, giving them their characteristic scent.[364] Bisabolol is commonly utilized in topical formulations to help molecules of similar size and polarity cross the epidermal layers of the skin.[365]

Bisabolol has been shown to have anti-inflammatory and anti-neuralgic (nerve pain) properties in rodents.[366] Bisabolol has also been shown to have anti-cancer properties, at least in some cancer cell lines, like glioma.[367]

# B-EUDESMOL

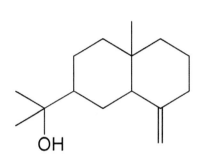

**B-Eudesmol** has demonstrated antiangiogenic effects both *in vitro* and *in vivo*.[368] Angiogenesis is a term referring to the formation of new blood vessels. An antiangiogenic drug slows down or limits the production of new blood vessels. This can be useful in slowing the growth of cancer cells by limiting the blood flow to the cancer cells. This hypothesis was tested in a 2008 study when researchers suppressed the growth of cancer cells on mouse tumors *in vivo*.[369] Eudesmol has a woody odor.

falciparum. Antimicrobial Agents Chemother 48: 2502–2509. Press: Boca Raton, FL. https://doi.org/10.1128/aac.48.7.2502-2509.2004

[364] Kamatou, G.P.P., Viljoen, A.M. A Review of the Application and Pharmacological Properties of $\alpha$-Bisabolol and $\alpha$-Bisabolol-Rich Oils. J Am Oil Chem Soc 87, 1–7 (2010). https://doi.org/10.1007/s11746-009-1483-3

[365] Kamatou, G.P.P., Viljoen, A.M. A Review of the Application and Pharmacological Properties of $\alpha$-Bisabolol and $\alpha$-Bisabolol-Rich Oils. J Am Oil Chem Soc 87, 1–7 (2010). https://doi.org/10.1007/s11746-009-1483-3

[366] Gadotti, V.M., Huang, S. & Zamponi, G.W. The terpenes camphene and alpha-bisabolol inhibit inflammatory and neuropathic pain via Cav3.2 T-type calcium channels. Mol Brain 14, 166 (2021). https://doi.org/10.1186/s13041-021-00876-6

[367] Cavalieri E, Mariotto S, Fabrizi C, de Prati AC, Gottardo R, Leone S, Berra LV, Lauro GM, Ciampa AR, Suzuki H. alpha-Bisabolol, a nontoxic natural compound, strongly induces apoptosis in glioma cells. Biochem Biophys Res Commun. 2004 Mar 12;315(3):589-94. https://doi.org/10.1016/j.bbrc.2004.01.088 PMID: 14975741.

[368] Tsuneki H, Ma EL, Kobayashi S, Sekizaki N, Maekawa K, Sasaoka T, Wang MW, Kimura I. 2005. Antiangiogenic activity of B-eudesmol in vitro and in vivo. European Journal of Pharmacology. 512(2-3):105-115. https://doi.org/10.1016/j.ejphar.2005.02.035

[369] Ma EL, Li YC, Tsuneki H, Xiao JF, Xia MY, Wang MW, Kimura I. 2008. B-Eudesmol suppresses tumour growth through inhibition of tumour neovascularisation and tumour cell proliferation. Journal of Asian Natural Products Research. 10(2):159-167. https://doi.org/10.1080/10286020701394332

## GUAIOL

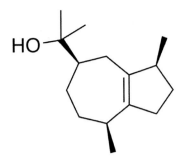

**Guaiol** is a terpene that is more commonly found in wide leaflet drug varieties of Cannabis of Afghani origin.[370] These are usually plants typically thought of as "Cannabis indica." This terpene is usually also found in relatively high ratios along with Eudesmol. It is described as having an odor like that of tea roses or violets.

---

## TRY THIS! COMPARING PLANT AROMAS

In this simple activity (which is best done as a group activity) gather as many of the listed herbs as possible. Then gather as many different Cannabis varieties as possible. If known, note the dominant terpenoids in each Cannabis variety and pair them with a non-Cannabis plant that also features that terpenoid. Compare and contrast the aromas of each pairing. If the terpenoid concentrations of the Cannabis flowers are unknown, simply smell each non-Cannabis plant component carefully and compare/contrast with the aromas of each of the Cannabis flowers.

Which non-Cannabis plants contained aromas detected in the Cannabis flowers? Did everyone agree with how plants were paired? Which aromas do you prefer?

| Recommended Plants / Plant Components | |
|---|---|
| **Plant** | **Dominant Terpenoids** |
| Orange Peel | Limonene and Nerolidol |
| Hops | Myrcene and Humulene |
| Black Pepper | Beta-Caryophyllene |
| Lemon Balm | Caryophyllene Oxide, Eucalyptol, Limonene |
| Lavender | Linalool |
| Pine or Fur Needles | Pinene |
| Green Tea | Phytol |
| Tea Tree Oil | Terpinolene and Terpinene |
| Violets | Guaiol |
| Chamomile | Bisabolol |
| Eucalyptus | Eucalyptol, Phellandrene |

---

[370] Hillig, K. W. (2004). A chemotaxonomic analysis of terpenoid variation in Cannabis. Biochemical systematics and ecology, 32(10), 875-891.  https://doi.org/10.1016/j.bse.2004.04.004

# CANNABIS DITERPENOIDS

## (20 Carbons)

### PHYTOL

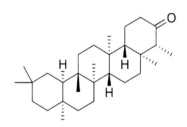

**Phytol** is a diterpene (20 carbon terpene) breakdown product of chlorophyll and is usually present in Cannabis extracts.[371] Phytol can exhibit relaxing effects.[372] It is reported to have little to no smell.

# COMMON CANNABIS TRITERPENOIDS

## (30 Carbons)

### FRIEDELIN

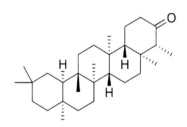

**Friedelin** is a triterpenoid (30 carbon terpene) found in Cannabis roots. Prior research on Friedelin from other plant sources reveals it may be an effective anti-inflammatory, analgesic (pain reliever), and antipyretic (anti-fever).[373]

### EPIFRIEDELANOL

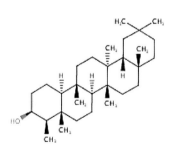

**Epifriedelanol** is another triterpenoid found in Cannabis roots. There is some research indicating that it could be a therapeutic target due to its demonstrated anti-tumor and cytoprotective (cell protective) effects among others.[374]

---

[371] McGinty D, Letizia CS, Api AM (2010). Fragrance material review on phytol. Food Chem Toxicol 48 (Suppl. 3): S59–S63. https://doi.org/10.1016/j.fct.2009.11.012

[372] Bang MH, Choi SY, Jang TO, Kim SK, Kwon OS, Kang TC et al. 2002. Phytol, SSADH inhibitory diterpenoid of Lactuca sativa. Arch Pharm Res 25: 643–646. https://doi.org/10.1007/bf02976937

[373] Antonisamy P, Duraipandiyan V, Ignacimuthu S. 2011. Anti-inflammatory, analgesic, and antipyretic effects of friedelin isolated from Azima tetracantha Lam. In mouse and rat models. Journal of Pharmacy and Pharmacology. Vol. 63, Issue 8. https://doi.org/10.1111/j.2042-7158.2011.01300.x

[374] Russo EB, Marcu J. 2017. Cannabis Pharmacology: The Usual Suspects and a Few Promising Leads. Adv. Pharmacol. 80:67-134. https://doi.org/10.1016/bs.apha.2017.03.004

| Terpene | Common Source | Notes |
|---|---|---|
| Limonene | Oranges, Lemons | Reduces acne bacteria<br><br>Stimulates the immune system when inhaled<br><br>Modulates psychoactive effects of THC |
| a-Pinene | Pine Needles | Assists memory |
| b-Myrcene | Hops | Sedative effects<br><br>Possibly primary culprit in the "couch lock" phenomenon |
| Linalool | Lavender | Anti-anxiety<br><br>Anticonvulsant |
| b-Caryophyllene | Black Pepper | Attracts predatory insects while discouraging herbivory while the plant is growing<br><br>May hold promise in treating gastric ulcers |
| Caryophyllene oxide | Lemon Balm | Serves as an insecticidal anti-feedant and broad-spectrum antifungal<br><br>May be the compound responsible for identification by drug sniffing dogs |
| Nerolidol | Orange Peel | Sedative<br><br>Potent antimalarial |
| Phytol | Tea | Relaxant<br><br>Results from the breakdown of chlorophyll |

FIGURE 31: COMMON TERPENES IN CANNABIS

**SOURCE:** Russo E. 2011. Taming THC: potential cannabis synergy and phytocannabinoid-terpenoid entourage effects. British Journal of Pharmacology. 163(7): 1344-1364. http://www.ncbi.nlm.nih.gov/pmc/articles/pmc3165946/

# Previously Reported Boiling Points of Common Cannabinoids and Terpenoids in Cannabis

| Boiling Point °C* | Boiling Point °F* | Compound |
|---|---|---|
| 119°C | 246°F[1] | β-caryophyllene |
| 156°C | 312°F[1] | α-pinene |
| 157°C or 200°C? | 315°F[1] - 392°F[3] | Δ9-THC Δ9-Tetrahydrocannabinol |
| 160-180°C | 320-356°F[1] | CBD Cannabidiol |
| 166-168°C | 330-334°F[1] | β-myrcene |
| 168°C | 334°F[1] | Δ3-carene |
| 175-178°C | 347-352°F[1] | Δ8-THC Δ8-Tetrahydrocannabinol |
| 176°C | 349°F[2] | eucalyptol |
| 177°C | 350°F[1] | d-limonene |
| 177°C | 350°F[1] | p-cymene |
| 185°C | 365°F[1] | CBN Cannabinol |
| 198°C | 388°F[1] | linalool |
| 209°C | 408°F[1] | terpineol-4-ol |
| 210°C | 410°F[1] | borneol |
| 217-218°C | 422-424°F[1] | α-terpineol |
| 220°C | 428°F[1] | CBC Cannabichromene |
| ~220°C | ~428°F[1] | THCV Tetrahydrocannabivarin |

FIGURE 32: PREVIOUSLY REPORTED CANNABINOID AND TERPENOID BOILING POINTS

**Note**: These are *reported* boiling points, presumably at atmospheric pressure unless otherwise noted. Other reports may vary (see d9-THC for an example)

(1) McPartland, John M. and E. Russo. "Cannabis and cannabis extracts: greater than the sum of their parts?" Journal of Cannabis Therapeutics. 2001. Vol. 1. No. 3/4. pp. 103-132;
(2) Downs, David Victor, et al. "Extraction of pharmaceutically active components from plant materials." U.S. Patent No. 7,344,736. 18 Mar. 2008.;
(3) PubChem (pubchem.ncbi.nlm.nih.gov) – measured at 0.02 mmHg pressure

Until recently, the **boiling points** of cannabinoids and terpenoids was not well understood due to commonly perpetuated mistakes in commonly cited scientific literature. Often studies that reported the boiling points of cannabinoids and terpenoids from Cannabis would fail to include the associated temperatures and pressures under which those boiling points were determined. Other times some of the reports were simply mistaken in what phenomenon they were describing. While a researcher may label a value as a boiling point, they may have been more correct to refer to it as a vaporization point, or evaporation point – which are different concepts than the boiling point. Technically the boiling point of a compound is the point at which its vapor pressure meets that of atmospheric pressure, while the evaporation point is the point at which a compound starts becoming a gas before its boiling point.

A study published in 2022 sought to correct some of these errors by publishing a thorough investigation of the boiling points and vapor pressures of common Cannabis constituents. Their results revealed that some compounds, like THC, had been subject to severe under-reporting, with an actual boiling point at atmospheric pressure at425°C, or 797°F as opposed to the previously reported range of 157°C to 200°C.

> "There is no practical direct way of measuring the temperature at which the vapor pressures of THC and CBD reach normal room pressure (about 760 torr), since at such elevated temperatures, these cannabinoids are instable and decompose. The normal boiling points can, however, be estimated by extrapolating vapor pressure at lower temperatures, using the Clausius Clapeyron equation. For example, the vapor pressures of THC at 155C and 190C are about 0.05 torr and 0.3 torr, respectively, leading to boiling points higher than 400C"

You may be asking yourself, "If the boiling point of THC is so high, why is it so easy to vape?" Remember that compounds, like THC, form into gasses well before their boiling points, which is why vaporizers work. This process of a liquid becoming a gas below the boiling point is called **evaporation** (think about water, which begins evaporating well before it starts boiling). Additionally, when cannabinoids and terpenoids are in the presence of other compounds with different boiling points, vapor pressure in the liquid increases, promoting faster evaporation.

| Corrected Boiling Points (at Atmospheric Pressure) of Common Cannabinoids and Terpenoids in Cannabis (Eyal et al, 2022)[375] | | |
|---|---|---|
| **Compound** | **Boiling Point (°C)** | **Boiling Point (°F)** |
| THC | 425 | 797 |
| CBD | 463.9 | 867.02 |
| a-Pinene | 155 | 311 |
| Sabinene | 163 | 325.4 |
| B-Pinene | 166 | 330.8 |
| B-Myrcene | 168 | 334.4 |
| Limonene | 176 | 348.8 |
| Terpinolene | 185 | 365 |
| Linalool | 198 | 388.4 |
| a-Fenchol | 201 | 393.8 |
| a-Terpineol | 217 | 422.6 |
| B-Caryophyllene | 263 | 505.4 |
| a-Humulene | 276 | 528.8 |
| Guaiol | 290 | 554 |
| Eudesmol | 295 | 563 |
| Bisabolol | 314 | 597.2 |

FIGURE 33 CORRECTED BOILING POINTS OF COMMON CANNABINOIDS AND TERPENOIDS IN CANNABIS

[375] Eyal AM, Berneman Zeitouni D, Tal D, Schlesinger D, Davidson EM, Raz N. Vapor Pressure, Vaping, and Corrections to Misconceptions Related to Medical Cannabis' Active Pharmaceutical Ingredients' Physical Properties and Compositions. Cannabis Cannabinoid Res. 2022 Apr 18. https://doi.org/10.1089/can.2021.0173

# BEYOND STRAIN NAMES: IDENTIFYING CHEMICAL VARIATION AMONG THC-RICH CANNABIS CULTIVARS

In 2017, Cannabis terpenoid researcher Dr. Justin Fischedick published a paper presenting results of terpene tests on over 200 samples across 30 cultivars (aka "strains").[376] In this study, Fischedick proposes a classification system by which a cultivar is categorized based on its dominant terpenoids, ratios of major terpenes, the presence of unique terpenes, and the presence of any other characteristic terpenes. After reviewing the resulting data, Fischedick found that 5 primary groups of terpene chemotypes could be easily identified among the samples tested, with unique classes under each of those 5 groups, comprising a total of 13 unique terpene chemotype classes. Identifying patterns in terpene profiles across cultivars is critical for establishing a new nomenclature that does not rely on strain names or indica/sativa designations.

The following figure summarizes the 5 primary groups and 13 total classes of terpene profiles that Fischedick identified among the samples tested for this particular study. If this classification system is applied to larger data sets, it is plausible that other groups and classes would be identified, which would begin to construct a more meaningful and reliable system of classifying Cannabis cultivars based on terpenoid and cannabinoid content.

It is important to note that this model is not the end all be all model of differentiating Cannabis varieties by terpenoid content. Instead, the work presented by Fischedick should be considered the beginning of the exercising of this technique which will gain sophistication over time as other researchers analyze more Cannabis samples and examine more chemical constituents of Cannabis.

As an example, in 2020, The American Chemistry Society Cannabis Chemistry Subdivision's ElSohly Award winner Jacqueline von Salm, PhD announced that her work examining the chemical variation of Cannabis cultivars revealed the unique presence of a terpenoid rarely measured by most Cannabis testing laboratories, alpha-thujene, which may be an important differentiator between certain cultivars (*viva voce*). This highlights how much more work needs to be done before jumping to conclusions about how we should differentiate cultivars based on their chemical profiles.

---

[376] Fischedick JT. 2017. Identification of Terpenoid Chemotypes Among High (−)-trans-Δ9-Tetrahydrocannabinol-Producing Cannabis sativa L. Cultivars.Cannabis and Cannabinoid Research.Dec 2017.34-47. https://doi.org/10.1089/can.2016.0040

| Group | Characteristics | Class | Cultivars (Strain Names) |
|---|---|---|---|
| **Terpinolene Dominant** | a-Phellandrene, b-phellandrene 3-carene, a-terpinene | Terpinolene | Trainwreck, Jack Herer, Ace of Spades, Sage |
| **Beta-Caryophyllene Dominant** | 1:1 Limonene : Humulene | Cookie | Animal Cookies, Blue Cookies, Fortune Cookies, Girl Scout Cookies, Thin Mints, Cookie, Phantom Cookies |
| | 2:1 Limonene : Humulene linalool, endo-fenchyl-alcohol, and a-terpineol | Sherbet | Sherbet, Sunset Sherbet |
| | 1:1 Limonene : Myrcene | Glue | Gorilla Glue #4, Super Glue |
| **Limonene / Myrcene Dominant** | 1:1 Limonene : Myrcene | OG Kush | Crown OG, Gas, OG Kush, Skywalker OG Kush, Superman OG Kush, Tahoe OG Kush, Hardcore OG, Louis XIII OG Kush, Milky Way OG Kush, Wifi OG Kush |
| | 2:1 Limonene: Myrcene | Limonene OG Kush | Miami White Kush, Triple OG, Headband |
| | 3:1 Limonene : Linalool Endo-fenchyl-alcohol, alpha terpineol, geranyl acetate | Gelato | Gelato |
| **Limonene / Myrcene / Beta-Caryophyllene Dominant with alpha-Bisabolol** | 2:2:1 Limonene : Beta-Caryophyllene : Myrcene | Kush | Bubba Kush, Master Kush |
| | 1:1:1 Limonene : Myrcene : Beta-caryophyllene | Mr. Nice | Mr. Nice |
| **Myrcene Dominant** | 4:1 myrcene : alpha-pinene Alpha-pinene > trans-ocimene | Purple | Grape Ape, Purple Cream, Purple Princess, Purple Urkle, Blue Mazaar, Granddaddy Purple, Purple Max, Watermelon |
| | 2:1:4 alpha-pinene : beta-pinene : myrcene | Blue Dream | Blue Dream |
| | Trans-ocimene > limonene | Strawberry | Strawberry Haze, Strawberry Cough |
| | Alpha-pinene > limonene Low in beta-caryophyllene and humulene | High Myrcene | Godfather, AK-47 |

FIGURE 34: TERPENE CHEMOTYPE GROUPS AMONG COMMON CANNABIS CULTIVARS[377]

[377] Fischedick JT (2017) Identification of terpenoid chemotypes among high ()-trans-D9 - tetrahydrocannabinol-producing Cannabis sativa L. cultivars, Cannabis and Cannabinoid Research 2:1, 34–47, https://doi.org/10.1089/can.2016.0040

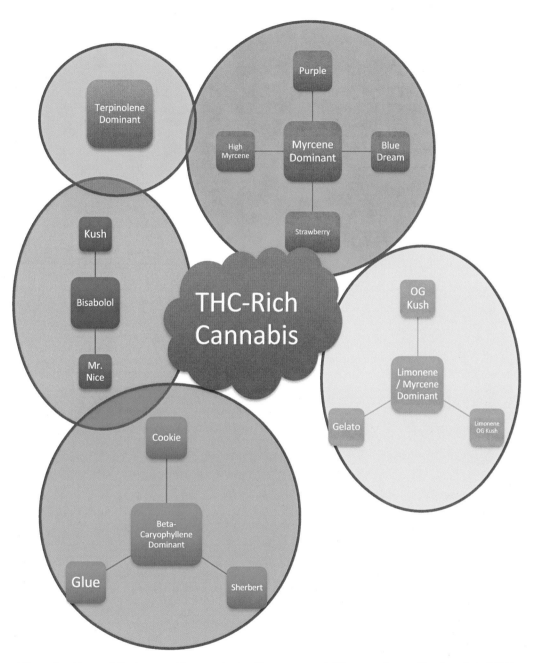

Visualization of Terpene Chemotype Groups and Classes from Fischedick 2017

# TERPENOIDS AS SKIN PENETRATION ENHANCERS

Terpenes have been used with varying degrees of success to enhance the drug delivery of compounds through the skin. Terpenes can be used with cannabinoids to increase the efficiency of drug delivery for epicutaneous and transdermal drug delivery systems through the skin. There are a variety of characteristics that affect a terpene's potential to serve as a potent skin penetration enhancer.

A terpene's **lipophilicity** (its affinity for lipids) is a major characteristic that influences its ability to help other lipophilic compounds, like cannabinoids, pass through the skin.

A terpene's **boiling point** is inversely related to its level of skin penetration (Aqil et al, 2007). Low boiling point terpenes can serve as better skin penetration enhancers than higher boiling point terpenes. Likewise, smaller terpene compounds serve as better skin penetration enhancers than larger terpene compounds. The following are some terpenes that are also found in Cannabis that have been studied for their effects of assisting in skin penetration:

| Terpene | Type | Permeant | Description |
|---|---|---|---|
| **Limonene** | Monoterpene | Butyl paraben, mannitol | Limonene enhances permeation of lipophilic drugs but ineffective for hydrophilic drugs |
| **Linalool** | Monoterpene alcohol | Haloperidol | Linalool reported as the potent enhancer for transdermal delivery of Haloperidol, an antipsychotic medication used to treat schizophrenia. |
| **Nerolidol** | Sesquiterpene alcohol | Nicardipine hydrochloride, hydrocortisone, carbamazepine, tamoxifen | Nerolidol is found to be good candidate for the enhancement of hydrophilic drugs rather than lipophilic drugs |
| **Terpinolene** | Monoterpene | Dapiprazole | Terpinolene is found to be effective enhancer for the transdermal delivery of Dapiprazole through mouse skin. |
| **Geraniol** | Monoterpene alcohol | Caffeine | Geraniol provided a 16x increase in permeation of caffeine |

FIGURE 35: SKIN PENETRATION EFFECTS OF COMMON TERPENES IN CANNABIS [378]

Many terpenes can serve as effective skin penetration enhancers for nonpolar compounds like cannabinoids due to their lipophilic structures. Terpene alcohols can often serve as carriers for both polar and nonpolar compounds due to the addition of oxygen atoms to the molecular structure. For instance, Nerolidol and Geraniol, two terpene alcohols, have both been demonstrated as permeation enhancers for more water-soluble compounds like caffeine.[379]

---

[378] Aqil M, Ahad A, Sultana Y, Ali A. Status of terpenes as skin penetration enhancers. Drug Disc Today. 12:1061-1067 https://doi.org/10.1016/j.drudis.2007.09.001
[379] Aqil M, Ahad A, Sultana Y, Ali A. Status of terpenes as skin penetration enhancers. Drug Disc Today. 12:1061-1067 https://doi.org/10.1016/j.drudis.2007.09.001

# TERPENE TOXICOLOGY

Many terpenes found in Cannabis are classified as GRAS, or "generally recognized as safe", when consumed in low concentrations *orally*, or when exposed to low concentrations on the skin. There is very little information available regarding how safe any terpenes are to inhale, and it is very important to acknowledge that something that may be safe to consume orally may not be safe to consume through other methods.

Low molecular weight terpenoids, like those found in Cannabis, can act as allergens in some people. Many terpenes oxidize very easily, resulting in compounds which may be more irritating to the skin or to tissues in the body. This can sometimes trigger allergic reactions in sensitive individuals. If manufacturing with terpenoids, it is very important to protect them from exposure to air, light, and heat so that their integrity is maintained, and potential allergens are not formed.

LIMONENE-2-HYDROPEROXIDE, AN IRRITANT FORMED FROM THE OXIDATION OF LIMONENE

| Examples of Unwanted Byproducts of Vaping or Dabbing Cannabis at High Temperatures | |
|---|---|
| Benzene | Toluene |
| Ethylbenzene | Methyl Vinyl Ketone |
| Styrene | Isoprene |
| Xylenes | Hydroperoxides of Limonene and other terpenes |

Additionally, when heated terpenes can form potent allergens and irritants, as well as some toxic byproducts, presenting unique health risks for Cannabis smokers. When smoking Cannabis extracts, often referred to as "dabbing", terpenes can breakdown and form new chemical compounds which can be much more toxic than any of the terpenes initially present in the extract. Primarily, terpenes like myrcene, limonene, and linalool can form products like benzene, which is very carcinogenic, and methacrolein, which is a potent lung irritant.[380]

As the smoking of Cannabis extracts continues to grow in popularity, researchers will surely be further examining the health effects of terpene and terpene byproduct inhalation, to determine what, if any, additional health risks may be associated with Cannabis extract smoking.

## AROMA IS ABOUT MORE THAN TERPENOIDS

While it is true that terpenes impart a lot of the aromas and flavors of unique Cannabis varieties, terpenes are only part of the picture. As we will cover in the next chapter, there are other chemicals at play that are also affecting the aromas and flavors of Cannabis, including terpenoid esters, aldehydes, and flavonoids – to name a few. A recent study examining the chemicals responsible for the aroma of Cannabis found that,

---

[380] Meehan-Atrash J, Luo W, Strongin RM. 2017. Toxicant formation in dabbing: the terpene story. ACS Omega 2017: 6112-6117 https://doi.org/10.1021/acsomega.7b01130

*"The compounds found to be responsible for the overall aroma of dry marijuana ... are 1) Benzaldehyde, 2) Myrcene, 3) Decanal, 4) Heptanal, 5) Methyl anthranilate, 6) Octanal, 7) Hexanal, 8) Methylisohexenyl ketone, 9) Linalool, 10) β-Caryophyllene, 11) α-Humelene, and 12) Acetic acid. Highly odorous compounds...from fresh marijuana...are A) Nonanal, B) Decanol, C) o-Cymene, D) Isobutyraldehyde, E) 1-Chloroacetophenone, F) Nerol, G) Propylamine, H) o-Guaiacol, I) Linalyl acetate, J) Methyl anthranilate, K) Benzaldehyde, L) Limonene."*

(Rice and Koziel, 2015)[381]

You may notice that many of the compounds listed in this study are *not* terpenoids. This is very important because many consumers and producers rely on organoleptic properties, like aroma, to make purchasing decisions. There are cultural memes that claim to relate Cannabis aromas to therapeutic profiles, largely relying on clinical research about terpenoids. This focus on associated aroma with terpenoids could be leading many to miss the forest for the trees.

---

## Enduring Understandings

- Cannabis produces over 200 different terpenoids.
- Lightweight terpenes are often somewhat responsible for the aromas and flavors of the Cannabis plant.
- Terpenes are highly influenced by the environment and are used as a way for the plant to communicate and react to its environment such as attracting predatory insects, repelling pests, changing the flavor of leaves to discourage herbivory, and more.
- Researchers have attempted to categorize Cannabis varieties based on terpenoid variation.
- Terpenes can act as skin penetration enhancers in topical formulas.
- At high temperatures, terpenes can form carcinogenic and irritating byproducts, like benzene.
- Although terpenes have been used safely in foods and cosmetics, there is little information available about the health effects of inhaling terpenes.
- Terpenes are only a piece of the Cannabis aroma puzzle. Research has shown that there are many other chemical types influencing the overall aroma of Cannabis besides terpenes.

---

[381] Rice S, Koziel JA. 2015. Characterizing the smell of marijuana by odor impact of volatile compounds: an application of simultaneous chemical and sensory analysis. PLOS ONE 10(12): e0144160. https://doi.org/10.1371/journal.pone.0144160

# Chapter 15:
## WHAT ARE THESE OTHER CANNABIS COMPOUNDS?

## Learning Questions

- What are flavonoids? What are some unique flavonoids found in Cannabis?
- What are esters? What are some common cannabinoid derived esters found in Cannabis?
- What are stilbenoids? What stilbenoids are commonly found in Cannabis?
- What essential fatty acids are found in the Cannabis plant?
- What other chemical compounds may be found in Cannabis?

### FLAVONOIDS

Flavonoids are polyphenolic compounds found in plants that are responsible for various color pigments. They are responsible for giving fruit skins their color, for example. Flavonoids are responsible for all sorts of color pigments in plants, including hues of blue, red, purple, yellow, and even some shades of green.

Cannabis produces approximately twenty different flavonoids either as free flavonoids or as conjugated glycosides.[382] There are several flavonoids that are thought to be unique to Cannabis, like **Cannflavin** A, B, and C. During extractions in the laboratory, some flavonoids like **anthocyanins** and **anthocyanidins** leave a rosy or purple color in the solvent. Many flavonoids, like **kaempferol** and **quercetin** have a yellow tint.

There are some flavonoids that have been shown to easily penetrate cell membranes and maintain their pharmacological activity in Cannabis smoke.[383] Flavonoids might have chemoprotective properties by inhibiting certain enzymes responsible for the activation of carcinogens, including some carcinogens thought to exist in Cannabis smoke.[384] Flavonoids have demonstrated antioxidant and anti-inflammatory effects in a variety of research models. Many flavonoids elicit effects from the body by interacting with estrogen receptors.

---

[382] Turner, C.E., M.A. Elsohly, and E.G. Boeren. 1980. Constituents of Cannabis sativa L. XVII. A review of the natural constituents. J Nat Prod 43:169-304.

[383] Sauer, M.A., S.M. Rifka, R.L. Hawks, G.B. Cutler, and D.L. Loriaux. 1983. Marijuana: interaction with the estrogen receptor. J Pharm Exper Therap 224:404-7.

[384] McPartland JM, Pruitt PL. Medical marijuana and its use by the immunocompromised. Altern Ther Health Med. 1997 May;3(3):39-45. https://pubmed.ncbi.nlm.nih.gov/9141290/

IN THIS EXAMPLE, THREE DIFFERENT CANNABIS FLOWER VARIETIES PRODUCE VARYING COLORS OF POLAR EXTRACTS, POSSIBLY INDICATING VARYING FLAVONOID OR QUINOID CONTENT

In addition, it has been shown that some of the anthocyanin flavonoids in cannabis exhibit affinity for CB1 and CB2 receptors. Particularly, cyanidin and delphinidin have shown moderate affinity for CB1 receptors, and cyanidin, delphinidin, and peonidin exhibit moderate affinity for CB2 receptors. This means that these flavonoids could be interacting with the endocannabinoid system directly to promote other pharmacological effects in the body other than the typical antioxidant and neuroprotective effects often associated with flavonoids.[385]

Some flavonoids, like kaempferol and hydroxyflavone, can inhibit the enzyme fatty acid amide hydrolase (FAAH), which is responsible for breaking down the endocannabinoid anandamide.[386] This in turn can mean that anandamide will circulate in the body longer, interacting with cannabinoid receptors in the body longer.

---

[385] Korte G, Dreiseitel A, Schreier P, Oehme A, Locher S, Hajak G, Sand PG. An examination of anthocyanins' and anthocyanidins' affinity for cannabinoid receptors. J Med Food. 2009 Dec;12(6):1407-10. https://doi.org/10.1089/jmf.2008.0243
[386] Thors L, Belghiti M, Fowler CJ. Inhibition of fatty acid amide hydrolase by kaempferol and related naturally occurring flavonoids. Br J Pharmacol. 2008 Sep;155(2):244-52. https://doi.org/10.1038/bjp.2008.237

# TRY THIS! PIGMENT EXTRACTIONS AT HOME

You can extract flavonoids and other pigments from Cannabis or other colorful plants at home (assuming your home resides in a state or country where Cannabis is legal). Simply find a Cannabis "bud" that has purple, blue, or red hues, grind it up, put it in a tea bag, and soak in water. Within minutes the pigment compounds will transfer to the water. This water is now infused with antioxidant bioflavonoids!

## Materials

Cannabis Inflorescence (Flower)

Glass Cup

Herb Grinder

Water

Cheesecloth, coffee filter, or tea bag

## Procedures

1. Ensure the Cannabis inflorescence is dry to facilitate grinding
2. Grind the plant material up using a hand grinder or other grinding method. The material does not need to be a powder – this is about increasing surface area, but it doesn't have to be perfect.
3. Fill a glass with water.
4. Option 1:
   a. Pour the ground plant matter into the water.
   b. Stir and let sit for approximately 5 to 10 minutes.
   c. Pour the water over a cheesecloth or strainer to remove the plant matter
5. Option 2:
   a. Place the ground plant matter in a tea bag and place into water. Note: a coffee filter can be stapled or otherwise sealed together to make an impromptu tea bag, if needed.
   b. Stir and let sit for approximately 5 to 10 minutes.
   c. Remove the teabag from the water.
6. Evaluate the pigments of the water! I recommend shining light through the water to better see the pigments present.

Congratulations! You just extracted pigments, including flavonoids, from Cannabis! What colors did you notice?

# Common Cannabis Flavonoids

## CANNFLAVIN A, B AND C

CANNFLAVIN A

**Cannflavin A, B, and C** are thought to be unique to Cannabis, as they have not been discovered or described in any other organism, so far. These compounds are potent anti-inflammatory agents and exhibit antioxidant and analgesic effects.

An isomer of Cannflavin B, known as FBL-03G or **Caflanone**, is currently being studied for its potential to treat pancreatic cancer (Moreau et al, 2019).

CANNFLAVIN B

CANNFLAVIN C

## LUTEOLIN

➢ Anti-inflammatory; inhibits pro-inflammatory immune system signaling[387]
➢ Some anti-cancer effects demonstrated *in vitro*.[388]
➢ Yellow pigment

---

[387] Nabavi SF, Braidy N, Gortzi O, Sobarzo-Sanchez E, Daglia M, Skalicka-Woźniak K, Nabavi SM. Luteolin as an anti-inflammatory and neuroprotective agent: A brief review. Brain Res Bull. 2015 Oct;119(Pt A):1-11. https://doi.org/10.1016/j.brainresbull.2015.09.002

[388] Imran M, Rauf A, Abu-Izneid T, Nadeem M, Shariati MA, Khan IA, Imran A, Orhan IE, Rizwan M, Atif M, Gondal TA, Mubarak MS. Luteolin, a flavonoid, as an anticancer agent: A review. Biomed Pharmacother. 2019 Apr;112:108612. https://doi.org/10.1016/j.biopha.2019.108612

## QUERCETIN

- ➤ More potent antioxidant than ascorbic acid (Vitamin C).[389]
- ➤ Prevents immune cells from releasing histamine *in vitro*. May exhibit anti-inflammatory effects[390]
- ➤ Anti-cancer effects *in vitro*
- ➤ Antiviral properties[391]
- ➤ Anti-inflammatory properties[392]
- ➤ Bone protecting effects[393]

## KAEMPFEROL

- ➤ Wide range of proposed pharmacological actions including antioxidant, anti-inflammatory, antimicrobial, anticancer, cardioprotective, neuroprotective effects and more.[394]
- ➤ Can induce apoptosis in breast[395], pancreatic[396], and other cancer cells
- ➤ Can inhibit FAAH, an enzyme that breaks down the endocannabinoid anandamide[397]

[389] Xu D, Hu MJ, Wang YQ, Cui YL. Antioxidant Activities of Quercetin and Its Complexes for Medicinal Application. Molecules. 2019 Mar 21;24(6):1123. https://doi.org/10.3390/molecules24061123

[390] Mlcek J, Jurikova T, Skrovankova S, Sochor J. Quercetin and Its Anti-Allergic Immune Response. Molecules. 2016 May 12;21(5):623. https://doi.org/10.3390/molecules21050623

[391] Li Y, Yao J, Han C, Yang J, Chaudhry MT, Wang S, Liu H, Yin Y. Quercetin, Inflammation and Immunity. Nutrients. 2016 Mar 15;8(3):167. https://doi.org/10.3390/nu8030167

[392] Li Y, Yao J, Han C, Yang J, Chaudhry MT, Wang S, Liu H, Yin Y. Quercetin, Inflammation and Immunity. Nutrients. 2016 Mar 15;8(3):167. https://doi.org/10.3390/nu8030167

[393] Wong SK, Chin KY, Ima-Nirwana S. Quercetin as an Agent for Protecting the Bone: A Review of the Current Evidence. Int J Mol Sci. 2020 Sep 3;21(17):6448. https://doi.org/10.3390/ijms21176448

[394] Calderón-Montaño JM, Burgos-Morón E, Pérez-Guerrero C, López-Lázaro M. A review on the dietary flavonoid kaempferol. Mini Rev Med Chem. 2011 Apr;11(4):298-344. https://doi.org/10.2174/138955711795305335

[395] Zhu L, Xue L. Kaempferol Suppresses Proliferation and Induces Cell Cycle Arrest, Apoptosis, and DNA Damage in Breast Cancer Cells. Oncol Res. 2019 Jun 21;27(6):629-634. https://doi.org/10.3727/096504018x15228018559434

[396] Wang F, Wang L, Qu C, Chen L, Geng Y, Cheng C, Yu S, Wang D, Yang L, Meng Z, Chen Z. Kaempferol induces ROS-dependent apoptosis in pancreatic cancer cells via TGM2-mediated Akt/mTOR signaling. BMC Cancer. 2021 Apr 12;21(1):396. https://doi.org/10.1186/s12885-021-08158-z

[397] Thors L, Belghiti M, Fowler CJ. Inhibition of fatty acid amide hydrolase by kaempferol and related naturally occurring flavonoids. Br J Pharmacol. 2008 Sep;155(2):244-52. https://doi.org/10.1038/bjp.2008.237

## APIGENIN

- ➤ Potential applications for diabetes, amnesia, Alzheimer's disease, depression, insomnia, cancer, metabolic disease, and more.[398]
- ➤ Potent anti-prostaglandin activity
- ➤ Inhibits tumor necrosis factor induced inflammation[399]
- ➤ Potent inhibitor of Cytochrome P450 2C9 liver enzyme that is responsible for breaking down many drugs.[400]
- ➤ Yellow pigment

## CHRYSOERIOL

- ➤ Very stable compound with potential applications for cancer, diabetes, inflammation, osteoporosis, Parkinson's disease, and cardiovascular diseases[401]
- ➤ May have vasorelaxant and hypotensive properties[402]
- ➤ Exhibits bronchodilation effects when administered in tea[403]
- ➤ Exhibits antioxidant activity[404]
- ➤ Yellow pigment

[398] Salehi B, Venditti A, Sharifi-Rad M, Kręgiel D, Sharifi-Rad J, Durazzo A, Lucarini M, Santini A, Souto EB, Novellino E, Antolak H, Azzini E, Setzer WN, Martins N. The Therapeutic Potential of Apigenin. Int J Mol Sci. 2019 Mar 15;20(6):1305. https://doi.org/10.3390/ijms20061305

[399] Ding F, Li X. Apigenin Mitigates Intervertebral Disc Degeneration through the Amelioration of Tumor Necrosis Factor α (TNF-α) Signaling Pathway. Med Sci Monit. 2020 Sep 19;26:e924587. https://doi.org/10.12659/msm.924587

[400] Si D, Wang Y, Zhou YH, Guo Y, Wang J, Zhou H, Li ZS, Fawcett JP. Mechanism of CYP2C9 inhibition by flavones and flavonols. Drug Metab Dispos. 2009 Mar;37(3):629-34. https://doi.org/10.1124/dmd.108.023416

[401] Aboulaghras S, Sahib N, Bakrim S, Benali T, Charfi S, Guaouguaou FE, Omari NE, Gallo M, Montesano D, Zengin G, Taghzouti K, Bouyahya A. Health Benefits and Pharmacological Aspects of Chrysoeriol. Pharmaceuticals (Basel). 2022 Aug 7;15(8):973. https://doi.org/10.3390/ph15080973

[402] Gorzalczany S, Moscatelli V, Ferraro G. Artemisia copa aqueous extract as vasorelaxant and hypotensive agent. J Ethnopharmacol. 2013 Jun 21;148(1):56-61. https://doi.org/10.1016/j.jep.2013.03.061

[403] Khan AU, Gilani AH. Selective bronchodilatory effect of Rooibos tea (Aspalathus linearis) and its flavonoid, chrysoeriol. Eur J Nutr. 2006 Dec;45(8):463-9. https://doi.org/10.1007/s00394-006-0620-0

[404] Mishra B, Priyadarsini KI, Kumar MS, Unnikrishnan MK, Mohan H. Effect of O-glycosilation on the antioxidant activity and free radical reactions of a plant flavonoid, chrysoeriol. Bioorg Med Chem. 2003 Jul 3;11(13):2677-85. https://doi.org/10.1016/s0968-0896(03)00232-3

More commonly found in passionflower and a variety of other medicinal plants, **vitexin** is a flavonoid derived from apigenin. It is a glycoside, meaning that it contains a sugar (glucose/glucoside) in the molecule. Vitexin, and it's related molecular family member **isovitexin**, are commonly used in traditional Chinese medicine. Vitexin is recognized as having antioxidant, anti-cancer, anti-inflammatory, anti-hyperalgesia, and neuroprotective effects.[405]

## FBL-03G (CAFLANONE)

CAFLANONE (FBL-03G)

CANNFLAVIN B

In 2019, a paper was published identifying the potential therapeutic applications of a flavonoid derivative of Cannabis called **FBL-03G**, also known as **caflanone**. This compound is not actually naturally occurring in Cannabis, but rather is a synthetic isomer of Cannflavin B, which *is* a naturally occurring flavonoid in Cannabis.

Specifically, this compound has been identified as being a potential treatment for pancreatic cancer.[406] Orphan drug status was granted to caflanone in 2019, and the drug is due to enter clinical trials.[407] It should be noted that the designation of orphan drug does not indicate whether the drug actually holds promise for treating pancreatic cancer. Rather, this status allows researchers a seven-year window to exclusively research the drug for the treatment of pancreatic cancer. Time will tell

---

[405] He M, Min JW, Kong WL, He XH, Li JX, Peng BW. A review on the pharmacological effects of vitexin and isovitexin. Fitoterapia. 2016 Dec;115:74-85. https://doi.org/10.1016/j.fitote.2016.09.011
[406] Moreau M, Ibeh U, Decosmo K, Bih N, Yasmin-Karim S, Toyang N, Lowe H, Ngwa W. Flavonoid Derivative of Cannabis Demonstrates Therapeutic Potential in Preclinical Models of Metastatic Pancreatic Cancer. Front Oncol. 2019 Jul 23;9:660. https://doi.org/10.3389/fonc.2019.00660
[407] https://www.newsfilecorp.com/release/48491/Flavocure-Biotech-Announces-Orphan-Designation-Granted-by-FDA-for-Caflanone-FBL03G-in-Pancreatic-Cancer Flavocure Press Release, October 3, 2019 "Flavocure Biotech Announces Orphan Designation Granted by FDA for Caflanone (FBL-03G) in Pancreatic Cancer"

whether this flavonoid compound of Cannabis holds clinically significant therapeutic value.

## MISCELLANEOUS PIGMENT COMPOUNDS

There are a variety of pigment compounds, other than flavonoids, that produce some of the various colorations in the Cannabis plant. These include compounds like chlorophyll, which is responsible for the green color of plants, and carotenoids, which typically provide orange and yellow colors to plants. Xanthophylls are a type of carotenoid found in Cannabis that produces yellow pigments in leaves. Many of these pigment compounds exhibit antioxidant properties. Additionally, oxidative products of Cannabis compounds, such as the quinone derivatives of cannabinoids, can produce red color in Cannabis extracts.

## THIOLS

Thiols are compounds that feature a sulfur and hydrogen group attached to them. As you might imagine when thinking of the smell of sulfur, thiols often have sharp sulfurous or skunky odors. In 2021 the research and development team at Abstrax Tech published a study[408] identifying a variety of terpenoid thiols in Cannabis that contribute to the characteristic skunky aromas of fresh and cured Cannabis flowers.

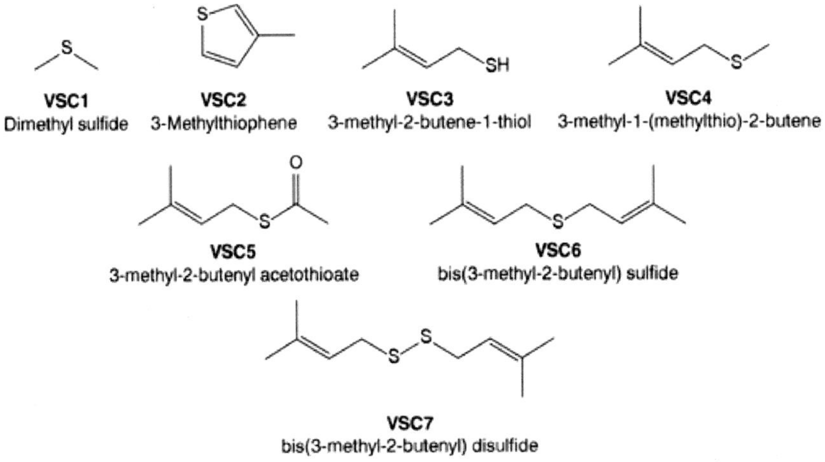

**VSC1**
Dimethyl sulfide

**VSC2**
3-Methylthiophene

**VSC3**
3-methyl-2-butene-1-thiol

**VSC4**
3-methyl-1-(methylthio)-2-butene

**VSC5**
3-methyl-2-butenyl acetothioate

**VSC6**
bis(3-methyl-2-butenyl) sulfide

**VSC7**
bis(3-methyl-2-butenyl) disulfide

**FIGURE 36 PRENYLATED VOLATILE SULFUR COMPOUNDS FOUND IN CANNABIS[409]**

Figure from Oswald et al. Identification of a New Family of Prenylated Volatile Sulfur Compounds in Cannabis Revealed by Comprehensive Two-Dimensional Gas Chromatography. ACS Omega 2021, 6, 47, 31667–31676 Publication Date: November 12, 2021 https://doi.org/10.1021/acsomega.1c04196

---

[408] Oswald et al. Identification of a New Family of Prenylated Volatile Sulfur Compounds in Cannabis Revealed by Comprehensive Two-Dimensional Gas Chromatography. ACS Omega 2021, 6, 47, 31667–31676 Publication Date: November 12, 2021 https://doi.org/10.1021/acsomega.1c04196
[409] Oswald et al. Identification of a New Family of Prenylated Volatile Sulfur Compounds in Cannabis Revealed by Comprehensive Two-Dimensional Gas Chromatography. ACS Omega 2021, 6, 47, 31667–31676 Publication Date: November 12, 2021 https://doi.org/10.1021/acsomega.1c04196

# ESTERS

Esters are compounds that are formed by joining together an alcohol and a carboxylic acid with an oxygen atom. These compounds are widespread throughout nature and are responsible for giving many fruits and vegetables their characteristic aromas and flavors. Some esters are even used as perfumes. While terpenes are the compounds that are often most discussed when thinking about essential oils and plant aromas, esters compliment terpenes in critical ways to provide the smells and tastes of plants that we are familiar with.

Very few esters have been characterized in Cannabis so far. In 1995, hexyl acetate was discovered in the volatile components of Cannabis.[410] In 2008, two esters of CBGA were discovered as well as an assortment of THCA esters.[411] The table below lists most of the esters that have been characterized in Cannabis so far.

| THCA Esters | | CBGA Esters |
|---|---|---|
| B-fenchyl-delta-9-tetrahydrocannbinolate | a-terpenyl-delta-9-tetrahydrocannbinolate | y-eudesmyl cannabigerolate |
| a-fenchyl-delta-9-tetrahydrocannbinolate | 4-terpenyl-delta-9-tetrahydrocannabinolate | a-cadinyl cannabigerolate |
| Epi-bornyl-delta-9-tetrahydrocannbinolate | a-cadinyl-delta-9-tetrahydrocannabinolate | |
| Bornyl-delta-9-tetrahydrocannabinolate | y-eudesmyl-delta-9-tetrahydrocannbinolate | |
| **Volatile Esters** | | |
| hexyl acetate | methyl anthranilate | linalyl acetate |

FIGURE 37: COMMON CANNABIS ESTERS

A synthetic cannabinoid that is gaining popularity among limited circles of Cannabis users seeking a more psychedelic high is a compound called THC-O-Acetate. THC-O-Acetate is a cannabinoid ester formed by replacing the -OH group on THCA with an acetate group. This leads to several distinct changes in effects. THC-O-Acetate is said to be as much as three times as potent as THC, however it takes as much as 30 minutes for the effects to set in. This is because the body must perform extra work to metabolize this compound before enabling the drug to take effect. Technically, THC-O-Acetate could be thought of as a prodrug for THC.[412]

# KETONES

Ketones are compounds which consist of two different carbon containing compounds are joined together by a double bonded oxygen. Very few ketones have been characterized in Cannabis so far. A review of the volatile components of Cannabis revealed two ketones: 2-methyl-4-

[410] Ross SA, ElSohly MA. 1996. The volatile oil composition of fresh and air-dried buds of Cannabis sativa. J Nat Prod 59: 49–51. https://doi.org/10.1021/np960004a

[411] Ahmed SA, Ross SA, Slade D, Radwan MM, Zulfiqar F, Matsumoto RR, Xu YT, Viard E, Speth RC, Karamyan VT, ElSohly MA. Cannabinoid ester constituents from high-potency Cannabis sativa. J Nat Prod. 2008 Apr;71(4):536-42. https://doi.org/10.1021/np070454a

[412] Holt AK, Poklis JL, Peace MR. Δ8-THC, THC-O Acetates and CBD-di-O Acetate: Emerging Synthetic Cannabinoids Found in Commercially Sold Plant Material and Gummy Edibles. J Anal Toxicol. 2022 Jun 8:bkac036. https://doi.org/10.1093/jat/bkac036

heptanone and 2-methyl-3-heptanone.[413] One of those compounds, 2-methyl-4-heptanone, is also present in bananas and has been speculated to be responsible for contributing to the flavor profile of Cannabis in some way. The ketones methylisohexenyl ketone and 1-chloroacetophenone were reported as a volatile ketone contributing to the characteristic aroma of dry Cannabis.[414]

## ALDEHYDES

Volatile aldehydes are responsible for the aromas of Cannabis arguably just as much as terpenes. An aldehyde functional group consists of a carbon with a double bond to an oxygen and a single bond to a hydrogen. Examples of volatile aldehydes found in Cannabis include Benzaldehyde, Decanal, Heptanal, Octanal, Hexanal, and Isobutyraldehyde.[415]

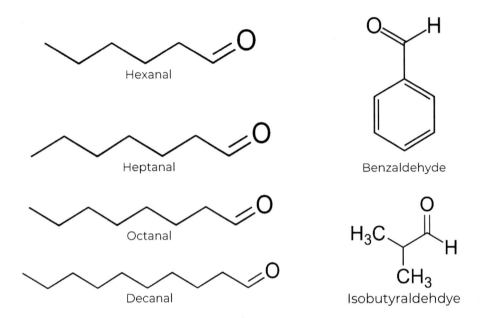

Hexanal

Heptanal

Octanal

Decanal

Benzaldehyde

Isobutyraldehdye

## STILBENOIDS

Stilbenoids are phenolic compounds, technically phenylpropanoids, that are derivatives of the compound stilbene. One of the most popular stilbenoids is resveratrol, found in the skin of grapes, among other plant products. In plants, stilbenoids play an important role in plant defense responses to stresses like fungal or bacterial infections, insect attacks, or herbivory. The presence and abundance of stilbenoids in plants is often associated with disease and pest resistance in plants.

---

[413] Ross SA, ElSohly MA. The volatile oil composition of fresh and air-dried buds of Cannabis sativa. J Nat Prod. 1996 Jan;59(1):49-51. https://doi.org/10.1021/np960004a
[414] Rice, S., & Koziel, J. A. (2015). Characterizing the smell of marijuana by odor impact of volatile compounds: An application of simultaneous chemical and sensory analysis. PloS one, 10(12), e0144160. https://doi.org/10.1371/journal.pone.0144160
[415] Rice S, Koziel JA. Characterizing the Smell of Marijuana by Odor Impact of Volatile Compounds: An Application of Simultaneous Chemical and Sensory Analysis. PLoS One. 2015 Dec 10;10(12):e0144160. https://doi.org/10.1371%2Fjournal.pone.0144160

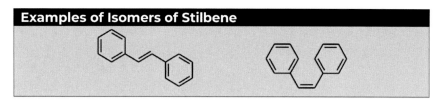

**Examples of Isomers of Stilbene**

There are a variety of stilbenoids found in Cannabis, detectable in the stems, leaves, resins, and flowers. There are three primary categories of stilbenoids found in Cannabis, including phenanthrenes, dihydrostilbenes, and spiroindans.[416][417]

| Stilbenoid Class | Examples Found in Cannabis |
|---|---|
| **Phenanthrenes** | Denbinobin |
| **Dihydrostilbenes** | Canniprene, Cannabistilbene I, Cannabistilbene IIa, Cannabistilbene IIb |
| **Spiroindans** | Cannabispirone, Cannabispiradienone, Beta-Cannabispiranol |

FIGURE 38: EXAMPLES OF STILBENOIDS IN CANNABIS

## DENBINOBIN

**Denbinobin** is one of the most understood stilbenoids found in Cannabis. It is an interesting stilbenoid because it is not terpenoid derived, like many other stilbenoids. In research that has been done with denbinobin, it has been discovered that this compound can induce apoptosis in cells, with implications for cancer treatment.[418] In one study, denbinobin was shown to have significant anti-cancer effects on leukemia cells through inhibition of the NF-kB pathway. It may also be an inhibitor of the HIV-1-lentiviral promotor, with implications for treating HIV. It may be worth noting as well that denbinobin is also a quinone derivative.

---

[416] Guo T , Liu Q , Hou P , Li F , Guo S , Song W , Zhang H , Liu X , Zhang S , Zhang J , Ho CT , Bai N . Stilbenoids and cannabinoids from the leaves of Cannabis sativa f. sativa with potential reverse cholesterol transport activity. Food Funct. 2018 Dec 13;9(12):6608-6617. https://doi.org/10.1039/c8fo01896k

[417] Andre CM, Hausman JF, Guerriero G. Cannabis sativa: The Plant of the Thousand and One Molecules. Front Plant Sci. 2016 Feb 4;7:19. https://doi.org/10.3389/fpls.2016.00019

[418] Sánchez-Duffhues G, Calzado MA, de Vinuesa AG, Appendino G, Fiebich BL, Loock U, Lefarth-Risse A, Krohn K, Muñoz E. Denbinobin inhibits nuclear factor-kappaB and induces apoptosis via

# CANNIPRENE

**Canniprene** has been isolated from the leaves of the Cannabis plant and has been found to be a potent inhibitor of inflammatory signaling compounds in the body.[419]

# PHYTOSTEROLS

**Phytosterols** are plant-derived steroid alcohols. Steroids are organic compounds that all share a common four ring structure, as seen in the following examples for campesterol, stigmasterol, and beta-sitosterol. Phytosterols are formed in the plant from the precursor cycloartenol, which is derived from a triterpene called squalene.

Phytosterols can modulate the way the body absorbs cholesterol, primarily by competing with cholesterol in the body, effectively lowering cholesterol over time. In one human study, "the consumption of 1.5 – 1.8 g/day of plant sterols or stanols reduced cholesterol absorption by 30 – 40%".[420] [421] It should be noted, however, that phytosterols are not absorbed readily in the body. Usually less than 5% of consumed phytosterols are absorbed into the blood. In contrast, the body absorbs approximately 40% of cholesterol that is consumed.

In general, the consumption of phytosterols is considered safe and even health promoting, possibly reducing the risk of heart disease, however there are some people that possess a rare genetic disorder called phytosterolemia, or sterolemia, that can cause the body to absorb far too many sterols, leading to a number of symptoms including elevated cholesterol levels, accumulation of fatty deposits in blood vessels, development of small growths called xanthomas which can cause pain and difficulty moving, and sometimes blood abnormalities, including a shortage of red blood cells, also called anemia.[422] [423]

---

reactive oxygen species generation in human leukemic cells. Biochem Pharmacol. 2009 Apr 15;77(8):1401-9. https://doi.org/10.1016/j.bcp.2009.01.004

[419] Allegrone G, Pollastro F, Magagnini G, Taglialatela-Scafati O, Seegers J, Koeberle A, Werz O, Appendino G. The Bibenzyl Canniprene Inhibits the Production of Pro-Inflammatory Eicosanoids and Selectively Accumulates in Some Cannabis sativa Strains. J Nat Prod. 2017 Mar 24;80(3):731-734. https://doi.org/10.1021/acs.jnatprod.6b01126

[420] Ogbe, R. J., Ochalefu, D. O., Mafulul, S. G., & Olaniru, O. B. (2015). A review on dietary phytosterols: Their occurrence, metabolism and health benefits. Asian J. Plant Sci. Res, 5(4), 10-21. https://hal.archives-ouvertes.fr/hal-03690226

[421] Lena Normén, Paresh Dutta, Ågot Lia, Henrik Andersson, Soy sterol esters and $\beta$-sitostanol ester as inhibitors of cholesterol absorption in human small bowel , The American Journal of Clinical Nutrition, Volume 71, Issue 4, April 2000, Pages 908–913, https://doi.org/10.1093/ajcn/71.4.908

[422] Knut Erik Berge (2003) Sitosterolemia: a gateway to new knowledge about cholesterol metabolism, Annals of Medicine, 35:7, 502-511, https://doi.org/10.1080/07853890310014588

[423] Salen, G., Patel, S. and Batta, A.K. (2002), Sitosterolemia. Cardiovascular Drug Reviews, 20: 255-270. https://doi.org/10.1111/j.1527-3466.2002.tb00096.x

## CAMPESTEROL

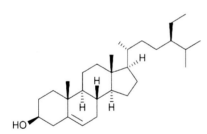

**Campesterol** is a common steroid alcohol (sterol) found in plants. While it is found in all sorts of vegetables, fruits, nuts, and seeds, it is found in greater concentrations in concentrated plant oils, including Cannabis oils.[424] Campesterol and other sterols have been found in refined Cannabis ethanol extracts as well as the Cannabis smoke.[425]

## STIGMASTEROL

**Stigmasterol** is one of the most abundant phytosterols and is commonly used as a food additive in an attempt to lower LDL cholesterol. It is often used as a precursor to progesterone[426] and vitamin D3[427].

## BETA-SITOSTEROL

**Beta-sitosterol** is another very common sterol found in plants, including Cannabis. Higher levels of beta-sitosterol in the blood may be correlated with increase heart attack risk in men that have already had a previous heart attack, although research is conflicting on this issue.[428]

[424] Fenselau, C., & Hermann, G. (1972). Identification of phytosterols in red oil extract of cannabis. Journal of Forensic Science, 17(2), 309-312. https://doi.org/10.1520/JFS10682J

[425] Adams, T. C., & Jones, L. A. (1975). Phytosterols of cannabis smoke. Journal of Agricultural and Food Chemistry, 23(2), 352-353. https://doi.org/10.1021/jf60198a007

[426] Sundararaman, P., & Djerassi, C. (1977). A convenient synthesis of progesterone from stigmasterol. The Journal of organic chemistry, 42(22), 3633-3634. https://doi.org/10.1021/jo00442a044

[427] Kametani, T., & Furuyama, H. (1987). Synthesis of vitamin D3 and related compounds. Medicinal research reviews, 7(2), 147-171. https://doi.org/10.1002/med.2610070202

[428] Assmann, G., Cullen, P., Erbey, J., Ramey, D. R., Kannenberg, F., & Schulte, H. (2006). Plasma sitosterol elevations are associated with an increased incidence of coronary events in men: results of a nested case-control analysis of the Prospective Cardiovascular Münster (PROCAM) study. Nutrition, Metabolism and Cardiovascular Diseases, 16(1), 13-21. https://doi.org/10.1016/j.numecd.2005.04.001

# SPIRANS

**Spirans** are compounds which have two rings, each featuring two single bonds in each ring. Several unique spirans have been identified in Cannabis including cannabispirketal and $\alpha$-cannabispiranol 4'-O-$\beta$-D-glucopyranose, among others.[429] The potentail antitumor properties of cannabispirketal and $\alpha$-cannabispiranol 4'-O-$\beta$-D-glucopyranose were assessed. Neither of these compounds exhibited significant effects on cancer cells.

# PHENANTHRENES

**Phenanthrenes** are compounds that feature a backbone of...you guessed it – phenanthrene. Recently there have been several unique phenanthrenes that have been found in Cannabis. In a study published in 2022, researchers investigating Type V (cannabinoid-free) Cannabis, they discovered three new dihydrophenanthrenes that as of this writing are yet-to-be-named.[430] These phenanthrene compounds exhibit some potentially therapeutic effects.

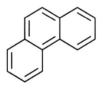

**PHENANTHRENE**

> *"We conclude that the discovered compounds likely contribute to the anti-inflammatory properties of Cannabis sativa L. chemotype V and might promote inflammation resolution by promoting a lipid mediator class switch."*[431]

It should be noted that these compounds were discovered in Type V Cannabis, not Type I (THC), Type II (THC:CBD), Type III (CBD), or Type IV (CBG) Cannabis as of yet. It is likely that researchers will try to find these compounds in commercial Type I and Type III Cannabis in coming years.

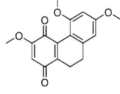

**Examples of Dihydrophenanthrenes Found in Cannabis**

---

[429] Tian-Tian Guo, Jian-Chun Zhang, Hai Zhang, Qing-Chao Liu, Yong Zhao, Yu-Fei Hou, Lu Bai, Li Zhang, Xue-Qiang Liu, Xue-Ying Liu, Sheng-Yong Zhang & Nai-Sheng Bai (2016): Bioactive spirans and other constituents from the leaves of Cannabis sativa f. sativa, Journal of Asian Natural Products Research, https://doi.org/10.1080/10286020.2016.1248947

[430] Salamone, Stefano, Lorenz Waltl, Anna Pompignan, Gianpaolo Grassi, Giuseppina Chianese, Andreas Koeberle, and Federica Pollastro. 2022. "Phytochemical Characterization of Cannabis sativa L. Chemotype V Reveals Three New Dihydrophenanthrenoids That Favorably Reprogram Lipid Mediator Biosynthesis in Macrophages" Plants 11, no. 16: 2130. https://doi.org/10.3390/plants11162130

[431] Salamone, Stefano, Lorenz Waltl, Anna Pompignan, Gianpaolo Grassi, Giuseppina Chianese, Andreas Koeberle, and Federica Pollastro. 2022. "Phytochemical Characterization of Cannabis sativa L. Chemotype V Reveals Three New Dihydrophenanthrenoids That Favorably Reprogram Lipid Mediator Biosynthesis in Macrophages" Plants 11, no. 16: 2130. https://doi.org/10.3390/plants11162130

# TRYPTOPHAN DERIVATIVES

## Kynurenine (KYN)

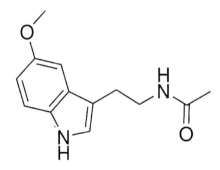

**Kynurenine** (KYN) is typically found in animals as a metabolic product of tryptophan, and not commonly found in plants. Kynurenine is primarily found in Cannabis leaves compared to the stem or roots.[432]

## Kynurenic acid

**Kynurenic acid** is another tryptophan metabolite usually found in animals, but also found in Cannabis. Kynurenic acid has antioxidant, anti-inflammatory, neuroprotective, and hypolipidemic (lipid reducing) properties.[433]

## Melatonin (N-acetyl-5-methoxytryptamine)

**Melatonin** is assumed to be present in the vast majority, if not all, plants. In 2019 a study was published identifying melatonin in both Cannabis seeds and aerial parts.[434] There is no correlation between melatonin production and cannabinoid concentration.

---

[432] Russo F, Tolomeo F, Vandelli MA, Biagini G, Paris R, Fulvio F, Laganà A, Capriotti AL, Carbone L, Gigli G, Cannazza G, Citti C. Kynurenine and kynurenic acid: Two human neuromodulators found in Cannabis sativa L. J Pharm Biomed Anal. 2022 Mar 20;211:114636. https://doi.org/10.1016/j.jpba.2022.114636 Epub 2022 Jan 31. PMID: 35124451.

[433] Russo F, Tolomeo F, Vandelli MA, Biagini G, Paris R, Fulvio F, Laganà A, Capriotti AL, Carbone L, Gigli G, Cannazza G, Citti C. Kynurenine and kynurenic acid: Two human neuromodulators found in Cannabis sativa L. J Pharm Biomed Anal. 2022 Mar 20;211:114636. https://doi.org/10.1016/j.jpba.2022.114636 Epub 2022 Jan 31. PMID: 35124451.

[434] Allegrone, G., Razzano, F., Pollastro, F. et al. Determination of melatonin content of different varieties of hemp (Cannabis sativa L.) by liquid chromatography tandem mass spectrometry. SN Appl. Sci. 1, 720 (2019). https://doi.org/10.1007/s42452-019-0759-y

## FATTY ACIDS IN SEED OIL

33 fatty acids have been found in Cannabis seed oil. Most of these fatty acids are unsaturated fatty acids.[435] The fatty acid variety in Cannabis seed oil does not differ substantially between different types of Cannabis.[436] Some of the fatty acids contained in Cannabis seed oil are essential fatty acids required by the body which the body cannot produce. These include omega-3 and omega-6 fatty acids.

## OTHER CANNABIS COMPOUNDS

Cannabis seeds contain a novel lignanamide called Cannabisin A, which has been identified as a potential inhibitor of an enzyme involved in the infection of SARS-CoV-2 (COVID-19).[437] There are also a variety of mono and polysaccharides found in Cannabis. Vitamin K has been found in the Cannabis plant.[438] Vitamin E has been found in the plant's seeds. There are also a number of nitrogenous compounds (amines), amino acids, proteins, other alcohols, and other steroids that have been described of Cannabis. The alternative sweetening compound quebrachitol has been identified in Cannabis as well as other sugars like arabinose, D-manno-heptulose, altro-heptulose, D-glycero-D-manno-octulose, myo-inositol, glycerol, erythritol, arabinitol and xylitol.[439][440]

### Reported Boiling Points of Other Cannabis Compounds

| Boiling Point °C* | Boiling Point °F* | Compound | Class |
|---|---|---|---|
| 134 | 273 | B-sitosterol[1] | Phytosterol |
| 170 | 338 | Stigmasterol[2] | Phytosterol |
| 178 | 352-353 | Apigenin[1] | Flavonoid |
| 182 | 360 | Cannflavin A[1] | Flavonoid |
| 250 | 482 | Quercetin[1] | Flavonoid |

FIGURE 39 BOILING POINTS OF MISC CANNABINOID COMPOUNDS

**Data Sources:**

1 McPartland, John M. and E. Russo. "Cannabis and cannabis extracts: greater than the sum of their parts?" Journal of Cannabis Therapeutics. 2001. Vol. 1. No. 3/4. pp. 103-132

2 PubChem (pubchem.ncbi.nlm.nih.gov)

[435] Brenneisen R. 2007. Chemistry and analysis of phytocannabinoids and other Cannabis constituents. In: Elsohly M (ed.). Marijuana and the Cannabinoids. Humana Press: Totowa, NY, pp. 17–49.

[436] Ross, S., ElSohly, H., ElKashoury, E., and ElSohly, M. (1996) Fatty acids of Cannabis seeds. Phytochem. Anal. 7, 279–283.

[437] Ngo ST, Quynh Anh Pham N, Thi Le L, Pham DH, Vu VV. Computational Determination of Potential Inhibitors of SARS-CoV-2 Main Protease. J Chem Inf Model. 2020 Dec 28;60(12):5771-5780. https://doi.org/10.1021/acs.jcim.0c00491

[438] Turner CE, Elsohly MA, Boeren EG. Constituents of Cannabis sativa L. XVII. A review of the natural constituents. J Nat Prod. 1980 Mar-Apr;43(2):169-234. https://doi.org/10.1021/np50008a001

[439] Groce JW, Jones LA. Carbohydrate and cyclitol content of cannabis. J Agric Food Chem. 1973 Mar-Apr;21(2):211-4. https://doi.org/10.1021/jf60186a003

[440] Haustveit G, Wold JK. Some carbohydrates of low molecular weight present in Cannabis sativa L. Carbohydr Res. 1973 Aug;29(2):325-9. https://doi.org/10.1016/s0008-6215(00)83018-9

# Enduring Understandings

- Flavonoids are a class of polyphenol compounds which are often pigment compounds that give plants their various colors.
- Cannflavin A, B and C are flavonoids thought to be unique to Cannabis – although it is possible that they may be found in other plants in the future.
- Esters are another set of compounds, like terpenes, that are often responsible for the aromas and flavors of plants.
- Very few ketones have been studied in Cannabis, although one ketone found in Cannabis is also found in bananas and may contribute to the flavor of some Cannabis varieties.
- Aldehydes are as responsible for the aromas of Cannabis as terpenes.
- Stilbenoids are commonly associated with pest resistance in plants.
- Phenanthrenes found in Cannabis may act as anti-inflammatory compounds
- Cannabis seeds are rich sources of essential fatty acids including Omega-3 and Omega-6 fatty acids. They also contain Cannabisin A which may be a drug target for treating SARS-CoV-2 (COVID-19)

# Review

Which cannabinoid is considered to be the parent compound of THCA, CBDA, and CBCA?

_____

True or False: Monoterpenes are lighter compounds than Sesquiterpenes and are more likely to volatilize quickly.

TRUE                FALSE

What compound does GPP have to bind with to begin the synthetic pathway to CBGV, THCV, CBDV, and CBCV?

_____

What is a "breakdown" product of THC that is commonly found in Cannabis though not actually synthesized in the plant?

_____

# Chapter 16:
## SYNTHETIC AND SEMI-SYNTHETIC CANNABINOIDS

### Learning Questions

- What are synthetic cannabinoids?
- What are the health risks of ingesting synthetic cannabinoids?
- What are semi-synthetic cannabinoids?

To research the endocannabinoid system and the role of cannabinoid receptors in the body, synthetic cannabinoids have been developed which perform a variety of functions, typically **agonizing** (stimulating) or **antagonizing** (blocking/muting) a specific cannabinoid receptor type. By using synthetic cannabinoids for *in vitro* (cell culture) and *in vivo* (animal) research studies, researchers can better understand what functions cannabinoid receptors serve and how their activity affects other cells, organs, and physiological systems.

Over time, some of these cannabinoids escaped the laboratory and made their appearance on internet retail outlets and in a variety of "herbal incense blends", namely herbal blends produced under the brands *Spice* or *K2*. These herbal blends have been found to contain a wide variety of herbs that have been sprayed with highly potent synthetic cannabinoid compounds to provide intoxicating effects like THC. These products are sometimes sought after as a Cannabis alternative because the metabolites of these synthetic cannabinoids will not cause the user to fail a standard drug test.

| Herbs That Have Been Identified In "Spice" [441] | |
|---|---|
| **Common Name** | **Scientific Name** |
| Beach Bean | *Canavalia maritima* |
| Blue Lotus | *Nelumbo nucifera* |
| Dog Rose | *Rose canina* |
| Dwarf Skullcap | *Scutellaria nana* |
| Honeyweed | *Leonotis leonurus* |
| Indian Warrior | *Pedicularis densiflora* |
| Wild Dagga | *Leonotis leonurus* |
| Marshmallow | *Althaea officinalis* |
| White/Blue Water Lily | *Nymphaea alba / caerulea* |

---

[441] European Monitoring Centre for Drugs Drug Addiction (2009). Understanding the 'Spice' phenomenon. European Monitoring Centre for Drugs and Drug Addiction. doi:10.2810/27063. ISBN 9789291684113. ISSN 1725-5767.

Consumption of synthetic cannabinoid laced materials such as *Spice* or *K2* have been associated with nausea, vomiting, increased blood pressure, and chest pain.[442] Several fatal case studies have been reported including suicides and fatal heart ischemia, or dangerous narrowing of the heart arteries. According to the Drug Abuse Warning Network, 11,406 emergency room visits in 2010 were associated with the consumption of herbal products containing synthetic cannabinoids.[443]

It is important to note that synthetic cannabinoids are not all inherently more toxic than phytocannabinoids. It is very common for people to talk about synthetic cannabinoids as if they are all super CB1 agonists that act like "THC on steroids."[444] But the catalog of synthetic cannabinoids is vast, comprised of chemicals that exhibit a wide range of activity on CB1 and CB2 receptors (among others).

Another common misunderstanding about synthetic cannabinoids is that they do not occur in nature. First of all, it is important to recognize how much we still have to learn about plants and their chemical constituents. As analytical technology improves,

## Did You Know?

Most synthetic cannabinoids are derived from **resorcinol**. By adding isoprenoids, including some common terpenoids, to resorcinol, a chemist can synthesize many compounds that resemble common phytocannabinoids in their structure.

$$HO \qquad OH$$

scientists can look at more and more trace compounds that they were unable to see before. This has led to discoveries that have confirmed the natural occurrence of what

---

[442] Fattore L, Fratta W. 2011. Beyond THC: the new generation of cannabinoid designer drugs. Frontiers in Behavioral Neuroscience. 5(60): 1-12 https://doi.org/10.3389/fnbeh.2011.00060
[443] Bush DM, Woodwell DA. Update: Drug-Related Emergency Department Visits Involving Synthetic Cannabinoids. 2014 Oct 16. In: The CBHSQ Report. Rockville (MD): Substance Abuse and Mental Health Services Administration (US); 2013: https://www.ncbi.nlm.nih.gov/books/NBK350768/
[444] This phrase has become very common on Cannabis blogs when discussing synthetic cannabinoids. Check out https://www.google.com/search?q=synthetic+cannabinoids+%22thc+on+steroids%22&rlz=1C1GCEA_enUS939US939&oq=synthetic+cannabinoids+%22thc+on+steroids%22 and see for yourself.

was previously considered strictly synthetic. An example of this is THCP. THCP was initially synthesized in a lab and referred to as THC-C7 (referring to the number of carbons in the carbon chain off the primary THC moiety – 7). But then, years later, THC-C7 was discovered in trace concentrations in Cannabis.[445]

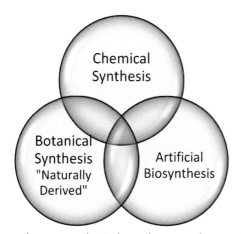

$K_i$ CB1 = 1.32 nM
$K_i$ CB2 = 0.032 nM

**C9/C11 modifications**

*increasing binding affinity*

$K_i$ CB1 = >10000 nM
$K_i$ CB2 = 32 nM

$K_i$ CB1 = 15850 nM
$K_i$ CB2 = 20 nM

**C1 phenol**
*increasing CB2 selectivity*

**B-ring opening**
*CBD derivatives*

**C3 side chain**

*increasing potency*

$K_i$ CB1 = 75 nM
$K_i$ CB2 = 63 nM

$K_i$ CB1 = 4350 nM
$K_i$ CB2 = 2860 nM

$K_i$ CB1 = 0.83 nM
$K_i$ CB2 = 0.49 nM

$\Delta^9$-THC
$K_i$ CB1 = 41 nM
$K_i$ CB2 = 36 nM

$\Delta^8$-THC
$K_i$ CB1 = 47 nM
$K_i$ CB2 = 39 nM

[446]

Chemical Synthesis

Botanical Synthesis "Naturally Derived"

Artificial Biosynthesis

There is good reason to believe that the primary constituents of Cannabis like THCA, CBDA, THC, CBD, CBG, CBC, etc will be synthesized outside of the plant more and more to meet consumer demand for cannabinoid products. These compounds are all "naturally occurring", but also commonly available as synthetic cannabinoids. As Cannabis laws loosen up around the world, it seems inevitable that synthetic cannabinoids will play a big role in emerging Cannabis markets. In the legal hemp market in the United States, delta-8-THC and other THC analogue products have become increasingly popular, especially in states with prohibitive Cannabis laws. Although some of these THC analogues can be found in nature, all of them are primarily produced through chemical synthesis in labs for the general hemp market.

[445] Citti, C., Linciano, P., Russo, F. et al. A novel phytocannabinoid isolated from Cannabis sativa L. with an in vivo cannabimimetic activity higher than Δ9-tetrahydrocannabinol: Δ9-Tetrahydrocannabiphorol. Sci Rep 9, 20335 (2019). https://doi.org/10.1038/s41598-019-56785-1

[446] Figure 2 from Prandi C, Blangetti M, Namdar D, Koltai H. Structure-Activity Relationship of Cannabis Derived Compounds for the Treatment of Neuronal Activity-Related Diseases. Molecules. 2018 Jun 25;23(7):1526. doi: 10.3390/molecules23071526. PMID: 29941830; PMCID: PMC6099582.

| Name | Pharmacology | Notes | Indications |
|------|--------------|-------|-------------|
| **Nabilone** | Partial CB1 and CB2 agonist | delta-6a,10a-dimethyl heptyl tetrahydrocannabinol (DMHP) – the first synthetic cannabinoid pharmaceutical | Primarily to treat nausea and anxiety; has been demonstrated to be effective for treating multiple sclerosis, pain, dementia-related agitation, PTSD nightmares, and headache |
| **Dronabinol (Marinol; Cesamet)** | Partial CB1 and CB2 agonist | Synthetic THC | Primarily to treat nausea and lack of appetite; has been demonstrated to be potentially effective for treatment of GI problems, spasticity, schizophrenia, OCD, trichotillomania, and more. |
| **Liquid Dronabinol (Syndros)** | See Dronabinol | Synthetic THC | See Dronabinol |

FIGURE 40: EXAMPLES OF CLINICALLY APPROVED SYNTHETIC CANNABINOID PRODUCTS APPROVED FOR USE IN THE UNITED STATES

Data Source: Ware MA. 2015. Synthetic Psychoactive Cannabinoids Licensed as Medicines. Handbook of Cannabis. Oxford University Press. Chapter 21. pp. 393-414

# Examples of Synthetic Cannabinoids

## Cannabicyclohexanol (CCH)

**Cannabicyclohexanol** is a cannabinoid receptor agonist produced by Pfizer in 1979. In 2009 it was announced that this compound was one of the primary active ingredients in *Spice* products.[447] It is a potent CB1 receptor agonist.

## JWH-018

**JWH-018** is a full CB1 and CB2 receptor agonist. It causes tolerance more quickly than other related cannabinoids, like THC.[448] This is also a primary psychoactive compound found in *Spice* products. JWH stands for John W. Huffman, the organic chemist at Clemson University that synthesized this and other synthetic cannabinoid compounds.

---

[447] Ciolino, L.A. (2015), Quantitation of Synthetic Cannabinoids in Plant Materials Using High Performance Liquid Chromatography with UV Detection (Validated Method). J Forensic Sci, 60: 1171-1181. https://doi.org/10.1111/1556-4029.12795

[448] Atwood, B.K. et al. (2010). JWH018, a common constituent of 'Spice' herbal blends, is a potent and efficacious cannabinoid CB1 receptor agonist. British Journal of Pharmacology 160 (3): 585–593. https://doi.org/10.1111/j.1476-5381.2009.00582.x

# JWH-073

**JWH-073** is a partial agonist of the CB1 and CB2 receptors. It produces effects similar to that of THC. This was also a primary psychoactive compound found in *Spice* products.

# HU-210

"HU" stands for Hebrew University, where this compound was synthesized. **HU-210** is a highly potent compound that exhibits an extended duration of action and greater potency than that of THC.[449] Research employing HU-210 and other similar synthetic cannabinoids have revealed the endocannabinoid system's role in affecting inflammation and neuroprotection (Ramirez et al, 2005; Jiang et al, 2005; Darlington, 2003).[450] [451]

---

[449] Devane WA, Breuer A, Sheskin T, Jarbe TU, Eisen MS, Mechoulam R. 1992. A novel probe for the cannabinoid receptor. J Med Chem. 35(11):2065-2069. https://doi.org/10.1021/jm00089a018
[450] Ramírez, B. G., Blázquez, C., del Pulgar, T. G., Guzmán, M., & de Ceballos, M. L. (2005). Prevention of Alzheimer's disease pathology by cannabinoids: neuroprotection mediated by blockade of microglial activation. Journal of Neuroscience, 25(8), 1904-1913. https://doi.org/10.1523/JNEUROSCI.4540-04.2005
[451] Jiang, W., Zhang, Y., Xiao, L., Van Cleemput, J., Ji, S. P., Bai, G., & Zhang, X. (2005). Cannabinoids promote embryonic and adult hippocampus neurogenesis and produce anxiolytic-and antidepressant-like effects. The Journal of clinical investigation, 115(11), 3104-3116. https://doi.org/10.1172/JCI25509

# EXAMPLES OF SEMI-SYNTHETIC CANNABINOIDS

Semi-synthetic cannabinoids are formed by removing or adding simple functional groups to existing phytocannabinoids, effectively altering their pharmacological activity and affinity for chemical receptors like cannabinoid receptors. As researchers discovered the downsides of full or ultra-agonistic synthetic cannabinoids, a lot of focus began shifting toward the realm of semi-synthetics – most notably with the VCE-003 class of cannabigerol derivatives and the hexahydrocannabinoids.

## VCE-003 AND DERIVATIVES

**VCE-003** is, at its core, a CBG molecule that has had its aromatic ring changed to a quinone structure, featuring two double bonded oxygens. One consequence of this change is that VCE-003 is better at stimulating PPAR receptors.[452] This cannabigerol quinone derivative has been shown to demonstrate neuroprotective and anti-inflammatory effects in experimental models of multiple sclerosis.[453]

## HYDROGENATED CANNABINOIDS, AKA HEXAHYDROCANNABINOIDS (HHCs)

**Hydrogenation** is the process of saturating a molecule with hydrogens, essentially replacing any double bonds in the molecule. To date there have been hydrogenated versions of THC, THCA, CBD, and CBDA produced synthetically, as well as others. The resulting molecules are hexahydrocannabinol (HTHC),

---

[452] https://www.beyondthc.com/wp-content/uploads/2015/12/Appendino-to-ICRS.pdf

[453] Granja AG, Carrillo-Salinas F, Pagani A, Gomez-Canas M, Negri R, Navarrete C, Mecha M, Mestre L, Fiebich BL, Cantarero I, Calzado MA, Bellido ML, Fernandez-Ruiz J, Appendino G, Guaza C, Munoz E. 2012. A Cannabigerol Quinone Alleviates Neuroinflammation in a Chronic Model of Multiple Sclerosis. J Neuroimmune Pharmacol. 7: 1002-1016. https://doi.org/10.1007/s11481-012-9399-3

hexahydrocannabinolic acid (HTHCA), hexacannabidiol (HCBD), hexacannabidiolic acid (HCBDA), respectively. Some of these hydrogenated cannabinoids have been studied as potential anti-cancer compounds and have been shown in cell culture models to inhibit the proliferation of cancer cells as well as the formation of tumors.[454]

## SYNTHETICALLY DERIVED PHYTOCANNABINOIDS

Synthetic compounds are not necessarily always "artificial" compounds. This is something we all know, but sometimes forget when discussing "synthetic chemicals." Around half of our pharmaceuticals are natural products that are synthesized rather than extracted from their natural source, after all. Similarly, the supply of synthetically derived phytocannabinoids is proliferating with a lot of help from loose and ambiguous language of hemp legislation.

In the United States, synthetically derived phytocannabinoids like delta-9-THC, delta-8-THC, THCV, THCP and others are widely available in hemp stores, gas stations, and grocery stores. This is because the language of the 2018 Farm Bill which initially legalized hemp in the US was loosely written to apply not only to hemp and its immediate byproducts, but also any chemicals that may be produced from anything in the hemp plant. This, accompanied by a glut of CBD available in the industry resulting in a price crash, led many producers to begin converting CBD into compounds with more valuable – namely intoxicating THC isomers.

The problem is that even at the time of this writing, most of the labels for these synthetically derived products do not indicate to the consumer that they were produced synthetically and not directly extracted from the Cannabis plant. You may say, "Why should that matter? A chemical is a chemical, regardless of where it is from." While, yes, that is true – the problem comes up in the form of non-target chemical synthesis byproducts. Chemical synthesis is not a perfect process, and often results in the production of all sorts of chemical byproducts. If not properly remediated before use as an ingredient, these byproducts make their way into finished products.

There are a number of chemical byproducts that have shown up in synthetically derived THC isomers in the hemp market of the United States. The most popular THC isomer on the market at the time of this writing is delta-8-THC. In a 2022 article, authors Geci, Scialdone and Tishier point out that these delta-8-THC is produced through acid-catalyzed ring closure of cannabidiol (ACRCC). Basically, producers expose CBD to a warm acid bath which eventually transforms CBD to delta-9-THC, and then to delta-8-THC. When this is done, a number of byproducts form including delta-7-THC, delta-10-THC, delta-9,11-THC, delta-8-iso-THC, delta-4(8)-iso-THC, 9-MeO-HHC, 10-MeO-HHC, 9-EtO-HHC, 10-EtO-HHC, delta-9-iso-THCBF, Olivetol, o-delta-9-THC, o-delta-8-THC, o-delta-8-iso-THC, o-delta-4(8)-iso-THC, p-cymene, MPTP, and MPPP.[455] Many of

---

[454] Thapa, D., Lee, J. S., Heo, S. W., Lee, Y. R., Kang, K. W., Kwak, M. K., ... & Kim, J. A. (2011). Novel hexahydrocannabinol analogs as potential anti-cancer agents inhibit cell proliferation and tumor angiogenesis. European journal of pharmacology, 650(1), 64-71. https://doi.org/10.1016/j.ejphar.2010.09.073

[455] Geci M, Scialdone M, Tishler J. The Dark Side of Cannabidiol: The Unanticipated Social and Clinical Implications of Synthetic Δ8-THC. Cannabis Cannabinoid Res. 2022 Oct 19. https://doi.org/10.1089/can.2022.0126

these compounds do not occur naturally in Cannabis, and there is little to no safety data available about them. For some, like olivetol, it is well documented that they can be potent irritants. Additionally, once these compounds are heated, they will further transform into as of yet unstudied pyrolization byproducts.

As the Cannabis and cannabinoid markets grow, it will become ever more important for consumers to understand the quality of the products that they are consuming and whether the active constituents were naturally extracted from the Cannabis plant, or whether they were synthetically derived. If a cannabinoid ingredient is synthetically derived, it is then important that the producer of that ingredient did their diligence to ensure the ingredient was pure and free of non-target compounds. However, this requires analytical laboratories to have adequate methods for differentiating these many synthetic by-products.

Many of the non-target compounds that were listed in the previous paragraph in relation to synthetic delta-8-THC manufacturing, for instance, are very similar, many having identical chemical formulas. This makes them easy to miss using traditional analytical methods used for cannabinoid potency, and labs must validate entirely unique methods to ensure they can really separate these many chemically similar byproducts.

---

## Enduring Understandings

- Synthetic cannabinoids are typically cannabinoids produced in laboratories to study cannabinoid receptor activity by dramatically stimulating or antagonizing receptors.
- Many synthetic cannabinoids have escaped from the research laboratory and made their way into consumer products.
- Some of the effects associated with potent synthetic cannabinoid agonists that may be found in products like Spice or K2 include nausea, vomiting, increased blood pressure, and in some cases temporary loss of consciousness (passing out).
- Semi-synthetic cannabinoids are derived from naturally occurring phytocannabinoids by manipulating the functional groups or saturation of the molecules.
- Several semi-synthetic cannabinoids have demonstrated greater neuroprotective, anti-inflammatory, and anti-cancer activity compared to naturally occurring phytocannabinoids.
- The safety of semi-synthetic and synthetic cannabinoids needs to be further elucidated.
- Phytocannabinoids and isomers of phytocannabinoids are commonly synthetically derived and supplied in hemp markets around the world, with delta-8-THC products being some of the most popular
- Synthetically derived products can contain a host of chemical byproducts, some of which have never been found in nature

# PART III: CANNABIS EXTRACTION AND TESTING

## Essential Questions

What services do commercial Cannabis testing laboratories typically offer?

How do labs prove their accuracy?

What are some ways Cannabis testing can go wrong?

What questions could you ask a laboratory to evaluate their competency?

# Chapter 17:
## CANNABIS EXTRACTION SCIENCE AND TECHNOLOGY

**SCAN ME**

**Learning Questions**

- What are the various ways that Cannabis extracts are commonly produced?
- What is supercritical fluid?
- Why is ethanol a generic solvent for extracting a broad spectrum of phytochemicals?
- Why are hydrocarbons a powerful solvent for selectively extracting cannabinoids and terpenoids?
- How are Cannabis extracts refined?

As highlighted previously, most of the "active" chemical constituents of Cannabis are found within the glandular heads of capitate-stalked and capitate-sessile trichomes (though there are therapeutically valuable compounds in leaves and roots as well). For as long as we have records for Cannabis use, we can find evidence of humans using different methods to separate these trichomes from the plant to concentrate the "essence" of the Cannabis plant and produce something that can more readily be used in various formulations. This can be as simple as running one's hands along a Cannabis inflorescence to gather resin on the hands which can then be rolled into a ball. On the other end of the spectrum of complexity, today's modern Cannabis extraction laboratories employ a wide variety of mechanical and chemical separation technologies to concentrate and refine Cannabis resins.

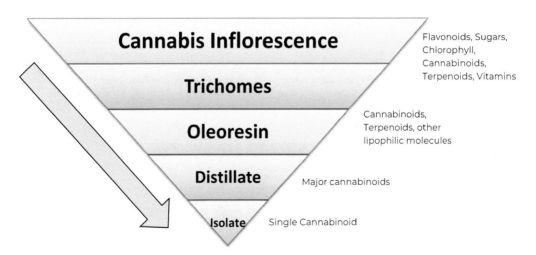

Some simple methods of resin separation include shaking the plant material over varying sized mesh filters that dry sift the trichomes from the plant. Cannabis resins can also be pressed out of the plant using heat and pressure. More commonly, though, Cannabis extractions are being conducted using a variety of **solvent** systems. A solvent is a liquid that can dissolve things. The most popular solvents used for Cannabis extractions are alcohol, organic solvents like butane and propane, lipids (fats), and supercritical fluid $CO_2$. In this chapter we will review some of the most common extraction methods applied to Cannabis, including solventless mechanical separation, solvent-assisted extraction, extract refinement, and cannabinoid isolation.

## SOLVENTLESS SEPARATION

Before we dive into the science behind many of the most common Cannabis extraction methods that utilize solvents – let's discuss a class of Cannabis extracts that do not use solvents. In fact, many argue that this class of "extracts" are not even extracts at all (I've never been too interested in semantics). Instead, many argue that "solventless extracts" are the products of separation and are simply concentrated trichomes. But whatever you choose to call them – all these products have one thing in common – their production relies on mechanical means of separation rather than chemical (for the most part).

This group of extracts includes dry sift hash (kief, hash), wet sift hash (bubble hash), and rosin. Each of these extracts are produced with methods that are designed to capture Cannabis trichomes in their purest form before mechanically processing them into different textures or consistencies.

**Dry sift hash** is any hash produced by rubbing Cannabis flowers across something so that the trichomes separate from the plant. This can be done with a metal mesh screen, cloth mesh screen, or even one's own hands – as has been a long-standing traditional way of making hashish. Charas is made by rubbing freshly harvested Cannabis plants to collect resin, rather than the cured buds. Sometimes hashmakers will press together the sifted hash into shapes like bricks or spheres which are then allowed to cure.

**Wet sift hash** involves submerging Cannabis in water within a series of mesh bags. The plant material is then agitated, often with the addition of ice, to break off the trichomes and collect the trichomes in the mesh bags. The mesh bags help filter out unwanted plant particulates, with pure trichome heads falling into mesh bags with smaller mesh sizes that can exclude bits of plant and even trichome stalks. Wet sift hash is most commonly referred to as "**bubble hash**". Once the wet trichome containing goop is collected from the mesh bags, it is often spread across trays and placed in freeze driers to remove the moisture and prevent the hash from starting to melt together.

BUBBLE HASH THAT HAS BEEN PRESSED TOGETHER | PHOTO: ADOBE STOCK

It is worth noting that some might say that water is a solvent used in bubble hash production and thus bubble hash is not "solventless". While it is true that water is a fantastic solvent for many things, it is not an effective solvent for oils, like

Cannabis trichomes. The water and ice used in bubble hash production is used to cool the plant material down and agitate the trichomes off the plant material. Because oil and water do not mix, these trichomes specifically do NOT solubilize in the water and instead clump together, making them easier to recover and dry. So, yes, water is a solvent – but only when it is solubilizing a solute. Trichomes are not solutes in water.

The morphology of trichomes is very important when considering producing high quality hash. In general, hash makers look for Cannabis material that features lots of capitate-stalked trichomes with thin "necks" adjoining the trichome head and stalk. The vast majority of trichomes should still be unruptured and free – not stuck to other nearby trichomes.

Once trichomes have been sifted and collected, it is possible to assess the quality of the has based on how cleanly the product vaporizes. The purist hash should leave no char or residue behind when burned. These pure forms of hash are referred to as "**full melt**" hash because the product will completely melt away on a dab rig. These products also tend to have better flavor and taste compared to "**half melt**" hash which does not vaporize cleanly and leaves behind residue and tar that must be cleaned. Hash is also often rated on a scale of 1 to 6 stars, with 1 or 2 representing things like kief which contain a lot of plant parts besides trichomes, and 6 representing pure full melt hash.

**Rosin** is a product produced by placing Cannabis trichomes (often bubble hash) under gentle heat and pressure to break the trichome cuticles and release the cannabinoid and terpenoid-rich oil contained within. Rosin can also be produced by placing Cannabis inflorescences under heat and pressure; however, this often results in a lower quality product due to contamination from non-target plant tissues and chlorophyll.

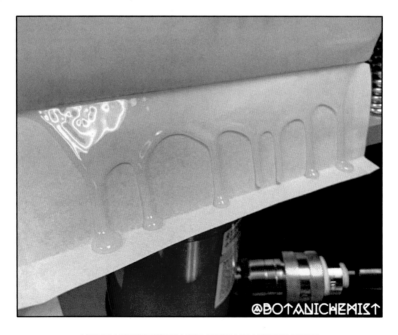

A ROSIN PRESS EXPELLING FRESH CANNABIS ROSIN
PHOTO BY JONATHAN MINTLE (AKA BOTANICHEMIST)

ROSIN ART PRODUCED BY JONATHAN MINTLE (AKA BOTANICHEMIST)

ROSIN "COINS" | PHOTO BY JONATHAN MINTLE (BOTANICHEMIST)

**Lipids** are oily things like waxes and fats. Lipids are nonpolar, so they can act as efficient solvents for extracting cannabinoids and other nonpolar compounds from Cannabis. Traditionally butter and various plant oils (olive, avocado, coconut, sunflower) are used for lipid extractions. Cannabis infused butters and food oils have the advantage of being safe and ready to consume. Not only can lipids serve as efficient carriers for cannabinoids, but they may also enhance the bioavailability of cannabinoids and other compounds in the body.[456]

Caprylic acid, an MCT oil component featuring an 8-carbon chain tail.

Some Cannabis products including tinctures and salves are produced with "MCT" oil. MCT stands for medium chain triglyceride. Medium chain triglycerides are fatty acids that have tails of 6 – 12 carbon atoms long. Because medium chain triglycerides have these long tails of hydrogen and carbon, they are oily and nonpolar – perfect for extracting or mixing with other oils like cannabinoids or terpenoids.

| # of Carbons in Tail | Common Name | Categorical Name | Molecular Structure of MCT Oil Component |
|---|---|---|---|
| 6 | Caproic acid | Hexanoic acid | |
| 8 | Caprylic acid | Octanoic acid | |
| 10 | Capric acid | Decanoic acid | |
| 12 | Lauric Acid | Dodecanoic acid | |

FIGURE 41: COMMON MCT OILS

Some lipids can help serve as dietary supports for the endocannabinoid system. For instance, extra virgin olive oil contains phenolic compounds which may boost the production of cannabinoid receptors in the body.[457] In addition, olive oil has been demonstrated as a mildly effective skin penetration enhancer and can boost bioavailability. Omega fatty acids have been demonstrated to exhibit anti-inflammatory effects via cannabinoid receptors and can also be used as carriers for cannabinoids and terpenoids.[458]

---

[456] Nanjwade BK, Patel DJ, Udhani RA, Manvi FV. Functions of lipids for enhancement of oral bioavailability of poorly water-soluble drugs. Sci Pharm. 2011 Oct-Dec;79(4):705-27. https://doi.org/10.3797/scipharm.1105-09

[457] Notarnicola M, Tutino V, Tafaro A, Bianco G, Guglielmi E, Caruso MG. 2016. Dietary olive oil induces cannabinoid CB2 receptor expression in adipose tissue of ApcMin/+ transgenic mice. Nutrition and Healthy Aging. 4(1): 73–80. https://doi.org/10.3233/nha-160008

[458] McDougle DR, Watson JE, et al. 2017. Anti-inflammatory omega-3 endocannabinoid epoxides. Proceedings of the National Academy of Sciences Jul 2017, 114 (30) E6034-E6043; https://doi.org/10.1073/pnas.1610325114

# HYDROCARBON SOLVENT EXTRACTION

**Hydrocarbon solvents** are, as the name implies, solvents that are composed of hydrogen and carbon. Cannabinoids and terpenes are nonpolar, so they mix easily with organic nonpolar hydrocarbon solvents like propane or butane. During the extraction process, the solvent passes across the plant material and the nonpolar compounds in the plant attach to the solvent, producing a liquid mixture of solvent and Cannabis extract. The solvent is then evaporated off, or **purged**, resulting in the final Cannabis concentrate product, typically referred to as a "hash oil", such as **butane hash oil**, or **BHO**.

PROPANE

BUTANE

| Alkanes Table (Simple to Complex; Most Volatile to Least Volatile) | |
|---|---|
| **Alkane** | **Molecular Formula** |
| Methane | CH4 |
| Ethane | C2H6 |
| Propane | C3H8 |
| Butane | C4H10 |
| Pentane | C5H12 |
| Hexane | C6H14 |
| Heptane | C7H16 |
| Octane | C8H18 |
| Nonane | C9H20 |
| Decane | C10H22 |

FIGURE 42: ALKANES TABLE

An **alkane** is another term used to describe a carbon compound surrounded by hydrogen. Alkanes are the bases for other organic compounds. For instance, if you add an oxygen-hydrogen group to any alkane, like ethane, it becomes an alcohol, like ethanol.

The fewer carbons present in the compound, the higher the volatility. Methanol is the most volatile alcohol while Ethanol is slightly less volatile. Solvent that is left behind in a concentrated extract is called a **"residual solvent."**

# ETHANOLIC EXTRACTION

**Ethanolic extractions** are those involving alcohol, specifically ethanol, or ethyl alcohol. Alcohol acts as a good solvent for extracting cannabinoids and other terpenoids because it can bind to both polar and nonpolar compounds. Alcohol is easy to obtain, and the extraction process is relatively simple, making the extraction method more feasible for home preparations. Usually, ethanolic extractions result in a tincture that can be consumed alone or diluted in a drink. Sometimes extractions are conducted with a sugar alcohol called **glycerol**, or **glycerin**. Final products utilizing glycerol as a solvent are called **glycerites**, whereas extracts suspended in alcohol or more commonly referred to as **tinctures**.

Basic ethanolic extractions result in a tincture product that is seemingly low in cannabinoid content by weight, usually between 1-10%. However, because the product is weighed down by the alcohol, and possibly sugar, it is very easy to consume heavy quantities of the material. For instance, a 3% THC tincture would contain 30 mg/g of THC. A gram of tincture could easily be consumed in a single spoonful.

Ethanolic extraction products can be made more potent by evaporating, or "purging", the alcohol out of the extract, resulting in a thick resin sometimes called "RSO".

### REMOVING GREEN COLOR IN ETHANOLIC CANNABIS EXTRACTS

Ethanolic concentrates or extracts might exhibit a green color, due to chlorophyll that has been extracted. This usually happens when material has soaked in alcohol for a long period of time. Chlorophyll is very soluble in alcohol. Peak chlorophyll extraction will usually be obtained if plant material soaks in alcohol in the dark for 24 hours or more.[459]

Chlorophyll has a melting point of around 152°C, or 306°F.[460] To avoid chlorophyll in extracts, reduce temperatures and time spent in solvent. Using chilled ethanol will greatly reduce the amount of chlorophyll in the final extract. UV radiation will break down chlorophyll, among other compounds in the extract, leading to a reduction of green color in the extract over time if exposed to sun light or other UV sources, changing the color from green to an amber or brown color. Washing the extract quickly with alcohol repeatedly can recapture some of the cannabinoids from the extract while leaving the chlorophyll behind. More commonly, adsorbents like activated charcoal can be used to remove more water-soluble components of an extract, like chlorophyll, while allowing other compounds to pass through.

## DIMETHYL ETHER (DME) EXTRACTION

**Dimethyl Ether** is an isomer of ethanol, featuring the same molecular formula of $C_2H_6O$. Due to its similarities to ethanol, one could infer that dimethyl ether would be a similarly useful compound for extracting cannabinoids and terpenoids from Cannabis. DME is very easy to remove from extracts due to its very low boiling point of -23°C (-9°F). This feature is also attractive because it allows the extraction to occur at very low temperatures, protecting the integrity of the chemical compounds that are extracted. DME has a relatively toxicity profile but is highly flammable like ethanol.[461] Sometimes the Cannabis extract produced from DME extraction are referred to as DHO (DME Hash Oil).

---

[459] Sartory, D.P., Grobbelaar, J.U. Extraction of chlorophyll a from freshwater phytoplankton for spectrophotometric analysis. Hydrobiologia 114, 177–187 (1984). https://doi.org/10.1007/BF00031869
[460] https://pubchem.ncbi.nlm.nih.gov/compound/5748352
[461] https://pubchem.ncbi.nlm.nih.gov/compound/Dimethyl-ether

# TRY THIS!
## HOME ETHANOL EXTRACTION EXPERIMENT: MACERATION VERSUS PERCOLATION

**Disclaimer**: Check your local laws before performing an extraction on Cannabis. Cannabis extraction might be illegal where you live. The author and publisher of Curious About Cannabis™ do not accept responsibility for any illegal activity that may be conducted using the information shared here.

There are a variety of ways that someone can make an ethanolic tincture at home. In fact, herbalists have been making botanical tinctures for thousands of years! There are two primary ways to make ethanolic tinctures: maceration and percolation. Maceration is the most common method and involves letting the plant material soak in ethanol for an extended period of time before filtering the solids out of the liquid. Percolation, on the other hand, is like brewing coffee. A tool called a percolation cone is used to hold the plant material in place. The plant material is lightly soaked in ethanol to soften up the plant tissues before ethanol is poured over the plant material and allowed to drip through the percolation cone, drip by drip. But which method is better? I have my thoughts, but why don't you try an experiment for yourself!

## Materials:

| | | |
|---|---|---|
| Glass Jars w/ Lids | Conical Metal Strainer | Coffee Filters |
| High Proof Ethanol (Everclear) – NO RUBBING ALCOHOL | Cheesecloth or Metal Strainer | Permanent Marker |
| Optional: Balance/Scale | | |

## Procedures:

1. Before beginning, if you would like to measure the amount of alcohol that is recovered in each process, it is important to measure the weights of the jars with lids prior to starting. These weights are called tare weights and will be used later.
2. To perform a maceration extraction:
   a. Measure ground Cannabis into a jar.
   b. There should be approximately 4x as much ethanol as Cannabis. Take the amount of Cannabis used and multiply by 4. Then measure that much ethanol into the jar.
   c. Seal the jar.
   d. Shake well for at least 1 minute.
   e. Store in a cool, dark area (light and heat will alter the chemistry of the tincture).
3. To perform a percolation extraction:
   a. Measure ground Cannabis into coffee filter. For sake of example, let's assume you start with 10 grams of ground Cannabis.

b. Measure an amount of ethanol equal to four times that of the amount of Cannabis into a small jar. For example, if starting with 10 grams of Cannabis, measure out 40 grams of ethanol.

c. Lightly moisten the ground Cannabis with a small amount of ethanol. I recommend moistening with an amount of ethanol equal to the amount of Cannabis used. For instance, if 10 grams of Cannabis is being used, moisten with 10 grams of ethanol.

d. Begin pouring the remainder of the ethanol slowly over the Cannabis material and allow to drip into the jar. Be careful not to overfill. Continuing the previous example, after moistening the plant material with the 10 grams of ethanol, 30 grams of ethanol would then be poured on top.

e. When finished pouring ethanol, remove the conical strainer and filter and seal the jar.

f. Store in a cool, dark area

4. To measure the amount of alcohol recovered from each trial, simply weigh the sealed jar and subtract the tare weight for that jar from the total weight measured.

5. Optional: Submit each sample to a third-party Cannabis testing lab to identify the cannabinoid content in each tincture.

a. Which one was more potent?

# SUPERCRITICAL/SUBCRITICAL FLUID CO2 EXTRACTION (SFE)

*"CO2 is a flexible solvent. CO2 is capable of being an excellent solvent for terpene extraction. It's also capable of extracting a lot of water, wax, and nonsense..."*

Murphy Murri, BTS #17 Curious About Cannabis Podcast

As an alternative to more toxic solvents like hexane, methanol, or butane, carbon dioxide (CO2) can be used to extract cannabinoids and terpenoids from Cannabis. $CO_2$ extractions result in amber or yellow-orange oils that are commonly used in portable electronic vaporizer pens. The extraction process involves heating and pressurizing carbon dioxide to the point that it becomes a super or subcritical fluid.

A **supercritical fluid** is a phase state at which the solvent is neither a gas nor a liquid but has the properties of both. It can creep into tiny spaces and pores like a gas while dissolving substances like a liquid. This makes it very efficient for extracting compounds from plants and other materials. The heat and pressure parameters can be customized to efficiently extract particular compounds, like cannabinoids or terpenes.

Although some extractors use true supercritical fluid extraction, most Cannabis extractors actually heat and pressurize carbon dioxide just below the supercritical state, to a point called a **subcritical** state. The process is relatively quick and can be standardized easily with good manufacturing practices.

SFE is an often-preferred extraction method since it does not typically leave residual solvent in the produced oil and the process can be more environmentally friendly than organic solvent extraction. Commercial supercritical fluid extraction is already used commercially to decaffeinate coffee beans, extract the oils of hops for beer production, and produce essential oils from plants.

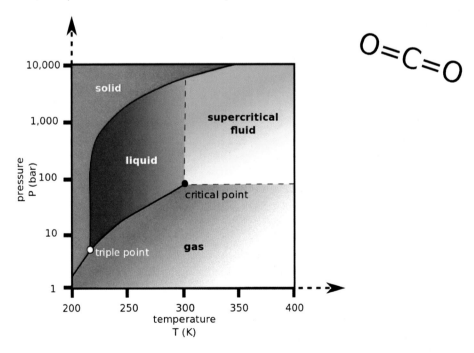

# R134A (Refrigerant) Extraction

**R134a** is **1,1,1,2-tetrafluoroethane**, which is a hydrofluorocarbon commonly used in refrigeration which you may be more familiar with as Freon™. R134a is generally preferred by some producers because it is non-flammable and cold, requiring less energy to extract. Exposure to R134a concentrations of up to 8000 ppm in healthy individuals did not result in significant adverse reactions.[462] R134a poses very low toxicity risk to aquatic organisms, making it a more ecologically friendly solvent. Due to the properties of R134a, it is possible to put the solvent under pressure and decarboxylate acidic cannabinoids at lower temperatures.

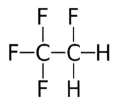

## Cosolvent Extractions

While each of these extraction methods has been presented in isolation, processors often utilize mixtures of solvents and extraction techniques to achieve their preferred product. There are several solvents that are often used together to produce Cannabis extracts including, but not limited to: ethanol/water, ethanol/carbon dioxide (carbon dioxide expanded ethanol), carbon dioxide/butane, butane/propane, carbon dioxide/butane/propane, propane/butane/hexane, etc. Using different solvents together allows an extractor to gain better selectivity for whatever chemical fraction they are targeting.

## Assistive Techniques for Extraction

### Microwave Assisted Extraction (MAE)

Microwave assisted extraction, or MAE, is a relatively newer extraction technique that combines traditional solvent extraction techniques with microwave heating. This heating of the solvent increases the energy present in the extraction. This typically results in shorter extractions times, less solvent used, higher yields, and lower costs. Microwave heating can be applied to supercritical fluid extraction techniques to enhance the efficiency of the technique and potentially increase yield.[463]

### Ultrasound Assisted Extraction (UAE)

The extraction process can often be enhanced by utilizing a process called focused ultrasound extraction. Focused ultrasound utilizes sound waves to generate bubbles in the solvent which gather energy and eventually pop, resulting in a forceful implosion that hits the sample matrix, effectively disintegrating the cells of the sample, allowing target compounds to better interact with the solvent and extract more effectively. This method can be especially effective for the extraction of highly volatile compounds like terpenes. Ultrasound assisted extraction, also called sonication, can be combined with supercritical fluid extraction processes, like carbon dioxide (CO2)

---

[462] https://pubchem.ncbi.nlm.nih.gov/compound/1_1_1_2-Tetrafluoroethane#section=Toxicity
[463] Staudt R, Nitzsche J, Harting P. 2003. Supercritical Fluid Extraction Using Microwave Heating. Proceedings 6th International Symposium on Supercritical Fluids, Versailles, France, April 2003.

extraction, to **speed up production times and obtain better yields at lower temperatures and pressures all while using less solvent.**[464]

## EXTRACT REFINEMENT TECHNIQUES

### UNDERSTANDING THE EXTRACT REFINEMENT PROCESS

When a Cannabis inflorescence undergoes extraction, the crude oil produced, which contains essential oil and resinous components of the plant, is called an "oleoresin." Most product manufacturers do not use crude Cannabis oleoresin as an ingredient. Instead, they prefer to use extracts that have been minimally refined to remove heavy fats, waxes, and pigments. The resulting "cleaned up" extract is called an "absolute."

Many Cannabis extracts, including CO2 extracts and ethanol extracts, are absolutes. These absolute extracts may then be even further refined to distillates, which contain only a handful of target compounds, such as cannabinoids or terpenes. A distillate can then be further refined to a single isolated compound, like CBD or THC. The following sections describe the processes associated with these various steps of Cannabis extract refinement.

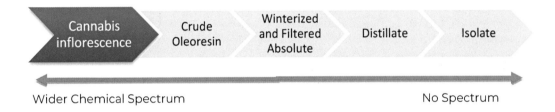

### WINTERIZATION

During the extraction process, many other compounds other than cannabinoids and terpenes are pulled from the product, like various waxes and fats. To remove these products from the extract or concentrate, a technique called **winterization** is often employed. Winterization involves bathing the extract in a solvent, typically alcohol, and then exposing the solution to cold temperatures for an extended period of time so that the waxes and fats precipitate out and clump together. The fats and waxes are then filtered out resulting in a final product that contains a higher concentration of cannabinoids by weight.

### FILTERING

Extracts can also be cleaned up by passing them through various types of filters, the most common being simple mesh filters and activated charcoal filters. Mesh filters can help remove particulates and heavy fats and waxes, especially when done after winterization. Charcoal filters can help reduce dark pigments in extracts while also

---

[464] Yang Y, Wei MC. 2016. A combine procedure of ultrasound-assisted and supercritical carbon dioxide for extraction and quantitation of oleanolic and ursolic acids from Hedyotis corymbosa. Industrial Crops and Products. 79: 7-17. https://doi.org/10.1016/j.indcrop.2015.10.038

helping to remove some contaminants and solvents, though it can also remove some target compounds like cannabinoids and other terpenoids.

## WASHING

Extracts can also be cleaned up by adding a different solvent which cannabinoids or other target compounds will exhibit a greater affinity for, but other non-target compounds will not and vice versa – adding solvents which non-target compounds will exhibit greater affinity for, leaving target compounds behind. For instance, an extract can be mixed with water and another solvent, such as ethanol or hexane, and then mixed and separated, removing some non-target compounds in the water and pulling target compounds into the other solvent. When the mixture is allowed to settle, stratified layers appear and the layer containing the target compounds can be removed and purged, resulting in an overall cleaner extract in the end.

## DISTILLATION

Fractionated distillation is a method of separating a mixture of compounds into its various components, or fractions, by taking advantage of the unique boiling points of the compounds found in the mixture. A solution can be slowly heated to various temperatures to boil off and then condense certain compounds from the mixture. By starting at the lowest boiling point and working the temperature up slowly, a variety of target compounds can be separated out and collected. Special columns called **fractionating columns** are also used to help separate compounds that have very similar boiling points. This basic concept can be applied on a variety of industrial scales to produce high quality, pure compounds of interest, like cannabinoids or terpenes.

Wiped film and short path distillation are commonly used in Cannabis extractions to produce clear distillates containing 70% or more THC or CBD. Wiped film distillation involves the use of a spinning series of paddles which spread the extract into a very thin film, allowing it to easily evaporate at lower temperatures, preventing degradation of target compounds like terpenoids and cannabinoids. Short path distillation utilizes techniques which cause the distillate to travel a very short distance to a reception flask. This is a technique commonly used for compounds that are unstable at high temperatures. Typically, terpenes will be distilled first and captured in a flask, followed by cannabinoids, leaving behind a dark non-volatile fraction that is often discarded or put through a secondary distillation. The captured terpenoids may be mixed back into the cannabinoid fraction to produce unique extract products.

## CRYSTALLIZATION AND CANNABINOID ISOLATION

If the concentration of a particular cannabinoid reaches an adequate purity, the molecules of that cannabinoid will begin to order themselves together into solid structures called crystals. This process is called crystallization. Different cannabinoids begin the crystallization process at different concentrations and conditions. It is most common to see CBD and THCA crystallize in concentrated Cannabis extract products.

There are various methods that are used to obtain cannabinoid crystallization, but they often begin with a distilled Cannabis extract product. One simple method is to simply obtain a concentrated extract that is of adequate purity that it will slowly crystallize on its own over time. Then the extract is simply allowed to rest until the cannabinoid of interest has crystallized and all other components of the extract have separated away from the crystals. This is the effect responsible for some Cannabis extract products labeled as "diamonds."

Another crystallization method involves dissolving the cannabinoids in a powerful solvent and then exposing the compounds to a solvent for which the cannabinoids have little affinity. This causes the cannabinoids to move closer to each other as they try to escape the unsuitable solvent, facilitating a crystallization reaction. Often a variety of cold and hot temperature treatments are also used to facilitate the crystallization process. After a successful crystallization process and harvest, the purity of the resulting crystals may be anywhere from 90 – 99%+ pure. If a purity of 95% or greater is reached, the product is often considered an "isolate".

### CANNABINOID ISOLATION VIA CHROMATOGRAPHY

In additional to crystallization techniques, cannabinoids like THC and CBD can be isolated from an extract using various forms of chromatography, like flash chromatography, centrifugal partition chromatography, or basic column chromatography. In chromatographic methods, a crude oil or distillate is usually dissolved in a solvent and then passed through a stationary phase consisting of silica and various adsorbents to neutralize non-target compounds while separating the components of the sample into purified fractions.

Flash chromatography involves sending the sample through the column at a high rate of speed and pressure. Rotary Centrifugal Partition Chromatography involves sending a sample through a series of columns while they are spinning, which helps the sample separate into separate phases, which then makes it easier for each phase to separate into its unique chemical constituents.

Once the sample has separated into its various components, a producer simply needs to purge the solvent out of the sample to be left with purified forms of each component. Chromatography efficiency can vary greatly depending on the technology used and the consistency of operation.

## FULL SPECTRUM VS. BROAD SPECTRUM EXTRACTS

The terms "full spectrum" and "broad spectrum" are often used to describe Cannabis extracts – but what do these terms mean? The terms "full spectrum" and "broad spectrum" are not scientific and are not well-defined. Every Cannabis company has their own definition of what a "full spectrum" or "broad spectrum" extract is, making it very confusing for customers to compare products. While reviewing various types of Cannabis products, the only conclusion I could come to was that these terms are used consistently to differentiate Cannabis extracts from cannabinoid isolates, like CBD or THC isolate.

The term "**full spectrum**" tends to imply that the full chemical profile of the plant, or some part of the plant, such as the resins, is maintained in the extract. But this is a bit of a misnomer for several reasons. First of all, as mentioned before, most hemp extracts are at least minimally refined to remove heavy fats and waxes. This right away manipulates the chemical profile. In addition, extraction techniques are not perfect, and always target some limited range of chemical compounds.

While it is possible to do various types of extractions on Cannabis and then mix them together, very few companies are doing that. Finally, as of now most Cannabis testing labs cannot accurately identify all the compounds in a Cannabis sample in such a way as to enable a producer to verify whether they did indeed capture the "full spectrum" of a Cannabis plant or flower. This is because the Cannabis plant contains hundreds of compounds, and some of those have still not been very well characterized.

While preparing to write this section I encountered a listing on a hemp wholesale website for a "full spectrum" hemp distillate extract. I thought to myself, "How can a distillate be 'full spectrum'?" Perhaps at best the producer is using the term "full spectrum" to refer to the cannabinoid fraction of the compounds found in Cannabis.

I have also seen supercritical $CO_2$ extracts labeled as "full spectrum" and I've seen ethanol extracts that are also labeled as "full spectrum". The chemical profiles of these three extract types – distillate, $CO_2$, and ethanol – are *very* different, so the term "full spectrum" cannot be reasonably applied to all three types equally.

The term "broad spectrum" seems to be a bit more honest when describing most hemp extracts. However, the term "broad spectrum" is ambiguous and, dare I say...broad. Currently the term "broad spectrum" is often applied to extracts that have had the original chemistry of the plant altered in some way, usually by decarboxylating the cannabinoids or removing THC. But this is not always how the term "broad spectrum" is used.

How phytochemically diverse must an extract be to qualify as "broad spectrum"? Does a distillate that only contains cannabinoids count as "broad spectrum", since it contains multiple cannabinoids?

The best way for consumers to handle this issue is to always ask to see the Certificate of Analysis for any Cannabis product they are considering purchasing. The Certificate of Analysis should provide details about what cannabinoids, and possibly terpenes, are in the extract. Certificates of Analysis for extracts also sometimes indicate the production method, which can help consumers infer other information about the extract. For instance, if a Certificate of Analysis of an extract indicates that the extract is a concentrated ethanol extract, you can infer that the extract contains more phytochemical diversity.

The different cannabinoids, terpenes, flavonoids, and other plant compounds found in Cannabis other than the major cannabinoids like CBD and THC can change the behavior of cannabinoids in the body, sometimes enhancing CBD and/or THC's effects, and other times perhaps reducing their effects.

Some research indicates that phytochemically diverse Cannabis extracts that have not been heavily refined, may provide better therapeutic value, at lower dosages, with fewer side effects, compared to isolated CBD. However, more research is needed to understand this effect in such a way as to be able to take advantage of it in a targeted manner.

## CONTAMINANTS IN CANNABIS EXTRACTS AND CONCENTRATES

Contaminants in Cannabis extracts can come from a variety of sources at different points of the supply chain. When Cannabis resins are concentrated, chemical contaminants like pesticides and mycotoxins often will become concentrated as well. The feedstock (the raw plant material) for an extraction could be tested for pesticides prior to extraction and appear clean, but during the extraction and concentration process, trace amounts of pesticides present in the flower could get tripled, quadrupled, or more, resulting in pesticide concentrations which are then detectable at potentially dangerous levels.

Most extraction methods kill molds and bacteria. Supercritical fluid extraction exerts so much pressure that the process destroys most fungal spores. However, if mycotoxins were produced by any fungal contaminants in the plant material, those mycotoxins will remain intact and could become concentrated in the extract.

Solvents, pesticides, and mycotoxins can build up in extraction equipment if it is not well maintained and cleaned, resulting in the contamination of otherwise clean material that might run through the equipment. It is important to always clean extraction equipment in between runs to ensure that there are no carry-over contaminants that are unnecessarily contaminating multiple batches of extract, rather than just one.

Some refined Cannabis extracts may be at risk of becoming contaminated with foreign matter like clay particles or silica (glass). In general, this kind of contamination can be easily prevented through the use of proper screens and filters, however Cannabis extracts contaminated with these kinds of materials, which are often used in color remediation and other forms of extract refinement, have been identified in legal Cannabis markets.

Contaminants in Cannabis can also come about because of improper packaging or storage conditions. Typically, Cannabis extracts should only be stored in containers made of materials that will not react with terpenoids or cannabinoids. Many types of common plastics and cheap metals can break down over time and leach into the extract. Alternatively, the terpene content in an extract can sometimes dissolve some cheap plastics. To stay safe, the best materials for housing Cannabis extracts are those made of glass, stainless steel, and polytetrafluoroethylene (PTFE).

When trying to determine whether a material will possibly react with Cannabis extracts, you can use **Chemical Resistance Charts**, or **Chemical Compatibility Charts**, to understand whether the material is chemically compatible. These charts are readily available for free online from a wide variety of sources. These charts list a host of common chemicals or materials followed by a series of codes that indicate whether the material is compatible with the product or not.

# Common Sources of Cannabis Product Contamination

| Life Cycle Stage | Contaminants | Source |
|---|---|---|
| **Cultivation** | Pesticides | Applied during growth |
| | Growth Hormones | Applied during growth |
| | Metals | Soil uptake |
| | Molds | Wet conditions during flowering |
| **Post-Harvest Handling** | Bacteria | Unhygienic handling |
| | Mold | Humidity in storage |
| | Mycotoxins | Mold |
| **Extraction** | Pesticides | Feedstock |
| | Solvents | Inadequate desolvation |
| | Mycotoxins | Feedstock |
| **Refinement** | Pesticides | Feedstock |
| | Solvents | Inadequate desolvation |
| | Mycotoxins | Feedstock |
| | Clays | Color remediation |
| | Silica | Color remediation, chromatography |
| **Formulation / Product Assembly** | Pesticides | Feedstock |
| | Solvents | Inadequate desolvation of extract, or other ingredient contamination |
| | Metals | Feedstock or ingredient contamination |
| | Mycotoxins | Feedstock |
| | Bacteria | Unhygienic handling, lack of PPE |
| | Unapproved additives | Ingredient in product formula not GRAS for intended use |
| **Storage** | Plastics | Incompatible Packaging |
| | Rubbers | Incompatible Packaging |

FIGURE 43: COMMON SOURCES OF PRODUCT CONTAMINATION

# ADDITIVES IN CANNABIS EXTRACTS

Additives may be added to Cannabis extracts for a number of reasons – some benign, and others less so. Cannabis extracts are most commonly amended with terpenes and ethanol to obtain a desirable taste, smell, and fluid consistency. For Cannabis extract oils used for vaporizer pens, propylene glycol or vegetable glycerin may be found as additives used to thin the oil and help it smolder. In their article "How Safe Is Your Vape Pen?", the non-profit Cannabis education organization Project CBD points out that propylene glycol can actually convert to a variety of harmful compounds at high temperatures including carbonyls, like formaldehyde, which can be highly toxic and carcinogenic (Project CBD, "How Safe Is Your Vape Pen?").[465] In addition to propylene glycol, extracted oils intended for use in vaporizer pens may also include some flavoring agents which are safe to eat but may not be safe to inhale, such as diacetyl or acetyl propionyl.

Recently, in 2019, the Centers for Disease Control (CDC) in the United States announced that there was a health crisis affecting users of vape pens.[466] Vape pen users were turning up in hospitals exhibiting symptoms of respiratory failure and respiratory disease. Ultimately this resulted in over 2500 people suffering lung disease and over 50 deaths. Upon investigation, it was found that this issue was primarily limited to Cannabis oil vape pens found on the black market.

After evaluating fluids and tissues taken from affected patients, it was concluded that at least one of the culprits was an additive called tocopherol acetate, or vitamin E acetate. Tocopherol acetate was used as a thickening agent, as well as a cheap alternative to tocopherol. Tocopherol acetate is generally regarded as safe to apply topically or consume orally but is *not* regarded as safe to inhale. As of the time of this writing, the CDC and various research bodies are still trying to determine whether there are other culprits at play other than tocopherol acetate.

To make matters more complicated, further research revealed that THC can actually react with vitamin E acetate to form complex a THC/Vitamin E Acetate complex, which may end up resulting in a more toxic compound than vitamin E acetate itself.[467]

There is currently very little information available about the potential health effects of inhaling whatever additives may be present in Cannabis extracts. As researchers begin to focus their research efforts on investigating the compositions of commercial and black-market Cannabis extracts, more information will become available to help consumers make informed decisions that can support their health. In the meantime, if you are a Cannabis extract consumer, try to learn about how your products are made and only consume products from companies that you trust.

---

[465] https://www.projectcbd.org/ja/industry/how-safe-your-vape-pen-0
[466] https://www.cdc.gov/tobacco/basic_information/e-cigarettes/severe-lung-disease.html
[467] Lanzarotta, A., Falconer, T. M., Flurer, R., & Wilson, R. A. (2020). Hydrogen bonding between tetrahydrocannabinol and vitamin E acetate in unvaped, aerosolized, and condensed aerosol e-liquids. Analytical chemistry, 92(3), 2374-2378. https://doi.org/10.1021/acs.analchem.9b05536

# QUALITY CONTROL OF EXTRACTION OPERATIONS

To ensure that Cannabis extract and manufactured products are of the assumed potency and purity, Cannabis cultivators, extractors, and product manufacturers must instate a variety of common quality control measures.

Cultivator Quality Agreement

Cannabis Intake Inspection, Microextraction, and Testing

Equipment and Facilities Sanitation

Production Monitoring

Potency and Purity Testing of Final Products

Packaging and Labeling Verification

Release for Distribution

### CULTIVATOR QUALITY AGREEMENTS

One of the first quality control points in extraction operations is supplier evaluation and qualification. The extractor establishes a quality standard for incoming Cannabis materials which approved suppliers must adhere to as part of their quality agreement with each other. Extractors should seek to form relationships with farms that follow Good Agricultural Practices and Good Handling Practices. It is common for quality agreements to include provisions to allow the laboratory to visit the farm for the purposes of assessing quality.

### FEEDSTOCK INTAKE INSPECTION

When the cultivator is ready to deliver Cannabis to the extractor, the extractor typically quarantine's the material, keeping it separated from other "cleared for work" materials, while it undergoes a visual and chemical inspection. The extraction facility will ensure that there are no obvious signs of foreign matter in the Cannabis lot such as sticks, grass clippings, bugs, or mold. After the visual inspection, the material is often submitted to a laboratory, either in-house or third party, which tests the material for contaminants and potency.

### EQUIPMENT VALIDATION

Before any equipment is used in production, it should first be validated. Equipment validation is a process which gives a producer confidence that their equipment is meeting required specifications and can perform reliably with repeated use.

## PROCESS VALIDATION

Once equipment has been validated, production processes must be validated to ensure that product manufacturing procedures produce consistent results when followed. This typically involves performing a procedure multiple times and evaluating quality control data associated with the production events to determine whether the process is functioning properly.

## MICROEXTRACTIONS AND PILOT BATCHES

Producers can minimize their risk exposure by producing small "pilot" batches of a product to ensure that the final product meets their quality specifications before committing to a large, and costly, batch size. If problems arise during the pilot batch production, they can be addressed before scaling up to larger batch sizes, thus keeping the impact of those errors as small as possible.

This is particularly important for extraction labs that process Cannabis from a variety of farms. It is possible for there to be less than detectable residues of pesticides or other contaminants on Cannabis which can become concentrated to detectable levels in the final extract. Because of this, it is important for extractors to perform **microextractions** on incoming Cannabis lots. Microextractions are small-scale extractions on a very small sample from the lot for the purposes of testing for contaminants like pesticides or metals.

## EQUIPMENT AND FACILITIES UPKEEP

Laboratories featuring sound quality systems keep consistent records of equipment and facility maintenance and cleaning. Every extraction and product manufacturing event should be traceable to sanitation and maintenance records which prove that work surfaces, utensils, and equipment were clean and in good working order during production.

## ENVIRONMENTAL MONITORING AND CONTROL

It is critical that Cannabis accepted by a laboratory is maintained in its receiving condition by monitoring storage conditions and moisture content of the plant material to prevent conditions that might support the growth of micro-organisms. You might ask, "But won't the extraction process kill any mold or bacteria?" The answer is, yes, the extraction process will likely kill micro-organisms, but the problem is not limited to the micro-organisms themselves, but rather extends to the toxic chemicals that they can leave behind.

Some molds produce toxic byproducts called mycotoxins which can be highly carcinogenic. These mycotoxins persist after the mold dies, are highly heat tolerant, and can pass into Cannabis smoke or vapor when consuming contaminated Cannabis or a contaminated Cannabis extract. This is why careful monitoring of environmental conditions and product storage conditions is critical for quality control.

## PRODUCTION MONITORING

During the extraction and product manufacturing process, the extraction laboratory may track any number of variables and data points to ensure the production of reliable, consistent products. Typically, labs measure their extraction yields, product cannabinoid content, and equipment operating parameters like temperatures and pressures, at a minimum. This allows a laboratory to understand how every batch of extract or product was produced and its resulting characteristics. These details are often captured through records called batch manufacturing records.

### TESTING OF INTERMEDIATE AND FINISHED PRODUCTS

Random samples from batches of finished extracts or manufactured products are typically submitted for routine potency and contaminant testing prior to distribution. The most common tests that producers order for finished products are cannabinoid and terpene assays, pesticide screening, metals testing, and microbiological testing.

---

# Enduring Understandings

- The most common methods of extracting chemical compounds from Cannabis include lipid, hydrocarbon, ethanol, and supercritical fluid extraction.
- Lipid extractions involve the use of fats or oils like butter, vegetable oils, MCT oils, etc.
- Hydrocarbon extractions usually involve the use of simple alkanes like butane and/or propane to extract the nonpolar fractions of Cannabis resins.
- Ethanol is a broad non-target solvent that extracts a wide spectrum of chemical compounds from Cannabis. Ethanol's selectivity can be tightened by changing the temperature of ethanol.
- Carbon dioxide can be pressurized and heated to a point that it becomes a supercritical fluid which can dissolve and pass through tissues acting as both a liquid and a gas.
- Winterization is a process by which heavier fats and waxes in a solution are precipitated out under cold temperatures.
- Crystallization is a purification process where conditions are provided under which a target chemical will group together, precipitate out of solution, and form a crystalline structure.

---

# Chapter 18:
## CANNABIS TESTING

*"When you walk into a lab there should be evidence of quality all around..."*

Anthony Smith, PhD, BTS #6 Curious About Cannabis Podcast

**SCAN ME**

### Learning Questions

- What are the most common services offered by Cannabis testing labs?
- What technologies and methods do Cannabis testing labs use to test Cannabis for potency and purity?
- How do Cannabis testing labs measure their own accuracy?
- How should a Cannabis Certificate of Analysis (COA) be interpreted?
- What are the ways in which Cannabis testing can go wrong?

## LOOKING FORWARDS AND BACKWARDS AT THE WORLD OF CANNABIS TESTING

### by Kyle Boyar, Analytical Technologist and Cannabis Researcher

"Cannabis testing is still very much evolving on a regular basis. It has only recently emerged as a regular practice in the last decade and has only been subject to regulation in the last six years. Cannabis testing came about in regulated states like California due to the needs of patients to better understand dosing and to ensure that harmful contaminants were not being consumed. Cannabis businesses quickly realized that having "tested" products was a market differentiator in the California Prop 215 era as early as 2009. I entered the cannabis testing field only a few short years later in 2012.

This dynamic eventually evolved into a means of marketing products through services like Weedmaps and their partnerships with testing labs. While well intentioned, this created a market drive for high potency values which led consumers to shop for the highest THC values. For many reasons, I feel that this was a disservice to medical patients and those who truly use cannabis in a therapeutic manner, as accurate dosing is paramount.

Those were the early days and since then we've refined a lot of these techniques and learned a lot about what makes for great cannabis with more therapeutic attributes. Over my tenure at one of the first cannabis testing labs in the country, I tested over a hundred thousand samples of medical cannabis including some of the best in the world as the official testing partner for groups like The Emerald Cup. I've also tested some weird stuff that most people haven't even considered existed, one of my favorite examples being cannabis infused Vietnamese Pho. Consistently over the years we saw that high THC values do not dictate what makes cannabis effective or therapeutic and the data from the Emerald Cup reflects that. The varieties with cannabinoid content in the high teens or low twenties consistently produce the most complexity and highest concentration of terpenes and terpenoids. Meanwhile, the mainstream consumer has been led to believe that high THC values are most desirable.

This has led testing laboratories to inflate their numbers, especially when it comes to THC values, but also the concentrations of other things like CBD and terpenoids. Beyond that, many manufacturers and distributors have learned to shop for the most ideal result in a practice known as lab shopping. Some labs are notorious for their diligence and accurate reporting, a practice which I applaud. Unfortunately, these labs are at a major disadvantage as we are currently in an environment that rewards bad actors who inflate values or pass contaminated cannabis or cannabis products. In many circumstances, people will game the system, using the most sensitive and accurate lab for R&D samples while sending their compliance samples to the lab that inflates the most and sees the least in terms of contaminants. The inflation of these values also has ripple effects in production and manufacturing where one bad data point can cause headaches for accurate dosing.

The data also validates these claims. Recently in CA Napro Research, an independent lab has performed "round robin testing" sending the same sample of flower and distillate to different licensed labs in the state and saw drastically different values. In the case of flower, some labs exceeded a relative percent difference of 170% compared to Napro's own internal value (Lewis & Smith, 2022). In general, we see a preference for higher numbers. In 2021, Zoroob published a study titled "The frequency distribution of reported THC concentrations of legal cannabis flower products increases discontinuously around the 20% THC threshold in Nevada and Washington state" which demonstrated that there are disproportionately more flower samples testing above the 20% level in these states.

Testing not only involves chemistry but also microbiological analysis which is often overlooked but of paramount importance for those with any kind of compromised immune function. I was fortunate to travel extensively across the US and Canada exploring the rapidly evolving testing sector while working as a Field Application Scientist at Medicinal Genomics. During my time there, we built a strong case for the use of molecular methods for pathogens over commonly used plating techniques by exposing flaws in the existing methodology. Our team also produced notable innovations for the cannabis genetics space such as Point of Grow Genetic Testing and the Jamaican Lion Reference Genome, which is one of the most complete and highest quality cannabis genomes available to date. This involved taking a very unconventional path and utilized the cryptocurrency boom via the currency DASH as a vehicle to achieve groundbreaking science in a quasi-legal arena that would not otherwise obtain funding.

As the cannabis testing space boomed with more legal markets and regulations coming online, I became increasingly aware of the value of traceability and staying organized. This led me to my next role on the software side of testing at TagLeaf where we produced one of the first true Laboratory Information Management Systems (LIMS) designed for cannabis testing labs. As the climate has become more regulated there has been an ever-increasing need for labs to have customized tools that are tailored to their processes and the regulations, and this opportunity afforded many exercises in structuring lab workflows and the various data generating processes to be captured in cannabis testing labs.

The combination of all these factors have made for a very unlevel playing field that actually hurts the consumer and even more so patients who need to ensure what's reported on the Certificate of Analysis is rooted in reality and backed by quality science. This has also facilitated a need for the industry to step on the gas to develop consensus and reference methods, something that is commonplace in any regulated industry to help ensure consistent data is being generated from lab to lab.

There have been a number of instances highlighting this need. One example is the case of Michigan where an Emergency Response Validation (ERV) was conducted by AOAC for Total Yeast & Mold (TYM) in response to discordant results amongst the licensed labs. The ERV found that molecular methods were inadequate for assessing TYM in cannabis and these findings ultimately emerged as Michigan Regulatory Authority (MRA) regulations that testing labs cannot issue solely TYM molecular data and must perform a plating or culture-based method that is AOAC certified.

At the end of the day, we are still operating in a highly incongruent marketplace where regulations and testing requirements differ from state to state. Until there is some kind of consensus and standardization every state will be doing a little something different, with some being more rigorous and thorough than others.

In some places where Cannabis is legal for medical and/or recreational purposes, there are requirements that all Cannabis products are tested for potency and purity – or, in other words, how "strong" the product is and how "clean" the product is. Cannabis testing laboratories provide the technical services required to properly comply with product quality rules and regulations. Beyond the realm of the Cannabis industry, these kinds of laboratories would be considered natural products laboratories. Typically, Cannabis labs test Cannabis and Cannabis derived products for things like cannabinoids, terpenes, molds, bacteria, pesticides, residual solvents, and metals.

Although the Cannabis testing industry is relatively new with the unfolding of Cannabis legalization across the world, the natural products testing industry has been around for ages. Humans have been striving to investigate and understand the properties of nature all throughout history. The elements of nature have been sought after by philosophers, alchemists, physicists, mystics, and chemists alike. Today the analysis of natural products is a customary practice, using a variety of techniques to determine both common and trace elements of a target natural product, like Cannabis flowers. Natural products analysis and research is traditionally performed for a variety of reasons like certifying the safety of a product or isolating new compounds for therapeutic research."

KyBo

# COMMON CANNABIS TESTING SERVICES

Laboratories providing Cannabis testing services typically offer a variety of analytical services including potency, pesticide residue, microbiology, terpene, and residual solvent analysis. Pesticide panels may vary lab to lab, especially without any regulatory oversight. Microbiology analyses may consist of testing for such things as yeasts and molds, E. coli, Salmonella, coliforms, and other bacteria.

## FOREIGN MATTER SCREENING

One of the most basic forms of "testing" that labs do is called foreign matter screening. In this test, one or more samples of a Cannabis product are examined under a microscope to search for anything that does not belong, such as hair, insect parts, glass or mineral shards, and other contaminants.

## CANNABINOID TESTING

Potency testing is the most common type of analysis that a Cannabis laboratory performs. Potency analysis includes the identification and quantification of phytocannabinoids. If the laboratory utilizes gas chromatography (GC) for cannabinoid testing, the laboratory will typically report Total, or Max, THC and CBD values, at a minimum. If the laboratory utilizes liquid chromatography, the laboratory will report THCA, CBDA, THC, and CBD, at a minimum. Along with these major phytocannabinoids, Cannabis laboratories often report minor cannabinoids such as CBG, CBC, CBN, THCV, and/or CBDV.

## TERPENOID TESTING

Terpene analysis is a service that is in increasing demand from the Cannabis industry as cultivators want to better understand the chemotypes of their plants and patients want to better understand the therapeutic potential of Cannabis products. Terpenes have been shown to exhibit unique "entourage effects" with cannabinoids and some terpenes directly bind to cannabinoid receptors. Terpene tests offered by Cannabis labs typically report anywhere between five to thirty or more terpenes commonly found in Cannabis.

Because terpenoids are such volatile and sensitive compounds, the way a laboratory handles the sample can greatly affect the terpenoids measured. Labs must go to great lengths to ensure the integrity of a sample is maintained properly and the terpenoid profile has not been altered. This is often done by keeping the sample cold and using a headspace sampler to heat the sample and extract the resulting vapor for analysis.

The gas that makes up the headspace within a headspace vial must be controlled to ensure that compounds in the sample do not oxidize or otherwise react with compounds found in air. For instance, to highlight an example that affects both terpenoid testing and residual solvent testing, a 2022 study found that if terpene samples are not held under an inert gas, like argon, acetone is formed from the reaction of terpenoids with the air – leading to inaccurate and exaggerated concentrations of acetone to be measured in the sample, throwing off the overall results.[468]

## PESTICIDE SCREENING

Pesticide testing is one of the primary contaminant screens that Cannabis laboratories offer. Depending on the regulatory requirements in an area, a Cannabis lab may test for any variety of pesticides. It is important to understand exactly what pesticides a laboratory includes on their pesticide panels before ordering a test. In Oregon, state regulations require testing for approximately 60 different pesticides commonly utilized in Cannabis production including several commonly used organic OMRI listed pesticides.

## RESIDUAL SOLVENT SCREENING

Sometimes there may be solvents left behind during the production of Cannabis extracts and/or concentrates. Cannabis testing laboratories often offer residual solvent screening services to help ensure that producers are recovering their solvents out of the product prior to packaging and sales. Usually, a method called headspace gas chromatography with flame ionization detection (HS-GC-FID) is used to test Cannabis products for residual solvents.

Whenever a laboratory must sample a product for residual solvent testing, they must prepare several sampling tools in advance to avoid using cleaning solvents on tools while sampling which could contaminate the samples with trace amounts of solvent.

## MICROBIOLOGICAL TESTING

There are many different fungi and bacteria that may be present in Cannabis. Some of these microorganisms can be quite toxic to consumers with compromised immune systems. Dangerous bacteria can cause food poisoning and allergic reactions. Many Cannabis testing laboratories offer a variety of microbiological testing services to identify the presence of molds, spores, and bacteria to help provide producers and consumers with peace of mind. There are a variety of different microbiological tests that are conducted on cannabis and cannabis products, but the two main classes are total count tests, which measure broad classes of organisms, and pathogen tests, which are typically presence/absence and are specific to a known pathogen of interest.

---

[468] Elzinga, Sytze, Jorge Dominguez-Alonzo, Raquel Keledjian, Brad Douglass, and Jeffrey C. Raber. 2022. "Acetone as Artifact of Analysis in Terpene Samples by HS-GC/MS" Molecules 27, no. 18: 6037. https://doi.org/10.3390/molecules27186037

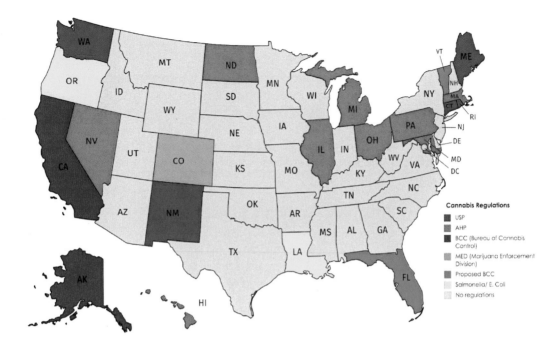

**FIGURE 44 CANNABIS MICROBIAL TESTING REGULATIONS BY STATE (BOYAR, 2019)**

Different states have different philosophies in their approach to microbial testing. Some like California, at the time of this writing in 2022, opt for pathogen only testing for things like STEC, Salmonella, and Aspergillus. This is likely due to the wide use of probiotic bacteria and fungi in organic outdoor cannabis cultivation. Other states, where outdoor cultivation would not be as common, choose to take a broader approach and follow guidelines set by the American Herbal Pharmacopeia (AHP) or the United States Pharmacopeia (USP) and include total count tests for things like Total Aerobic, Total Yeast and Mold, Total Coliforms, Bile Tolerant Gram-Negative bacteria, etc.

## TISSUE CULTURE SERVICES

Some Cannabis laboratories may offer tissue culturing services. Tissue culture plants can obtain a much higher rooting efficiency than cuttings, up to 95%[469], resulting in greater resource use efficiency. Tissue culture is also used to introduce genes to the **germplasm**. Germplasm is the term used to refer to the undifferentiated bundle of cells that can lead to the growth of a full plant. A bacterium is used to carry a new gene to the tissue. Then the tissue is exposed to an antibiotic that kills the bacteria but leaves the gene in the tissue. The plant can then adopt the gene and grow using the new genetic information. This is one form of genetic modification.

Tissue culture can also be used to create and maintain libraries of reliable plant genetics. It can also be used to produce **synthetic seeds** which are bundles of

---

[469] Lata H, S Chandra, IA Khan, MA ElSohly. 2010b. High Frequency Plant Regeneration from Leaf Derived Callus of High delta-9-Tetrahydrocannabinol Yielding Cannabis sativa L. Planta Med 76:1629-1633 https://doi.org/10.1055/s-0030-1249773

meristematic cells surrounded by a nutritive gel. These seeds can be stored for extended periods of time and then sown in soil to grow into a full clone.

## CHEMOTAXONOMY AND GENETICS

Some Cannabis labs primarily focus on performing chemotaxonomy and genetic work – attempting to better understand the varieties of Cannabis and the history of the plant's evolution. In chemotaxonomy, cannabinoid and terpenoid data are analyzed, and patterns are grouped together to find chemical "fingerprints" of Cannabis varieties.

Genetic sequencing can be performed to document the genetic code of a particular variety of Cannabis. By examining genetic information, researchers can identify how genes are flowing through plant populations and which genes are unique to certain plant varieties. Researchers can also use genetic sequencing to better understand what genes control the production of various chemical compounds of interest in the plant, so that they may be manipulated through targeted breeding practices or genetic modification.

## PLANT SEX DETERMINATION

Determining the sex of immature Cannabis plants is possible using PCR technology. **PCR** stands for **Polymerase Chain Reaction** and is a commonly used technology in molecular and cellular biology for analyzing DNA. It is a method of taking a small piece of DNA and replicating it many times to examine its contents. Both the germplasm of the plant seed and the cotyledons of a seedling (which were pre-formed in the embryo of the seed) can be analyzed to determine if the DNA indicates whether the plant is male, female, or likely to be a hermaphrodite.

## METALS ANALYSIS

Testing for metals like Arsenic, Lead, Cadmium, and Mercury is often very expensive and requires instrumentation that is usually not used for other types of analyses. For these reasons, most laboratories do not offer metals analysis unless metals testing is required for local or state regulatory compliance. Alternatively, environmental laboratories that already perform metals testing on other plants and soils may be more likely to offer metals testing.

## STABILITY STUDIES

Stability studies access how shelf stable a product is by undergoing one or more tests to assess thermal stability, photostability, and resistance to oxidation. To test thermal stability, a lab will take a product and store it in an incubator at a controlled temperature (usually 25-30°C) over an extended period of time, usually between 3 months to a year, while repeatedly testing the product to track how the chemical constituents in the product change over time. Photostability studies seek to determine how well a product can hold up when exposed to light. In photostability tests, a product is exposed to a controlled amount of light (usually around 1 million lux hours). To test for resistance to oxidation, a lab will take a sample of a product and expose it to hydrogen peroxide for 24 hours. The sample is then tested to determine how the primary active ingredients have been affected.

# THE LIFE OF A LAB SAMPLE

Once a Cannabis sample is either dropped off at a laboratory or collected in the field by a laboratory technician, it is assigned a unique identifier. When the sample is at the lab, waiting to be prepared, it typically is housed in refrigerators or freezers that feature temperature monitors and alarms to ensure that the sample is always properly preserved. Cannabis samples are typically stored in temperatures anywhere between -40°C to 20°C, depending on what analyses are required. Analyses of volatile compounds, like solvents, pesticides, and terpenoids, require colder preservation than analyses of less volatile compounds like metals.

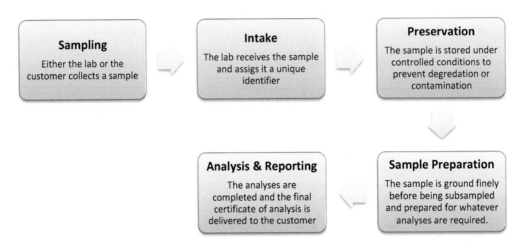

FIGURE 45: BASIC LAB TESTING WORKFLOW

At some point, either upon lab intake or prior to preparation, the sample is homogenized, meaning that it is ground and well mixed to ensure that the material is uniform throughout and any subsamples taken will be representative of the entire sample. Then, a laboratory technician will collect a subsample from the homogenized material to perform each requested analysis. Each type of lab test features unique sample size requirements that can range anywhere from 0.1g to 1g or more per analysis. The lab may prepare samples in duplicate or triplicate, requiring extra sample. Once any required samples are taken, the remainder of the original sample material is returned to controlled chilled storage.

Once a sample is collected per the requirements of the analytical method, sample preparation begins. This process can vary depending on what analyses are required, but it often involves exposing the sample to one or more solvents, cleaning the solution to filter out particulates, and then diluting the solution to a desired level. For microbiological testing, the solution is often plated onto growth media and incubated to promote the growth of target organisms like yeasts, molds, aerobic bacteria, or *E. coli* species.

Once the required tests are performed on the sample and the results are reported, the sample material is then marked for disposal. Some laboratories dispose of samples very quickly after reporting results while others retain samples for several weeks, months, or even years, just in case it is needed again for investigative reasons.

# ANALYTICAL METHODS FOR CHEMICAL ANALYSES

There are a wide range of tried-and-true analytical chemistry techniques available to explore the constituents of natural products. Throughout this next section, we will explore the most common analytical techniques utilized by laboratories that focus on testing Cannabis.

## ELISA (ENZYME-LINKED IMMUNOSORBENT ASSAY)

**ELISA** is a method traditionally used to detect pathogens in foods or bodily fluids as well as pesticide residues in water. It is a quick and inexpensive way of detecting the presence of a pesticide or a group of pesticides or toxins. Test kits are readily available that can quickly inform the analyst if a group of compounds are present in a sample by a simple change in the color of the liquid.

ELISA is limited by the fact that it can sometimes be hard or impossible to get quantitative data about one specific contaminant from an ELISA test if the kit is designed to test for multiple contaminants, like pesticides, at once. In other industries, ELISA tests are used as quality control to quickly and cheaply test samples to ensure they do not contain a particular group of contaminants, like a particular class of pesticides. If the test were to come up positive, the sample would then be sent to be analyzed on a GC or HPLC system to determine what pesticide is present and in what concentration.

## WHAT IS CHROMATOGRAPHY?

**Chromatography,** translated as "color writing", is a method of separating mixtures into constituent compounds. Solutions are forced through either a column or plate of particles. Different molecules pass through the column or across the plate at different speeds, resulting in similar molecules grouping together and separating from the mixture. A very basic example of chromatography can be demonstrated with water, a cup, a paper towel, and a water-soluble marker. If you tear off a strip of paper towel, place a dot on one end with the marker, and then dip the strip into a cup that has a shallow reservoir of water, the water will crawl up the paper through capillary action and smear the ink across the paper, separating the colors.

Chromatography involves a **stationary phase** and a **mobile phase**. The stationary phase, as the name implies, remains in place, while the mobile phase moves across the stationary phase. Usually, the sample is present in the mobile phase and the compounds separate as they move across and interact with the stationary phase. These relatively simple dynamics are the basic principles of all chromatography.

Chromatography results are visualized on graphs called **chromatograms**. The x axis is represented by the amount of time passed during the run, called **retention time**. The y axis represents the **signal** coming from the detector. The bumps on the graph are called "**peaks**" and represent the presence of different compounds: the greater the area of the peak, the greater the concentration of that compound in the sample.

There are several aspects of these peaks that are measured to determine the concentration of a compound: the **peak height, peak width, peak area, and peak**

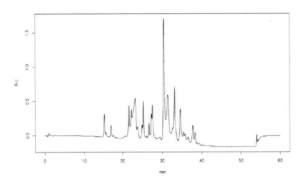

**symmetry**. **Peak width** and **symmetry** are usually indicators of the resolution of the data. If the peaks are tight, sharp, and symmetrical, the data is thought to have high resolution. **Peak height** and **peak area** correspond to the abundance of the measured compound.

## THIN LAYER CHROMATOGRAPHY

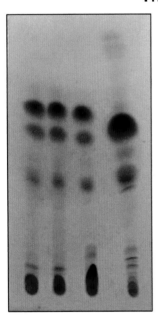

**Thin layer chromatography** is a relatively simple method of chromatography that uses a plate as the stationary phase and a solvent as the mobile phase. A sample is placed on to a specially designed TLC plate and allowed to dry. Then the plate is placed in a chamber that is saturated with a solvent and contains a bit of solvent at the base. The plate acts as a wick and sucks up the solvent. Capillary action carries the solvent all the way to the top of the plate. The plate is then removed and allowed to completely dry. Then the plate is sprayed with a special dye to give color to the compounds that have been separated on the plate. An assortment of colors, dots and smeared lines appear on the plate. These dots and lines can then be measured to get an estimation of the concentration of a chemical compound in the sample.

To make thin layer chromatography quantitative, sophisticated equipment or software that can perform pixel densitometry are used to quantify the total area of each analyte's dot. One limitation of thin layer chromatography is that it tends to over-estimate cannabinoids in low concentrations.

# TRY THIS! MARKER CHROMATOGRAPHY

The concept of chromatography can be easily demonstrated at home through a very simple experiment involving a marker, a piece of paper, and a little bit of water or rubbing alcohol. Have you ever wondered what colors are hidden within a marker's ink? Try this activity out and see for yourself!

## Materials

| | | |
|---|---|---|
| Pencil | Markers | Piece of white filter paper or card stock |
| Shallow glass or cup (glass recommended) | Water (for water soluble markers) | Rubbing Alcohol (for permanent markers) |

## Procedures

1. Fill the glass or cup with 1cm of water
2. Cut the filter paper or card stock into a long strip
3. Measure 1cm from the bottom of a strip of paper and draw a line with pencil.
4. Using the markers, place a single bold dot with each marker along the line, leaving approximately 0.5cm space between each dot.
5. Place the strip of paper into the cup.
6. Allow the water or alcohol to slowly wick up the paper. This can take several minutes.
7. Once the water or alcohol has completely saturated the piece of paper, remove the paper, and examine the results. You should see that the ink from each marker has spread out revealing all the component dyes that make up each color.

Congratulations! You have successfully performed a chromatography experiment!

Although this activity may seem very simple, it demonstrates all the major components of chromatography. The marker dot is your **sample**. The paper is your **stationary phase**, and the water or alcohol is your **mobile phase**. As the mobile phase moves the sample across the stationary phase, the sample separates into its component parts – or **constituents**. All forms of chromatography, however seemingly complex, all follow these basic principles illustrated in this simple experiment!

## GAS CHROMATOGRAPHY

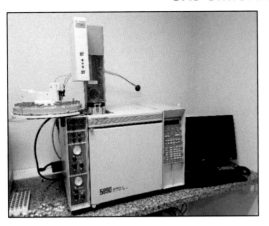

**Gas chromatography** is one of the most commonly used instruments used for compound separation and analysis. Samples are injected into the gas chromatograph and instantly vaporized. The vapor is then carried into the **column**, which is a long and very small tube which is lined with the stationary phase. A hot gas helps sweep the sample into the tube. The column is contained in an oven, as seen here. As the sample passes through the column, the oven heats up.

As the temperature rises, different compounds separate, stick to the column, and break away from the column. Eventually the compounds pass through a detector which sends a signal to a computer where a graph is created to visualize the compounds in the sample. This graph is called a **Chromatogram**.

Decarboxylated cannabinoid, terpenoid, and residual solvent analyses can all be performed on a gas chromatograph with reliability and accuracy. To perform residual solvent analyses on a gas chromatograph, a **head-space sampler** is needed. Residual solvents are highly volatile, meaning they evaporate easily under a little heat. For this reason, rather than sampling the liquid, the headspace sampler samples the gas that forms above the sample as the vial and the sample are gently heated to a programmed temperature.

## LIQUID CHROMATOGRAPHY

**Liquid chromatography** is another very common method of chemical analysis and involves a cooler method of separating and detecting compounds, as opposed to gas chromatography which is a very hot method. Specifically, **High Pressure Liquid Chromatography** (**HPLC**), also called High Performance Liquid Chromatography, is used in natural products analysis. Liquid chromatography is particularly useful for measuring the carboxylic acid cannabinoids like THCA, CBDA, CBCA, and CBGA. Since the method is cold, the acids are never heated enough to **decarboxylate** them.

To calculate the total potential decarboxylated THC content, the THCA and THC values must be combined. **These values cannot just simply be added**. When a 100mg/g of THCA is decarboxylated, $CO_2$ is lost and the weight of the molecule is reduced, ending up with approximately 88mg/g of THC after decarboxylation. So, if THCA and THC values are added together without accounting for this change, an exaggerated result is produced.

# FLASH CHROMATOGRAPHY

The final type of chromatography that a Cannabis laboratory is likely to utilize is flash chromatography. The "flash" in the name "flash chromatography" is in reference to the method's speed. When the technology was developed, it was thought that the process would be "over in a flash". As opposed to traditional gravity-fed column chromatography techniques, flash chromatography utilized pressurized gas to force a sample through a packed column and across an appropriate stationary phase.

Flash chromatography is typically used as a sample preparation technique, to quickly separate a sample into its constituents before being analyzed by an instrument like a mass spectrometer, or even a detector on a different type of chromatograph. Some Cannabis laboratories are turning to flash chromatography to better prepare complex samples, like Cannabis infused edibles.

# WHAT IS SPECTROMETRY?

**Spectrometry** is another method for analyzing the chemical components of materials. The word "spectrometry" gets its meaning from the fact that spectrometers measure ("-metry") spectra ("spectro-"), whether they be electromagnetic light spectra - as in infrared, ultraviolet, or x-ray spectrometry – or mass spectra, in mass spectrometry. For the purposes of Cannabis testing, mass spectrometry is the primary spectrometry method used, often in combination with gas or liquid chromatography.

In the case of mass spectrometry, the analytical instrument measures a sample's **mass spectrum**, which represents each of the mass-to-charge ratios for each ion in the sample as well as the velocity at which the ions passed through the instrument. The **mass-to-charge ratio** describes the mass of the ion in relation to the number of charges it is carrying. On a mass spectrum graph, the x axis represents the mass-to-charge ratio, and the y axis represents intensity.

Spectrometry is commonly used in Cannabis testing to detect and measure trace contaminants like pesticides, growth regulators, and residual solvents. When greater sensitivity is needed for detecting very trace amounts of compounds, tandem mass spectrometers may be used.

# MASS SPECTROMETRY

**Mass spectrometry** is a detection method that can be used in conjunction with gas or liquid chromatography to try to achieve a higher sensitivity of detection and greater confidence of compound identification. Once compounds are ionized through the gas or liquid chromatography, the ions are shot through the mass spectrometer where the ions pass between a series of magnets. The trajectory of the ions as they pass by the magnets is correlated with the mass of the compound, which can then be used to try and identify the compound. In Cannabis testing, mass spectrometry is primarily utilized in pesticide and residual solvent testing.

For particularly difficult to detect compounds, like trace pesticides, a triple quadrupole, or "triple quad", mass spectrometer is often used. A "triple quad" mass spectrometer provides greater sensitivity and the ability to detect very minute traces of compounds, sometimes in the parts per trillion range. In addition to ionizing compounds, a triple quad subsequently fragments the compounds and then ionizes the resulting fragments. Ultimately these fragments end up providing a unique "fingerprint" that can be used to identify the parent molecule. This can help differentiate compounds that are very similar and may otherwise interfere with each other on a standard mass spectrometer detector.

The mass spectra of a substantial number of compounds are stored in various libraries which can be accessed for a fee. Scientists can use these libraries to flag and tentatively identify compounds for which they do not have reference standards. These compounds are reported as Tentatively Identified Compounds, or TICs. TICs are supposed to be properly marked on test results and are not considered true quantitative results until confirmed against a reference standard. Mass spectra libraries are useful tools but are not fool-proof and can lead to misidentification of chromatographic peaks, especially for compounds in low concentrations. Mass spectrometry alone can be an inappropriate method for some analyses, as acknowledged in this excerpt from the blog of chromatography supplier, Restek:

> "When an interfering terpene, or other compound, coelutes with a terpene of interest, quantification will be compromised and, since many terpenes have the same molecular weight and share fragment ions, mass spectrometry cannot be relied upon to distinguish a terpene of interest from a coeluting interference terpene. The only way to accurately identify and quantify terpenes is to ensure that the terpenes of interest are chromatographically separated from all interfering compounds."[470]

## INDUCTIVELY COUPLED PLASMA MASS SPECTROMETRY (ICP-MS)

When it comes to testing natural products for metals, ICP mass spectrometry is the go-to method. ICP stands for "inductively coupled plasma" which refers to the torch used to dehydrate, separate, and ionize the materials being analyzed. Once ionized, the mass spectrometer detector scans the masses of the resulting fragments to identify them. ICP-MS systems usually use Argon as their primary gas for creating ICP. The ICP torch is approximately 6000°K, equal to the approximate temperature of the surface of the sun! Because the torch is so incredibly hot, it is very efficient at separating chemical constituents and elements that are very solid and hard at temperatures greater than 200 or 300°C, like metals!

| Commonly Tested Metals in Cannabis | |
|---|---|
| Lead (Pb) | Arsenic (As) |
| Cadmium (Cd) | Mercury (Hg) |
| Nickel (Ni) | Copper (Cu) |

FIGURE 46: COMMON METALS TESTED BY CANNABIS LABS

Cannabis testing labs will usually not offer metals testing unless it is required by state testing regulations simply because the equipment can be very expensive, and the process is technical in a manner that is dissimilar to other forms of mass spectrometry, requiring unique expertise.

---

[470] A Preliminary FET Headspace GC-FID Method for Comprehensive Terpene Profiling in Cannabis. http://www.restek.com/Technical-Resources/Technical-Library/Foods-Flavors-Fragrances/fff_FFAN2045-UNV

## ABSORBANCE SPECTROMETRY (SPECTROPHOTOMETRY)

Absorbance spectrometry is the use of electromagnetic radiation to measure the abundance of atoms or molecules in a substance. The two most common methods of absorbance spectrometry used for cannabinoid analysis include UV and IR absorbance spectrometry. Some analytical systems may use only UV or IR, while other systems sometimes mix the two. As the light hits the sample, the different compounds absorb the light differently, generating measurable levels of absorbance, which form graphs that look like chromatograms.

Spectrophotometers are often small and sometimes portable, compared to more traditional analytical equipment. Some commercially available portable Cannabis testing devices utilize an economical blend of liquid chromatography and absorbance spectrometry – using packed columns and liquid solvent to separate samples into their components. The sample is then fed into a spectrophotometer which measures the absorbance of each compound, allowing for the quantitation of major cannabinoids.

# ANALYTICAL METHODS FOR MICROBIOLOGICAL ANALYSES

## CULTURE PLATING

One of the most common methods of quantifying microbiological components is through using inoculated petri dishes containing nutritive media, or through using commercially available 3M Petrifilm™.[471] **Petrifilm**™ consists of a soft plate containing a nutritive surface used to culture fungi and bacteria. A plastic film covers the plate and is sealed after inoculation. To perform a mold/mildew test, a sample would be mixed with a special solvent used to collect the spores and cells without destroying them. Some of the liquid is then placed onto the Petrifilm™ where it is sealed in place. The plate is left to incubate for 2 to 5 days depending on the type of Petrifilm™ plate. Then the fungal or bacterial **colonies** on the plate are counted.

A limitation to plating methods is that sometimes non-target organisms will grow in the growth media. For instance, bacteria might grow on a culture designed for growing yeast and mold. Plating methods also generally do not inform the analyst whether any of the detected colonies on the plate are harmful to human health or not. Most plating methods do not target any particular species of micro-organism, sometimes leading samples to fail testing even if they do not present a risk to human health.

## QUANTITATIVE / REAL TIME POLYMERASE CHAIN REACTION (QPCR/RT-PCR)

To overcome some of the limitations of microbiological plating, laboratories also perform DNA testing using a quick and relatively easy method of amplifying DNA and comparing it to a reference standard through a method called polymerase chain reaction, or PCR. In PCR, a small sample of DNA is replicated many times so that it may be easily measured. PCR is typically used for microbiological testing in Cannabis.

---

[471] https://www.3m.com/petrifilm

Through DNA testing, it is possible to overcome one of the primary limitations of other forms of microbiological testing – poor selectivity.

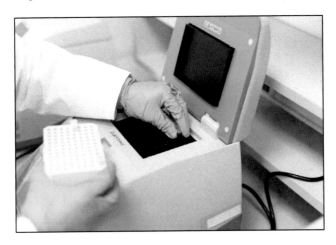

There are various ways of performing PCR tests. A simple method of using PCR is through a chemical reaction that changes the solution containing the DNA a unique color if the DNA matches the target organism. This allows for cheap, simple visual determination of whether a sample "passes" or "fails" without expensive equipment. Alternatively, there is a method called real-time or quantitative PCR, or qPCR. qPCR involves expensive equipment that amplifies DNA, makes it fluoresce, and then monitors the fluorescence to measure how much DNA is present and whether it matches a reference sample. qPCR monitors the changes to DNA, while the amplification process takes place, which is why it is referred to as "real time" PCR.

**CFX Opus 96 Real-Time PCR System**

Photo Courtesy of Bio-Rad Laboratories, Inc.

# COSTS OF TESTING

The costs of Cannabis testing services can vary quite a bit depending on the location of the laboratory, the methods used, and the quality of service. In essence, just like with most things in life – you get what you pay for. The following table demonstrates estimated costs of different testing services as of the time of this writing in 2022.

| Service | Typical Method(s) Used | Typical Price Range |
|---------|------------------------|---------------------|
| Cannabinoids | GC – decarboxylated cannabinoids<br>LC or LC/MS – cannabinoid acids | $40 - $150 |
| Terpenoids | GC or GC/MS<br>Headspace GC/MS | $50 - $200 |
| Pesticides | GC/MS-MS<br>LC/MS-MS<br>ELISA (qualitative) | $75 - $400 |
| Residual Solvents | GC/MS | $50 - $150 |
| Metals | ICP/MS | $100 - $300 |
| Moisture Content | Loss on Drying<br>Moisture Analyzer | $25 - $50 |
| Water Activity | Relative Humidity Probe | $25 - $50 |
| Yeast and Mold | Petrifilm™<br>ELISA (presence/absence) | $30 - $60 |
| E. coli or Salmonella | Petrifilm™<br>ELISA (presence/absence)<br>PCR | $30 - $75 |
| Aspergillus sp. | PCR | $50 - 100 |
| Mycotoxins | ELISA<br>Lateral Flow (presence/absence)<br>LC/MS | $30 - 100 |
| Sex Testing | PCR | $5 - $10 per plant |
| GC – Gas Chromatograph with Flame Ionization Detector<br>GC/MS – Gas Chromatograph with Mass Spectrometer Detector<br>LC – Liquid Chromatograph, usually High Pressure LC (HPLC)<br>LC/MS – Liquid Chromatograph with Mass Spectrometer Detector<br>GC/MS-MS – Gas Chromatograph with tandem Mass Spectrometer Detectors<br>LC/MS-MS – Liquid Chromatograph with tandem Mass Spectrometer Detectors<br>ICP/MS – Inductively Coupled Plasma Mass Spectrometer<br>PCR – Polymerase Chain Reaction | | |

FIGURE 47: CANNABIS TESTING SERVICES, EQUIPMENT USED, AND TYPICAL PRICE RANGES

# Evaluating a Cannabis Testing Laboratory

At the time of the writing of this book, the legal Cannabis industry in the United States is still young but is quickly maturing. As Cannabis is legalized and regulated, a myriad of ancillary businesses crops up to serve the industry in some way or another. One of these ancillary businesses in the Cannabis industry are Cannabis testing laboratories.

Unfortunately, in areas that have legalized Cannabis but not yet applied strict quality standards or regulations in place, it is common to see Cannabis testing laboratories appear seemingly overnight, run by individuals with no science background or sense of scientific integrity, willing to dish out the most favorable result money can buy. Because of this, **it is important that all participants in the Cannabis industry, including consumers, learn how to critically evaluate Cannabis testing laboratories** to identify those that are competent and will provide reliable data.

## Laboratory Credentials/Competency

When assessing the scientific competence of an analytical laboratory, it is important to investigate the credentials of laboratory staff closely. Many laboratory technicians and assistants hold bachelor or master's degrees in chemistry, biology, or some related science field. The executive scientist, or chief science officer, usually holds either an MS or a PhD, often with publications in peer-reviewed journals.

The laboratory manager or director should have prior experience employing a variety of analytical techniques for quantifying compounds in natural products of a variety of types of samples. The laboratory should have at least one employee that serves as quality manager who thoroughly understands how to build and manage quality assurance systems. Quality managers work with the laboratory manager or laboratory director to implement quality objectives, establish methods of measuring laboratory performance, and instituting programs for continuous improvement.

Laboratories that are accredited will maintain records called "demonstrations of capability." These records indicate exactly how each technician performed in a series of sample preparations. Typically, the technician will prepare a sample several consecutive times. The results from each of the samples is compared to one another as well as to the known concentration of the sample to determine the technician's precision and accuracy with the method being evaluated.

The consumer should feel comfortable calling a laboratory and asking for qualifications and credentials of laboratory staff to ensure that proper reliable results will be produced, especially as the Cannabis industry continues to mature. Depending on a state's rules on Cannabis testing and Cannabis testing laboratory oversight, the quality of available laboratories working with Cannabis can be extremely variable.

## What if a Laboratory Outsources Their Work?

While evaluating your local Cannabis laboratories, you might find that some of them do not perform all the services that they advertise, rather opting to outsource those services to another laboratory. Discovering this might make you a bit uneasy and skeptical. Don't worry. This behavior is called **subcontracting**, and alone is not a cause for concern. In fact, in the analytical chemistry world, it is very common for laboratories to subcontract work to one another so that each lab may specialize their expertise in a core set of services while still maintaining the ability to offer clients a full range of services.

If a laboratory subcontracts any of their services, it should be evident on their test reports, or certificates of analysis. Usually accrediting bodies will require accredited laboratories to let clients know in writing of any subcontracting relationships. Once you have found out who your laboratory subcontracts services to, you can apply all the information in this chapter to that laboratory. If the subcontracting laboratory is reputable, you can breathe easy. In fact, subcontracting can sometimes provide clients with access to very reputable high-quality laboratories indirectly, which they would not be able to access otherwise, perhaps even adding value to the service.

However, if you find that a laboratory is dishonest about how they produce their data or do not indicate subcontracting laboratories on their test reports, this could indicate an intention to deceive. Alternatively, it could simply be an oversight on the lab's part with no intention to deceive. Proper due diligence can easily decipher these kinds of dilemmas.

## QUALITATIVE VS QUANTITATIVE TESTING

One of the first things that is important to understand regarding lab testing is the difference between **qualitative** and **quantitative** analysis. A qualitative analysis tells you broad information about what is there, whereas a quantitative analysis tells you how much of that thing is present. For example, a test that only measures whether a pesticide is present or not in a Cannabis sample would be considered qualitative. A test that tells you the actual concentrations of pesticides present or not present in a Cannabis sample would be considered quantitative. When evaluating a laboratory's services, be sure to note whether their methods are going to give you the qualitative or quantitative information that you need. If you only need to know whether something is present or absent in a Cannabis sample, you will only need qualitative testing. If you need to know how much of any particular thing (including cannabinoids) is in a sample, you need quantitative testing.

The leap from qualitative testing to quantitative testing requires more detailed measurements and calculations, often requiring highly sensitive equipment calibrated to detect and measure the compounds in question. Because quantitative work is more technical, it often also requires more highly skilled and trained personnel to perform the work.

To summarize plainly, qualitative refers to "what", and quantitative refers to both "what" and "how much".

# How Low Can They Go? LODs and LOQs

> *"The Limit of Detection is the lowest analyte concentration likely to be reliably distinguished from the Limit of Blank and at which detection is feasible...The Limit of Quantification is the lowest concentration at which the analyte can not only be reliably detected but at which some predefined goals for bias and imprecision are met. The LOQ may be equivalent to the LOD, or it could be at a much higher concentration."*
>
> *(Armbruster and Pry, 2008; emphasis added)[472]*

Analytical instruments all have certain detection and quantification limits for different compounds. The **limit of detection and limit of quantification** refer to points at which a compound can confidently be measured. The limit of detection is the smallest concentration of an analyte that an analytical instrument can detect. It is technically defined as the lowest concentration at which an analyte can be distinguished from a **blank** with over 50% confidence. The blank is a sample that only contains a solvent and is used to clean and detect residues out of the analytical instrument. The limit of quantification is usually slightly higher than the LOD because the LOQ value must be reliably repeatable for quality assurance purposes.

For cannabinoids, the limit of detection is often somewhere around 0.005% or 0.001% when using gas or liquid chromatography. What this would mean is that if THC or CBD were present in a sample at 0.004%, the analyst would not be able to distinguish the result from the overall "noise" that is present in the data. Because there is always a small gap of uncertainty between the LOD or LOQ and 0, **a value of zero is almost never reported in analytical chemistry**. Instead, "not detected", "ND", "<LOQ", or some similar notation is used.

The LOD/LOQ of an analytical method is particularly important in relation to pesticide testing. It is possible for Cannabis flower to "pass" a pesticide analysis with no detectable levels of pesticides, but a resulting concentrated extract made from that material may still end up containing pesticide levels that *are* detectable. So, what's going on? Imagine that some Cannabis flower that would be used to make a batch of concentrated extract is contaminated with approximately 0.02 ppm of some pesticide. If the LOD/LOQ for the lab's pesticide method was 0.05 ppm, then this flower material would "pass" the lab's pesticide tests with results of "none detected" or "<LOQ".

When this flower is run through the extraction and concentration process, those pesticide residues would become concentrated up to 2 – 10x their original concentration as the cannabinoids are concentrated (keep in mind that many pesticides are chemically similar in structure to cannabinoids). This would mean that when the final concentrate is tested for pesticides, a result of 0.1 ppm or more could be detected, which could be very significant depending on the pesticide detected.

---

[472] Armbruster DA, T Pry. 2008. Limit of Blank, Limit of Detection and Limit of Quantitation. Clin Biochem Rev. 29:49-52 https://pubmed.ncbi.nlm.nih.gov/18852857

## SOURCES OF UNCERTAINTY

Uncertainty is inherent in science. Science does not usually produce hard facts. Instead, science produces assumptions and conclusions that have varying degrees of confidence. Barwick (1999) states "the evaluation of the uncertainty associated with a result is an essential part of quantitative analysis. Without knowledge of the measurement of uncertainty, the statement of an analytical result cannot be considered complete."[473] The International Organization for Standardization (ISO) lays out rules for how this uncertainty can be measured.

There are many sources of uncertainty, error, and bias throughout the testing process such as the client, the analyst, the instrument, and the computer – for instance. A client might sample their own batch using contaminated tools or an uncalibrated balance. The analyst might make slight measurement mistakes throughout sample preparation. The instrument might not inject samples correctly or the detector could malfunction. The software that integrates with the instrument might glitch.

Each setting on an analytical instrument affects many other variables, which is why calibration and control standards are important. Sources of uncertainty, when identified, can be measured to determine how strong an effect the errors might have on the final result. Standard Operating Procedures (SOPs) are used to standardize procedures to control sources of error, minimize errors and limit biases, where possible.

## RANGES OF "CORRECTNESS"

As mentioned above, rather than there being one "correct" value, in science there are often ranges of acceptable results that are considered accurate with varying levels of confidence. A result begins to become suspect when it falls outside of some acceptable range. **There is generally an accepted variance in Cannabis testing of between 10 and 20%, or approximately ±2-4 percentage points on average, for Cannabis flower**.

It is important for labs to work together to promote accuracy and reliability of results. **"Ring tests"**, or **proficiency tests**, are events where a third party provides a test sample with a known concentration of an analyte or analytes to a variety of labs to analyze. The results of the analyses are then reported, and the information is shared with the labs and potentially other parties. The information can help labs improve their methods and identify sources of variance. Ring testing helps keep labs sharp and on their toes, as they are aware that eventually they will have to compare their methods with the methods of other laboratories.

Repeated testing is always going to report slightly different results, but if quality control measures are in place, the repeated results will fall within a narrow range of variance. The lab's objective is to make that range as narrow as possible for any given sample.

---

[473] Barwick, V. J., & Ellison, S. L. (1999). Measurement uncertainty: approaches to the evaluation of uncertainties associated with recovery. Analyst, 124(7), 981-990. https://doi.org/10.1039/A901845J

# Understanding Positive and Negative Predictive Power

Confidence in an analytical method stems from establishing the method's predictive power. Different types of analyses require different types of predictive power – positive and negative predictive power.

**Positive predictive power**: If the result is positive, how likely is it that it is *actually* positive? How does the lab determine whether a result is *really* positive?

For example, if a Cannabis flower is tested for potency and is shown to contain 22% total THC, how does the analyst know that the sample did not contain more or less? How does the analyst know that a trace cannabinoid is *actually* THCV and not just noise from the analytical instrument? The laboratory uses reference standards containing known concentrations of target analytes, builds calibration curves that determine how little or great a concentration of a compound can be accurately quantified, performs duplicate sample preparations, and utilize validated methods to prove their positive predictive power.

**Negative predictive power**: If the result is negative, how likely is it that it is *actually* negative? How does the lab determine whether a result is *really* negative?

For example, if a sample is analyzed for pesticides and comes back clean, how does the analyst actually know that the sample does not have pesticides in it, as opposed to a potential problem with sample preparation or recovery efficiency? Maybe there *were* pesticides there, but the laboratory mishandled the sample, making it appear as if none are there. Or perhaps the instrument's detector is not working correctly, leading to constant negative results. How does an analyst get past these doubts? Laboratories must perform efficiency tests on their methods to prove their negative predictive power.

When evaluating laboratories, ask the laboratory what steps they go through to prove their positive and negative predictive power. The answers should lie in their quality management system.

# Quality Management Systems in Laboratories

Quality control in analytical laboratories is primarily about good record keeping, adhering to defined procedures, and engaging in regular quality assurance practices to achieve constant improvement. There are a variety of activities and documentation that make up a laboratory's quality management system. Anything that affects the quality of the data being collected must be documented and tracked. Analysts date and initial all notes in notebooks belonging to the lab that must remain at the lab. Laboratory Information Management Systems (LIMS) are used to digitally manage the laboratories methods, sampling workflow, employees, clients, orders, etc. Other aspects of a laboratory's quality management system include:

## Standard Operating Procedures

Standard operating procedures are documents which describe in detail the procedures to be used in the laboratory for each task performed. These are very important because these unchanged procedures help to differentiate sources of error. SOPs are used to train new laboratory workers while theoretically ensuring that performance will not change significantly.

## REFERENCE STANDARDS

Reference standards are samples that contain a known amount of an analyte. These samples are run alongside legitimate test samples to calibrate results and ensure that suspected compounds are correctly identified.

## INTERNAL VS. EXTERNAL STANDARDS

Internal reference standards are samples of known concentrations that are developed in-house and used for the purposes of instrument and result calibration and correction. External reference standards are obtained from a third-party source to check the accuracy and validity of the internal standard as well as to use as a tool for instrument and result calibration and correction.

## IDENTIFYING AND CALCULATING UNCERTAINTY AND ERROR

Error can arise from a wide variety of sources. It is important for labs to recognize and calculate some of these errors to make corrections to results to make them more accurate.

## PROFICIENCY TESTING/RING TESTING

It is important for laboratories to participate in proficiency testing to ensure the accuracy of their methods and results as well as helping to better the overall natural products testing industry. If a laboratory is ISO 17025[474] or NELAP[475] accredited, proficiency testing is mandatory.

## CONTROLLED DOCUMENTATION

All documents produced by the laboratory must be tightly monitored and controlled. Changes to paperwork must be dated and initialed. Laboratory notebooks are property of the lab and should remain at the lab. Usually, a piece of software called a LIMS (Laboratory Information Management System) is used to manage data concerning clients, analysis requests, and results. Accredited labs are subject to audits, so tight document control is crucial.

## RECORDS

Records of all happenings in the lab must be kept in a safe location for the purposes of auditability and accountability.

## CUSTOMER COMMUNICATIONS AND COMPLAINTS

A laboratory's quality assurance system needs to have a protocol for handling customer/client communications and complaints. A laboratory will make a mistake at some point. A system must be in place to handle complaints and customer issues in a way that does not sacrifice the laboratory's integrity or deviate from the laboratory's mission.

## DATA DRIVEN QUALITY OBJECTIVES

Accredited laboratories must demonstrate that they are meeting current goals while striving to achieve new goals. To do this, specifically defined quality objectives

---

[474] https://www.iso.org/ISO-IEC-17025-testing-and-calibration-laboratories.html
[475] https://nelac-institute.org/content/NELAP/index.php

must be chosen that can be measured to demonstrate whether the lab is meeting those objectives.

## INTERNAL AND EXTERNAL AUDITS

To ensure the integrity of the lab's quality assurance system, a laboratory will routinely perform self-audits. Along with self-audits, external audits from accreditation bodies may be performed to ensure quality assurance standards compliance.

## THE QUALITY MANUAL

For both ISO 17025 and NELAP accreditation a physical copy of a quality manual is necessary. The quality manual is a document that details the laboratories quality assurance system. The manual contains information about employees and their credentials, protocols, SOPs, etc.

Control Data

**Lab Sample Name:** CCV1
**Lot Number:** CCV1
**Control Type:** CCV - Continuing Calibration Verification
**Valid Sample:** true
**Test Type:** BCL-03: Cannabinoid Potency by HPLC-UV

| Analyte | Amount | Target | Units | Recovery | Lower | Upper | Pass |
|---------|--------|--------|-------|----------|-------|-------|------|
| CBD | 69.085 | 62.5 | ug/ml | 110.536 | 70 | 130 | true |
| CBG | 66.551 | 62.5 | ug/ml | 106.482 | 70 | 130 | true |
| CBN | 65.438 | 62.5 | ug/ml | 104.701 | 70 | 130 | true |
| CBCA | 55.447 | 62.5 | ug/ml | 88.715 | 70 | 130 | true |
| CBDA | 61.582 | 62.5 | ug/ml | 98.531 | 70 | 130 | true |
| CBDV | 65.083 | 62.5 | ug/ml | 104.133 | 70 | 130 | true |
| CBGA | 57.320 | 62.5 | ug/ml | 91.712 | 70 | 130 | true |
| THCA | 58.091 | 62.5 | ug/ml | 92.946 | 70 | 130 | true |
| THCV | 66.105 | 62.5 | ug/ml | 105.768 | 70 | 130 | true |
| CBDVA | 58.217 | 62.5 | ug/ml | 93.147 | 70 | 130 | true |
| THCVA | 59.569 | 62.5 | ug/ml | 95.31 | 70 | 130 | true |
| Delta-8-THC | 66.664 | 62.5 | ug/ml | 106.662 | 70 | 130 | true |
| Delta-9-THC | 66.387 | 62.5 | ug/ml | 106.219 | 70 | 130 | true |

**FIGURE 48 EXAMPLE OF CONTINUING CALIBRATION VERIFICATION DATA**

# How Does a Lab Know Its Results Are Accurate?

As now previously described, a laboratory must utilize strict quality control standards to prove their accuracy and precision. This chart sums up some, but by no means not all, of the ways in which laboratories assess and defend their own accuracy (and precision). Find more detail about each of these quality measures on the next several pages.

| Basic Ongoing Quality Measures | |
|---|---|
| Proficiency Tests/Ring Tests | Laboratory "blindly" analyzes a sample provided by a third party who knows the actual concentrations of the target analytes in the sample |
| Demonstrations of Capability (DOC) | Used to document a laboratory technician's suitability for performing a sample preparation or analytical method |
| **Sampling Quality Control Samples** | |
| Sample Acceptance Policy | Defines the sample conditions necessary for acceptance by the laboratory |
| Random/Representative Sampling Procedures and Policies | Procedures that the lab will use to obtain a sample that is adequately representative of its source |
| **Sample/Matrix Specific Quality Control Samples** | |
| Matrix Spike | A sample is spiked with known concentrations of target analytes to measure matrix specific accuracy |
| Matrix Spike Duplicate | A second sample is spiked with known concentrations of target analytes to measure matrix specific precision |
| Matrix Duplicate | A duplicate sample used to measure general precision |
| **Preparation Batch Specific Quality Control Samples** | |
| Method Blank | Monitors contamination during sample preparation |
| Laboratory Control Sample (LCS) | A blank spike or other laboratory reference sample used to measure accuracy |
| Laboratory Control Sample Duplicate (LCSD) | A duplicate blank spike or other laboratory reference sample used to measure precision |
| **Instrument Specific Quality Control Samples** | |
| Solvent Blank | Monitors instrument contamination during analysis |
| Initial Calibration Verification (ICV) | A calibration check using reference standards obtained from a different source than those used for the initial calibration |
| Continuing Calibration Verification (CCV) | A sample containing a known concentration of a reference standard used to confirm the ongoing calibration of an instrument, often run before and after an analytical batch |

FIGURE 49: HOW DOES A LAB KNOW THAT ITS RESULTS ARE ACCURATE AND PRECISE?

# Understanding Laboratory Quality Controls

There are distinct types of samples that laboratories use to monitor the accuracy and precision of their data. These QC samples are broken down into batch specific, sample specific, and instrument specific samples.

## BATCH-SPECIFIC QUALITY CONTROL SAMPLES

Batch specific quality control samples may be prepared and analyzed alongside every batch of prepared samples to monitor contamination, accuracy, and precision. If a batch-specific QC measure is unsatisfactory, it disqualifies the entire batch and all the affected samples must be re-prepared.

### METHOD BLANK

A method blank is quality control sample which monitors whether any analyte contamination is occurring during the sample preparation process. A sample that is known to have zero analytes of interest is prepared in the typical fashion as a normal sample would be prepared. The sample is analyzed, and the results should reveal that no analytes of interest are present. If the method blank reveals significant levels of target analytes, like cannabinoids, the laboratory must review their sample preparation procedures, identify the source of contamination, and re-prepare and re-analyze all samples associated with the failed method blank.

### LABORATORY CONTROL SAMPLE (LCS)/LCS DUPLICATE

A laboratory control sample consists of a sample that contains known concentrations of target analytes. Sometimes this is a sample that is spiked with chemicals at certain concentrations. Other times, an LCS may simply be a well characterized material that the laboratory uses as a reference. An LCS is run for every analytical batch. If the LCS is determined to be "out-of-control", meaning that it falls out of the lab's specifications, then the entire associated batch of samples must be re-prepared and re-analyzed. A second LCS may be prepared for an analytical batch to measure ongoing precision.

## SAMPLE-SPECIFIC QUALITY CONTROL SAMPLES

Laboratories also utilize a series of other quality control sample types to gain insight about specific samples and sample types, monitoring things like matrix effects. **Matrix effects** are effects unique to the sample type that affect the quality of analytical results. For instance, if a laboratory is testing a new sample type that they have never seen before, like a Cannabis infused candy, they might include sample-specific quality control samples which monitor whether the applied method is properly extracting all the cannabinoids from the candy. If the quality control sample reveals that the lab's recovery of cannabinoids is too low, a different method would have to be used.

Some of the sample-specific quality control sample types are described below.

## MATRIX SPIKE/MATRIX SPIKE DUPLICATE

A matrix spike is specific to a sample and identifies interfering matrix effects that limit the ability to effectively extract analytes of interest from the sample. Typically, a client sample is chosen at random and prepared in duplicate. One sample will be prepared like usual and the other will be spiked with known concentrations of a reference standard. The results of the spiked and un-spiked sample will be compared to determine how efficiently the target compounds were recovered. Sometimes a duplicate spiked sample will be prepared to also measure precision.

## MATRIX DUPLICATE

A matrix duplicate is another sample specific QC sample. A matrix duplicate is simply a duplicate preparation of a sample of a particular type. Labs typically prepare at least one matrix duplicate for each matrix type featured in an analytical batch. For instance, if a lab is analyzing Cannabis flowers and extracts, they would prepare a duplicate of a flower sample and a duplicate of an extract sample. The results of the duplicate samples are compared to ensure they are precise.

# INSTRUMENT-SPECIFIC QUALITY CONTROL SAMPLES

In addition to batch-specific and sample-specific quality control samples, laboratories also utilize instrument-specific quality control samples, which monitor instrument performance and look for signs of contamination or loss of calibration. These types of samples are generally run with every analytical batch of samples. Some of the primary instrument-specific quality control sample types are described below.

## SOLVENT BLANK

The solvent blank is a way of measuring instrument contamination and actively cleaning instrumentation. Solvent blanks are simply preparations of clean solvent which are analyzed to determine if any analytes have been left behind in the instrument from a prior analysis. This is particularly important for contaminant screenings like residual solvent and pesticide screenings. If instruments are not carefully monitored with solvent blanks, contaminants may build up in the instrument and the instrument may start reporting false positives.

## INITIAL CALIBRATION VERIFICATION (ICV)

An ICV is a sample used to test the initial calibration of an instrument and is typically a reference standard obtained from a secondary source or secondary lot. This helps to ensure that the initial reference standard was trustworthy, and the established calibration curve is reliable.

## CONTINUING CALIBRATION VERIFICATION (CCV)

A CCV is another instrument specific QC sample. CCVs are typically pure reference standards, formulated to a known concentration, which are used to monitor instrument performance throughout an analytical run. Usually, a CCV will be placed at the beginning (initial CCV) and end (final CCV) of an analytical run with the expectation that the results will match the expected target concentration. If a CCV is out of control, the lab must examine the instrument and determine whether maintenance or recalibration is required.

## WHY DO TEST RESULTS VARY ACROSS LABS?

States that have legalized Cannabis and instituted mandatory product testing are beginning to see stark discrepancies across laboratories. Products seem to receive widely different potency results across laboratories. A report released in 2018 revealed that there was a huge variance in potency values produced by Cannabis testing labs in the state of Washington.[476] The authors found that the chemotypes attributed to different strain names can vary substantially across laboratories – which is likely attributable to issues related to the "strain" concept discussed in earlier chapters of this book. Namely, strain names are largely unreliable, and plants can exhibit unique chemical profiles depending on environmental effects and genetic variability associated with seed propagation. It is easy to imagine that a variety of plants might receive the same strain identification, even if they are not genetically identical.

This report also discovered that among the laboratories investigated, some laboratories consistently reported high potency values, while others consistently reported low values, as compared to the overall spread of data analyzed. This sort of trend leads consumers to "number shop" – looking for laboratories that tend to report higher THC values than others. Overall, this behavior leads to distorted data sets that make it difficult for researchers to work with and abstract meaningful insight. This trend also reveals that it's not just the heterogeneity of the products that is to blame for the disparities seen across testing labs.

The authors of the 2018 report comment that after controlling for various confounding variables, "these results suggest that the observed differences between laboratories cannot be explained by differences in the producers, product types, or strain names of the samples being processed by each lab." This means, then, that the variability must come from details in a laboratory's protocols or quality system. Until greater quality standards are placed on testing laboratories, it will be impossible to ascertain whether an appreciable level of variability for Cannabis and cannabinoid product potency will remain.

Because of the discrepancies seen across laboratories, it is recommended that if you are a producer trying to collect data for product or process improvement, you should carefully vet laboratories and choose a lab that you trust. After picking a laboratory, stick with that laboratory throughout a project – otherwise you might end up with a bunch of data that is impossible to compare.

## HOW CAN CANNABIS TESTING GO WRONG?

There are many ways in which Cannabis testing can go wrong. When trying to find a good Cannabis testing laboratory to work with, it is important to understand some of the common ways in which Cannabis testing can become compromised so that you can ask your lab probing questions to identify the quality of work that they are providing or claiming to provide. The following are some of the most common ways

---

[476] Jikomes N, Zoorob M. The Cannabinoid Content of Legal Cannabis in Washington State Varies Systematically Across Testing Facilities and Popular Consumer Products. Sci Rep. 2018 Mar 14;8(1):4519. https://doi.org/10.1038/s41598-018-22755-2 Erratum in: Sci Rep. 2020 Aug 27;10(1):14406.

that Cannabis testing can go wrong in the laboratory followed by some questions that you should ask when deciding whether to use a laboratory's services or not.

## Improper Total THC or Total CBD Calculation

When analyzing Cannabis for potency using a High-Pressure Liquid Chromatograph (HPLC), the results include the carboxylic acid forms of the cannabinoids, including THCA, CBDA, and CBCA, among others. To determine the total THC, the THCA and the THC are combined. It is tempting, but incorrect, to simply add them without applying the **decarboxylation correction factor**. Failure to use this conversion factor could be a sign of incompetence and unreliability, or an attempt to boost result numbers.

When the cannabinoid acids are heated and decarboxylated, they lose $CO_2$, and become lighter molecules. All in all, approximately 10-12% of the weight of a cannabinoid is lost after decarboxylation. So, 20% THCA (200 mg/g) becomes approximately 17% THC (170 mg/g) after decarboxylation. This conversion factor is approximately 0.88 and can be found throughout scientific literature, however you can calculate this correction factor yourself by simply dividing the molecular weight of THC (314.45 g/mol) by the molecular weight of THCA (358.47 g/mol) to reach the value 0.877 (314.45/358.47 = 0.877). In other words, THC is 87.7% of the mass of THCA.

Always pay close attention to cannabinoid test results produced via HPLC and ensure that the Total THC and Total CBD calculations are utilizing the proper decarboxylation correction factor and not simply adding up the carboxylic acid cannabinoids and neutral cannabinoids together.

## Low Decarboxylation or Vaporization Efficiency (GC)

When a gas chromatograph is running, the first thing that occurs is a sample is injected into an inlet port where the sample is then quickly vaporized. This step is critical because if the sample is not vaporized at the proper temperature, the cannabinoid acids will not properly decarboxylate, resulting in dramatically low result numbers.

It is important for labs using gas chromatography to determine their decarboxylation efficiency to determine the accuracy of the equipment and the need for any corrections to be applied to the result. This can be done by taking a sample and manually decarboxylating half of it while preparing the other half as usual. Both samples are run through the machine and the difference is calculated. This is repeated multiple times to determine the decarboxylation efficiency.

At the time of this writing, most Cannabis testing labs are moving away from measuring cannabinoids with gas chromatographs, so the decarboxylation efficiency problem is becoming less significant. However, this issue is also related to the measurement of other Cannabis compounds, like terpenoids. This is especially true if the laboratory is using a headspace sampling method, instead of a liquid injection. If measuring terpenoids using a headspace sampler, it is important to ensure that the volatilization of terpenes in the sample is adequate, otherwise the results obtained may be biased toward the terpenes with the lightest weight (and thus easiest to volatize) and heavier terpenes in the sample, like sesquiterpenoids, diterpenoids, etc, may be left behind.

## Measuring "Ghost Peaks"

After repeated analyses on an instrument, residues may build up if certain components are not cleaned or replaced. If this happens, the instrument's detector will detect not only the sample passing through, but the leftover residues in the machine as well, leading to exaggerated results, or "ghost peaks." To avoid this, routine maintenance and servicing is necessary. Labs should also utilize "blank" injections of known clean solvent to detect ghost peaks before running any samples. If you are concerned about ghost peaks, simply ask your lab how they monitor and prevent instrument contamination or "analyte carryover".

## Co-Eluting, or "Stacked" Peaks

When using relatively simple analytical techniques, like GC or HPLC, it is sometimes easy to be fooled into thinking that you are looking at one peak on your chromatogram, when in reality that peak represents two or more compounds that are similar enough in their chemistry that they passed through the instrument's detector at the same time, forming one giant peak. This is called "coelution." This is particularly a problem with measuring terpenoids, because there are a lot of them at similar weights and chemical configurations, but this is also an issue with cannabinoids. It is important when a lab is validating a testing method that they go to extra lengths to confirm that the peaks that they see on their chromatograms actually only represent a single compound each.

## Lack of Reference Standards or Adequate Quality Controls

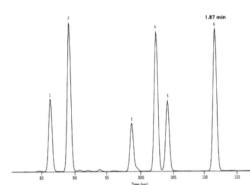

It is essential that laboratories use quality assurance practices, including quality control samples and reference standards, to monitor the accuracy of analysis results. A cannabinoid **reference standard** is a specially formulated sample that has a known concentration of cannabinoids present in it. When tests are run, the results can be compared and calibrated with the results of the reference standard to determine whether the instrument is performing correctly. Reference standards can be "spiked" onto a sample to measure how well an analytical method is "recovering" the target compounds.

For pesticide analysis quality control, for example, a sample is spiked with a known amount of pesticide. When the sample is analyzed, the result for that pesticide should correlate with the amount calculated to have been added to the sample. If it is off, the lab knows to examine their processes for sources of error.

It is tempting to try and produce results without using reference standards, especially for laboratories utilizing mass spectrometry which compares results against a database to tentatively identify compounds. However, it is entirely possible for mass spectra libraries to be inadequate for identifying compounds, or alternatively tentative chemical matches may be of such a low quality that they cannot be trusted with any high degree of confidence.

When evaluating laboratories, always ask them if they utilize reference standards for all the compounds that are measured and reported.

## MANIPULATING CHROMATOGRAM PEAKS

One way that laboratories can fudge numbers is by manipulating the way that the instrument's computer software interprets the chromatogram peaks. It is possible to boost cannabinoid results, for instance, by redefining the amount of area on the graph that is representative of THC or CBD. This is why traceable records and auditing are important to ensure that laboratories are held accountable for the data they produce. Auditors are very sensitive to instances of "manual integration" of chromatogram peaks and require that laboratories maintain pre and post edit versions of any chromatograms that are manipulated along with the edit date, the initials of the editor, and a rationale for the edit. Manual integrations are a common activity in labs and do not necessarily indicate nefarious behavior but repeated manual integration without a proper rationale is cause for concern.

## USE OF EXCESSIVELY LENIENT QUALITY CONTROL PARAMETERS

It is entirely possible for a laboratory to have quality control parameters in place, but still deliver poor results, if those parameters are set too generously so that the laboratory allows itself a wide margin of error. For instance, a laboratory may allow technicians to use a standardized sample mass for result corrections, rather than the sample's actual mass, if that mass is within a certain range. A laboratory could say that if a weighed sample falls between 175 to 225mg, the result is corrected for a sample mass of 200mg. This would then allow technicians to consistently weigh samples under the standardized correction, ultimately causing results to be higher than they should be.

Other examples relate to other thresholds like accuracy and precision measurements. A laboratory could make their acceptable analyte recovery limits quite wide so that they never have an analytical batch that falls out of compliance with their own quality control parameters. This kind of behavior is particularly common in unregulated laboratory industries in states that have recently legalized medical or recreational cannabis, where laboratories testing Cannabis are not under scrutiny of third party or government agency auditors.

## IMPROPER SAMPLING AND HANDLING OF SAMPLE MATERIAL

A common way that Cannabis testing goes awry is at the time of sampling and sample preparation. Client-provided samples tend to be the most cherry-picked samples from the available lot, perhaps not really representing an average of the lot. In addition, laboratories may feel pressure to manipulate samples by removing stems and trimming away excess plant material prior to sample preparation, further manipulating the final result. In some cases, laboratories have reported that samples have been received demonstrating unambiguous evidence of adulteration or manipulation, often in the form of inflorescences that have been sprinkled with sifted trichomes to boost cannabinoid content.

Great care must be taken while handling samples in the lab. Sterile gloves are used to avoid physical contact with the sample while also avoiding microbiological contamination. Our hands produce oils which mix with the oily trichomes of Cannabis, potentially manipulating the sample, if handled without gloves. If sample material comes into contact with an unsterile surface, the material must be discarded.

Samples must be well-mixed, or **homogenized**, before being prepared. If a sample is not properly mixed, or if a sample is "cherry picked", the analysis results might not be representative of the sample or the batch from which the sample was collected. For instance, when grinding up a Cannabis inflorescence, the trichomes are likely to dry sift to the bottom of the pile. If an analyst were to use the top portion of this sample in a potency preparation, they would get a lower result than if they tested the bottom of the pile. To avoid this problem, special homogenization equipment or methods for grinding samples within sterile test tubes is utilized so no material is lost or misrepresented.

## QUESTIONS TO ASK A LAB

In a September 2003 issue of *Natural Products Insider*, Dr. Steven Dentali, PhD published a list of ten questions[477] to ask an analytical laboratory that are just as relevant to Cannabis testing laboratories as they are to any other natural products laboratory. Here is a summary of those questions:

Is your lab certified/accredited? If so, by what accrediting body?

Do you outsource any analyses? If so, to whom? What quality controls do you have in place to ensure my samples are not contaminated by any subcontracted facilities?

What are the credentials of the lab's staff? How much experience do they have performing these sorts of analyses?

What systems do you use for recording and managing data?

How long would my raw data be stored and is the data available upon request?

Do you use validated methodologies for analyses and are method and procedural summaries available to review upon request? How do you validate your methods?

Do you have established laboratory instrument maintenance, servicing, and calibration schedules? Are these activities documented?

How are samples stored and protected from contamination?

What are typical turn-around times for each analysis? Will turn-around-times vary depending on the time of year?

How do you assure the validity of results if I am suspicious or unhappy with a result?

Keep in mind that these are just some of the questions you could ask to quickly evaluate a laboratory. After reading this chapter, what other questions might you ask your local laboratory?

---

[477] https://www.naturalproductsinsider.com/labstesting/choosing-analytical-lab

# Enduring Understandings

- Cannabis testing laboratories typically provide services to evaluate the potency and purity of Cannabis and Cannabis infused products.
- Some of the common tests performed by Cannabis testing laboratories are cannabinoids analyses, terpenoid analyses, microbiological testing, pesticide testing, metals testing, residual solvent testing, and sex testing.
- Chromatography is a process of separating a mixture into its unique chemical constituents.
- Mass spectrometry is a way of analyzing chemicals by evaluating the effects that their weight has on the trajectory of the chemical as it passes by a magnet.
- Polymerase chain reaction (PCR) is a technology used to amplify and measure DNA to detecting the presence of micro-organisms or particular genes.
- Analytical laboratories can utilize a variety of quality control methods to measure their own accuracy and precision.
- Due to product heterogeneity, natural batch-to-batch variation, lack of standardized methods across laboratories, and a lack of standardized sample methods, results across laboratories and across regions of the world can differ substantially.

# Chapter 19:
## CERTIFICATES OF ANALYSIS

---

### Learning Questions

- What information is commonly found on a Cannabis COA?
- What does LOQ mean?
- What happens if someone disagrees with a lab's test results?
- How can Cannabis test results be converted to other units of measurement?

---

If you have ever had any Cannabis or Cannabis product tested by a laboratory for potency or contaminants, you have inevitably been faced with the task of deciphering a laboratory's "**certificate of analysis**", sometimes referred to as a "C of A", but more often referred to as a test report. These reports feature technical jargon, graphs, a myriad of numbers, interpretations, narrations, and a lot of other data.

Usually when someone is faced with a Cannabis test report, they ultimately want to know a few very basic things:

- What are the Total THC and Total CBD values?
- Were any contaminants detected?
- If so, what contaminants were detected and in what concentrations?

However, finding this seemingly simple information is not always so straightforward. Lab results can feature any assortment of technical jargon, columns of seemingly irrelevant data, and qualifier codes that appear to only have meaning to the laboratory, not the customer. Throughout this chapter, topics will be reviewed related to interpreting a Cannabis test report to identify some short-cuts to finding the information you need.

### FIND THE PRIMARY INFORMATION

The first thing you should do when reviewing a test report is hunt down the primary pieces of data that answer your big question(s). If you ordered a potency analysis, immediately **search for the results for THC, THCA, Total THC, CBD, CBDA, and/or Total CBD**. If you ordered a contaminants screening, find the appropriate analysis section and **determine if any results other than "ND", "None Detected" or "<LOQ" are listed.** If "<LOQ" is listed for some analytes, while others are listed as "ND" or "<LOD", then the lab may have detected trace amounts of the analyte in concentrations above the lab's limit of detection, but not above their limit of quantitation.

If there were any values listed for any contaminants, review those values and determine what units the values are being reported. For bacterial and fungal analyses, results are typically reported as **CFU/g**, or colony forming units per gram. Pesticide and residual solvent results are typically reported as **PPM**, or parts per million. Terpenoid and cannabinoid results are often reported as **%** w/w, or percent concentration by weight.

# COMMON TERMS FOUND ON CANNABIS TEST REPORTS

| Term | Description |
|------|-------------|
| **LOD** | Limit of Detection; The laboratory's lowest concentration that they can confidently detect |
| **LOQ** | Limit of Quantitation; The laboratory's lowest concentration that they can confidently detect and report – usually slightly higher than the LOD. |
| **ND** | "Not Detected" or "None Detected"; Indicates the lack of identified presence of something |
| **Dry Weight** | Dry weight results represent the concentration of the total dry, non-water, components of the sample. Dry weight results provide more value than wet weight results because dry weight results can always be corrected by moisture content to determine actual concentration of a sample. |
| **Action Level** | Concentration of an analyte required at which a sample "fails" for regulatory compliance or some other action is required |
| **%** | Percent; Parts per hundred; 1/100 |
| **ppm** | Parts per million; 1/1,000,000 |
| **ppb** | Parts per billion; 1/1,000,000,000 |
| **ppt** | Parts per trillion; 1/1,000,000,000,000 |
| **g** | Gram |
| **mg** | Milligram; 0.001g |
| **mL** | Milliliter; 0.001 L |
| **mg/g** | Milligram per gram; commonly used when reporting results for manufactured products |
| **mg/mL** | Milligrams per milliliter; commonly used when reporting results for liquid products; calculated by multiplying the mg/g result by the product's density in g/mL |
| **mg/unit** | Milligrams per unit; commonly used when reporting results for manufactured products; calculated by multiplying the mg/g result by the unit mass in grams |
| **CFU** | Colony Forming Units; Represent colonies identified on cultures which may be caused either by spores or living microbiological organisms present in the sample |
| **CFU/g** | Colony Forming Units per gram; Represents the number of colonies formed on a culture from one gram of sample. |
| **TIC** | Tentatively Identified Compound; a compound that was identified using mass spectrometry but not verified using reference standards. |

FIGURE 50: GUIDE TO COMMON TERMS FOUND ON CANNABIS TEST REPORTS

## EVALUATE THE RESULTS

Actual values should be reported for quantitative analyses, rather than a simple "pass/fail" designation. There are good reasons for this. For example, assume that there is a limit of 10,000 cfu/g of yeasts or molds allowed in Cannabis. **A pass/fail system for reporting microbiological results would not distinguish between Cannabis with non-detectable mold levels from a contaminated batch with 9900 cfu/g of black mold** – just below the allowable limit. Almost assuredly buyers at wholesalers and dispensaries would take such a discrepancy into consideration when deciding what product to purchase, however a pass/fail system of result reporting prevents such an informed decision-making process.

Test results should also be examined for **Tentatively Identified Compounds (TICs)**. These are usually seen in pesticide, residual solvent, or terpene analyses that use mass spectrometers and mass spectra libraries to identify compounds. **These values, usually of trace concentrations of compounds, are not truly quantitative or properly** identified, however, until they have been verified against a chemical reference standard.

### How did the lab calculate "Total" THC, CBD, CBG, etc?

When reviewing cannabinoid potency results, it is important to determine how the "Total THC" and "Total CBD" values are calculated by the lab. First, look to see if the certificate of analysis notes what instrumentation was used for each analysis. If the instrument used for potency is an HPLC, immediately check to see if the **decarboxylation conversion factor** was applied to the THCA concentration to calculate total potential THC. When the decarboxylation factor is not applied correctly, the result becomes exaggerated, sometimes quite substantially.

As mentioned in previous chapters, decarboxylation refers to the process by which a carbon dioxide, or $CO_2$, group is removed from a carboxylic acid compound. When a bunch of THCA is decarboxylated to THC, a significant amount of weight is lost due to the loss of the $CO_2$. This is why it is inaccurate to simply add THCA and THC to calculate available or potential THC.

This is the proper equation for calculating total THC:

%THC + (%THCA x 0.877) = Max/Total THC

The decarboxylation factor is calculated by dividing the weight of the lighter compound by the weight of the heavier compound. For instance, the molecular weight of THC is 314.45 g/mol while the weight of THCA is 358.473 g/mol. Dividing these weights results in **0.877**, or an ~88% loss. For each compound, these decarboxylation factors might be slightly different, but for cannabinoids most of them are right around 0.88. So, all in all, around 12% of the total weight of THCA is lost once it is heated and decarboxylated to THC.

## Max/Total THC Calculation

Using the following THC and THCA values, calculate the total or max THC.

THCA: 16.8%       THC: 3.4%       Max or Total THC: _____%

| Cannabinoid | Molecular Weight | Neutral Molecular Weight | Decarboxylation Correction Factor |
|---|---|---|---|
| THCA | 358.478 | 314.469 | 0.877 (87.7%) |
| CBDA | 358.5 | 314.464 | 0.877 (87.7%) |
| CBGA | 360.5 | 316.48 | 0.878 (87.8%) |
| CBCA | 358.5 | 314.46 | 0.877 (87.7%) |
| CBNA | 354.4 | 310.4319 | 0.876 (87.6%) |
| THCVA | 330.42 | 286.41 | 0.867 (86.7%) |
| CBDVA | 330.42 | 286.41 | 0.867 (86.7%) |

## What Do They Mean by "Total Cannabinoids"?

It is common to see a value referred to as "total cannabinoids" on test reports from Cannabis testing laboratories. It is important to understand that there is not a Cannabis testing laboratory in operation that is reporting results for all 100+ cannabinoids that have been identified in Cannabis. For one thing, commercial labs cannot even obtain reference standards for most of them. At best, a Cannabis testing laboratory will report somewhere between 10 and 15 cannabinoids. For this reason, any value labeled as "total cannabinoids" is a bit misleading because it can only include the cannabinoids that the lab is actually quantifying. Don't be fooled by this specter of a test result.

## Are Results In Dry Weight or Wet Weight?

Sometimes a certificate of analysis might show two separate cannabinoid or terpenoid results, one for wet weight, and one for dry. In the natural products industry, results for the analysis of things like terpenes, vitamins, or cannabinoids are typically reported as dry matter. **Dry matter** refers to all the solids of a material, or everything that is not water. When a natural product is measured for vitamin content, for example, the concentration that is reported is the concentration of *solids* in the plant material that are vitamins.

To determine dry weight results, laboratories often either calculate each sample's moisture content or use a standardized procedure for drying samples completely before analysis, usually by using a programmable dehydrator or temperature-controlled oven.  One way to measure the moisture content of a sample is to track the mass of a sample as it dries until the sample mass stabilizes. Then the starting weight and final weight can be compared to calculate the moisture content.

This process of calculating moisture content through tracking the mass during drying is called "loss on drying."  In addition, the length of time of drying and temperature may be tracked. A standardized drying temperature and time can be calculated and used to ensure all samples reach proper desiccation regardless of starting moisture content. There are other methods of measuring moisture content using various chemical reactions such as Karl Fisher titrations or sophisticated moisture content analytical equipment such as a moisture balance, which automates the loss on drying process.

**The analyte concentration of a dry sample will always be slightly higher than in a wet sample**. This is not because there are any fewer total molecules of cannabinoids present in the sample when it is wet compared to when it is dry, but rather because more of the total weight of the sample has become water, thus manipulating the overall concentration of cannabinoids by mass of the sample. The following pie charts demonstrate this change.

Wet weight corrections are most commonly seen in the pharmaceutical industry because slight changes in weight can have significant consequences when working with highly potent compounds consumed in very small quantities, like powdered drugs.

If both wet weight and dry weight results are listed on a certificate, try to find out how the dry weight correction was determined. Was the analysis performed on the wet sample and then adjusted to represent dry weight, or was the analysis performed on a dry sample and then adjusted to represent a wet sample? How were these adjustments performed? Was the samples true moisture content calculated, or was an assumed moisture content used?

The moisture level of a sample is often thought of as a predictor for microbial contaminants, but this not quite correct, because the water in a sample varies in its availability to microbial organisms like fungi and bacteria. The water in a sample is chemically "bound", or stuck in place, to varying degrees. A sample can potentially have significant water content, but the water could be very immobile and thus unavailable to microbes. This is why measuring **water activity,** or the mobility of water in a sample, is important. Water activity is measured by sealing a sample in a chamber and then measuring the humidity of the air in the chamber over time until it stabilizes.

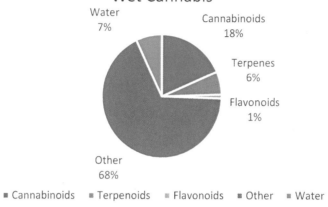

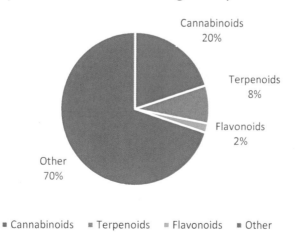

FIGURE 51: WET VS DRY WEIGHT CONCENTRATIONS OF CANNABIS COMPOUNDS

## WHO CERTIFIED THE RESULTS?

Other things to note include **the identity of the representative certifying the certificates of analysis**. This person should be able to attest to the validity of the results. A disconnected party does not satisfy this requirement. This signature should be by someone who is managing the lab or reviewing and verifying results as they are produced, as required by ISO and NELAC standards. **The date of the analysis** should also be noted. A certificate of analysis is only valid for a determined length of time set by the lab. Typically, this is approximately ninety days. After the validity date, the batch should be retested to produce a more accurate snapshot of the chemical profile of the material after long term storage.

## DISPUTING TEST RESULTS WITH A LAB

It is common for anyone getting Cannabis testing performed regularly to run into situations where one might want to better understand the results or dispute the results of a testing lab. Most professional laboratories serving Cannabis clients will be happy to address concerns that may arise from laboratory results. Typically, the reasons that test result disputes arise is because of a less-than-expected potency value or an unexpected pesticide detection.

## HANDLING UNEXPECTED POTENCY RESULTS

Potency result discrepancies may be caused by any number of reasons. Sometimes a CBD:THC ratio of a Cannabis flower may be different than what is typical for the associated cultivar, or "strain". Sometimes this may be due to unexpected genetic variability, especially in seed cultivation. Other times strains may be incorrectly labeled, leading the cultivator to expect a particular chemotype of resin yield which it simply cannot produce. The following are more factors that may affect the cannabinoid potency of a Cannabis flower sample:

- Excess leaf (untrimmed or lightly trimmed Cannabis)
- Excess moisture (if lab does not report results in dry weight)
- Excess stem
- Sampling conditions (random vs. client provided; homogeneity)
- Premature harvest

Keep in mind that when dealing with natural products like Cannabis flowers, it is completely normal to see some mild variation in potency results. If a Cannabis batch is tested by three different labs and the three labs report the total THC as 21%, 17%, and 19% respectively - these are considered to be essentially the same result and is *not* indicative of foul play or inadequate laboratory method standardization.

Sometimes the manufacturing of Cannabis extracts can produce unexpected results, particularly regarding distillation. The result that many Cannabis distillate manufacturers have learned is that a distilled product may be anywhere from 30% to over 80% pure, which seems counterintuitive. When a distillate manufacturer receives a test result revealing that the product is only 30% THC or CBD, it leaves them scratching their head. The answers to this enigma can be found in the lab's chromatograms for the distillate sample.

A close inspection of a distillate sample's chromatogram typically reveals a variety of "mystery peaks", representing unique chemical compounds in the distillate which were not present in either the beginning flower, or intermediate extract. Throughout the course of the distillate production process, the Cannabis resin is exposed to a variety of temperatures, pressures, stirring, oxygen, and light – all of which provide conditions suitable for chemical reactions to take place in the extract. Scientists are still in the process of identifying exactly what these compounds are, with many speculating that they are various THC or CBD isomers.

If you suspect that a potency result that you have received from a lab is incorrect, ask to meet with the lab director or other available lab representative to review your results with you. The lab should be able to share what quality controls were in place to ensure the validity of your result. Alternatively, if there is sufficient cause to doubt the validity of the initial result, the laboratory may reanalyze the sample to confirm the initial result.

## UNEXPECTED PESTICIDE OR SOLVENT RESULTS

Unexpected pesticide results often arise from the use of systemic or translaminar pesticides. These pesticide types linger for prolonged periods of time in the plant, potentially appearing in detectable concentrations months after application. Sometimes pesticide contamination occurs from sources such as run-off from neighboring farms, airborne pollution, contact with clothing that has previously come in contact with pesticides, or even from the use of irrigation supplies which have come into contact with pesticides. It is important to rule out all sources of pesticide contamination prior to contesting a pesticide detection result. Sometimes agrochemical products might even feature unlabeled active pesticides.

A lab error that could be responsible for false positive pesticide detections in Cannabis is pesticide residue carryover in the analytical instrument used to test the samples. If a sample that is contaminated with pesticides is run prior to a "clean" sample, it is possible for traces of those pesticides from the first sample to linger in the instrument and pass through during the analysis of the "clean" sample. Typically, laboratories have various quality control measures in place to detect these kinds of phenomenon including running clean solvent blanks periodically throughout analyses to detect residual pesticides in the instrument.

## COMMON CAUSES OF UNEXPECTED POTENCY RESULTS

| Sample Type | Common Causes | Remedy |
|---|---|---|
| Flowers | Excess leaf and stem; Excess moisture; Premature harvest | Trim flowers adequately; Dry flowers until stems snap when bent; Monitor cannabinoid concentration in plant using thin layer chromatography or other technique during flowering to optimize harvest time |
| Distillates | Exposure to excess heat, light, oxygen; Inadequate system parameters | Ensure extraction process is tightly controlled with all systems properly sealed off from exposure to light and air; Avoid excess heat |
| Edibles | Using volume vs mass for recipes; No test results for feedstock; Ignoring density conversions; Ingredients with co-eluting compounds (i.e. essential oils) | Always use *mass*, rather than volume, for product recipes requiring precise dosages; Always have Cannabis flower or extract ingredients tested to properly calculate recipes; If the edible is a liquid, always have the lab convert your potency result from % or mg/g to mg/mL based on the product's density; If using complex ingredients, send the lab samples of ingredients as well as "blanks" of the finished product without cannabinoids so the lab can make sure that none of the ingredients are causing any interference with cannabinoids |

FIGURE 52: COMMON CAUSES OF UNEXPECTED POTENCY RESULTS

A lab error that could be responsible for false positive solvent detections is solvent contamination associated with the cleaning of lab tools. It is a common habit for lab technicians to clean tools in between handling. However, if a sample is to be tested for the presence of solvents, it is critical that the laboratory *not* clean tools when handling samples. Instead, samples are cleaned ahead of time and often baked or dried to ensure they are free of solvent residue. Then the technician will use as many clean tools as needed to complete the job without performing any cleaning. If a tool becomes dirty, a new one is used. A laboratory should have detailed procedures for ensuring against and detecting solvent contamination at the time of sampling and sample preparation.

Should you suspect a false positive pesticide or solvent detection, ask to meet with the lab director or other lab representative to go over your results with you. The lab should be able to share with you any quality control information associated with your sample to prove that care was taken to avoid cross contamination and ensure the validity of the lab's results.

### COMMON CONVERSIONS AND CALCULATIONS

Once you have test results in hand, it might seem challenging to convert those results into something meaningful. For instance, let's say that I wanted to make my own batch of Cannabis infused brownies, using some of my recently harvested homegrown Fire OG variety of Cannabis. I send a sample to the lab and receive results revealing that my Cannabis is 20% THC. How does this tell me how much Cannabis to use in my recipe? How can I predict the final dosage of each brownie? To answer these and related questions, we must perform some basic conversions and calculations.

| What Kind of Potency Result Do You Need? | |
|---|---|
| **Product Type** | **Result Units** |
| Flower | % |
| Flower (to be used as ingredient) | Mg/g |
| Extract | % |
| Extract (to be used as ingredient) | Mg/g |
| Edible (solid) | Mg/g |
| Edible (liquid) | Mg/mL |

FIGURE 53: WHAT POTENCY RESULT FORMAT DO YOU NEED?

The rest of this chapter will explore many commonly utilized math conversions and dosage calculations which I highly recommend learning.

### HOW MANY MILLIGRAMS PER GRAM (MG/G)?

To properly produce consistent dosages, it is important to understand how to calculate how many milligrams of something, like THC, are in a product. Some test results may feature these conversions. Other times, you may need to perform the calculations yourself. Luckily, the math is not too complicated.

When dealing with percentages, it helps to break the word "percent" down and remember that you are dealing with numbers that are "per 100" (think "per century" if it helps). In other words, to convert a percentage to a fraction, you just take the number and divide it by 100. So, 25 percent THC also means 25 divided by 100, or 25/100. We want to measure milligrams, so we just add those units to form 25mg/100mg. We know we want our final units to be mg/g, so we need to get the bottom number of the fraction, or denominator, converted to grams. A gram (g) is comprised of 1000 milligrams (mg), so if we multiply 25mg/100mg by 10, we get 250mg/1000mg, or 250mg/g.

1g (gram) of Cannabis = 1000mg (milligrams)

25% THC = 250mg/g because 25% of 1000mg is 250mg.

25 *per***cent** (per 100) = 25/100 = 25mg/100mg = 250mg/1000mg = 250mg/g

And so, 16% THC = 160 mg/g

**SHORTCUT**: to convert percent to mg/g, simply multiply the percent number by 10. For example, 20% THC or CBD is equal to 200mg/g THC or CBD.

### How Many Milligrams Per Milliliter (mg/mL)?

To find out how many milligrams are in a liquid Cannabis product like a tincture, you may need to convert the potency result from percent to milligrams (mg) per milliliter (mL). To do this, you must first know the approximate **density** of the product. A Cannabis infused tincture will primarily consist of ethanol. The known density of pure ethanol is 0.789g/mL. This means that every 1mL of ethanol weighs 0.789 grams.

A product's mass per volume is its density and is often reported in grams per milliliter (g/mL). This means that **an accurately measured milliliter of the product should be weighed to determine its weight per milliliter**. This measurement must be accurate; otherwise, any potency calculations made with it will be exaggerated.

To convert a potency result from percent to mg/mL, all you have to do is to calculate the mg/g result and then multiply that number by the product density. For instance, if a tincture contained 3% THC, it could then be determined that it contained 30mg/g THC. Assuming the product's density is 0.789g/mL, because it is primarily ethanol, we can multiply 30mg/g THC by 0.789g/mL to get 23.67mg of THC per mL of tincture.

| Solvent | Density (g/mL) |
|---|---|
| Ethanol | 0.789 |
| Everclear (95%) | 0.8 |
| Everclear (75%) | 0.84 |
| Coconut Oil | 0.924 |
| Glycerin | 1.26 |
| Most Vegetable Oils | ~0.920 |
| Medium Chain Triglyceride (MCT) Oil | ~0.93-0.96 |
| **Measures of Mass (Solids)** | |
| 1 gram (g) | = 1000 milligrams (mg) |
| 1 kilogram (kg) | = 1000 grams |
| **Measures of Volume (Liquids)** | |
| 1 liter (L) | = 1000 milliliters (mL) |
| 1 deciliter (dL) | = 1/10 liter |

FIGURE 54: COMMON SOLVENT DENSITIES AND MEASUREMENT CONVERSIONS

# TYPICAL POTENCY RANGES FOR CANNABIS PRODUCTS

Disclaimer: The following information is meant only to serve as a general guide to some of the common trends found among the potencies of Cannabis products. There are always exceptions.

| Product Type | Typical Potency Range (Total THC or CBD) |
|---|---|
| Inflorescence (flower) | 5 – 25% |
| Cannabis Leaves (trim) | 1 – 8% |
| Tinctures and MCT Solutions | 0.1 – 10% |
| Edibles and Topicals | Highly variable; 5 – 1000mg per unit |
| Concentrates (sifted hash) | 30 - 50% |
| Concentrates (rosin) | 40 - 60%+ |
| Concentrates (reduced ethanolic extract) | 40 – 65%+ |
| Concentrates (CO2 extract) | 45 – 70%+ |
| Concentrates (butane, propane, etc) | 60 - 80%+ |
| Distillates | 70 – 90%+ |
| Isolate | 95%+ |

FIGURE 55: TYPICAL CANNABIS PRODUCT POTENCY RANGES

## INFLORESCENCE (FLOWERS)

The typical potency ranges for dried and cured Cannabis inflorescence is anywhere between 10% and 25%. It is common for flowers to fall somewhere between 13% and 25%. It is uncommon, though possible, to see flower potencies above 25%. It is very rare to find flowers that reach 30% or more. It is important to note that Cannabis potency values are influenced by the amount of leaf and stem present. Tightly trimmed "buds" will have higher potencies.

## EXTRACTS

Sifted forms of concentrated Cannabis extracts such as **Kief** and **Bubble hash** often feature total THC or total CBD potencies between 25% and 45%. The potency of desolvated ethanolic extracts, sometimes referred to by names like "**Rick Simpson Oil**" **(RSO)** or **FECO (Full Extract Cannabis Oil)**, typically range between 45% to 70% total THC or CBD. The potency values of these types of products are less than that of other concentrated extract types primarily because these extracts contain a wide variety of non-cannabinoid plant compounds like chlorophyll, flavonoids, glycoproteins, and more.

**BHO/PHO** concentrated extract products usually have a total THC or CBD potency somewhere between 55% and 85%. **$CO_2$ extracted resins** usually have total THC potencies between 40-55% on average prior to refinement. Winterized versions of these extracts will often reach potency values between 60% and 75%. **Distilled** and **isolated** extracts can sometimes reach purities of 85% or more. Cannabinoid **isolates** are usually found at purities of 95%+.

## How Does Extract Color Relate to Potency?

The color of a concentrate can *sometimes* be an indicator of cannabinoid content, but there are many exceptions. The higher the THC or CBD potency, usually the lighter in color and more transparent the product will be, in general. Cannabinoids themselves do not have much color, except for sometimes a very faint yellow or orange hue. Flavonoids, chlorophyll, quinones, and other compounds contribute colors like shades of green, red, yellow, and orange. Additionally, as an extract ages and the polyphenolic components of the extract oxidize, the color can change, usually becoming darker. Waxes and fats affect the clarity and viscosity of extract products, distorting light as it passes through the extract. Therefore, if a product does not feature excess compounds other than cannabinoids and terpenes, the product should be relatively free of color and less opaque.

Concentrates between 50% and 70% cannabinoid content often display amber to orange-yellow color, respectively. Concentrates usually exhibit a yellowish tint at around 80% concentration. At 90% or greater THC or CBD concentration, most color is gone, and only faint yellow and gold color remains.

However, this is not to say that all light colored or transparent concentrates must contain high concentrations of cannabinoids. Product color can be manipulated using different techniques like charcoal filtering, celite filtering or solvent washing. Some otherwise transparent concentrates may feature additional ingredients like terpenes which ultimately dilute the product's cannabinoid concentration while maintaining product clarity. Also, be aware that extracted oils can appear darker in color when contained in bulk but can actually be quite light in color and transparent when handled in small amounts.

To summarize, color can *sometimes* relate to potency, but it does not *always* directly correlate to potency.

## Edibles and Infused Products

**Potency results for edibles are usually reported in mg per g, mg per mL, mg per serving or mg per product** (brownie, sucker, chocolate, etc). The average potency of a Cannabis infused edible usually ranges between 0.1-6% THC or CBD by weight, or 1 to 60 mg/g. Many edible products are between 10 and 100 mg THC or CBD total, although there are some products available in legal Cannabis markets that range upwards to 1000 mg per serving.

The average potency of an edible is highly sensitive to product weight. 10 unique Cannabis infused suckers of the same production batch, even with adequate quality control, will each weigh differently. So, if the tested infused sucker is reported to contain 5mg/g of THC, the suckers could have a wide range of potencies, with a 5-gram sucker containing 25mg THC, but a 6.5 gram sucker in the same batch containing 32.5mg. That's a 77% increase in potency between suckers! This is a distinction that customers need to understand to achieve proper dosing.

| EXAMPLE OF POTENCY VARIABILITY IN A 5mg/g THC EDIBLE | | |
|---|---|---|
| | Sucker Weight (g) | Total mg THC |
| **Sucker 1** | 5 | 25 |
| **Sucker 2** | 6.5 | 32.5 |
| **Sucker 3** | 5.2 | 26 |
| **Sucker 4** | 4.8 | 24 |
| **Sucker 5** | 6.8 | 34 |
| **Total mg THC Range Throughout Batch** | | 24 – 34mg THC |

FIGURE 56: EXAMPLE OF POTENCY VARIABILITY IN A 5MG/G THC EDIBLE

**A more representative way of displaying potency values for edibles would probably be best as a _range_ of values**. For instance, the label for a brownie could indicate 60 ± 3 mg/brownie. This lets the consumer know that each of the brownies in the batch do not have the same potency due to their different weights and natural variations, but no brownie in the batch should contain more than 63 mg/g THC or less than 57 mg/g THC. This would allow consumers to prepare for potential worst-case scenarios if they happen to be particularly sensitive to the effects of THC.

## CANNABINOID RATIOS CAN TELL A STORY

Cannabinoid ratios can sometimes be used to determine certain qualitative information about the material. For instance, **THC breaks down into CBN when exposed to oxygen and heat**. If CBN is present in high concentrations in a sample, it could be possible that the material was stored improperly, and the THC has been breaking down. Likewise, CBD can break down to a compound called cannabinodiol, or CBND – which may have psychoactive effects like THC – although CBND has not been well studied.

This is one reason why it may be a good idea to retest Cannabis batches for potency every few months. A product that tests high in THC or CBD early after curing, might measure significantly lower after poor storage over time. The presence of CBG and CBGA can also tell the story of a Cannabis sample. CBGA is synthesized to THCA, CBDA, CBCA, and then later to THC, CBD, and CBC, thus **high CBG and/or CBGA content could be an indicator of premature harvesting or a genetic issue affecting the enzymes that convert CBGA to THCA and CBDA (unless the plant is a CBG dominant cultivar).**

**Additionally, various cannabinoids and terpenes may modulate the pharmacological effects of THC or CBD**. Some examples of compounds that might reduce the psychotropic effects of THC are CBD, CBG, CBC, and limonene. High CBN, myrcene, and linalool levels all demonstrate sedative activity in various studies indicating a potential utility for insomnia. Citrus compounds like limonene and nerolidol have been thought to demonstrate antidepressant effects like CBD and CBC. **The complex interactions between competing and complementing compounds are little understood, making it difficult to predict the efficacy of a Cannabis product in treating a health condition.** The more research reveals about these compounds and their synergies, the more qualitative information will be able to be drawn from lab test results.

331

TAGLEAF LABS // 123 FAKE ST FAKETOWN CA 12345 // PH: (123) 456-7890

CA LICENSE #: TL-0000001-LIC

## CERTIFICATE OF ANALYSIS

PRODUC-ID: MAR 24, 2021

**SAMPLE:** SAUCY GOODNESS (CONCENTRATE) // **CLIENT:** CURIOUS ABOUT CANNABIS // **BATCH:** PASS

**BATCH NO.:** IZ352829234
**LOT NO.** A7532
**MATRIX:** CONCENTRATE
**CATEGORY:** INHALABLE
**SAMPLE ID:** TAG-210324-001
**COLLECTED ON:** MAR 24, 2021
**RECEIVED ON:** MAR 24, 2021
**BATCH SIZE:** 1000 UNITS
**SAMPLE SIZE:** 13 UNITS
**PACKAGE SIZE:** 1 G
**SERVING SIZE:** 0.1 G

### CANNABINOID OVERVIEW

| | |
|---|---|
| $\Delta^9$-THC PER SERVING: | 1.45 mg |
| CBD PER SERVING: | 0.01 mg |
| TOTAL CANNABINOIDS: | 87.34 mg |

## MANUFACTURER INFO

**MANUFACTURER**
CAC MFG
710 CURIOUS ABOUT CANNABIS ROAD
CANNAVILLE, CA 92107

**LICENSE**
MFG09R372
ADULT-USE - MANUFACTURING
LICENSE

## DISTRIBUTOR INFO

**DISTRIBUTOR**
CAC DISTRIBUTION
710 CURIOUS ABOUT CANNABIS ROAD
CANNAVILLE, CA 92107

**LICENSE**
DL3252674
ADULT-USE - DISTRIBUTOR LICENSE

### BATCH RESULT: PASS

| | | | |
|---|---|---|---|
| POTENCY | PASS | MYCOTOXINS | PASS |
| FOREIGN | PASS | PESTICIDES | PASS |
| METALS | PASS | SOLVENTS | PASS |
| MICROBIAL | PASS | | |

## SOP-T02: CANNABINOID POTENCY BY HPLC-DAD // MAR 24, 2021

| ANALYTE | LIMIT | AMT | AMT | LOD/LOQ | PASS/FAIL | ANALYTE | LIMIT | AMT | AMT | LOD/LOQ | PASS/FAIL |
|---|---|---|---|---|---|---|---|---|---|---|---|
| CBC | | ND | ND | | N/A | TOTAL THC ** | | 72.689 % | 726.89 mg/g | | N/A |
| CBCA | | 0.300 % | 3.00 mg/g | | N/A | TOTAL CBD ** | | 0.405 % | 4.05 mg/g | | N/A |
| CBD | | 0.010 % | 0.10 mg/g | | N/A | CBD/SRV | | 0.01 mg | | | N/A |
| CBDA | | 0.450 % | 4.50 mg/g | | N/A | $\Delta^9$-THC/SRV | | 1.45 mg | | | N/A |
| CBG | | 0.400 % | 4.00 mg/g | | N/A | TOTAL CBD/SRV ** | | 0.41 mg | | | N/A |
| CBGA | | 3.500 % | 35.00 mg/g | | N/A | TOTAL THC/SRV ** | | 72.69 mg | | | N/A |
| CBN | | ND | ND | | N/A | CBD/PKG | | 0.10 mg | | | N/A |
| $\Delta^8$-THC | | ND | ND | | N/A | $\Delta^9$-THC/PKG | | 14.50 mg | | | PASS |
| $\Delta^9$-THC | | 1.450 % | 14.50 mg/g | | N/A | TOTAL CBD/PKG ** | | 4.05 mg | | | N/A |
| THCA | | 81.230 % | 812.30 mg/g | | N/A | TOTAL THC/PKG ** | | 726.89 mg | | | N/A |
| THCV | | ND | ND | | N/A | | | | | | |

** TOTAL THC = (THCA X 0.877) + THC
** TOTAL CBD = (CBDA X 0.877) + CBD

ALL LQC SAMPLES REQUIRED BY SECTION 5730 OF CALIFORNIA CODE OF
REGULATIONS TITLE 16 DIVISION 42 BUREAU OF CANNABIS CONTROL WERE
PERFORMED AND MET THE ACCEPTANCE CRITERIA.

: JANE SMITH, PHD
SCIENTIFIC DIRECTOR, TAGLEAF LABS
MAR 24, 2021

*Jane Smith*

**5OP-T06: PESTICIDE ANALYSIS BY GC-MS // MAR 24, 2021**

| ANALYTE | LIMIT | AMT (µg/g) | LOD/LOQ | PASS/FAIL | ANALYTE | LIMIT | AMT (µg/g) | LOD/LOQ | PASS/FAIL |
|---|---|---|---|---|---|---|---|---|---|
| CAPTAN | 0.7 µg/g | ND | | PASS | CYFLUTHRIN | 2 µg/g | ND | | PASS |
| CHLORDANE | Any amt | ND | | PASS | METHYL PARATHION | Any amt | ND | | PASS |
| CHLORFENAPYR | Any amt | ND | | PASS | PENTACHLORONI-TROBENZENE | 0.1 µg/g | ND | | PASS |

**5OP-T05: PESTICIDE ANALYSIS BY LC-MS // MAR 24, 2021**

| ANALYTE | LIMIT | AMT (µg/g) | LOD/LOQ | PASS/FAIL | ANALYTE | LIMIT | AMT (µg/g) | LOD/LOQ | PASS/FAIL |
|---|---|---|---|---|---|---|---|---|---|
| ABAMECTIN | 0.1 µg/g | ND | | PASS | MALATHION | 0.5 µg/g | ND | | PASS |
| ABAMECTIN BA | | ND | | N/A | MALATHION A | | ND | | N/A |
| ABAMECTIN BB | | ND | | N/A | METALAXYL | 2 µg/g | ND | | PASS |
| ACEPHATE | 0.1 µg/g | ND | | PASS | METHIOCARB | Any amt | ND | | PASS |
| ACEQUINOCYL | 0.1 µg/g | ND | | PASS | METHOMYL | 1 µg/g | ND | | PASS |
| ACETAMIPRID | 0.1 µg/g | ND | | PASS | MEVINPHOS | Any amt | ND | | PASS |
| ALDICARB | Any amt | ND | | PASS | MEVINPHOS I | | ND | | N/A |
| AZOXYSTROBIN | 0.1 µg/g | ND | | PASS | MEVINPHOS II | | ND | | N/A |
| BIFENAZATE | 0.1 µg/g | ND | | PASS | MYCLOBUTANIL | 0.1 µg/g | ND | | PASS |
| BIFENTHRIN | 3 µg/g | ND | | PASS | NALED | 0.1 µg/g | ND | | PASS |
| BOSCALID | 0.1 µg/g | ND | | PASS | OXAMYL | 0.5 µg/g | ND | | PASS |
| CARBARYL | 0.5 µg/g | ND | | PASS | PACLOBUTRAZOL | Any amt | ND | | PASS |
| CARBOFURAN | Any amt | ND | | PASS | PERMETHRIN | 0.5 µg/g | ND | | PASS |
| CHLORANTRANIL-IPROLE | 10 µg/g | ND | | PASS | PERMETHRIN CIS | | ND | | N/A |
| | | | | | PERMETHRIN TRANS | | ND | | N/A |
| CHLORPYRIFOS | Any amt | ND | | PASS | PHOSMET | 0.1 µg/g | ND | | PASS |
| CLOFENTEZINE | 0.1 µg/g | ND | | PASS | PIPERONYLBUTO-XIDE | 3 µg/g | ND | | PASS |
| COUMAPHOS | Any amt | ND | | PASS | | | | | |
| CYPERMETHRIN | 1 µg/g | ND | | PASS | PRALLETHRIN | 0.1 µg/g | ND | | PASS |
| DAMINOZIDE | Any amt | ND | | PASS | PROPICONAZOLE | 0.1 µg/g | ND | | PASS |
| DIAZINON | 0.1 µg/g | ND | | PASS | PROPOXUR | Any amt | ND | | PASS |
| DICHLORVOS | Any amt | ND | | PASS | PYRETHRINS | 0.5 µg/g | ND | | PASS |
| DIMETHOATE | Any amt | ND | | PASS | PYRETHRINS PYRETHRIN I | | ND | | N/A |
| DIMETHOMORPH | 2 µg/g | ND | | PASS | PYRETHRINS PYRETHRIN II | | ND | | N/A |
| DIMETHOMORPH I | | ND | | N/A | PYRIDABEN | 0.1 µg/g | ND | | PASS |
| DIMETHOMORPH II | | ND | | N/A | SPINETORAM | 0.1 µg/g | ND | | PASS |
| ETHOPROPHOS | Any amt | ND | | PASS | SPINETORAM J | | ND | | N/A |
| ETOFENPROX | Any amt | ND | | PASS | SPINETORAM L | | ND | | N/A |
| ETOXAZOLE | 0.1 µg/g | ND | | PASS | SPINOSAD | 0.1 µg/g | ND | | PASS |
| FENHEXAMID | 0.1 µg/g | ND | | PASS | SPINOSAD A | | ND | | N/A |
| FENOXYCARB | Any amt | ND | | PASS | SPINOSAD D | | ND | | N/A |
| FENPYROXIMATE | 0.1 µg/g | ND | | PASS | SPIROMESIFEN | 0.1 µg/g | ND | | PASS |
| FIPRONIL | Any amt | ND | | PASS | SPIROTETRAMAT | 0.1 µg/g | ND | | PASS |
| FLONICAMID | 0.1 µg/g | ND | | PASS | SPIROXAMINE | Any amt | ND | | PASS |
| FLUDIOXONIL | 0.1 µg/g | ND | | PASS | TEBUCONAZOLE | 0.1 µg/g | ND | | PASS |
| HEXYTHIAZOX | 0.1 µg/g | ND | | PASS | THIACLOPRID | Any amt | ND | | PASS |
| IMAZALIL | Any amt | ND | | PASS | THIAMETHOXAM | 5 µg/g | ND | | PASS |
| IMIDACLOPRID | 5 µg/g | ND | | PASS | TRIFLOXYSTROB-IN | 0.1 µg/g | ND | | PASS |
| KRESOXIM-METHYL | 0.1 µg/g | ND | | PASS | | | | | |

https://lims.tagleaf.com/coa_/dh203vbE8k

Page 2 of 3

333

# REGULATORY COMPLIANCE TESTING

## SOP-T10: STEC AND SALMONELLA BY QPCR // MAR 24, 2021

| ANALYTE | LIMIT | AMT (CFU) | PASS/FAIL | ANALYTE | LIMIT | AMT (CFU) | PASS/FAIL |
|---------|-------|-----------|-----------|---------|-------|-----------|-----------|
| SALMONELLA SPP. | Any amt in 1 gram | ND | PASS | SHIGA TOXIN-PRODUCING E. COLI | Any amt in 1 gram | ND | PASS |

## SOP-T11: ASPERGILLUS BY QPCR // MAR 24, 2021

| ANALYTE | LIMIT | AMT (CFU) | PASS/FAIL | ANALYTE | LIMIT | AMT (CFU) | PASS/FAIL |
|---------|-------|-----------|-----------|---------|-------|-----------|-----------|
| ASPERGILLUS FLAVUS | Any amt in 1 gram | ND | PASS | ASPERGILLUS NIGER | Any amt in 1 gram | ND | PASS |
| ASPERGILLUS FUMIGATUS | Any amt in 1 gram | ND | PASS | ASPERGILLUS TERREUS | Any amt in 1 gram | ND | PASS |

## SOP-T07: MYCOTOXIN ANALYSIS BY LC-MS // MAR 24, 2021

| ANALYTE | LIMIT | AMT (µg/kg) | LOD/LOQ | PASS/FAIL | ANALYTE | LIMIT | AMT (µg/kg) | LOD/LOQ | PASS/FAIL |
|---------|-------|-------------|---------|-----------|---------|-------|-------------|---------|-----------|
| AFLATOXIN B1 | | ND | | N/A | AFLATOXIN G2 | | ND | | N/A |
| AFLATOXIN B2 * | | ND | | N/A | AFLATOXINS * | 20 µg/kg | ND | | PASS |
| AFLATOXIN G1 * | | ND | | N/A | OCHRATOXIN A | 20 µg/kg | ND | | PASS |

* BEYOND SCOPE OF ACCREDITATION

## SOP-T03: HEAVY METALS DETECTION BY ICPMS // MAR 24, 2021

| ANALYTE | LIMIT | AMT (µg/g) | LOD/LOQ | PASS/FAIL | ANALYTE | LIMIT | AMT (µg/g) | LOD/LOQ | PASS/FAIL |
|---------|-------|------------|---------|-----------|---------|-------|------------|---------|-----------|
| ARSENIC | 0.2 µg/g | ND | | PASS | LEAD | 0.5 µg/g | ND | | PASS |
| CADMIUM * | 0.2 µg/g | ND | | PASS | MERCURY * | 0.1 µg/g | ND | | PASS |

* BEYOND SCOPE OF ACCREDITATION

## SOP-T01: FOREIGN MATERIAL TEST // MAR 24, 2021

| ANALYTE | LIMIT | AMT (%) | PASS/FAIL | ANALYTE | LIMIT | AMT (%) | PASS/FAIL |
|---------|-------|---------|-----------|---------|-------|---------|-----------|
| IMBEDDED FOREIGN MATERIAL | 25 % | ND | PASS | MOLD | 25 % | ND | PASS |
| INSECT FRAGMENTS, HAIR, MAMMAL EXCREMENT | 1 Unit | ND | PASS | SAND, SOIL, CINDERS, DIRT | 25 % | ND | PASS |

## SOP-T09: RESIDUAL SOLVENT ANALYSIS BY HS-GC-FID/MS // MAR 24, 2021

| ANALYTE | LIMIT | AMT (µg/g) | LOD/LOQ | PASS/FAIL | ANALYTE | LIMIT | AMT (µg/g) | LOD/LOQ | PASS/FAIL |
|---------|-------|------------|---------|-----------|---------|-------|------------|---------|-----------|
| 1,2-DICHLOROETHANE | 1 µg/g | ND | | PASS | ISOPROPYL ALCOHOL | 5000 µg/g | ND | | PASS |
| ACETONE | 5000 µg/g | ND | | PASS | METHANOL | 3000 µg/g | ND | | PASS |
| ACETONITRILE | 410 µg/g | ND | | PASS | METHYLENE CHLORIDE | 1 µg/g | ND | | PASS |
| BENZENE | 1 µg/g | ND | | PASS | PENTANE | 5000 µg/g | 0.500 | | PASS |
| BUTANE | 5000 µg/g | 490.000 | | PASS | PROPANE | 5000 µg/g | 120.000 | | PASS |
| CHLOROFORM | 1 µg/g | ND | | PASS | TOLUENE | 890 µg/g | ND | | PASS |
| ETHANOL | 5000 µg/g | ND | | PASS | TRICHLOROETHY-LENE | 1 µg/g | ND | | PASS |
| ETHYL ACETATE | 5000 µg/g | ND | | PASS | M-XYLENE | | ND | | N/A |
| ETHYLENE OXIDE | 1 µg/g | ND | | PASS | O-XYLENE | | ND | | N/A |
| ETHYL ETHER | 5000 µg/g | ND | | PASS | P-XYLENE | | ND | | N/A |
| HEPTANE | 5000 µg/g | ND | | PASS | P- AND M-XYLENE | | ND | | N/A |
| HEXANE | 290 µg/g | ND | | PASS | TOTAL XYLENES | 2170 µg/g | ND | | PASS |

https://lims.tagleaf.com/coa_/dh203vbE8k

# Enduring Understandings

- A certificate of analysis (COA) should always be certified by a qualified analyst with a signature present directly on the COA.
- An LOQ is a laboratory's limit of quantitation which is the lowest value that can be measured and distinguished from the background noise of the analytical instrument.
- A result of "<LOQ" is not necessarily the same as 0 or "not present".
- Total THC or Total CBD is calculating according to the formula: THC + (THCA * 0.877) or CBD + (CBDA * 0.877)
- The decarboxylation factor used in Total THC or Total CBD calculations is derived by dividing the molecular mass of the neutral cannabinoid into the molecular mass of the acidic cannabinoid and multiplied by 100.
- Percent concentration results can easily be converted into milligram per gram values by multiplying the percent concentration value by 10.

# Pop Quiz!

Practice Converting Potency Results!

A Cannabis flower is determined to contain 16% THC. Convert this value to milligrams per gram (mg/g).

An ethanolic tincture is labeled as 5% THC. Convert this value to milligrams per milliliter. Use the solvent density chart for assistance.

Approximately how many milligrams of CBD are in 2 gallons of Cannabis infused glycerin tincture that contains 7 mg/g CBD?

(Hint: convert gallons to liters)

Answers: 160mg/g; 39.45mg/mL; ~66,774mg CBD

# PART IV: CANNABIS, CANNABINOIDS, AND YOU

## Essential Questions:

How does Cannabis elicit effects from the human body?

What are the components of the Endocannabinoid System?

How are phytocannabinoids, endocannabinoids, and synthetic cannabinoids similar and different?

How might Cannabis use affect human health?

# Chapter 20:
## MEET YOUR ENDOCANNABINOID SYSTEM

*"I look at the endocannabinoid system as a lipid signaling network...it's at the bottom of a pyramid, with all other physiological systems stacked on top of it..."*

Kevin Spelman, PhD, BTS #4 Curious About Cannabis Podcast

**SCAN ME**

## Learning Questions

- What is the endocannabinoid system?
- What are endocannabinoids and cannabinoid receptors?
- What are examples of common endogenous cannabinoids produced by the human body?
- How do exogenous cannabinoids, like THC or CBD, affect the endocannabinoid system?
- What happens when the endocannabinoid system is disturbed or out of balance?
- How do lifestyle choices like exercise, diet and meditation affect the ECS?

Cannabis elicits effects from the human body through a number of different mechanisms. However, one of the primary methods that many cannabinoids in Cannabis interact with the body is through a physiological system called the **endocannabinoid system**. It was only within recent decades that the endocannabinoid system was described and recognized.[478]

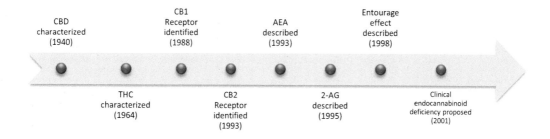

The endocannabinoid system is a lipid signaling system in the body which shows activity beginning in very early stages of brain development.[479] The system consists of

---

[478] Di Marzo V, Melck D, Bisogno T, De Petrocellis L. Endocannabinoids: endogenous cannabinoid receptor ligands with neuromodulatory action. Trends Neurosci. 1998 Dec;21(12):521-8. https://doi.org/10.1016/s0166-2236(98)01283-1

[479] Trezza V, Patrizia C. 2013. The endocannabinoid system as a possible target to treat both the cognitive and emotional features of post-traumatic stress disorder (PTSD). Frontiers in Behavioral Neuroscience. 100(7):1-6 https://doi.org/10.3389/fnbeh.2013.00100

three parts: the cannabinoid **receptors**, the **endocannabinoids**, and the various **enzymes** responsible for endocannabinoid synthesis and breakdown.[480] [481] Cannabinoid receptors are found all throughout the body and control movement, memory, sleep cycles, body temperature regulation, appetite, and the body's ability to sense harmful stimuli.[482] [483] [484] There has also been some evidence that **the endocannabinoid system plays an important role in modulating the immune system**.[485] Although there are many theories of how the endocannabinoid system might modulate the immune system, much more research is needed to further elucidate how this might occur and what various compounds, receptors, and enzymes might be involved.

The modulation of endogenous cannabinoids and receptors is now thought by some researchers to be a key component of several adverse medical conditions. For example, some animal models have shown that **obesity might be correlated with excess production of endocannabinoids**, leading to over excitation of the endocannabinoid system resulting in irregular hunger cravings and dysregulated insulin activity.[486]

Fibromyalgia is a complex pain disorder that is frequently diagnosed but not understood. It is generally characterized by an increased sensitivity to pain which manifests a variety of symptoms. In one study, mice were given an injection of a compound that blocks cannabinoid production to see how it affects their sensitivity to pain.[487] The result was an increased sensitivity to pain, or **hyperalgesia**. In another study, a synthetic cannabinoid was used to block capsaicin (the spicy compound in chili peppers) induced hyperalgesia in rodents.[488] Although there seems to be some correlation, further research is needed before determining any causal connections between medical conditions like fibromyalgia with endocannabinoid derangements.

---

[480] Di Marzo V, DePetrocellis L, Bisogno T. 2005. The biosynthesis, fate and pharmacological properties of endocannabinoids. Handb. Exp.Pharmacol. 168, 147–185. https://doi.org/10.1007/3-540-26573-2_5

[481] Piomelli D. The molecular logic of endocannabinoid signalling. Nat Rev Neurosci. 2003 Nov;4(11):873-84. https://doi.org/10.1038/nrn1247

[482] Bellocchio, L., Cervino, C., Pasquali, R., Pagotto, U., 2008. The endocannabinoid system and energy metabolism. J. Neuroendocrinol. 20, 850–857. https://doi.org/10.1111/j.1365-2826.2008.01728.x

[483] Kano, M., Ohno-Shosaku, T., Hashimotodani, Y., Uchigashima, M., Watanabe, M., 2009. Endocannabinoid-mediated control of synaptic transmission. Physiol. Rev. 89, 309–380. https://doi.org/10.1152/physrev.00019.2008

[484] Sagar, D.R., Gaw, A.G., Okine, B.N., Wong, A., Woodhams, S.G., Kendall, D.A., Chapman, V., 2009. Dynamic regulation of the endocannabinoid system: implications for analgesia. Mol. Pain 8, 5–59. https://doi.org/10.1186/1744-8069-5-59

[485] Killestein J, ELJ H, M Reif, B Blauw, M Smits, BMJ Uitdehaag, L Nagelkerken, CH Polman. (2003). Immunomodulatory effects of orally administered cannabinoids in multiple sclerosis. Journal of Neuroimmunology. 137:140-143 https://doi.org/10.1016/s0165-5728(03)00045-6

[486] Pagotto U, Vicennati V, Pasquali R (2205). The endocannabinoid system and the treatment of obesity. Ann Med 37(4):270-275. https://doi.org/10.1080/07853890510037419

[487] Richardson JD, Aanonsen L, Hargreaves KM. SR 141716A, a cannabinoid receptor antagonist, produces hyperalgesia in untreated mice. Eur J Pharmacol 1997; 319:R3–4. https://doi.org/10.1016/s0014-2999(96)00952-1

[488] Li J, Daughters RS, Bullis C, Bengiamin R, Stucky MW, Brennan J, et al. The cannabinoid receptor agonist WIN 55,212-2 mesylate blocks the development of hyperalgesia produced by capsaicin in rats. Pain 1999; 81:25–33. https://doi.org/10.1016/s0304-3959(98)00263-2

# CANNABINOID RECEPTORS

Phytocannabinoids are effective in humans because they bind to certain receptors in the human body. **Receptors** are biochemical mechanisms that rest along cell walls and have the ability to send signals to the inside of the cell by interacting with compounds outside of the cell. It is the cell's way of perceiving what is outside of the cell, so to speak. Receptors have **receptor sites** that are shaped in such a way that only certain compounds can fit, sort of like a lock and key.

Once a compound binds with the receptor site, the receptor is either **agonized** or **antagonized**. If the cell is agonized, it has been excited or activated. If the receptor is antagonized, it means that the compound is hogging up space on the receptor site, blocking other compounds from binding to the site or reducing the effects of other compounds that might come and bind to the cell's receptors. This limits or prevents **signal transduction** within the cell. Signal transduction is the series of events that follow inside the cell after a compound has attached to a receptor.

## CB1 RECEPTORS

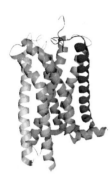

**CB1** receptors are located primarily throughout the brain and spine[489] affecting cognition, emotion, learning, memory, movement, pain, digestion, and immune function. They are the most abundant g-coupled protein receptor in the brain, making it a critical component of the way that different components of the brain communicate with one another. To put this into perspective, other examples of g-protein coupled receptors that you might be familiar with are dopamine, serotonin, metabotropic glutamate, and GABA receptors.

There are an abundant number of CB1 receptors located in the **hippocampus**, which is the part of the brain responsible for memory. Depending on what cannabinoids are interacting with the CB1 receptors in the hippocampus, memory might be protected or compromised. CB1 receptors are also found on various periphery tissues and organs, such as the skin.

## CB2 RECEPTORS

**CB2** receptors are smaller than CB1 receptors and found primarily in immune cells[490] but are also found throughout the body and even on neurons.[491] Many of these cells modulate **cytokine** release, which affects immune system responses like the production of **Killer T cells**. Because inflammation is largely an

---

[489] Elphick, M. R.; Egertova, M. (2001). "The neurobiology and evolution of cannabinoid signalling". Philosophical Transactions of the Royal Society B: Biological Sciences 356 (1407): 381–408. https://doi.org/10.1098/rstb.2000.0787

[490] Pertwee RG, Ross RA. 2002. Cannabinoid receptors and their ligands. Protaglandins, Leukotrienes, and Essential Fatty Acids (PLEFA). 66(2-3):101-121. https://doi.org/10.1054/plef.2001.0341

[491] Onaivi ES, Ishiguro H, Gu S, Liu QR. 2012. CNS effects of CB2 caannabinoid receptors: beyond neuro-immuno-cannabinoid activity. J Psychopharmacol. 26(1): 92-103. https://doi.org/10.1177/0269881111400652

immune system response, cannabinoids can reduce inflammation by suppressing the immune system.

> *"Changes in endocannabinoid levels and/or CB2 receptor expressions have been reported in almost all diseases affecting humans, ranging from cardiovascular, gastrointestinal, liver, kidney, neurodegenerative, psychiatric, bone, skin, auto-immune, lung disorders to pain and cancer, and modulating CB2 receptor activity holds tremendous therapeutic potential in these pathologies."[492]*

## CB1/CB2 Receptor Complexes

The story of CB1 and CB2 receptors is a bit more complex than it may seem, as chemical receptors, in general, do not always appear separate from one another. Chemical receptors can form complexes, often referred to as heteromers, where their activity can be unique compared to if the receptors were separated. Heteromerization occurs in various circumstances in the endocannabinoid system, with one example being the presence of CB1/CB2 receptor complexes, where CB1 and CB2 receptors appear side by side and influence each other's activity.

Another example are heteromers formed between CB1 and 5HT2A (serotonin) receptors.[493] So far at the time of this writing, CB1 has been found to form heteromers "with serotonin, angiotensin, opioid, GPR55, somatostatin, orexin, dopamine, and adenosine receptors among others".[494] These receptor complexes have not been thoroughly investigated; however, some limited research has been done with individual cannabinoids to understand how different cannabinoids may affect these complexes.

### Did You Know?

CB1 receptor signaling is crucial to newborn survival according to a study conducted by Fride et al (2001). Endocannabinoids like Anandamide and 2-AG stimulate CB1 receptors which signal the newborn mouse pup to suckle for food. If CB1 receptors are blocked in a newborn pup, the pup will not suckle and will eventually die of starvation.

[492] Pacher P, Mechoulam R. 2011. Is lipid signaling through cannabinoid 2 receptors part of a protective system? Prog Lipid Res. 50(2):193-211. https://doi.org/10.1016/j.plipres.2011.01.001

[493] Galindo, L., Moreno, E., López-Armenta, F. et al. Cannabis Users Show Enhanced Expression of CB1-5HT2A Receptor Heteromers in Olfactory Neuroepithelium Cells. Mol Neurobiol 55, 6347–6361 (2018). https://doi.org/10.1007/s12035-017-0833-7

[494] Morales P, Reggio PH. An Update on Non-CB1, Non-CB2 Cannabinoid Related G-Protein-Coupled Receptors. Cannabis Cannabinoid Res. 2017 Oct 1;2(1):265-273. https://doi.org/10.1089/can.2017.0036

## MISCELLANEOUS G-PROTEIN COUPLED RECEPTORS (GPRs)

There are several other miscellaneous g-protein coupled receptors in the body that cannabinoids interact with, including, but not limited to, GPR55, GPR18, GPR119, GPR3, GPR6, and GPR12. "GPR" stands for **g-protein coupled receptor**. Both the CB1 and the CB2 receptors are also g-protein coupled receptors. THC activates **GPR55** just as potently and with greater efficacy than the CB1 receptor.[495] The over-stimulation of GPR55 receptors is now implicated in conditions like osteoporosis and cancer. The activation of the **GPR18** receptor by certain cannabinoids has been shown to affect blood pressure in rodent models.[496] **GPR35** signaling could play a role in metabolic disease, like diabetes, hypertension, asthma, pain, and inflammatory bowel disease.[497]

| Class A G-Protein Coupled Receptors Involved in the ECS | |
|---|---|
| **GPR55 (aka LPI1)** | Over-activity involved in pain, cancer, metabolic syndromes, osteoporosis, and motor coordination; lysophosphatidylinositol (LPI) is considered GPR55's endogenous ligand; sometimes referred to as LP1 receptor or CB3 receptor.[498] |
| **GPR35** | 2-acyl lysophosphatidic acid receptor; endocannabinoid 2-AG can be metabolized to 2-arachidonoyl LPA[499] |
| **GPR18** | High density of receptors in lymphoid tissues; moderately distributed in lungs, brain, testis, ovaries, and other organs; involved in intraocular pressure, cancer, metabolic disorders, and more; N-arachidonoyl glycine and Resolvin D2 (RvD2) are being investigated as endogenous ligands of GPR18.[500] |
| **GPR3 GPR6 GPR12** | Predominantly found in the brain and reproductive system; involved in neuron growth, synaptic formation, and neuronal differentiation; may play a role in Alzheimer's disease, neuropathic pain, emotional responses, Parkinson's disease, and more; CBD is a GPR3 and GPR6 inverse agonist[501] |
| **GPR119** | Endocannabinoid congeners OEA and PEA interact with GPR119 directly; GPR119 regulates energy balance in the pancreas; GPR119 may be involved in the regulation of metabolic disorders and obesity.[502] |

[495] Ryberg E, Larsson N, Sjö¨gren S, Hjorth S, Hermansson N-O, Leonova J et al. 2007. The orphan receptor GPR55 is a novel cannabinoid receptor. Br J Pharmacol 152: 1092–1101. https://doi.org/10.1038/sj.bjp.0707460

[496] Penumarti A, Abdel AR. (2014) The novel endocannabinoid receptor gpr18 is expressed in the rostral ventrolateral medulla and exerts tonic restraining influence on blood pressure. J Pharmacol Exp Ther. 349:29-38 https://doi.org/10.1124/jpet.113.209213

[497] Milligan G. Orthologue selectivity and ligand bias: translating the pharmacology of GPR35. Trends Pharmacol Sci 2011;32:317–25. https://doi.org/10.1016/j.tips.2011.02.002

[498] Morales P, Reggio PH. An Update on Non-CB1, Non-CB2 Cannabinoid Related G-Protein-Coupled Receptors. Cannabis Cannabinoid Res. 2017 Oct 1;2(1):265-273. https://doi.org/10.1089/can.2017.0036

[499] Zhao P, Abood ME. GPR55 and GPR35 and their relationship to cannabinoid and lysophospholipid receptors. Life Sci. 2013 Mar 19;92(8-9):453-7. https://doi.org/10.1016/j.lfs.2012.06.039

[500] Morales P, Reggio PH. An Update on Non-CB1, Non-CB2 Cannabinoid Related G-Protein-Coupled Receptors. Cannabis Cannabinoid Res. 2017 Oct 1;2(1):265-273. https://doi.org/10.1089/can.2017.0036

[501] Morales P, Reggio PH. An Update on Non-CB1, Non-CB2 Cannabinoid Related G-Protein-Coupled Receptors. Cannabis Cannabinoid Res. 2017 Oct 1;2(1):265-273. https://doi.org/10.1089/can.2017.0036

[502] Ye L, Cao Z, Wang W, Zhou N. New Insights in Cannabinoid Receptor Structure and Signaling. Curr Mol Pharmacol. 2019;12(3):239-248. https://doi.org/10.2174%2F1874467212666190215112036

## CANNABINOID RECEPTOR AFFINITY AND EFFICACY

A compound's **affinity** for a receptor is a measure of its likelihood to bind to a receptor. If the compound exhibits no affinity for a receptor, it will steer clear and not interact with the receptor. If a compound exhibits affinity for a receptor, that affinity can then be characterized in a variety of ways according to a spectrum of **efficacy** measured in terms of agonism vs antagonism, or action vs. non-action.

FIGURE 57: CANNABINOID RECEPTOR AFFINITY PER COMMON PHYTOCANNABINOIDS AND ENDOCANNABINOIDS

| Cannabinoid | CB1 Affinity | CB2 Affinity |
|---|---|---|
| THC | Partial agonist | Partial agonist |
| CBD | Inverse agonist/Allosteric Modulator | Inverse agonist |
| CBG | Protean agonist? | Partial agonist |
| CBC | Antagonist/Weak agonist | Antagonist/Weak agonist |
| CBN | Weak agonist | Potent partial agonist |
| THCV | Antagonist at low dose; Agonist at high dose | Partial agonist |
| Anandamide | Partial agonist | Partial agonist |
| 2-AG | Potent agonist | Potent agonist |
| *CB1 binding affinity data for CBG is currently contradictory and inconclusive | | |

If a compound binds to a receptor but elicits no response, it is an **antagonist**. It does not stimulate the cell in any way, and just takes up space on the receptor site, effectively blocking other compounds from binding to that receptor location. If a compound binds to a receptor and elicits a positive response, it is classified as an **agonist**. This is usually thought of as "stimulating" or "activating" the cell. THC is a CB1 and CB2 **partial agonist**. Many synthetic cannabinoids are **full** or **super agonists** of CB1 receptors. If a compound binds to a receptor and elicits a negative response, it is classified as **an inverse agonist**. CBD acts as an inverse agonist to CB2 receptors.

## Receptor Binding Efficacy

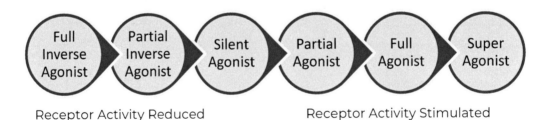

Imagine receptor binding like turning a volume knob. A super agonist would be equal to turning the volume up. An inverse agonist would be like turning the volume down. A silent antagonist would be as if the volume knob were stuck and could not be turned up or down. In much the same way, agonists stimulate receptors and increase activity in the cell. Antagonists do not affect the activity of the receptor but can block other compounds from reaching the receptor. Finally inverse agonists reduce the natural, or basal, level of activity of the cell. If the cell already exhibits zero activity, then it cannot be inversely agonized.

To make things a bit more complicated there are activities like allosteric modulation and protean agonism, which are much less straightforward. **Allosteric modulation** occurs when a compound binds to part of a receptor, but not necessarily the "bullseye" of the receptor, technically referred to as the **orthosteric site**, or "primary site" of action. An allosteric action is one that typically changes the shape of a receptor or otherwise affects a receptor in such a way that it will behave dfiferently when something attempts to bind to the orthosteric site. CBD is an allosteric modulator of CB1 receptors, for instnace, and it is thought that this allosteric modulation activity is how CBD antagonizes the activity of THC.

**Protean agonism** is a concept which describes a compound's ability to elicit different effects depending on the state of a receptor. Proteus was a Greek god that could manipulate his form depending on who viewed him. In this same spirit, protean agonists are able to stimulate a receptor when the receptors' sites are largely inactive, but it may perofrm the opposite action when many of the receptor's sites are already active. CBG is thought to potentially be a protean agonist of CB1 receptors, because in some cases CBG has been shown to stimulate CB1 receptors, however it is not good at competing with other compounds for access to CB1 receptors, and may even serve as an inverse agonist if CB1 receptors are already being stimulated be another compound.

## FOUR CLASSES OF CANNABINOID RECEPTOR AGONISTS[503]

| Class Type | Description | Examples |
|---|---|---|
| **Classical Cannabinoids** | ABC-tricyclic benzopyrans | THC, CBD; HU210 |
| **Non-classical Cannabinoids** | Characterized by opening of dihydropyran ring; many have high affinity for both CB1 and CB2 receptors | CP55,940 |
| **Aminoalkylindoles** | Initially developed as anti-inflammatory drugs and analgesics, later found to be CB receptor agonists; These cannabinoids have provided assistance in developing selective CB2 agonists | WIN55,212-2 |
| **Eicosanoids** | Acylethanolamides | Anandamide |
| | Acylesters | 2-AG |

FIGURE 58: CLASSES OF CANNABINOID RECEPTOR AGONISTS

## THE ENDOCANNABINOIDS

Endocannabinoids belong to two primary chemical families: N-acylethanolamines and acylesters.[504] Much of the endocannabinoid research going on currently is exploring

---

[503] Yao B, Mackie K. 2009. Endocannabinoid Receptor Pharmacology. Current Topics in Behavioral Neurosciences. 37-63
[504] Fezza F, Bari M, Florio R, Talamonti E, Feole M, Maccarrone M. Endocannabinoids, related compounds and their metabolic routes. Molecules. 2014 Oct 24;19(11):17078-106. https://doi.org.10.3390/molecules191117078

what enzymes might be responsible for the synthesis and breakdown of these varying compounds in order to better understand the chemical "map" of endocannabinoid synthesis and metabolism pathways.

Unlike many other types of chemicals in neurons, endocannabinoids are not stored up in the body, but rather are produced on demand. They are also considered **retrograde messengers** because they are often produced in post-synaptic neurons and travel *backwards* across the synapse to the pre-synaptic neuron, the opposite of how most neurotransmitters travel.[505] Basically, endocannabinoids have a unique ability to travel upstream, so to speak.

One primary effect that cannabinoid receptors have on neurons, is that when activated they affect the opening and closing of ion channels around the cell, which changes how the cell releases neurotransmitters, ultimately affecting their sensitivity and how the cell communicates with other cells. This usually blocks the release of neurotransmitters into the synapse between neurons. **This is how pain responses are thought to be diminished after endocannabinoid receptor stimulation.** It has been demonstrated that cannabinoids also can modulate calcium, sodium, potassium, and TRPV1 ion channels through a receptor independent mechanism.[506]

Endocannabinoids are also utilized by the body to regulate appetite, sleep, mood, and many other functions in the body. Beyond the central nervous system, endocannabinoids are utilized by the body to coordinate inflammation responses to physical trauma or infection, protect healthy cells while coordinating the destruction of problematic out-of-control cells, like cancer, and more.

Generally, endocannabinoids are derived from the combination of arachidonic acid with either an ethanolamine or a glycerol. The most well studied n-acylethanolamine is Anandamide, and the most well studied acylester is 2-arachidonoyl glycerol, or 2-AG. These are considered the body's primary endocannabinoids, so far. In the next sections we will review these primary endocannabinoids as well as other endocannabinoids that are receiving attention from researchers.

## ANANDAMIDE / N-ARACHIDONOYL ETHANOLAMINE (AEA)

**Anandamide** gets its name from the Sanskrit word *ananda* which means "bliss". It is sometimes called "the bliss compound." Anandamide is a partial CB1 and CB2 receptor agonist, similar to THC, and was the first endocannabinoid discovered.[507] Anandamide and similar

---

[505] Castillo PE, Younts TJ, Chávez AE, Hashimotodani Y. Endocannabinoid signaling and synaptic function. Neuron. 2012 Oct 4;76(1):70-81. https://doi.org/10.1016/j.neuron.2012.09.020
[506] Oz M. Receptor-independent effects of endocannabinoids on ion channels. Curr Pharm Des. 2006;12(2):227-39. https://doi.org/10.2174/138161206775193073
[507] Devane WA, Breuer A, Sheskin T, Jarbe TU, Eisen MS, Mechoulam R. 1992. A novel probe for the cannabinoid receptor. J Med Chem. 35(11):2065-2069. https://doi.org/10.1021/jm00089a018

compounds have been discovered in dark chocolate.[508] Although anandamide was discovered first, it is not in as high concentrations in the body as other endocannabinoids, like 2-AG.

## 2-Arachidonoylglycerol (2-AG)

**2-AG** was the second endocannabinoid discovered[509] and is a potent CB1 receptor agonist. 2-AG is the most abundant endocannabinoid present in the body. CBD administration triggers the production and release of 2-AG throughout the body. 2-AG is degraded by the enzyme monoacylglycerol lipase (MAGL).

## The Biosynthesis and Degradation of Endocannabinoids

All endocannabinoids are **eicosanoids**, which are oxidative products of long carbon chain molecules derived from omega-3 or omega-6 fatty acids which control many different bodily functions like inflammation, immunity, and central nervous system signaling. Other examples of eicosanoids include leukotrienes, prostaglandins, and thromboxanes. Many of these compounds are involved in biological activity like inflammation responses and bronchoconstriction and are key components of inflammatory conditions like asthma.

**OMEGA 6 FATTY ACID, LINOLEIC ACID**

**OMEGA 3 FATTY ACID, ALPHA LINOLEIC ACID**

Eicosanoid biosynthesis typically begins with a compound called **arachidonic acid (AA)**. Arachidonic acid is not an essential fatty acid, but many different compounds rely on it and depending on certain chemical deficiencies in the body, it could become a "**conditional essential fatty acid**." Usually mammals will metabolize linoleic acid, a polyunsaturated omega-6 fatty acid, into arachidonic acid.[510] If there is a problem with the enzymes involved in this breakdown, arachidonic acid must be obtained from other

---

[508] Tomaso ED, Beltramo M, Piomelli D. 1996. Brain cannabinoids in chocolate. Nature. 382:677-678. https://doi.org/10.1038/382677a0

[509] Sugiura T, Kondo S, Sukagawa A, Nakane S, Shinoda A, Itoh K, Yamashita A, Waku K. 2-Arachidonoylglycerol: a possible endogenous cannabinoid receptor ligand in brain. Biochem Biophys Res Commun. 1995 Oct 4;215(1):89-97. https://doi.org/10.1006/bbrc.1995.2437

[510] Simopoulos AP. An Increase in the Omega-6/Omega-3 Fatty Acid Ratio Increases the Risk for Obesity. Nutrients. 2016 Mar 2;8(3):128. https://doi.org/10.3390/nu8030128

sources. When endocannabinoids break down, they generally break down into arachidonic acid along with whatever other base chemical groups may be present, like glycerol in the case of 2-AG, or dopamine in the case of NADA.

## ANANDAMIDE BIOSYNTHESIS AND METABOLISM

**Anandamide** production is said to begin with a compound called **N-arachidonoyl phosphatidylethanolamine** (NAPE). A variety of enzymatic activities can follow involving α/β-hydrolase 4 (ABHD4), lyso-phospholipase (lysoPLD), protein tyrosine phosphatase non-receptor type 22 (PTPN22), and N-acyl-phosphatidylethanolamines-hydrolyzing phospholipase D (NAPE-PLD) which would transform NAPE directly or indirectly into Anandamide (AEA).

There are several known degradation enzymes that break AEA down into various other components. Fatty acid amide hydrolase (FAAH) can degrade AEA to arachidonic acid and ethanolamine. 12-lipoxygenase (12-LOX) will degrade AEA to 12-hydroxyanandamide (12-HAEA). Cyclooxygenase-2 (COX-2) degrades AEA to prostamides F2a (PMF2a). Finally, cytochrome p450 degrades AEA into 5,6-epoxyeicosatrienoyl ethanolamides (5,6-EET-EA).

There are many known compounds that can inhibit the activity of FAAH, affecting the breakdown of anandamide and helping it circulate in the body longer. Many pharmaceutical companies have been examining FAAH inhibitors for a long time to determine if they could be valuable as treatments for anxiety, chronic pain, and neurodegenerative disorders. However, manipulating enzymes can be tricky, and dangerous.

In 2016 a clinical trial examining the effects of an FAAH inhibitor on endocannabinoids in human subjects went horribly wrong, leaving one volunteer dead and five others hospitalized.[511] It turned out, upon further examination, that the FAAH inhibitor used in the trial also inhibited other enzymes. It was also found that the dose is incredibly important, because some FAAH inhibitors are active and safe at low dosages but can become dangerous at higher dosages. Rodent models used to examine the safety of these compounds are not always helpful as the results don't necessarily scale to humans.

| Examples of Naturally Derived FAAH Inhibitors ||
| Compound | Example of Natural Source |
| --- | --- |
| Cannabidiol (CBD) | Cannabis |
| Alkylamides | Echinacea |
| Kaempferol | Many Vegetables |
| Guinensine | Black Pepper |

FIGURE 59: NATURALLY DERIVED FAAH INHIBITORS

---

[511] Kaur R, Sidhu P, Singh S. What failed BIA 10-2474 Phase I clinical trial? Global speculations and recommendations for future Phase I trials. J Pharmacol Pharmacother. 2016 Jul-Sep;7(3):120-6. https://doi.org/10.4103%2F0976-500X.189661

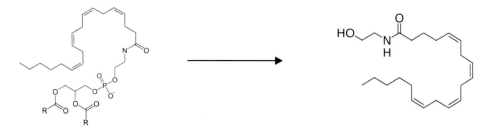

N-ARACHIDONOYL PHOSPHATIDYLETHANOLAMINE (NAPE) CAN TRANSFORM DIRECTLY OR INDIRECTLY INTO ANANDAMIDE THROUGH VARIOUS ENZYMATIC PROCESSES.

| Enzyme | Chemical Byproduct(s) |
|---|---|
| Fatty acid amide hydrolase (FAAH) | Arachidonic acid and ethanolamine |
| 12-lipoxygenase (ALOX12) | 12-hydroxyanandamide |
| Cyclooxygenase-2 (COX-2) | Prostamides F2a |
| Cytochrome p450 complex (CYP) | 5,6-epoxyeicosatrienoyl ethanolamides |

FIGURE 60: COMMON ANANDAMIDE METABOLIC PRODUCTS

## 2-AG BIOSYNTHESIS AND METABOLISM

2-AG, on the other hand, goes through a much different synthetic mechanism. 2-AG is synthesized either through diacylglycerol lipase or phospholipase C from 1-acyl-2-arachidonoylglycerol (DAG) or 2-arachidonoylglycerol-3-phosphate (2-AG-3P), respectively. The enzymes monoacylglycerol lipase (MAGL), a/B-hydrolase domain 6 and a/B-hydrolase domain 12 break 2-AG down into arachidonic acid and glycerol.

Alternatively, 12-lipoxygenase (12-LOX) can degrade 2-AG into 12-hydroxyarachidonoyl-glycerol (12-HETE-G) and cyclooxygenase-2 (COX-2) can degrade 2-AG into prostaglandinglycerol $E_2$-G (PGE$_2$-G). These are only the pathways that have been illuminated thus far. It is likely that other synthetic and metabolic pathways will be described after future research.[512]

The synthetic and degradation pathways of other endocannabinoids are not well described or understood. Understanding these pathways will help identify new targets of drug therapy for a wide variety of ailments. Already, research is beginning to support the concept of a "clinical endocannabinoid deficiency" syndrome.[513] [514]

It is thought that clinical endocannabinoid deficiency could be an underlying factor behind many ailments such as migraine, fibromyalgia, and irritable bowel

[512] Fezza F, Bari M, Florio R, Talamonti E, Feole M, Maccarrone M. 2014. Endocannabinoids, Related Compounds and Their Metabolic Routes. Molecules. 19:17078-17106. https://doi.org/10.3390/molecules191117078

[513] Smith SC, Wagner MS. 2014. Clinical endocannabinoid deficiency (CECD) revisited: can this concept explain the therapeutic benefits of cannabis in migraine, fibromyalgia, irritable bowel syndrome, and other treatment-resistant conditions?. Neuro Endocrinol Lett. 35(3):198-201. https://pubmed.ncbi.nlm.nih.gov/24977967/

[514] Russo E. 2004. Clinical Endocannabinoid Deficiency (CECD): Can this concept explain therapeutic benefits of cannabis in migraine, fibromyalgia, irritable bowel syndrome and other treatment-resistant conditions?. Neuroendocrinology Letters. 25:31-39 https://pubmed.ncbi.nlm.nih.gov/15159679/

syndrome. Others have proposed the concept of a spectrum of endocannabinoid derangements including conditions involving surpluses of endocannabinoid signaling, potentially contributing to conditions such as schizophrenia, obesity, metabolic disorders and more[515] [516]

MAGL or other enzymes degrade 2-AG

**2-AG CAN DEGRADE TO ARACHIDONIC ACID AND GLYCEROL**

# Novel Endocannabinoids

## Lysophosphatidylinositol (LPI)

**Lysophosphatidylinositol**, besides being a difficult word to pronounce, is a ligand associated with the putative cannabinoid receptor GPR55. This is interesting because most cannabinoids exhibit low affinity for the GPR55 receptor type. The shape of the GPR55 receptor is much different than other cannabinoid receptors, ultimately compromising the ability of most cannabinoids to bind to it.[517]

GPR55 receptors can be found in a variety of tissues including breast adipose, or fatty, tissues, the testis, spleen, and the brain.[518] [519] Despite the locations of these receptors, the function of GPR55 receptors is mostly a mystery, though it's over stimulation has recently been associated with carcinogenesis and osteoporosis.

[515] Leweke, F.M., Koethe, D., 2008. Cannabis and psychiatric disorders: it is not only addiction. Addiction Biology 13, 264–275. https://doi.org/10.1111/j.1369-1600.2008.00106.x

[516] Alvheim AR, Malde MK, Osei-Hyiaman D, Lin YH, Pawlosky RJ, Madsen L, Kristiansen K, Frøyland L, Hibbeln JR. Dietary linoleic acid elevates endogenous 2-AG and anandamide and induces obesity. Obesity (Silver Spring). 2012 Oct;20(10):1984-94. https://doi.org/10.1038/oby.2012.38

[517] Oka S, Nakajima K, Yamashita A, Kishimoto S, Sugiura T. Identification of GPR55 as a lysophosphatidylinositol receptor. Biochem Biophys Res Commun. 2007 Nov 3;362(4):928-34. https://doi.org/10.1016/j.bbrc.2007.08.078

[518] Sawzdargo M, Nguyen T, Lee DK, Lynch KR, Cheng R, Heng HH, George SR, O'Dowd BF. Identification and cloning of three novel human G protein-coupled receptor genes GPR52, PsiGPR53 and GPR55: GPR55 is extensively expressed in human brain. Brain Res Mol Brain Res. 1999 Feb 5;64(2):193-8. https://doi.org/10.1016/s0169-328x(98)00277-0

[519] https://patents.google.com/patent/WO2001086305A3/en

# VIRODHAMINE (OAE)

Opposite of Anandamide, whose name is rooted in the Sanskrit word *ananda*, meaning "bliss", **this endocannabinoid gets its name from the Sanskrit word for "opposition", *virodha*.** This is because this compound utilizes a chemical bond that is somewhat opposite than what is seen in Anandamide. Virodhamine utilizes an ester bond where Anandamide utilizes an amine bond. Virodhamine was the first endocannabinoid discovered that *antagonizes* the CB1 receptor, rather than agonizing it like Anandamide.[520] This can effectively reduce the effects of Anandamide and other CB1 agonist endocannabinoids by taking up space on CB1 receptors without affecting signal transduction.

Despite this antagonist activity, **Virodhamine** acts as a full agonist at CB2 receptors, which are most densely located in immune system cells.[521] **While Virodhamine has been reported to be found in brain tissues, subsequent studies have failed to demonstrate its presence.**[522]

# N-ARACHIDONOYL DOPAMINE (NADA)

**ARACHIDONIC ACID**

**DOPAMINE**

The endocannabinoid N-**Arachidonoyl dopamine (NADA)** is a newer endocannabinoid of interest isolated from the brains of rats that acts as both a CB1 and Vanilloid TRPV-1 receptor agonist, similar to Anandamide (AEA) but different as NADA is a more potent Vanilloid receptor agonist and a more effective CB1 receptor agonist than AEA.[523] NADA has been demonstrated as a potent vasorelaxant, or blood pressure reducer,

[520] Porter AC, Sauer JM, Knierman MD, Becker GW, Berna MJ, Bao J, Nomikos GG, Carter P, Bymaster FP, Leese AB, Felder CC. 2002. Characterization of a novel endocannabinoid, Virodhamine, with antagonist activity at the CB1 receptor. JPET. 301:1020-1024. https://doi.org/10.1124/jpet.301.3.1020
[521] Porter AC, Sauer JM, Knierman MD, Becker GW, Berna MJ, Bao J, Nomikos GG, Carter P, Bymaster FP, Leese AB, Felder CC. 2002. Characterization of a novel endocannabinoid, Virodhamine, with antagonist activity at the CB1 receptor. JPET. 301:1020-1024. https://doi.org/10.1124/jpet.301.3.1020
[522] Yao B, Mackie K. 2009. Endocannabinoid Receptor Pharmacology. Current Topics in Behavioral Neurosciences. 37-63
[523] Marinelli S, Di Marzo V, Florenzano F, Fezza F, Viscomi MT, van der Stelt M, Bernardi G, Molinari M, Maccarrone M, Mercuri NB. 2007. N-Arachidonoyl-Dopamine Tunes Synaptic Transmission onto Dopaminergic Neurons by Activating both Cannabinoid and Vallinoid Receptors. Neuropsychopharmacology. 32:298-308. https://doi.org/10.1038/sj.npp.1301118

by both this interaction with CB1 and TRPV-1 receptors as well as with CB1 and particular endothelial receptors, depending on where the blood vessels are located in the body.[524]

Even though NADA has the word dopamine in its name, it does not exhibit much direct affinity for dopamine receptors.[525] **NADA breaks down into its primary components: dopamine and arachidonic acid**.

## NOLADIN ETHER (2-ARACHIDONYL GLYCERYL ETHER)

Noladin ether was discovered in pig brains and appeared in the scientific literature in 2001.[526] It is an agonist of CB1 and CB2 receptors, and has been found to cause sedation and reduce blood pressure in rodents.[527] Noladin ether is very stable in the body compared to anandamide and 2-AG, making it a target for drug development.

## PENTADECANOYLCARNITINE

In 2022 researchers published a study indicating that the fatty acid pentadecanoic acid's metabolite, **pentadecanoylcarnitine**, exhibited dose-dependent anti-inflammatory activity while also agonizing both CB1 and CB2 receptors. In addition to cannabinoid receptors, pentadecanoylcarnitine also agonizes 5-HT1A and 5-HT1B, while antagonizing Histamine H1 and Histamine H2 receptors.[528]

## WHAT HAPPENS WHEN THE ENDOCANNABINOID SYSTEM IS OUT OF WHACK?

In 2004 Dr. Ethan Russo published a paper entitled Clinical Endocannabinoid Deficiency (CECD): Can this Concept Explain Therapeutic Benefits of Cannabis in Migraine,

---

[524] O'Sullivan SE, Kendall DA, Randall MD. 2004. Characterisation of the vasorelaxant properties of the novel endocannabinoid N-arachidonoyl-dopamine (NADA). Bri J of Pharm. 141:803-812. https://doi.org/10.1038/sj.bjp.0705643

[525] Bisogno T, Melck D, Bobrov MY, Gretskaya NM, Bezuglov VV, De Petrocellis L, Di Marzo V. 2000. N-acyl-dopamines: novel synthetic CB(1) cannabinoid-receptor ligands and inhibitors of anandamide inactivation with cannabimimetic activity in vitro and in vivo. Biochem. J. 351:817-824. http://www.ncbi.nlm.nih.gov/pmc/articles/pmc1221424/

[526] Hanus L, Abu-Lafi S, Fride E, Breuer A, Vogel Z, Shalev DE, Kustanovich I, Mechoulam R. 2-arachidonyl glyceryl ether, an endogenous agonist of the cannabinoid CB1 receptor. Proc Natl Acad Sci U S A. 2001 Mar 27;98(7):3662-5. https://doi.org/10.1073/pnas.061029898

[527] Shoemaker JL, Joseph BK, Ruckle MB, Mayeux PR, Prather PL. The endocannabinoid noladin ether acts as a full agonist at human CB2 cannabinoid receptors. J Pharmacol Exp Ther. 2005 Aug;314(2):868-75. https://doi.org/10.1124/jpet.105.085282

[528] Venn-Watson, S., Reiner, J. & Jensen, E.D. Pentadecanoylcarnitine is a newly discovered endocannabinoid with pleiotropic activities relevant to supporting physical and mental health. Sci Rep 12, 13717 (2022). https://doi.org/10.1038/s41598-022-18266-w

Fibromyalgia, Irritable Bowel Syndrome and other Treatment-Resistant Conditions?[529] As indicated by the subtitle, this paper hypothesized that certain treatment resistant pain conditions might be explained by endocannabinoid deficiencies. If these conditions are in fact caused by endocannabinoid deficiencies, they might be best treated with cannabinoid compounds and certain enzyme inhibitors to maintain cannabinoid concentrations in the body for longer periods of time.

Conditions like migraine and fibromyalgia can be thought of as pain sensitivity disorders. Some cannabinoid research has shown that pain sensitivity in animals is increased when cannabinoid receptors are blocked. This would lead one to assume that if someone had a deficient endocannabinoid system, they might be more sensitive to pain. These conditions along with irritable bowel syndrome are also heavily affected by inflammation. The anti-inflammatory effects of cannabinoids have been repeatedly demonstrated. Additionally, these conditions have a relatively high comorbidity rate, meaning that these three conditions (migraine, fibromyalgia, and IBS) often appear together. If endocannabinoid deficiency is a critical component of these diseases, then one treatment target could be effective in alleviating symptoms of all three conditions at once.

Along with studying endocannabinoid deficiencies, researchers are also interested in exploring endocannabinoid surpluses which may be responsible for increased risks of obesity and diabetes. **The concept of endocannabinoid derangements as the pathology for disease is new and will require much more research before it is better understood to the point that dosage and formulation can be based on information about a patient's endocannabinoid levels.**

## HOW DO LIFESTYLE CHOICES INFLUENCE THE ECS?

As researchers have begun to better understand how the endocannabinoid system is connected to various physiological processes, it has become clear that our lifestyle choices can influence our endocannabinoid system tone substantially. When the endocannabinoid system becomes deranged in some way, it can be possible to therapeutically affect it without the use of exogenous cannabinoids at all. Instead, it is possible to "feed" the endocannabinoid system with positive lifestyle choices.

Aerobic exercise has been shown to increase anandamide in both rodent and human research studies.[530] This release of anandamide has been associated with some of the mechanisms underlying the "runner's high" phenomenon.[531] A study published in 2020 that examined the endocannabinoid levels of meditation retreat attendees found that meditation led to an approximate 70% increase in all endocannabinoid markers measured

[529] Russo EB. Clinical endocannabinoid deficiency (CECD): can this concept explain therapeutic benefits of cannabis in migraine, fibromyalgia, irritable bowel syndrome and other treatment-resistant conditions? Neuro Endocrinol Lett. 2004 Feb-Apr;25(1-2):31-9. https://pubmed.ncbi.nlm.nih.gov/15159679/

[530] Desai S, Borg B, Cuttler C, Crombie KM, Rabinak CA, Hill MN, Marusak HA. A Systematic Review and Meta-Analysis on the Effects of Exercise on the Endocannabinoid System. Cannabis Cannabinoid Res. 2022 Aug;7(4):388-408. https://doi.org/10.1089/can.2021.0113

[531] Fuss J, Steinle J, Bindila L, Auer MK, Kirchherr H, Lutz B, Gass P. A runner's high depends on cannabinoid receptors in mice. Proc Natl Acad Sci U S A. 2015 Oct 20;112(42):13105-8. https://doi.org/10.1073/pnas.1514996112

including anandamide, 2-AG, 1-AG, DEA, and OEA.[532] These increases in endocannabinoid levels were also associated with decreased depression and anxiety scores.

Diet is another important tool that can be used to influence the endocannabinoid system. Because the body relies on polyunsaturated fatty acids as base substrates for making endocannabinoids and many endocannabinoid-like compounds, it would follow that a diet rich in polyunsaturated fatty acids could help support a deficient endocannabinoid system. Care should be taken to avoid excessive dietary intake of polyunsaturated fatty acids chronically. Excessive endocannabinoid production in the body could then lead to a reduction in cannabinoid receptor expression and the development of an endocannabinoid system derangement.[533]

Additionally, many fruits and vegetables contain compounds, including certain flavonoids and terpenoids, which are known to either influence cannabinoid metabolism or interact with cannabinoid receptor targets like CB1, CB2, and TRPV1. It has also been found that fasting can trigger the production of endocannabinoids. A 2013 study that examined endocannabinoid levels in a small sample of individuals participating in Ramadan fasting found that serum concentrations of endocannabinoids increased by days 7 and 21 compared to the day before Ramadan.[534]

---

[532] Sadhasivam S, Alankar S, Maturi R, Vishnubhotla RV, Mudigonda M, Pawale D, Narayanan S, Hariri S, Ram C, Chang T, Renschler J, Eckert G, Subramaniam B. Inner Engineering Practices and Advanced 4-day Isha Yoga Retreat Are Associated with Cannabimimetic Effects with Increased Endocannabinoids and Short-Term and Sustained Improvement in Mental Health: A Prospective Observational Study of Meditators. Evid Based Complement Alternat Med. 2020 Jun 5;2020:8438272. https://doi.org/10.1155/2020/8438272

[533] McPartland JM, Guy GW, Di Marzo V. Care and feeding of the endocannabinoid system: a systematic review of potential clinical interventions that upregulate the endocannabinoid system. PLoS One. 2014 Mar 12;9(3):e89566. https://doi.org/10.1371/journal.pone.0089566

[534] Lahdimawan, A., 2013. Effect of Ramadan fasting on endorphin and endocannabinoid level in serum, PBMC and macrophage. https://repo-dosen.ulm.ac.id/handle/123456789/17325

# Enduring Understandings

- The endocannabinoid system (ECS) is a lipid signaling system primarily consisting of cannabinoid receptors, endogenous cannabinoids, and enzymes responsible for building or breaking down receptors and cannabinoids – although the definition of the ECS is rapidly expanding as non-cannabinoid receptors, like TRPV1, are included.
- The most common cannabinoid receptors in the body are cannabinoid type 1 and type 2 (CB1 and CB2) receptors.
- CB1 receptors are the most abundant receptor of its type in the brain and central nervous system.
- The most common endogenous cannabinoids produced by the body are Anandamide and 2-AG.
- The concept of the endocannabinoid system is rapidly expanding and evolving, now often referred to as the endocannabinoidome which encompasses the many non-cannabinoid receptors, ligands and enzymes involved in the activity of the endocannabinoid system.
- Endocannabinoid system functioning can become deranged, characterized by either too little or too much endocannabinoid signaling. Overactive endocannabinoid signaling is associated with obesity and metabolic syndrome while underactive endocannabinoid signaling is associated with pain, inflammatory conditions, anxiety, and depression.
- The general tone of the endocannabinoid system can be influenced by lifestyle choices like exercise, yoga, meditation, diet and fasting

# Chapter 21: BEYOND THE ECS AND INTO THE ENDOCANNABINOIDOME

*"... [The endocannabinoid system] seemed to be quite complicated to study. It became even more complicated when we could see that this system was not as simple as we thought in the beginning, but was quickly expanding into a much bigger signaling system which we will probably end up discovering controls all aspects of human physiology...*

*...A lifetime will not be sufficient to understand these mediators and how they interact with each other..."*

> Vincenzo di Marzo, PhD
> The Curious About Cannabis Podcast, BTS Episode #35

---

## Learning Questions

- What is the Endocannabinoidome?
- How are the endocannabinoidome and endocannabinoid system different?
- What are the components of the endocannabinoidome?
- How does the endocannabinoidome relate to other systems in the body?

---

## THE EVER-EXPANDING ENDOCANNABINOID SYSTEM

Since it was first introduced in the scientific literature in the late 1990s, the concept of the endocannabinoid system has been rapidly evolving. When researchers first discovered the presence of cannabinoid receptors and the endogenous cannabinoids anandamide and 2-AG in the late 1980s and early 1990s, many were left wondering how these proteins are affected by other endogenous and exogenous compounds. The discovery of bioactive arachidonic acid derivatives, like anandamide and 2-AG, and their endogenous receptors inspired a huge explosion of research that has created a wave of interest that is still growing.

In fact, the first time the term "entourage effect" was published, it was in reference to research indicating that the effects of 2-AG seem to change when "non-active" fatty acids are co-administered with it. Little did these researchers appreciate at the time that this would be the beginning of a greater discovery of not just the body's own cannabinoids and their receptors, but also the discovery of a whole host of enzymes, chemical receptors, and non-cannabinoid or cannabinoid-like compounds which exhibit very little to no activity at cannabinoid receptors, but profoundly influence the activity of endocannabinoids and cannabinoid receptors. This "expanded endocannabinoid system" would later be dubbed, the "endocannabinoidome."

When endocannabinoids and cannabinoid receptors are broken down in the body, they can form other pharmacologically active compounds, making it even more challenging to understand how endocannabinoids influence physiology. It is becoming more and more clear that the components of the endocannabinoid system perform different functions in different tissues and cells. In some ways it is like the body consists of a series of interconnected, but unique endocannabinoid systems.

The concept of the endocannabinoidome is very much an emerging concept that requires refinement and further study but demonstrates how the discovery of the initial components of the endocannabinoid system is affecting the entire way that researchers conceptualize human physiology.

## Beyond Cannabinoid Receptors

Cannabinoids not only act on cannabinoid receptors, but a variety of other receptor types as well. For instance, CBD has been shown to interact with vanilloid, adenosine, serotonin, and GPR55 receptors. Understanding how the endocannabinoid system is tied in with other receptor types and pathways will be critical to learning how cannabinoids can best be utilized in medicine. Below are brief descriptions of other receptor types that some cannabinoids interact with.

### Vanilloid Receptors (TRPV-1, TRPA-1, TRPV-2, etc)

Vanilloid receptors are primarily involved in pain perception, temperature regulation, and taste. The chemical compound capsaicin is a vanilloid compound primarily found in chili peppers and is the culprit behind the burning sensation felt when eating spicy food. Capsaicin binds to TRPV1 receptors, causing a burning sensation, although no tissue damage is occurring. There are a variety of types of vanilloid receptors. The endocannabinoid NADA exhibits affinity for both cannabinoid and vanilloid receptors. CBD exhibits affinity for TRPV1 receptors. TRPV1 receptors have recently been suggested to be included as part of the endocannabinoid system.

### Adenosine Receptors (A1, A2A)

Adenosine receptors have varying functions throughout the body but are primarily implicated in regulating the heart, controlling neurotransmitters like glutamate and dopamine, and signaling anti-inflammatory action. CBD causes a variety of A2A receptor mediated actions, like neuroprotection (protection of brain cells).

### Serotonin Receptors (5HTx)

Serotonin receptors are heavily implicated in many psychological disorders such as anxiety and depression as well as pain disorders like chronic migraine. Serotonin receptor signaling affects blood vessel constriction and dilation. In heavy doses, CBD exhibits affinity for serotonin receptors. THC has been shown to stimulate 5HT production and limit uptake.

Serotonin and cannabinoid receptors often appear together throughout the brain as receptor heteromers. Chronic THC consumption increases this heteromerization of cannabinoid and serotonin receptors. It should be noted that these kinds of heteromers are commonly seen in models of anxiety, depression, and other mental health disorders, indicating that chronic THC consumption may change the structure of chemical receptors in neurons in the brain to reflect these patterns, and may explain why some chronic Cannabis users sometimes develop anxiety and depressive conditions.

This kind of heteromerization also occurs with dopamine receptors in the brain, and THC administration strengthens the connections between dopamine receptors and cannabinoid receptors. It should be noted that research has indicated that CBD may reverse these heteromer effects and help restore the original phenotype of neurons in the brain that express these chemical receptors.

### PPARs (Peroxisome Proliferator Activated Receptors)

PPARs are unique receptor types found in the nucleus of cells that, when activated, can manipulate the transcription of genes. In other words, these receptors can manipulate DNA to influence the activation or prevention of gene expression. PPAR-gamma receptors are linked to things like insulin sensitivity, glucose storage, and other metabolic activities. As a result, the manipulation of PPAR receptors is a new target for diabetes therapies.

CBD agonizes PPAR-gamma receptors in the body, potentially indicating a therapeutic role for CBD in diabetes treatment. Along with stimulating PPAR receptors directly, CBD can lead to indirect stimulation of PPAR-gamma receptors through natural endocannabinoids. It was once thought that this activity was due to FAAH inhibition, however researchers discovered that, while it is the case in mice that CBD inhibits FAAH, which leads to a subsequent increase in endocannabinoid concentration in the body – in humans, this enzyme suppression effect has not been demonstrated.[535] Whatever the mechanism may be, CBD causes levels of Anandamide to increase in the body which then go on to interact with a myriad of chemical receptors including PPAR-gamma.

---

[535] Elmes, M. W., Kaczocha, M., Berger, W. T., Leung, K., Ralph, B. P., Wang, L. et al. (2015). Fatty Acid-binding Proteins (FABPs) Are Intracellular Carriers for Δ9-Tetrahydrocannabinol (THC) and Cannabidiol (CBD). The Journal of Biological Chemistry, 290(14), 8711–8721. http://doi.org/10.1074/jbc.M114.618447

# Endocannabinoid Congeners and Other Endocannabinoid Modulators

## N-Palmitoylethanolamine (PEA)

Discovered in the 1960s and sold as Normast® (ultramicronized PEA) and Pelvilen®, **PEA** has demonstrated anti-inflammatory, analgesic, and neuroprotective activity. PEA exhibits activity at PPARa receptors, GPR55, TRPV receptors, and K+ channels. Today PEA is widely available as a dietary supplement.

## N-Oleoylethanolamine (OEA)

In the body, **OEA** is found primarily in the pancreas. It exhibits activity via PPARa receptors, GPR119, GPR55, TRPV receptors, and K+ channels. Like PEA, OEA is also widely available as a dietary supplement.

## N-Stearoylethanolamine (SEA)

Although not much is known about **SEA**, it has been shown to exhibit potential anti-inflammatory and immunomodulating activity.[536] In a rodent study, SEA was found to have memory enhancing effects.[537]

---

[536] Berdyshev AG, Kosiakova HV, Onopchenko OV, Panchuk RR, Stoika RS, Hula NM. N-Stearoylethanolamine suppresses the pro-inflammatory cytokines production by inhibition of NF-κB translocation. Prostaglandins Other Lipid Mediat. 2015 Sep;121(Pt A):91-6. https://doi.org/10.1016/j.prostaglandins.2015.05.001 Epub 2015 May 18. PMID: 25997585.

[537] Lykhmus O, Uspenska K, Koval L, Lytovchenko D, Voytenko L, Horid'ko T, Kosiakova H, Gula N, Komisarenko S, Skok M. N-Stearoylethanolamine protects the brain and improves memory of mice treated with lipopolysaccharide or immunized with the extracellular domain of α7 nicotinic acetylcholine receptor. Int Immunopharmacol. 2017 Nov;52:290-296. https://doi.org/10.1016/j.intimp.2017.09.023 Epub 2017 Sep 28. PMID: 28963942.

# N-Arachidonoylglycine (NAGly)

**N-arachidonoylglycine** has demonstrated anti-inflammatory properties[538] and is a likely FAAH inhibitor[539], potentially influencing the levels of endocannabinoids in the body by modulating their breakdown. N-arachidonoylglycine is known to interact with GPR18 and GPR132.[540]

# N-Arachidonoylserine (ARA-S)

**N-arachidonoyl serine** (ARA-S) has exhibited vasodilation properties, meaning that it can make blood vessels expand (dilate).[541] ARA-S only binds very weakly with CB1, CB2, or TRPV1 receptors. ARA-S may be the endogenous ligand for an otherwise orphaned receptor present in endothelial cells that was discovered through the investigation of the synthetic cannabinoid Abnormal CBD (Abn-CBD).[542]

---

[538] Burstein SH, McQuain CA, Ross AH, Salmonsen RA, Zurier RE. Resolution of inflammation by N-arachidonoylglycine. J Cell Biochem. 2011 Nov;112(11):3227-33. https://doi.org/10.1002/jcb.23245 PMID: 21732409; PMCID: PMC3196844.

[539] Grazia Cascio M, Minassi A, Ligresti A, Appendino G, Burstein S, Di Marzo V. A structure-activity relationship study on N-arachidonoyl-amino acids as possible endogenous inhibitors of fatty acid amide hydrolase. Biochem Biophys Res Commun. 2004 Jan 30;314(1):192-6. https://doi.org/10.1016/j.bbrc.2003.12.075 PMID: 14715265.

[540] Foster JR, Ueno S, Chen MX, Harvey J, Dowell SJ, Irving AJ, Brown AJ. N-Palmitoylglycine and other N-acylamides activate the lipid receptor G2A/GPR132. Pharmacol Res Perspect. 2019 Nov 21;7(6):e00542. https://doi.org/10.1002/prp2.542 PMID: 31768260; PMCID: PMC6868653.

[541] Milman G, Maor Y, Abu-Lafi S, Horowitz M, Gallily R, Batkai S, Mo FM, Offertaler L, Pacher P, Kunos G, Mechoulam R. N-arachidonoyl L-serine, an endocannabinoid-like brain constituent with vasodilatory properties. Proc Natl Acad Sci U S A. 2006 Feb 14;103(7):2428-33. https://doi.org/10.1073/pnas.0510676103 Epub 2006 Feb 7. PMID: 16467152; PMCID: PMC1413724.

[542] Offertáler L, Mo FM, Bátkai S, Liu J, Begg M, Razdan RK, Martin BR, Bukoski RD, Kunos G. Selective ligands and cellular effectors of a G protein-coupled endothelial cannabinoid receptor. Mol Pharmacol. 2003 Mar;63(3):699-705. https://doi.org/10.1124/mol.63.3.699 PMID: 12606780.

# N-Oleoyl-Dopamine (OLDA)

**OLDA** is an endogenous inverse agonist of the GPR6 receptor[543] and an agonist of the GPR119 receptor[544] and the TRPV1 receptor.[545]

OLDA triggers the release of a glucagon like peptide in the small intestine. Glucagon is a hormone that helps regulate glucose in the body.

Plasma levels of OLDA are negatively correlated with PTSD[546]

OLDA is metabolized by COMT.[547] Cannabinoid Hyperemesis Syndrome patients may have COMT mutation and TRPV1 mutation, which may then affect the behavior of endocannabinoid congeners like OLDA.

[543] Shrader SH, Song ZH. Discovery of endogenous inverse agonists for G protein-coupled receptor 6. Biochem Biophys Res Commun. 2020 Feb 19;522(4):1041-1045. https://doi.org/10.1016/j.bbrc.2019.12.004 Epub 2019 Dec 7. PMID: 31818461; PMCID: PMC7218748.

[544] Chu ZL, Carroll C, Chen R, Alfonso J, Gutierrez V, He H, Lucman A, Xing C, Sebring K, Zhou J, Wagner B, Unett D, Jones RM, Behan DP, Leonard J. N-oleoyldopamine enhances glucose homeostasis through the activation of GPR119. Mol Endocrinol. 2010 Jan;24(1):161-70. https://doi.org/10.1210/me.2009-0239 Epub 2009 Nov 9. PMID: 19901198; PMCID: PMC5428146.

[545] Joffre J, Wong E, Lawton S, Lloyd E, Nguyen N, Xu F, Sempio C, Kobzik L, Zlatanova I, Schumacher M, Klawitter J, Su H, Rabl K, Wilhelmsen K, Yeh CC, Hellman J. N-Oleoyl dopamine induces IL-10 via central nervous system TRPV1 and improves endotoxemia and sepsis outcomes. J Neuroinflammation. 2022 May 24;19(1):118. https://doi.org/10.1186/s12974-022-02485-z PMID: 35610647; PMCID: PMC9131699.

[546] Hauer D, Schelling G, Gola H, Campolongo P, Morath J, Roozendaal B, Hamuni G, Karabatsiakis A, Atsak P, Vogeser M, Kolassa IT. Plasma concentrations of endocannabinoids and related primary fatty acid amides in patients with post-traumatic stress disorder. PLoS One. 2013 May 7;8(5):e62741. https://doi.org/10.1371/journal.pone.0062741 PMID: 23667516; PMCID: PMC3647054.

[547] Zajac D, Spolnik G, Roszkowski P, Danikiewicz W, Czarnocki Z, Pokorski M. Metabolism of N-acylated-dopamine. PLoS One. 2014 Jan 22;9(1):e85259. https://doi.org/10.1371/journal.pone.0085259 PMID: 24465516; PMCID: PMC3899008.

## N-Arachidonoyl-Serotonin

**N-arachidonoyl serotonin** was first synthesized in 1998 before it would be discovered in mammalian tissues in 2010. N-arachidonoyl serotonin is a FAAH inhibitor, boosting anandamide and 2-AG levels, and a TRPV1 antagonist.[548] This dual activity of blocking FAAH and antagonizing TRPV1 was considered unique when first discovered, which inspired the development of a number of research chemicals and pharmaceuticals that exhibit these same effects.

## Omega-3 Fatty Acid Derived Endocannabinoids

While most of the endocannabinoid system modulators that we have focused on so far have been derivatives of omega-6 fatty acids, there are several omega-3 fatty acid derived endocannabinoids, or endocannabinoid-like compounds, that are worth mentioning, including docosahexaenoyl ethanolamide (DHA-EA or synaptamide), docosahexanoyl-glycerol (DHG), eicosapentaenoyl ethanolamide (EPA-EA), eicosapentanoylglycerol (EPG), and more. These compounds are generally formed from conjugations between DHA or EPA and various glycerols, ethanolamines, and amino acid derivatives.

The most studied of these omega-3 derived endocannabinoid modulators is docosahexaenoyl ethanolamide, also known as synaptamide Synaptamide has been found to exhibit pain relieving effects in rodents, potentially through improvement of neuronal plasticity in the brain.[549] Synaptamide has also exhibited neuroprotective properties in other pre-clinical studies.[550] Additionally, synaptamide's metabolite n-docosahexaenoylethanolamine may also exhibit neuroprotective and neurotrophic effects.[551]

---

[548] Gobira PH, Lima IV, Batista LA, de Oliveira AC, Resstel LB, Wotjak CT, Aguiar DC, Moreira FA. N-arachidonoyl-serotonin, a dual FAAH and TRPV1 blocker, inhibits the retrieval of contextual fear memory: Role of the cannabinoid CB1 receptor in the dorsal hippocampus. J Psychopharmacol. 2017 Jun;31(6):750-756. https://doi.org/10.1177/0269881117691567  Epub 2017 Feb 21. PMID: 28583049.

[549] Tyrtyshnaia A, Bondar A, Konovalova S, Manzhulo I. Synaptamide Improves Cognitive Functions and Neuronal Plasticity in Neuropathic Pain. Int J Mol Sci. 2021 Nov 26;22(23):12779 https://doi.org/10.3390/ijms222312779

[550] Ponomarenko A, Tyrtyshnaia A, Ivashkevich D, Ermolenko E, Dyuizen I, Manzhulo I. Synaptamide Modulates Astroglial Activity in Mild Traumatic Brain Injury. Mar Drugs. 2022 Aug 21;20(8):538. https://doi.org/10.3390/md20080538

[551] Kim HY, Spector AA. N-Docosahexaenoylethanolamine: A neurotrophic and neuroprotective metabolite of docosahexaenoic acid. Mol Aspects Med. 2018 Dec;64:34-44. https://doi.org/10.1016/j.mam.2018.03.004

## Prostaglandin F-2a Ethanolamide

**Prostaglandin F-2A Ethanolamide** is a COX2 metabolite of anandamide with its own therapeutic activities, working to regulate adipocyte (fat cell) production in the body. This contrasts with Anandamide's effects, which promote adipocyte production. This example of one compound exerting one effect, while its metabolite has the opposite effect, is a perfect representation of one of the many ways our bodies stay in balance.

Bimatoprost[552] is an analog of Prostamide F2a that was approved as a drug to treat glaucoma and hypotrichosis (thinning hair/hair loss) under the brand names Latisse and Lumigan.

## Pepcans

The term "pepcan" is an abbreviation of the words "peptide cannabinoid" and it refers to certain peptides which exhibit activity at cannabinoid receptors. Probably the best studied example is hemopressin, which is a peptide subunit of hemoglobin. Hemopressin antagonizes CB1 and does not seem to exhibit much effect on CB2 receptors. Modified forms of hemopressin, such as RVD-hemopressin, have been identified in animals and have been found to act as a CB1 antagonist or inverse agonist in rodent heart, brain, and blood cells. From studying hemopressin, researchers have concluded that the longer the form of hemopressin, the greater activity it seems to have a CB1 receptors.

**HEMOPRESSIN**

The concept of pepcans is particularly interesting because these compounds are so polar in nature. They are full of oxygen and nitrogen making them non-lipids and quite different in structure than traditional endocannabinoids or phytocannabinoids. By

---

552 "Bimatoprost Monograph for Professionals". Drugs.com. American Society of Health-System Pharmacists.

understanding how pepcans interact with cannabinoid receptors, we may find that many other nonlipid compounds interact with cannabinoid receptors and the endocannabinoidome as a whole.

## Enduring Understandings

- The concept of the endocannabinoidome includes the endocannabinoid system plus endocannabinoid congeners and their receptor targets, metabolites, and enzymes.

- The endocannabinoidome is intertwined with other major systems like the genome, metabolome, proteome, and microbiomes.

- Endocannabinoid congeners are cannabinoid-like compounds that do not directly interact with cannabinoid receptors but influence the activity of cannabinoids.

- Lipoaminoacids are long chains of carbon (fats) that feature an amino acid at the "head". Many lipoaminoacids are cannabinoid-like including n-arachidonoylglycine and n-arachidonoylserine

- There are a number of n-acyldopamines and n-acylserotonins that modulate the activity of cannabinoids, primarily via TRPV receptors

- A number of prostamides are derived from anandamide.

- Pepcans are peptide cannabinoids which were discovered based on the observed CB1 activity of hemopressin, a subunit of hemoglobin.

 Want to learn more? Scan this QR code to jump into the Curious About Cannabis self-paced course "The Endocannabinoidome"!

# Chapter 22:
## Side Effects and Risks of Cannabis Consumption

## Learning Questions

- What are the most common side effects of THC-rich Cannabis use?
- What are the most common side effects of CBD-rich Cannabis use?
- How does THC-rich Cannabis impact mental health?
- How does Cannabis affect men and women differently?
- How does Cannabis impact other areas of health such as the immune system, cardiovascular health, gastrointestinal health, sex and reproduction, or motor function?

This chapter focuses on highlighting some of the various side effects of Cannabis use – with the focus being on THC-rich Cannabis, though references are made to CBD-rich Cannabis where appropriate. Although from a physiological perspective Cannabis is a relatively safe plant to consume – meaning that it is not likely to kill you – it *does* present some risks for users, and it is important to understand the effects associated with Cannabis consumption.

# Cannabis Health Risks

## Common Cannabis Adverse Effects

Although there have been no reported overdose fatalities directly attributed to Cannabis, Cannabis and Cannabis derivative products can hold a variety of potential health risks, depending on the dose, method of ingestion, frequency of exposure, and internal biochemistry of the user. Although the health effects of acute administration of cannabinoids to humans has been studied to some extent, there is not much reliable information about the health risks of long term, or chronic, use of Cannabis in various forms and administration routes. Data that does exist often does not account for confounding factors like socioeconomic variables, diet, exercise, alternative drug delivery systems than smoking, other health conditions present, or other drug (licit or illicit) use present. A user's history of use can also influence adverse effects. **Many of the adverse psychological effects associated with acute high-THC Cannabis exposure such as anxiety and paranoia, are more common in naïve or anxious users and can often be controlled by dose modulation.**[553]

THC is the most studied cannabinoid, so many of the reported health effects of Cannabis are associated with the effects of THC consumption, but do not take other cannabinoids, Cannabis constituents or their synergies into account. Many Cannabis health reports also examine smoking without considering other administration routes. As

---

[553] Ashton, HC. 2001. Pharmacology and effects of cannabis: a brief review. The British Journal of Psychiatry. 178(2):101-106. https://doi.org/10.1192/bjp.178.2.101

research continues, a more mature picture of the toxicity and health effects of Cannabis compounds and Cannabis products will develop. Some primarily reported adverse health effects of high-THC Cannabis consumption include:[554] [555] [556]

| Adverse Health Effects of Short-Term High-THC Cannabis Use | Adverse Health Effects of Long-Term High-THC Cannabis Use |
|---|---|
| Short term memory loss; difficulty learning or retaining information | Tolerance and Dependence |
| Motor coordination dysfunction | Chronic bronchitis and emphysema (if smoking) |
| Anxiety, paranoia | Memory impairments |
| Increased heart rate (made worse by smoking) | Increased risk of heart attack and palpitations (made worse by smoking) |
| | Cannabinoid dependent hyperemesis (chronic nausea and vomiting) |

FIGURE 61: PRIMARY REPORTED ADVERSE HEALTH EFFECTS OF HIGH-THC CANNABIS CONSUMPTION

Along with these commonly reported adverse side effects, high-CBD Cannabis and CBD extracts have their own set of adverse side effects including hepatic drug metabolism inhibition, blood pressure changes, gastrointestinal irritation, drowsiness, and even increased tremor activity in some individuals with Parkinson's disease.[557] Although CBD has been demonstrated as safe in various clinical trials, it is still important to work with a physician when considering a CBD treatment, especially if you are taking other drugs, to ensure that CBD's effects on drug metabolism and bioavailability do not cause accidental overdose or toxicity of other medications.

| Potential Adverse Side Effects of CBD |
|---|
| Inhibition of drug metabolism |
| Manipulation of drug bioavailability |
| Immune system suppression |
| Tremor in Parkinson's disease patients |
| Decrease in blood pressure, resulting in lightheadedness or drowsiness |
| Minor gastrointestinal irritation |

FIGURE 62: REPORTED ADVERSE SIDE EFFECTS OF CBD

## HEALTH RISKS OF SMOKING AND VAPING

Many of the adverse health effects of Cannabis consumption can be directly linked to smoking, but less correlated with exposure to cannabinoids or other Cannabis compounds. Inhaling smoke into the lungs causes a variety of health effects including paralyzing of cilia throughout the lungs, increasing heart rate, and initiating pro-inflammatory responses. Smoking typically results in **carbon monoxide exposure** which

[554] Volkow, ND, Baler, RD, Compton, WM, Weiss, SRB. 2014. Adverse Health Effects of Marijuana Use. The N Engl J Med 370:2219-2227. https://doi.org/10.1056%2FNEJMra1402309
[555] Ashton, HC. 2001. Pharmacology and effects of cannabis: a brief review. The British Journal of Psychiatry. 178(2):101-106. https://doi.org/10.1192/bjp.178.2.101
[556] Hall, W, Degenhardt, L. 2009. Adverse health effects of non-medical cannabis use. Lancet. 374:1383-91. https://doi.org/10.1016/s0140-6736(09)61037-0
[557] Bergamaschi MM, Queiroz RH, Zuardi AW, Crippa JA. Safety and side effects of cannabidiol, a Cannabis sativa constituent. Curr Drug Saf. 2011 Sep 1;6(4):237-49. https://doi.org/10.2174/157488611798280924

increases carbon monoxide levels in the blood, reducing the ability of the blood to efficiently carry oxygen throughout the body. Chronic exposure to carbon monoxide can lead to heart disease and neurological damage.

Many of the negative health effects of smoking Cannabis can be alleviated by utilizing other delivery methods like sublingual sprays, Cannabis infused edibles or vaporizing the plant material at lower temperatures. Vaporizing, or "vaping", still produces particulates that are irritating to the lungs but avoids combustion and pyrolization, thus preventing exposure of the lungs to various aromatized hydrocarbons and other volatile organic compounds (VOCs) that can be dangerous and potentially carcinogenic. Vaporizing typically results in the same level of cannabinoid bioavailability as smoking while drastically reducing carbon monoxide exposure.[558]

| Examples of Unwanted Byproducts of Vaping or Dabbing Cannabis at High Temperatures | |
|---|---|
| Benzene | Toluene |
| Ethylbenzene | Methyl Vinyl Ketone |
| Styrene | Isoprene |
| Xylenes | Hydroperoxides of Limonene and other terpenes |

**Care should be taken when using portable vaporizers** as they can very easily heat up to the point of combusting the material. Vaporizers produced with glues, plastics, and other heat sensitive materials may present health risks. Some vaporizable products designed for portable vaporizers may contain additives to improve the smolder or draw of the vapor or smoke such as propylene glycol or vegetable glycerin. These additives can potentially present health risks such as respiratory irritation and damage upon chronic exposure. **Digital temperature programmable desktop vaporizers are generally preferred for minimizing health risks associated with smoking or vaporizing.**

*"It was shown that the ratio of the two primary cannabis concentrate ingredients, THC and terpenoids, impacts the release of VOCs and transfer of active ingredients. Specifically, increasing the mass percent of $\beta$-myrcene in THC for a synthetic cannabis oil from 7% to 14% led to significant decreases in the release of degradants and carcinogens such as benzene, 1,3-butadiene, and isoprene, and more efficient transfer of THC when vaping. However, the opposite effect was observed for dabbing: increased mass percent of this terpene led to an increased release of degradation products."[559]*

## PATHOGENIC INFECTIONS FROM CONTAMINATED CANNABIS

Cannabis can also serve as a vector for contaminants entering the body such as biological contaminants like yeasts, molds, and bacteria, as well as chemical contaminants such as pesticides, industrial contaminants, residual solvents, or metals. Consumers with compromised immune systems are especially at risk for suffering adverse reactions to

---

[558] Abrams DI, Vizoso HP, Shade SB, Jay C, Kelly ME, Benowitz NL. Vaporization as a smokeless cannabis delivery system: a pilot study. Clin Pharmacol Ther. 2007 Nov;82(5):572-8. https://doi.org/10.1038/sj.clpt.6100200
[559] Meehan-Atrash, J., 2021. Chemical Characterization of Toxicologically Relevant Molecules in Cannabis Concentrates and Vaporizer Aerosols (Doctoral dissertation, Portland State University).

## CANNABINOID HYPEREMESIS SYNDROME (CHS)

Cannabinoid hyperemesis syndrome, or CHS, is a condition usually characterized by severe nausea and vomiting precipitated by Cannabis use or cannabinoid exposure.[560] CHS generally affects chronic Cannabis users that have used Cannabis for more than a year, though reports are highly variable and inconsistent. Some users report having used Cannabis for nearly a decade or longer before CHS symptoms begin, while others experience symptoms much sooner.

It is unknown how prevalent CHS may be among chronic Cannabis users, for several reasons. Cannabis is still illegal in many places in the world, which dissuades users from reporting their Cannabis use to their physician. This can lead to underdiagnoses or misdiagnoses with conditions such as cyclical vomiting syndrome (CVS). On the other hand, in areas where Cannabis is legal and its use is prevalent, physicians may be more likely to assume that chronic nausea and vomiting symptoms are correlated with Cannabis use without performing in-depth investigations, leading to overdiagnosis and misdiagnosis. Additionally, the symptoms of CHS can overlap with a variety of other conditions, making it challenging to diagnose.

One of the tell-tale signs of CHS is frequent showering and hot baths, which can relieve the sensation of nausea. The primary treatment for CHS is to discontinue Cannabis use. It has been reported that other cannabinoids besides THC will trigger CHS symptoms, including CBD, and it is not advised that patients diagnosed with CHS engage the use of any cannabinoids for that reason (Alice Moon, *viva voce*). A reported remedy that may ease nausea symptoms is the application of capsaicin on the stomach.[561] Both the application of capsaicin, as well as the use of hot showers or baths, likely elicit their therapeutic actions through the stimulation of TRPV1 receptors, though other mechanisms are likely also at play.

The exact mechanisms of CHS are not well known. DeVuono and Parker (2020) speculated that chronic doses of THC lead to dysregulation of the endocannabinoid system through CB1 receptor downregulation, which in turn increases endocannabinoid system enzymes that go on to decrease the levels of endocannabinoids present at any time in the body.[562] This in turn would cause changes to TRPV1 receptor distribution. The upregulation of TRPV1 receptors could theoretically lead to symptoms like sweating, thirst, increased heart rate, decreased body temperature, and digestion disruption. These symptoms can go on to elicit anxiety and depression in patients, which can cause a

---

[560] Galli JA, Sawaya RA, Friedenberg FK. 2011. Cannabinoid Hyperemesis Syndrome. Curr Drug Abuse. 4(4): 241-249. https://doi.org/10.2174/1874473711104040241

[561] Stumpf JL, Williams LD. 2020. Management of Cannabinoid Hyperemesis Syndrome: Focus on Capsaicin. Journal of Pharmacy Practice. Jul 2. 897190020934289. https://doi.org/10.1177/0897190020934289

[562] DeVuono MV, Parker LA. Cannabinoid Hyperemesis Syndrome: A Review of Potential Mechanisms. Cannabis Cannabinoid Res. 2020 Jun 5;5(2):132-144. https://doi.org/10.1089/can.2019.0059

feedback loop that intensifies all the other symptoms, ultimately leading to the primary outwardly visible symptoms of CHS – nausea and vomiting.

In 2022 a groundbreaking genomics study was published that found potential genetic indicators of cannabinoid hyperemesis syndrome among a couple dozen patients.[563] This study found that patients exhibited mutations in COMT and TRPV1 receptor genes, CYP2C9 metabolism genes, DRD2 , and the ATP binding cassette transporter gene ABCA1. These findings may shed more light on the role of TRPV1 receptors in CHS, which was already becoming apparent in previous research, while also bringing into the question of the roles of these various other gene targets. CYP2C9 is a common cytochrome P450 isozyme responsible for breaking down common drugs and other chemicals our bodies consume. A mutation at this gene might mean that a person's body metabolizes cannabinoids differently – perhaps then leading to an unusually high exposure to THC metabolites.

| Genetic Mutations Associated with CHS (Russo et al, 2022)[564] | |
|---|---|
| COMT | Mutations associated with panic disorders, schizophrenia |
| TRPV1 | Mutations associated with pain sensitivity, heat sensitivity, nausea |
| CYP2C9 | Responsible for metabolism of fatty acids and common drugs; mutations associated with drug sensitivity |
| DRD2 | Mutations associated with substance abuse, depression |
| ABCA1 | Mutations associated with Tangier Disease, hypoalphalipoproteinemia (reduced alpha-lipoproteins) |

The endocannabinoid system modulator N-oleoyl-dopamine (OLDA) is metabolized by COMT. OLDA is a TRPV1 agonist as well as a GPR119 agonist. GPR119 is often associated with effects opposite those of anandamide or 2-AG (or THC). Thus, OLDA can act as a balancing ECS modulator, bringing down cannabinoid activity if it is too high. If COMT enzymes are not produced properly in the body, OLDA, among many other endogenous compounds commonly metabolized by COMT, would not function properly. Just with our example of OLDA, it is easy to see how a COMT mutation can affect TRPV1 signaling as well as the activities of CB1 agonists like anandamide, 2-AG, and THC.

The 2020s have, thus far, been a breakthrough decade for CHS research, and it is likely that as more places throughout the United States and the world legalize Cannabis, CHS will be diagnosed more frequently and thus recognized as a priority for clinical research.

If you are worried that you or someone you know may be experiencing CHS, talk to your doctor and seek community support resources. Outspoken CHS survivor and Cannabis advocate, Alice Moon, maintains a website, http://www.cannabinoid-hyperemesis.com, that compiles information about cannabinoid hyperemesis syndrome to assist those that may be suffering from this condition, as well as researchers hoping to learn more about the condition.

---

[563] Russo EB, Spooner C, May L, Leslie R, Whiteley VL. Cannabinoid Hyperemesis Syndrome Survey and Genomic Investigation. Cannabis Cannabinoid Res. 2022 Jun;7(3):336-344. https://doi.org/10.1089/can.2021.0046
[564] Russo EB, Spooner C, May L, Leslie R, Whiteley VL. Cannabinoid Hyperemesis Syndrome Survey and Genomic Investigation. Cannabis Cannabinoid Res. 2022 Jun;7(3):336-344. https://doi.org/10.1089/can.2021.0046

## OTHER POTENTIAL RISKS OF CANNABIS CONSUMPTION

A 2017 National Academy of Sciences study[565] identified the statistical evidence for various reported adverse effects of Cannabis. The health risks that they identified as being supported with substantial, moderate or limited statistical evidence are: **testicular tumors, heart attack and stroke risk, increased risk of prediabetes, chronic bronchitis, chronic obstructive pulmonary disease (COPD), increased risk of motor vehicle crashes, increased risk of injuries, lower birth weight of offspring, pregnancy complications, admission of infants to neonatal intensive care units (NICU), acute impairment of learning, memory and attention, development of schizophrenia or psychoses, increased risk of mania or hypomania, increased risk of suicidal ideation and suicide completion** in heavier users. It should be noted that these risks are associated with statistical significance, not necessarily clinical significance, and are primarily associated with THC-dominant Cannabis products.

## THC ANTIDOTES

Although it is nearly physically impossible to physiologically overdose on cannabinoids, it *is* possible to psychologically overdose on cannabinoids, like THC, and in up in a very uncomfortable experience for a prolonged period. What can someone do if they have consumed too much THC and find themselves in an uncomfortable experience? It turns out there are quite a few options available – though the jury is still out as to whether they are all effective. Most recommended THC antidote treatments are anecdotal with very little pre-clinical or clinical research available to validate their claims.

| What Might Help a THC "Overdose"? |
| --- |
| Distraction / Entertainment |
| Food and Water |
| Lemons / Lemon Water[566] |
| Calamus Root[240] |
| Pine Nuts[240] |
| Pistachio Nuts[240] |
| Black Pepper[240] |
| CBD or CBC |
| Beta-Caryophyllene[240] |
| Pinene[240] |
| Olivetol (Undoo®)[567] |

---

[565] National Academies of Sciences, Engineering, and Medicine; Health and Medicine Division; Board on Population Health and Public Health Practice; Committee on the Health Effects of Marijuana: An Evidence Review and Research Agenda. The Health Effects of Cannabis and Cannabinoids: The Current State of Evidence and Recommendations for Research. Washington (DC): National Academies Press (US); 2017 Jan 12.

[566] Russo EB. Taming THC: potential cannabis synergy and phytocannabinoid-terpenoid entourage effects. Br J Pharmacol. 2011 Aug;163(7):1344-64. https://doi.org/10.1111/j.1476-5381.2011.01238.x PMID: 21749363; PMCID: PMC3165946.

[567] Composition of olivetol and method of use to reduce or inhibit the effects of tetrahydrocannabinol in the human body https://patents.google.com/patent/EP3380092B1/

# SIDE-EFFECTS OF THC-RICH CANNABIS CONSUMPTION

## THE MUNCHIES – APPETITE STIMULATION

One of the most well-known side effects of Cannabis consumption is colloquially referred to as "the munchies" and is characterized by abnormally stimulated appetite and cravings. This is caused by CB1 receptor stimulation in the brain. Research has shown that mice that do not have CB1 receptors will not feel the need to eat and will die of malnourishment. That's how important our CB1 receptors are to our day-to-day regulation of food intake.

## RED EYES – CONJUNCTIVAL HYPEREMIA

**Conjunctival hyperemia**, or red eye, is a common acute side effect of Cannabis consumption. This is caused by altered blood flow in the body leading to **dilation of the blood vessels in the eye**, making them bigger and more visible, thus leading to a red appearance throughout the eye. Blood vessels exist throughout the eye in the vitreum, or jelly, of the eyeball. Most of the eye usually appears white because these blood vessels are very small. When the blood vessels enlarge, due to lack of sleep, allergies, or chemical initiated vasodilation, the eyeball appears red.

## DRY MOUTH - XEROSTOMIA

**Xerostomia** is the medical term for "dry mouth" or "cotton mouth," an effect common to many Cannabis users. Xerostomia is caused by effects elicited from cannabinoids or other compounds present in Cannabis and is not an artifact of smoking (Veitz-Keenan and Ferraiolo, 2011). Persistent xerostomia can lead to an increased risk of other oral conditions such as tooth loss and decay (Veitz-Keenan and Ferraiolo, 2011). To combat xerostomia, sugar-free gums, hard candies, and mints can be used to stimulate salivation (Gupta et al, 2006; Friedman and Isfeld, 2011). Products with alcohol compounds such as xylitol and sorbitol can be used to help fight the development of tooth decay (Burt, 2006).

## CANNABIS SMOKING AND MOUTH HEALTH

There are several studies that have attempted to determine what effects pulmonary use of Cannabis through smoking has on the environment within the mouth. The concern is not just because of the general effects that smoking, regardless of the material, has on the mouth. Part of the concern rests in the immunosuppressive properties of THC and other cannabinoids. This suppression of immune cell activity could mean that the body is more susceptible to bacterial and viral infections, but more research is needed to better understand these types of relationships.

One condition that seems to occur more frequently in Cannabis (smoking) users than non-smokers is **Leukoedema**.[568] Leukoedema is a condition which causes the oral

---

[568] Darling MR, Arendorf TM. 1992. Review of the effects of Cannabis smoking on oral health. Int Dent J. 42:19-22. https://pubmed.ncbi.nlm.nih.gov/1563817/

mucosa to alter in appearance, becoming wrinkled. This condition can also be caused by habitual oral activities such as cheek sucking or nut chewing.[569] [570]

Chronic Cannabis smoking has also been associated with **gingival enlargement**, or the enlargement of the gums. Heavy acute and chronic Cannabis smoking can also cause **uvulitis**, which is the swelling of the mucosal tissue around the uvula, causing the uvula to get very large. This can cause problems swallowing and breathing deeply. There is some evidence to suggest that Cannabis smokers have higher incidences of gingivitis, but it is hard to determine if this is because of Cannabis smoking, or from a lack of oral hygiene or other confounding factors.[571]

Chronic Cannabis smoking is also associated with increased populations of the fungus *Candida albicans* in the mouth, although it is not associated with an increased incidence of **candidiasis**, the term used for *C. albicans* infections (Versteeg et al, 2008).[572] *C. albicans* is responsible for conditions like thrush and the common yeast infection. It is a polymorphic species that can change between a yeast and a pseudomold depending on its environment. The increased presence of *C. albicans* is particularly of concern for immunocompromised patients because **candidemia**, the term used for a systemic *C. albicans* infection, can be fatal if the fungus reaches the bloodstream. Strains of *C. albicans* can be resistant to anti-fungal medications, increasing the severity of the infection.[573] The immunosuppressive properties of some cannabinoids might potentiate this effect.

There are mixed research results when it comes to Cannabis smoking and the likelihood of developing **oral cancers**. Theoretically it would seem like the hydrocarbons, benzopyrene, and other compounds in the smoke would promote premalignant tumors that could become cancerous. Indeed, one study does link Cannabis smoking with oral premalignant lesions, including **leukoplakia** and **crythroplakia**.[574] [575]Another series of studies, however found that **there was not an association between oral cancer prevalence and Cannabis smoking, whether acute or chronic**.[576]

## MEMORY LOSS

[569] Van Wyk CW, Breytenbach HS, Dreyer WP. 1979. The epidemiology of preventable oral mucosal lesions in the Cape Peninsula. J Dent Assoc 34:672-676.

[570] Pindborg JJ, Barmes D, Roed-Petersen B. 1968. Epidemiology and histology of oral leukoplakia and leukoedema among Papuans and New Guineans. Cancer. 22:379-384. https://doi.org/10.1002/1097-0142(196808)22:2%3C379::aid-cncr2820220215%3E3.0.co;2-a

[571] Silverstein SJ, Noel D, Heilbron D. 1978. Social drug use/abuse and dental disease. J calif Dent Assoc. 6:32-37. https://pubmed.ncbi.nlm.nih.gov/284013/

[572] Versteeg PA, Slot DE, Velden U, Weijden GAvander. 2008. Effect of cannabis usage on the oral environment: a review. Int J Dent Hygiene. 6:315-320. https://doi.org/10.1111/j.1601-5037.2008.00301.x

[573] Chong Y, Shimoda S, Yakushiji H, Ito Y, Miyamoto T, Shimono N, Kamimura T, Akashi K. 2012. Fatal candidemia caused by azole-resistant Candida tropicalis in patients with hematological malignancies. J Infect Chemother. 18(5):741-746. https://doi.org/10.1007/s10156-012-0412-9

[574] Hashibe M, Ford DE, Zhang ZF. 2002. Marijuana smoking and head and neck cancer. J Clin Pharmacol. 42:103S-107S https://doi.org/10.1002/j.1552-4604.2002.tb06010.x

[575] Versteeg PA, Slot DE, Velden U, Weijden GAvander. 2008. Effect of cannabis usage on the oral environment: a review. Int J Dent Hygiene. 6:315-320. https://doi.org/10.1111/j.1601-5037.2008.00301.x

[576] Rosenblatt KA, Darling JR, Chen C, Sherman KJ, Schwartz SM. 2004. Marijuana use and risk of oral squamous cell carcinoma. Cancer Research. 64:4049-4054. https://doi.org/10.1158/0008-5472.can-03-3425

Short term memory loss is a well-documented side-effect of the consumption of high THC/low CBD Cannabis products. The science behind this effect has to do with a region of the brain called the **hippocampus**, which **is involved with memory and learning and is saturated with CB1 receptors.** The hippocampus is very important for the formation of new memories about experiences (Eichenbaum and Cohen, 1993; Squire and Schacter, 2002). When THC or other cannabinoids stimulate CB1 receptors in the hippocampus, it often causes a disruption of normal functioning leading to altered and potentially impaired memory formation and retention. This can lead to one common effect where an individual may not remember the topic of a conversation by the time the conversation has ended. There are also rare reports of total temporary amnesia caused by acute Cannabis use (Stracciari et al, 2003).

It should be noted that Cannabis does not seem to disrupt all types of memory and learning, but rather primarily short-term memory and a specific subcategory of long-term memory, called **episodic memory**. In addition, researchers have found evidence that long term uses develop compensatory behaviors to compensate for these memory impairments (Schoeler and Bhattacharyya, 2013). Episodic memory is often called the "memory of events" and relates to memories of experiences in a particular time and place, as opposed to the memory of facts, called **semantic memory**, or **implicit memory**, which includes things like motor and cognitive skills, perceptual skills, conditioned responses, and habits. This is, for example, why many college students can get away with consuming copious amounts of Cannabis while still achieving good grades and actively learning. The downside is they may not remember many of the actual experiences that they had in college.

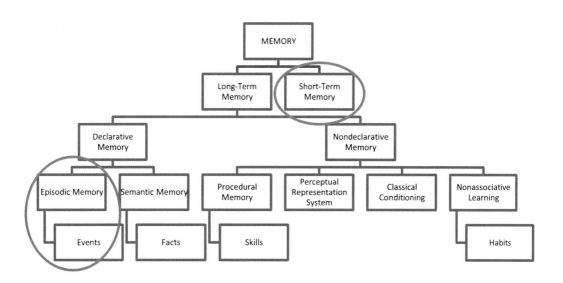

> **Did You Know?**
>
> Although THC may impair memory, some cannabinoids and terpenes exhibit memory *enhancement* effects, at least in rodent research models. The following cannabinoids and terpenes are reported to exhibit memory enhancement effects:
>
> Alpha-Pinene
> Cannabichromene (CBC)
>
> Beta-Caryophyllene
> Cannabigerol (CBG)
>
> Cannabidiol (CBD)

## CANNABIS AND MENTAL HEALTH

There is some evidence that Cannabis use can exacerbate underlying mental health conditions in particularly susceptible individuals. Cannabis use has demonstrated the **potential to facilitate mania symptoms** in bipolar patients. Cannabis use also has the potential to exacerbate anxiety or panic conditions, although this is usually the case with naïve or acute users, rather than chronic users. There is still no causal evidence to show that Cannabis use alone leads to any particular mental health disorder, although it can produce a variety of temporary acute psychological symptoms (paranoia, anxiety, etc) while also exacerbating existing mental health conditions.

## CANNABIS AND DISORDERS OF THE BIPOLAR SPECTRUM

Individuals with bipolar disorder (BD) are more likely to engage in substance use than any other "Axis 1" disorder such as major depressive disorder, schizophrenia, or panic attack disorder.[577] Many studies looking at Cannabis use in the bipolar population are limited due to low sample size and limited data on **comorbidity**, or co-occurrence, between BD and Cannabis use.[578] A meta-analysis performed by Agrawal et al revealed that BD patients are nearly seven times more likely to report a lifetime history of using Cannabis. One particularly interesting finding is that individuals diagnosed with BD tend to continue using Cannabis despite continuing or discontinuing the use of other drugs like alcohol, nicotine, or cocaine.

Zuardia et al (2010) looked at whether cannabidiol (CBD) was an effective treatment for manic episodes of bipolar affective disorder and found that doses of 600 to 1200 mg of CBD per day were ineffective, however the study was limited by a small sample size.[579] Another confounding caveat is that it has been demonstrated in other studies that

---

[577] Leweke, F.M., Koethe, D., 2008. Cannabis and psychiatric disorders: it is not only addiction. Addiction Biology 13, 264–275. https://doi.org/10.1111/j.1369-1600.2008.00106.x

[578] Agrawal A, Nurnberger Jr, JI, Lynskey, MT, The Bipolar Genome Study. 2011. Cannabis involvement in individuals with bipolar disorder. Psychiatry Research. 185:459-461. https://doi.org/10.1016/j.psychres.2010.07.007

[579] Zuardi A, Crippa J, Dursun S, Morais S, Vilela J, Sanches R, Hallak J. 2010. Cannabidiol was ineffective for manic episode of bipolar affective disorder. J Psychopharmacol. 24(1):135-137. https://doi.org/10.1177/0269881108096521

CBD might provide better symptom relief in the presence of THC or other cannabinoids rather than being administered alone.[580] [581]

Much of the reported Cannabis use among individuals with BD occurs immediately after a mood episode such as depression, mania, or hypomania.[582] Changes in frequency of psychosis, rapid cycling, and depressive episodes do not seem to be associated with Cannabis use, even Cannabis use at an early age, according to one review. However, per this same meta-analysis performed by Agrawal et al (2011), individuals with BD using Cannabis report general disability associated with life functioning more frequently compared to those with BD that do not use Cannabis frequently. Mania in people with BD is highly comorbid with Cannabis use, but so far there is no clear understanding of whether Cannabis use exacerbates mania episodes or, conversely, if mania symptoms encourage or exacerbate Cannabis use.

One challenge to interpreting some of the data relates to a discrepancy in how researchers describe the frequency of Cannabis use in users. Some studies define "lifetime Cannabis use" as simply having consumed Cannabis several times throughout life while other studies define chronic, or lifetime Cannabis use as having consumed Cannabis once or multiple times a year for multiple years. Some researchers define chronic use as consuming at least one Cannabis cigarette a day for multiple years. It is important to note how these terms are defined before interpreting a research paper looking at the effects of lifetime or chronic Cannabis use.

## CANNABIS USE AND DEPRESSION

Euphoria or elevated mood is a commonly reported side-effect of the consumption of high THC containing Cannabis products. It makes sense then that Cannabis might be an effective antidepressant. The endocannabinoid system has been investigated over recent years to determine its possible connection to depression. Some researchers have found that **patients with major depression tend to have reduced endocannabinoid levels which correlate with the length of the depressive episode.**[583] Studies have been performed with rodents that demonstrate **antidepressant effects elicited by the stimulation of CB1 receptors** by THC and Cannabis extracts.[584] Other studies contradict these findings. **Some research reveals that if CB1 receptors are blocked, anti-depressant effects can manifest.** Rodents were given drugs which

---

[580] Lemberger L, Dalton B, Martz R, Rodda B, Forney R. Clinical studies on the interaction of psychopharmacologic agents with marihuana. Ann N Y Acad Sci. 1976;281:219-28. https://doi.org/10.1111/j.1749-6632.1976.tb27933.x

[581] Karniol IG, Carlini EA. Pharmacological interaction between cannabidiol and delta 9-tetrahydrocannabinol. Psychopharmacologia. 1973 Oct 23;33(1):53-70. https://doi.org/10.1007/bf00428793

[582] Agrawal A, Nurnberger Jr, JI, Lynskey, MT, The Bipolar Genome Study. 2011. Cannabis involvement in individuals with bipolar disorder. Psychiatry Research. 185:459-461. https://doi.org/10.1016/j.psychres.2010.07.007

[583] Hill M, Miller G, Ho W, Gorzalka B, Hillard C. 2008. Serum endocannabinoid content is altered in females with depressive disorders: a preliminary report. Pharmacopsychiatry. 41(2):48–53.

[584] Hill MN, Gorzalka BB. Is there a role for the endocannabinoid system in the etiology and treatment of melancholic depression? Behav Pharmacol. 2005 Sep;16(5-6):333-52. https://doi.org/10.1097/00008877-200509000-00006

specifically block the CB1 receptor. The rodents subsequently displayed antidepressant-related behaviors in tail suspension and forced swim tests.[585] [586]

The phytocannabinoids cannabigerol (CBG), cannabidiol (CBD) and cannabichromene (CBC) have exhibited significant antidepressant effects in rodent models.[587] [588] CBC exhibits antidepressant behavior that is up to ten times more potent than CBD in tail suspension and forced swim tests.[589] Along with phytocannabinoids, there are a variety of terpenes present in Cannabis that exhibit anti-anxiety or antidepressant effects including limonene, linalool, and myrcene.[590]

## DID YOU KNOW?

Serotonin is one compound heavily implicated in depression and other mental health conditions.

Serotonin receptors and CB1 receptors are often found together in some brain tissues in animals (Hermann et al, 2002). CB1 receptors have been shown to help control serotonin release in mouse brain tissues (Nakazi et al, 2000). Research has also shown that serotonin receptors are a key component in the memory impairment effects of THC.

More research will help elucidate the endocannabinoid-serotonin relationship to better treat depression and related conditions!

On the other hand, **Cannabis use might also have the potential to exacerbate depression symptoms in some patients**. Graaf et al (2010) performed an in-depth review to determine if there might be an association between early Cannabis use and future depression spells.[591] Their results indicate a moderate risk association, with women more

[585] Shearman LP, Rosko KM, Fleischer R, Wang J, Xu S, Tong XS, Rocha BA. Antidepressant-like and anorectic effects of the cannabinoid CB1 receptor inverse agonist AM251 in mice. Behav Pharmacol. 2003 Dec;14(8):573-82. https://doi.org/10.1097/00008877-200312000-00001
[586] Witkin JM, Tzavara ET, Nomikos GG. A role for cannabinoid CB1 receptors in mood and anxiety disorders. Behav Pharmacol. 2005 Sep;16(5-6):315-31. https://doi.org/10.1097/00008877-200509000-00005
[587] Musty R, Deyo R (2006). A cannabigerol extract alters behavioral despair in an animal model of depression. Proceedings June 26; Symposium on the Cannabinoids. International Cannabinoid Research Society: Tihany, p. 32.
[588] Cascio MG, Gauson LA, Stevenson LA, Ross RA, Pertwee RG. Evidence that the plant cannabinoid cannabigerol is a highly potent alpha2-adrenoceptor agonist and moderately potent 5HT1A receptor antagonist. Br J Pharmacol. 2010;159:129–141. https://doi.org/10.1111/j.1476-5381.2009.00515.x
[589] Musty R, Deyo R (2006). A cannabigerol extract alters behavioral despair in an animal model of depression. Proceedings June 26; Symposium on the Cannabinoids. International Cannabinoid Research Society: Tihany, p. 32.
[590] Russo EB. Taming THC: potential cannabis synergy and phytocannabinoid-terpenoid entourage effects. Br J Pharmacol. 2011 Aug;163(7):1344-64. https://doi.org/10.1111/j.1476-5381.2011.01238.x
[591] de Graaf R, Radovanovic M, van Laar M, Fairman B, Degenhardt L, Aguilar-Gaxiola S, Bruffaerts R, de Girolamo G, Fayyad J, Gureje O, Haro JM, Huang Y, Kostychenko S, Lépine JP, Matschinger H, Mora ME, Neumark Y, Ormel J, Posada-Villa J, Stein DJ, Tachimori H, Wells JE, Anthony JC. Early cannabis use and estimated risk of later onset of depression spells: Epidemiologic evidence from the population-

likely to experience a depressive episode than men after consuming Cannabis early in life. This study did not identify distinct levels of Cannabis use (chronic vs acute use), thus somewhat limiting the quality of the data. A 2003 study conducted by Degenhardt et al discovered a "modest" association between depression and chronic Cannabis use but did not discover an association between depression and acute or infrequent use. Another 2008 study found a significant association between Cannabis use in early adulthood with later suicidal ideation, however, they did not discover any associations between *adolescent* Cannabis use and suicidal ideation or attempts.[592]

## PROBLEMS WITH RODENT MODELS OF MENTAL HEALTH

The **tail suspension test** and the **forced swim test**, also known as the **behavioral despair test**, are two commonly used techniques to study depression in non-human animal studies. Many of the research studies examining the effectiveness of cannabinoids as anti-depressants utilize these two models.

The tail suspension test involves suspending mice by their tails, usually by taping their tails to a beam, so that they cannot get away and they have no way of grabbing anything. The mouse's "escape oriented behaviors" are monitored and quantified. The more the mouse moves and acts like it is trying to free itself, the less depressed the mouse is said to be. Researchers expose different mice to different drug candidates and measure how long it takes the mouse to give up its fight to escape.

The forced swim, or behavioral despair test, involves introducing a mouse to a pool of water from which the mouse cannot escape. Similar to the tail suspension test, to evaluate the mouse's behavior, its time spent doing things other than just keeping its head above water to avoid drowning. The less the mouse fights to escape and avoid drowning, the less depressed it is said to be.

There is a lot of debate over the validity of these types of study models for depression. These study models are cheap and reliable, but it is hard to determine if the models *actually* measure what they aim to measure. Does the mobility behavior of the rodent *actually* represent depression in some useful way that applies to humans?

## CANNABIS USE AND POST TRAUMATIC STRESS DISORDER (PTSD)

Posttraumatic stress disorder (PTSD) is a condition characterized by heightened fear responses, inability to sleep, depression, anxiety, anger, avoidance behavior, recurrent memories, amnesia, and suicidal ideation after a high stress and traumatic event. PTSD is often comorbid with other psychological disorders and can be hard to diagnose or treat.[593] Commonly prescribed drugs for PTSD are often ineffective.[594] Recently, the

based World Health Organization World Mental Health Survey Initiative. Am J Epidemiol. 2010 Jul 15;172(2):149-59. https://doi.org/10.1093/aje/kwq096

[592] Pedersen W. 2008. Does cannabis use lead to depression and suicidal behaviours? A population-based longitudinal study. Acta Psychiatrica Scandinavica. 118(5):395-403. https://doi.org/10.1111/j.1600-0447.2008.01259.x

[593] Albucher RC, Liberzon I. Psychopharmacological treatment in PTSD: a critical review. J Psychiatr Res. 2002 Nov-Dec;36(6):355-67. https://doi.org/10.1016/s0022-3956(02)00058-4

[594] Ipser J, Seedat S, Stein DJ. Pharmacotherapy for post-traumatic stress disorder - a systematic review and meta-analysis. S Afr Med J. 2006 Oct;96(10):1088-96. https://pubmed.ncbi.nlm.nih.gov/17164942/

endocannabinoid system has been investigated as a potential site of treatment for PTSD.[595]

Many individuals with PTSD also use Cannabis. A study by the National Comorbidity Study showed that a patient with PTSD is three times more likely to use Cannabis regularly compared to someone without PTSD.[596] **Some researchers have suggested that individuals with PTSD often use Cannabis as a self-medication, taking advantage of Cannabis' amnesic, or memory impairing, properties**.[597] Cannabinoids can make it harder for the brain to recall memories while also making it easier for memories to be forgotten.[598 599 600 601] This effect can be of potential benefit to someone with PTSD that may be haunted by intrusive traumatic memories.

Researchers searching for evidence of this potential medicinal value of Cannabis have produced varying and contradictory results. Some studies show that stimulating cannabinoid receptors after a stressful event can actually promote harmful memory production and PTSD behavior[602 603] while other studies have shown that cannabinoid agonists given to rodents after a stressful event actually promoted a healthier response to the event.[604 605 606] A survey performed in California of 170 patients at a medical Cannabis dispensary revealed that the primary reason that patients with PTSD use Cannabis is for

---

[595] Neumeister A, Seidel J, Ragen BJ, Pietrzak RH. Translational evidence for a role of endocannabinoids in the etiology and treatment of posttraumatic stress disorder. Psychoneuroendocrinology. 2015 Jan;51:577-84. https://doi.org/10.1016/j.psyneuen.2014.10.012

[596] Kessler RC, Sonnega A, Bromet E, Hughes M, Nelson CB. Posttraumatic stress disorder in the National Comorbidity Survey. Arch Gen Psychiatry. 1995 Dec;52(12):1048-60. https://doi.org/10.1001/archpsyc.1995.03950240066012

[597] Trezza V, Campolongo P. The endocannabinoid system as a possible target to treat both the cognitive and emotional features of post-traumatic stress disorder (PTSD). Front Behav Neurosci. 2013 Aug 9;7:100. https://doi.org/10.3389/fnbeh.2013.00100

[598] Niyuhire F, Varvel SA, Martin BR, Lichtman AH. Exposure to marijuana smoke impairs memory retrieval in mice. J Pharmacol Exp Ther. 2007 Sep;322(3):1067-75. https://doi.org/10.1124/jpet.107.119594

[599] Atsak P, Roozendaal B, Campolongo P. Role of the endocannabinoid system in regulating glucocorticoid effects on memory for emotional experiences. Neuroscience. 2012 Mar 1;204:104-16. https://doi.org/10.1016/j.neuroscience.2011.08.047

[600] Marsicano G, Lafenêtre P. Roles of the endocannabinoid system in learning and memory. Curr Top Behav Neurosci. 2009;1:201-30. https://doi.org/10.1007/978-3-540-88955-7_8

[601] Lutz B. The endoc annabinoid system and extinction learning. Mol Neurobiol. 2007 Aug;36(1):92-101. https://doi.org/10.1007/s12035-007-8004-x

[602] Campolongo, P., Trezza, V., Palmery, M., Trabace, L., & Cuomo, V. (2009). Developmental exposure to cannabinoids causes subtle and enduring neurofunctional alterations. International review of neurobiology, 85, 117-133. https://www.nature.com/articles/npp2017162#article-info

[603] Hauer D, Ratano P, Morena M, Scaccianoce S, Briegel I, Palmery M, Cuomo V, Roozendaal B, Schelling G, Campolongo P. Propofol enhances memory formation via an interaction with the endocannabinoid system. Anesthesiology. 2011 Jun;114(6):1380-8. https://doi.org/10.1097/aln.0b013e31821c120e

[604] Ganon-Elazar E, Akirav I. Cannabinoids and traumatic stress modulation of contextual fear extinction and GR expression in the amygdala-hippocampal-prefrontal circuit. Psychoneuroendocrinology. 2013 Sep;38(9):1675-87. https://doi.org/10.1016/j.psyneuen.2013.01.014

[605] Ganon-Elazar E, Akirav I. Cannabinoid receptor activation in the basolateral amygdala blocks the effects of stress on the conditioning and extinction of inhibitory avoidance. J Neurosci. 2009 Sep 9;29(36):11078-88. https://doi.org/10.1523/jneurosci.1223-09.2009

[606] Ganon-Elazar E, Akirav I. Cannabinoids prevent the development of behavioral and endocrine alterations in a rat model of intense stress. Neuropsychopharmacology. 2012 Jan;37(2):456-66. https://doi.org/10.1038/npp.2011.204

help sleeping through the night.[607] It is speculated that this is because Cannabis use is often associated with reduced instances or conscious recall of dreams while sleeping. This could then mean that nightmares could be reduced or extinguished by cannabinoid receptor manipulation.

## CANNABIS USE AND SCHIZOPHRENIA

Patients with schizophrenia often consume Cannabis.[608] Some researchers have proposed that risks for both schizophrenia and Cannabis use are linked to common genetic causes, leading to high rates of comorbidity.[609] The effects of long-term Cannabis use in conjunction with schizophrenia are not well understood. A study performed in 2014 attempted to review published studies investigating the effects of Cannabis on schizophrenia symptoms. The researchers concluded that there is still not enough information to draw any practical conclusions about whether Cannabis improves or worsens the mental health of individuals with schizophrenia.[610] Many of the published studies so far report very small sample sizes, limiting the quality of the results. Different patterns in data may emerge when larger sample sizes are utilized.

A 2010 meta-analysis of Cannabis use in patients with schizophrenia published in the *Schizophrenia Bulletin* revealed that, of the data that was then available, schizophrenia patients that had also used Cannabis performed better on tests of visual memory, working memory, and executive functioning than patients that had not used Cannabis. This trend is generally associated specifically with chronic use of Cannabis. In contrast, the same 2010 study also found that schizophrenic patients that use Cannabis also tended to have displayed earlier ages of onset and more positive symptoms. If other substances, like cocaine or alcohol, are used in conjunction with Cannabis, mental performance usually decreases compared to the use of Cannabis alone.[611]

## CANNABIS USE AND HALLUCINATIONS

There is some evidence that Cannabis use may elicit auditory hallucinations, most remarkably in the form of "speech-illusions" while listening to white noise. Researchers in the Clinical Psychopharmacology Unit at University College in London presented participants with white noise and vaporized Cannabis or placebo and found:

*"On placebo, 35% of adolescents and 15% of adults heard speech illusion during the 'random noise only' stimuli, compared to 55% of adolescents and 45% of*

---

[607] Bonn-Miller, MO, Babson, KA, Vandrey, R. 2014. Using cannabis to help you sleep: Heightened frequency of medical cannabis use among those with PTSD. Drug and Alcohol Dependence. 136:162-165. https://doi.org/10.1016/j.drugalcdep.2013.12.008

[608] Koskinen J, Löhönen J, Koponen H, Isohanni M, Miettunen J. Rate of cannabis use disorders in clinical samples of patients with schizophrenia: a meta-analysis. Schizophr Bull. 2010 Nov;36(6):1115-30. https://doi.org/10.1093/schbul/sbp031

[609] Power RA, Verweij KJ, Zuhair M, Montgomery GW, Henders AK, Heath AC, Madden PA, Medland SE, Wray NR, Martin NG. Genetic predisposition to schizophrenia associated with increased use of cannabis. Mol Psychiatry. 2014 Nov;19(11):1201-4. https://doi.org/10.1038/mp.2014.51

[610] McLoughlin BC, Pushpa-Rajah JA, Gillies D, Rathbone J, Variend H, Kalakouti E, Kyprianou K. Cannabis and schizophrenia. Cochrane Database Syst Rev. 2014 Oct 14;(10):CD004837. https://doi.org/10.1002/14651858.cd004837.pub3

[611] Yücel M, Bora E, Lubman DI, Solowij N, Brewer WJ, Cotton SM, Conus P, Takagi MJ, Fornito A, Wood SJ, McGorry PD, Pantelis C. The impact of cannabis use on cognitive functioning in patients with schizophrenia: a meta-analysis of existing findings and new data in a first-episode sample. Schizophr Bull. 2012 Mar;38(2):316-30. https://doi.org/10.1093/schbul/sbq079

*adults on active cannabis. As predicted, relative to placebo, active cannabis led to a greater likelihood of experiencing speech illusion…"*[612]

Visual hallucinations are rarely reported from Cannabis use but may occur upon ingestion of very large doses. A study in 2006 looked to replicate another study examining whether Cannabis use in schizophrenic patients is associated with changes in hallucination symptoms. The authors conclude,

> *"The strong association between cannabis abuse and fewer negative symptoms in schizophrenia was thus replicated in this sample, but once co-morbid addictive disorders had been controlled no influence of cannabis abuse on hallucinations was detected."*[613]

It is more common for paranoid or delusional behavior or thinking to be reported after Cannabis use, though these symptoms are not really hallucinations, per se, but would be considered psychomimetic, or "imitating psychosis".

## CANNABIS, ANXIETY, AND PANIC ATTACK DISORDER

Cannabis' anxiety and paranoia inducing effects are generally well known and documented. Acute doses of Cannabis can induce fear, anxiety, and phobia.[614] One research group found that 21% of their study's subjects that used Cannabis had high levels of anxiety.[615] Cannabis use in teenagers and young adults is often associated with heightened levels of anxiety.[616] Cannabis use and panic attack disorder are also often comorbid.

There is debate about whether Cannabis can help treat anxiety and panic attack disorder or if it purely exacerbates anxiety and panic conditions. Although there is evidence supporting the idea that Cannabis can contribute to anxiety and panic attack disorder, there is also a growing body of evidence that *long-term* users of Cannabis achieve relief from anxiety and panic attack.[617]

Anxiety caused by Cannabis use is most likely to occur if the user is less familiar with the drug's effects, if the individual consumes Cannabis in a new or stressful

---

[612] Mokrysz C, Shaban N, Freeman TP, Curran HV. 2017. Acute effects of cannabis on the experience of speech illusion: a placebo-controlled study in adolescents and adults. European Neuropsychopharmacology. 27(1):S73

[613] Dubertret C, Bidard I, Ades J, Gorwood P. 2006. Lifetime positive symptoms in patients with schizophrenia and cannabis abuse are partially explained by co-morbid addiction. Schizophrenia Research. 86:284-290. https://doi.org/10.1016/j.schres.2006.05.006

[614] Crippa, JA, Zuardi, AW, Martin-Santos, R, Bhattacharyya, S, Atakan, Z, McGuire, P, Fusar-Poli, P. 2009. Cannabis and anxiety: a critical review of the evidence. Hum. Psychopharmacol Clin Exp. 24(7):515-523. https://doi.org/10.1002/hup.1048

[615] Reilly D, Didcott P, Swift W, Hall W. Long-term cannabis use: characteristics of users in an Australian rural area. Addiction. 1998 Jun;93(6):837-46. https://doi.org/10.1046/j.1360-0443.1998.9368375.x

[616] Dorard G, Berthoz S, Phan O, Corcos M, Bungener C. Affect dysregulation in cannabis abusers: a study in adolescents and young adults. Eur Child Adolesc Psychiatry. 2008 Aug;17(5):274-82. https://doi.org/10.1007/s00787-007-0663-7

[617] Crippa, JA, Zuardi, AW, Martin-Santos, R, Bhattacharyya, S, Atakan, Z, McGuire, P, Fusar-Poli, P. 2009. Cannabis and anxiety: a critical review of the evidence. Hum. Psychopharmacol Clin Exp. 24(7):515-523. https://doi.org/10.1002/hup.1048

environment, or if the individual consumes high concentrations of cannabinoids or Cannabis products. Crippa et al (2009) proposed this list of risk factors for anxiety produced by the consumption of Cannabis:

- Individual and Genetic Vulnerability
- Personality Traits
- Gender
- Frequency of Use
- Dose
- Proportions and concentration of cannabinoids

- History of previous anxiety episode
- Presence of anxiety disorders/symptoms
- Basal anxiety levels
- Abstinence states
- Environment and context of use (set and setting)

To minimize anxiety symptoms and risk of panic when consuming Cannabis,

➢ Familiarize yourself with Cannabis and its associated effects.
➢ Be careful consuming Cannabis in new settings.
➢ Avoid consuming Cannabis in uncomfortable or stressful settings.
➢ Be aware of the potency of the Cannabis product and monitor your dose.
➢ Schedule consumption appropriately. The psychoactive effects of inhaled Cannabis typically last approximately two to three hours. The effects of ingested Cannabis could last much longer.

## Is Cannabis Addictive?

Cannabinoids elicit effects from the brain's reward centers in much the same way as other drugs or pleasurable behaviors, potentially leading to dependence and tolerance symptoms. **After sudden cessation of chronic Cannabis use, non-life-threatening withdrawal symptoms can emerge such as sleeplessness, loss of appetite, depression, and irritation**. Although these withdrawal symptoms are often reported to be much milder than withdrawal symptoms from other substances of abuse including alcohol, nicotine, and caffeine, some users attempting cessation report relatively profound withdrawal symptoms for up to two weeks or longer after cessation.

When addressing the question of whether Cannabis is addictive, it is important to first define the term "addiction". Addiction is often characterized by compulsive behavior, despite negative consequences. The concept of "addiction" is often broken up into two primary categories: substance addiction (previously often referred to as chemical dependence) and process (or behavioral) addiction. A substance dependence is usually defined as a state of being in which the body reduces its own production of endogenous chemical compounds, creating a dependence for exogenous (outside the body) chemical compounds to avoid withdrawal effects. Process addictions are characterized as behavioral addictions that do not feature the administration of exogenous chemical compounds but still feature characteristics like tolerance, withdrawal, repetitive reward seeking behavior, and continued behavior despite negative consequences. Examples of process addictions include gambling addictions, shopping addictions, exercise addictions, etc.

Today it is more common to encounter the concept of substance use disorder spectra when studying addiction. The DSM-V, a diagnostic manual that mental health professionals use to diagnose behavioral and psychological disorders, identifies Cannabis Use Disorder as one of these substance use disorders, but is careful to point out that

Cannabis Use Disorder should not be diagnosed if the *only* symptom(s) a patient exhibits is the typical tolerance and/or withdrawal symptoms associated with the medical use of Cannabis (or any other drug). A key component of diagnosing substance use disorder is drug seeking or use behavior that *compromises relationships and obligations*. It should be noted, though, that a diagnosis of substance use disorder does not necessarily imply the presence of a chemical dependency on the substance. It simply reflects the fact that the substance is taken frequently despite consequences.

Some research has explored whether the potency of Cannabis has any effect on the likelihood of developing dependence symptoms. One report found that the symptoms of Cannabis dependence increase when tobacco is consumed in conjunction with Cannabis (Ream et al, 2008). Some evidence supporting the concept of Cannabis dependence lies in the fact that the brain experiences a deficit in dopamine release in certain areas of the brain during chronic Cannabis use (Giessen et al, 2016). Dopamine is a neurotransmitter commonly associated with pleasure and reward perceptions and behaviors. Primarily substance dependence is defined neurologically as decreased or blunted dopamine levels in the brain. If cannabis produces decreased functioning of dopamine receptors after use, an argument could be made that cannabis can produce dependence in users. The user would develop a need to stimulate dopamine receptors through the introduction of chemicals outside of the body because the body would not produce dopamine as easily on its own.

Cannabinoids do not cause the same sort of stark chemical dependencies that many other common drugs of abuse such as opiates or stimulants might cause. This may be because cannabinoids and their metabolites become stored in adipose, or fatty, tissue and steadily release over time after cessation of use. It may also be because phytocannabinoids do not cause drastic changes to the way the body produces its own cannabinoids.

To understand why the symptoms of Cannabis withdrawal are often mild, it is critical to understand the common cause of physical withdrawal symptoms. One of the causes for withdrawal is the body's sudden lack of a necessary neurotransmitter, which causes a myriad of physical problems. This generally happens because the targets of many drugs of abuse, like serotonin and dopamine, are slowly built up by the body, stored in little sacks called vesicles, and released on demand. When someone takes a drug like cocaine, it triggers a distinct release of chemicals from these vesicles in the brain, which the brain had spent considerable time building up. Once those chemicals are dumped and depleted, there is a considerable deficit, and the body must take time to recover. This physiological deficit is what produces most physical withdrawal effects. If this happens repeatedly, the body may stop producing endogenous compounds and depend on exogenous compounds, resulting in chemical dependence.

However, the body does not store endocannabinoids in vesicles like it does with serotonin and dopamine. Instead, endocannabinoids are synthesized on demand, as needed, escaping this effect of chemical dumping and deficit. However, repeated Cannabis use *can* cause a reduction in concentration of cannabinoid receptors in the body, leading to a tolerance effect, because there are fewer receptors to stimulate, resulting in less of an effect experienced by the user. Some cannabinoids, like CBD, can stimulate the body's own production of endogenous compounds.

To review, neurologically there may be evidence that Cannabis causes mild dependency, based on how Cannabis affects dopamine in the brain. Mental health professionals recognize a condition called Cannabis Use Disorder, which may or may not feature chemical dependency. Cannabis use does lead to tolerance and withdrawal symptoms. Typically, these withdrawal symptoms are relatively mild because the body rarely experiences a very sudden deficit of cannabinoids like it might with other targets of drugs of abuse, although some users report difficulty quitting or maintaining abstinence from Cannabis use. At the end of the day, if someone's Cannabis use is persisting despite negative consequences to the user and the user's relationships, it is highly probable that a substance addiction is present.

## ADOLESCENT CANNABIS USE

There is much debate over whether children are at a greater risk of developing long-term adverse health effects from THC-rich Cannabis consumption. There is some research that suggests that adolescent THC-rich Cannabis use can cause impaired adult memory function, particularly regarding emotional memory.[618]

A study published recently that investigated data from a longitudinal study found that adolescent Cannabis use did not seem to correlate with any significant mental or physical health risks later in life.[619] Other studies typically rely on broad drug-use survey data collected from school surveys which may or may not be reliable. Most studies looking at childhood Cannabis use are not longitudinal studies that follow subjects into adulthood. Many of these studies do not exclude confounding factors like cigarette smoking, non-Cannabis related health complications, diet, exercise, etc. More long-term research will have to be conducted before the long-term health effects of Cannabis use started during adolescence can be properly evaluated.

A negative effect that Cannabis use can have on adolescents is that it may affect the developing child's social behavior negatively, potentially delaying or stunting the child's emotional maturation and development of sophisticated social skills. If a child consumes Cannabis and consequently reduces social interaction or begins to associate Cannabis use with common activities like eating, entertainment, sports, etc, it may become difficult for the individual to later find as much pleasure in those activities without consuming Cannabis.

Cannabis' deleterious effects on memory can have profound consequences for a child's ability to learn. Cannabis can affect a person's ability to concentrate on a topic or comprehend complex information as is required in a school setting. Over time, if an individual repeatedly consumes Cannabis and has persistent difficulties keeping up with school, there may be a variety of other cultural and social consequences such as lower grades and less available educational and professional opportunities later in life.

---

[618] Ballinger MD, Saito A, Abazyan B, Taniguchi Y, Huang CH, Ito K, Zhu X, Segal H, Jaaro-Peled H, Sawa A, Mackie K, Pletnikov MV, Kamiya A. Adolescent cannabis exposure interacts with mutant DISC1 to produce impaired adult emotional memory. Neurobiol Dis. 2015 Oct;82:176-184. https://doi.org/10.1016/j.nbd.2015.06.006

[619] Bechtold J, Hipwell A, Lewis DA, Loeber R, Pardini D. Concurrent and Sustained Cumulative Effects of Adolescent Marijuana Use on Subclinical Psychotic Symptoms. Am J Psychiatry. 2016 Aug 1;173(8):781-9. https://doi.org/10.1176/appi.ajp.2016.15070878

# OTHER EFFECTS OF THC-RICH CANNABIS USE

## EFFECTS OF CANNABIS USE ON INSULIN SENSITIVITY AND BLOOD GLUCOSE STORAGE

There has been a long running debate over whether Cannabis helps a person lose weight. Many Cannabis consumers consume excess calories, but do not appear to be more overweight on average than non-Cannabis consumers. It turns out that there is some interesting science behind this idea.

Penner et al. examined data of Cannabis use, insulin levels, and blood glucose for over 4000 adult men and women and determined that individuals that were current users had on average **16% lower fasting insulin levels and smaller waist circumference**.[620] Fasting insulin is the insulin present in your blood before eating a meal. High insulin levels are typically associated with obesity.

Insulin helps glucose, or sugar, enter cells of tissues for storage or processing. When insulin binds to an insulin receptor on a cell, it triggers a cascade of effects. Channels on the cell wall are opened which allow glucose to enter. The glucose is then typically converted to a compound called pyruvate, which is then broken down into basic carbon chains, or fatty acids. Alternatively, glucose may end up getting linked together to form glycogen. This process is how the body stores energy away for later use. Glycogen is typically stored in muscles and the liver, while fatty acids are stored in adipose, or fatty, tissue throughout the body. When fatty acids and glycogen are metabolized, energy is released which fuels the work of the rest of the body.

Higher levels of insulin in a healthy person without insulin tolerance usually indicate that sugar will be readily processed and stored in tissues throughout the body. Lower fasting insulin levels would mean that sugar will have a harder time getting converted to fat, theoretically leading to smaller waist circumference on average, although this same effect could also result in significant increases in blood glucose (blood sugar).

Another study found that active Cannabis smoking seemed associated with **reduced incidences of diabetes mellitus**.[621] The authors of the study point out that the relationship is contrary to results obtained from previous preclinical animal studies and more research is needed to understand this effect.

Another study has found that Cannabis use is associated with a **lower risk of insulin resistance in HIV patients**. Insulin resistance is a serious condition preceding type 2 diabetes and heart disease in which the body's cells become resistant to insulin, so insulin ends up building up in the blood without serving a function. This can lead to increased blood pressure, obesity, and dyslipidemia. **Dyslipidemia** is a condition in which

---

[620] Penner EA, Buettner H, Mittleman MA. The impact of marijuana use on glucose, insulin, and insulin resistance among US adults. Am J Med. 2013 Jul;126(7):583-9. https://doi.org/10.1016/j.amjmed.2013.03.002

[621] Alshaarawy O, Anthony JC. Cannabis Smoking and Diabetes Mellitus: Results from Meta-analysis with Eight Independent Replication Samples. Epidemiology. 2015 Jul;26(4):597-600. https://doi.org/10.1097/ede.0000000000000314

there are elevated amounts of fats and other lipids in the blood because they are not being stored in other cells, either due to saturation or insulin resistance.

## EFFECTS OF CANNABIS ON THE IMMUNE SYSTEM

CB2 receptors are expressed in a variety of immune system cells including B and T lymphocytes, Th1 cells, Th2 cells, Treg cells, Macrophages, microglia, and natural killer cells.[622] Generally, **cannabinoids act as immunosuppressants**, meaning they inhibit the immune system response in one or more ways. Although most *in vitro* and *in vivo* research indicates a potent immunosuppressive effect of THC and CBD, research examining viral load in HIV positive patients indicates that neither smoked Cannabis nor synthetic THC seems to cause any negative effects on viral load over a 21-day.[623] [624]

**Cannabinoids primarily modulate the immune system by affecting cytokines**. Cytokines are a group of small proteins that affect cellular communication to help guide immune system cells toward areas of inflammation, infection, etc. Some cytokines are pro-inflammatory, while others are anti-inflammatory. **THC and CBD dampen the response of pro-inflammatory cytokines** and enhance the response of anti-inflammatory cytokines.[625]

Understanding how cannabinoids affect the immune system could lead to better treatment options for patients with inflammatory neurodegenerative diseases like Alzheimer's disease, Parkinson's disease, and Amyotrophic lateral sclerosis, as well as autoimmune disorders in which the patients are slaves to their own overactive immune systems, such as Behcet's disease, psoriasis, multiple sclerosis, rheumatoid arthritis, and more.

## EFFECTS OF CANNABIS ON HEART HEALTH

Cannabis can elicit numerous cardiovascular effects depending on the dominant cannabinoids present. Different cannabinoids have a variety of effects on the heart. The research on this topic is a bit difficult to wade through because cannabinoid effects on the heart, and other systems of the body, are dose dependent and can bring out varying effects and varying dosages.

Researchers found that when anesthetized animals are given THC, often blood pressure reduces, or alternatively blood pressure rises at first and then comes down followed by a condition called **bradycardia**, or an abnormal slowing of heart rate.[626] CBN has not typically affected heart rate or blood pressure when administered by itself.

---

[622] Galiègue S, Mary S, Marchand J, Dussossoy D, Carrière D, Carayon P, Bouaboula M, Shire D, Le Fur G, Casellas P. Expression of central and peripheral cannabinoid receptors in human immune tissues and leukocyte subpopulations. Eur J Biochem. 1995 Aug 15;232(1):54-61. https://doi.org/10.1111/j.1432-1033.1995.tb20780.x

[623] Abrams DI, Hilton JF, Leiser RJ, et al. 2003. Short-term effects of cannabinoids in patients with HIV-1 infection: a randomized, placebo-controlled clinical trial. Annals of Internal Medicine. 139:258-266. https://doi.org/10.7326/0003-4819-139-4-200308190-00008

[624] Ware MA. 2015. Synthetic Psychoactive Cannabinoids Licensed as Medicines. Handbook of Cannabis. Oxford University Press. Chapter 21. pp. 393-414.

[625] Cabral GA, Raborn ES, Ferreira GA. 2015. Phytocannabinoids and the Immune System. Handbook of Cannabis. Oxford University Press. 261-279.

[626] O'Sullivan SE, Kendall DA, Randall MD. 2004. Characterisation of the vasorelaxant properties of the novel endocannabinoid N-arachidonoyl-dopamine (NADA). Bri J of Pharm. 141:803-812. https://doi.org/10.1038/sj.bjp.0705643

In conscious humans, these effects are bit less predictable. Based on research done for the commercial cannabinoid product Sativex®, a product containing a 1:1 ratio of THC to CBD, researchers found that both Sativex® and smoked Cannabis cause **tachycardia**, or rapid heartbeat, with this effect decreasing among chronic users.[627] In other studies, both THC and THCV have been demonstrated as **vasoconstrictors**.

CBD alone seems to cause a reduction in heart rate and blood pressure in animal models, and this effect may be mediated by serotonin receptors, as administering a serotonin receptor antagonist blocks this action.[628] Several research reports indicate that long term administration of CBD does not result in a change to blood pressure or heart rate in subjects, but more research is needed to better understand how CBD affects the human cardiovascular system.[629] [630]

### EFFECTS OF CANNABIS ON THE STOMACH AND GASTROINTESTINAL SYSTEM

Endocannabinoid receptors are distributed throughout the gastrointestinal system including the stomach, gut, and colon. Endocannabinoids like 2-AG have been implicated as serving a protective role in the stomach.[631] CB1 receptor activation has been shown to reduce gastrointestinal motility in rodent models.[632] CB1 and CB2 receptor agonism is associated with reduced visceral sensitivity and pain in rodents.[633] CB1 and CB2 receptor agonism has also been demonstrated to effectively alleviate inflammation in models of Irritable Bowel Disease/Syndrome (IBD/IBS). These effects could be critical to treating painful GI inflammatory conditions like Crohn's Disease.

Referring to a retrospective observational study of Irritable Bowel Disease/Syndrome by Naftali et al (2011), Duncan and Izzo report:

> *"Of the 30 patients, 21 improved significantly after treatment with cannabis. The need for other medication was significantly reduced and the number of patients requiring surgery decreased during cannabis use."*

Cannabinoids have also been shown to have effects limiting colon cancer. Some cannabinoids have been shown effective at promoting apoptosis of colon cancer cells as

---

[627] Karschner, E., Darwin, W., McMahon, R., Liu, F., Wright, S., Goodwin, R. and Huestis, M. (2011), Subjective and Physiological Effects After Controlled Sativex and Oral THC Administration. Clinical Pharmacology & Therapeutics, 89: 400-407. https://doi.org/10.1038/clpt.2010.318

[628] O'Sullivan, S. E. (2015). Endocannabinoids and the cardiovascular system in health and disease. Endocannabinoids, 393-422.

[629] Benowitz NL, Jones RT. 1981. Cardiovascular effects of prolonged delta-9-tetrahydrocannbinol ingestion. Clinical Pharmacology and Therapeutics. 18-287-297. https://doi.org/10.1002/cpt1975183287

[630] Machado Bergamaschi, M., Helena Costa Queiroz, R., Waldo Zuardi, A., & Crippa, A. S. (2011). Safety and side effects of cannabidiol, a Cannabis sativa constituent. Current drug safety, 6(4), 237-249. https://doi.org/10.2174/157488611798280924

[631] Kinsey SG, Nomura DK, O'Neal ST, Long JZ, Mahadevan A, Cravatt BF, Grider JR, Lichtman AH. 2011. Inhibition of monoacylglycerol lipase attenuates nonsteroidal anti-inflammatory drug-induced gastric hemorrhages in mice. J Pharmacol Exp Ther. 338(3):795-802. https://doi.org/10.1124/jpet.110.175778

[632] Pinto L, Capasso R, Di Carlo G, Izzo AA. 2002. Endocannabinoids and the gut. Prostaglandins, Leukotrienes and Essential Fatty Acids. 66:333-341. https://doi.org/10.1054/plef.2001.0345

[633] Duncan, M., & Izzo, A. A. (2015). Phytocannabinoids and the gastrointestinal system. Handbook of Cannabis, 227-244.

well as limiting the cancer's proliferation. The oxidation of CBD leads to a compound called HU-331 which has demonstrated antiangiogenic and proapoptotic properties.[634]

Beyond cannabinoid receptors, vanilloid receptors also play important roles in the gastrointestinal system. Many cannabinoids interact with both TRPV1 and TRPV2 receptors including CBD, CBG, CBGV, and THCV.[635] One study has shown that CBC interacts with TRPV1, TRPV3, and TRPV4 receptors in the GI tract.[636] Vanilloid and cannabinoid receptors occur together in primary afferent nerves in the gut.[637]

Although Cannabis is sometimes used to treat nausea, it seems that chronic consumption of Cannabis in some users can precipitate nausea symptoms and even chronic vomiting in a condition referred to as Cannabinoid Hyperemesis Syndrome. Individuals suffering with this condition often learn various coping behaviors like frequent hot showers or baths, which help reduce the nausea. This condition was recognized relatively recently, and it is still unclear how prevalent Cannabinoid Hyperemesis Syndrome is, but symptoms typically are relieved through cessation of Cannabis use.

### EFFECTS OF CANNABIS ON SEX AND REPRODUCTION

As mentioned previously, the endocannabinoid system is intricately linked to the reproduction system in humans. Besides the ECS' involvement with various sexual hormones, the ECS is also associated with sperm availability in men and ova availability in women, implantation, basic physiology of the reproductive tract, and mating behavior.[638]

Gonadal hormones influence the endocannabinoid system, and endocannabinoids influence hormones. It turns out that endocannabinoid system components are found all throughout the hypothalamic-pituitary-gonadal (HPG) axis which controls reproduction and development. Rodent research indicates that females may produce more CB1 receptors if they lose function of their ovaries compared to females with intact reproductive systems.[639]

---

[634] Peters M, Kogan NM. HU-331: a cannabinoid quinone, with uncommon cytotoxic properties and low toxicity. Expert Opin Investig Drugs. 2007 Sep;16(9):1405-13. https://doi.org/10.1517/13543784.16.9.1405

[635] De Petrocellis L, Ligresti A, Moriello AS, Allarà M, Bisogno T, Petrosino S, Stott CG, Di Marzo V. Effects of cannabinoids and cannabinoid-enriched Cannabis extracts on TRP channels and endocannabinoid metabolic enzymes. Br J Pharmacol. 2011 Aug;163(7):1479-94. https://doi.org/10.1111/j.1476-5381.2010.01166.x

[636] De Petrocellis L, Orlando P, Moriello AS, Aviello G, Stott C, Izzo AA, Di Marzo V. Cannabinoid actions at TRPV channels: effects on TRPV3 and TRPV4 and their potential relevance to gastrointestinal inflammation. Acta Physiol (Oxf). 2012 Feb;204(2):255-66. https://doi.org/10.1111/j.1748-1716.2011.02338.x

[637] Izzo AA, Sharkey KA. Cannabinoids and the gut: new developments and emerging concepts. Pharmacol Ther. 2010 Apr;126(1):21-38. https://doi.org/10.1016/j.pharmthera.2009.12.005

[638] Stuart, J. M., Leishman, E., & Bradshaw, H. B. (2014). Reproduction and Cannabinoids: Ups and Downs, Ins and Outs. Handbook of Cannabis, 245.

[639] Castelli MP, Fadda P, Casu A, Spano MS, Casti A, Fratta W, Fattore L. Male and female rats differ in brain cannabinoid CB1 receptor density and function and in behavioural traits predisposing to drug addiction: effect of ovarian hormones. Curr Pharm Des. 2014;20(13):2100-13. https://doi.org/10.2174/13816128113199990430

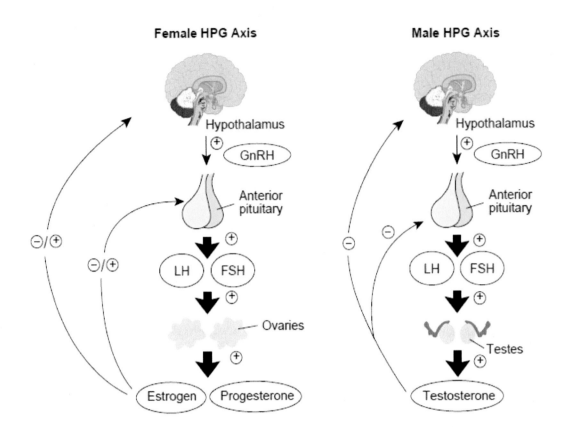

**Figure 63 Diagrams of the HPG Axis in Women and Men**

(From Kong et al, 2014) [640]

    Cannabinoids are involved in the release of a compound called gonadotropin-releasing hormone (GNRH) which influences the development of reproductive structures in the body. THC seems to have varying effects between males and females. A research study that examined how ovariectomized female rats (rats with ovaries removed) respond to THC with and without the addition of a sex hormone and found that the ovariectomized rats experienced less pain relief than those with the added hormone. [641] [642] More of the differences in cannabinoid receptor expression and cannabinoid pharmacology between men and women is discussed in the next section.

---

[640] Kong, Lu, Meng Tang, Ting Zhang, Dayong Wang, Ke Hu, Weiqi Lu, Chao Wei, Geyu Liang, and Yuepu Pu. 2014. "Nickel Nanoparticles Exposure and Reproductive Toxicity in Healthy Adult Rats" International Journal of Molecular Sciences 15, no. 11: 21253-21269. https://doi.org/10.3390/ijms151121253

[641] Craft, R. M., & Leitl, M. D. (2008). Gonadal hormone modulation of the behavioral effects of Δ9-tetrahydrocannabinol in male and female rats. European journal of pharmacology, 578(1), 37-42. https://doi.org/10.1016/j.ejphar.2007.09.004

[642] Stuart, J. M., Leishman, E., & Bradshaw, H. B. (2014). Reproduction and Cannabinoids: Ups and Downs, Ins and Outs. Handbook of Cannabis, 245.

It should be noted that at least one case study has suggested that the swings in blood pressure caused by cannabinoids, combined with the swings in blood pressure caused by the act of sex and orgasm, reportedly caused a stroke in a male subject.[643]

In men, the cannabinoid system may be linked to the regulation of erectile functioning. CB1 receptors are present on the neurons responsible for signaling the production of neurotransmitters and other compounds that cause erections.[644] In one study, researchers administered a CB1 antagonist to the paraventricular nucleus of the hypothalamus in the brains of male rats which induced erections.[645] It is possible that Cannabis use could impair reproductive ability for males as Cannabis smoke causes an increase in compounds that can cause oxidative damage in the body, which is associated with poor sperm quality, low fertilization rates, increased abortion rates, and increased incidence of disease in offspring.

In women, low doses of Cannabis may excite the libido, while increased doses are likely to depress the libido, though this effect is not consistent among women. This enhancement effect does not seem to extend to other characteristics like level of vaginal lubrication, orgasm frequency, or orgasm strength.[646] It is speculated that Cannabis was at one time, or another, used for several sex or reproductive treatments including menstrual irregularity, dysmenorrheal, childbirth, decreased libido, gonorrhea, urinary retention, menopausal symptoms, and more.[647]

Some epidemiological studies have found that Cannabis use during pregnancy is associated with low birth weight, cognitive defects, and other negative birth outcomes, but these studies are still limited in their ability to determine causality as they are often plagued by confounding variables like diet, cigarette and alcohol use, exercise, etc. At the same time, other longitudinal studies have determined that prenatal Cannabis exposure was not associated with these effects but rather does seem to be associated with hyperactivity and impulsivity in offspring, however the significance of the correlation weakens when other extraneous variables are considered.[648] [649]

In one study of mothers in Jamaica, researchers determined that babies that had been exposed to Cannabis during breastfeeding as newborns exhibited no differences

---

[643] Álvaro, L.C., Iriondo, I. and Villaverde, F.J. (2002), Sexual Headache and Stroke in a Heavy Cannabis Smoker. Headache: The Journal of Head and Face Pain, 42: 224-226. https://doi.org/10.1046/j.1526-4610.2002.02056.x

[644] Stuart, J. M., Leishman, E., & Bradshaw, H. B. (2014). Reproduction and Cannabinoids: Ups and Downs, Ins and Outs. Handbook of Cannabis, 245.

[645] Shamloul, R., & Bella, A. J. (2011). Impact of cannabis use on male sexual health. The journal of sexual medicine, 8(4), 971-975. https://doi.org/10.1111/j.1743-6109.2010.02198.x

[646] Gorzalka, B. B., Hill, M. N., & Chang, S. C. (2010). Male–female differences in the effects of cannabinoids on sexual behavior and gonadal hormone function. Hormones and behavior, 58(1), 91-99. https://doi.org/10.1016/j.yhbeh.2009.08.009

[647] Russo E. 2002. Cannabis treatments in obstetrics and gynecology: a historical review. Journal of Cannabis Therapeutics. 2:5-35. https://doi.org/10.1300/J175v02n03_02

[648] Goldschmidt, L., Day, N. L., & Richardson, G. A. (2000). Effects of prenatal marijuana exposure on child behavior problems at age 10. Neurotoxicology and teratology, 22(3), 325-336. https://doi.org/10.1016/S0892-0362(00)00066-0

[649] Fried, P. A., & Smith, A. M. (2001). A literature review of the consequences of prenatal marihuana exposure: an emerging theme of a deficiency in aspects of executive function. Neurotoxicology and teratology, 23(1), 1-11. https://doi.org/10.1016/S0892-0362(00)00119-7

from babies that had not been exposed to Cannabis.[650] During a five year follow up for a similar study that instead focused on Cannabis exposure during pregnancy, these results were confirmed. In fact, those children that had been exposed to Cannabis during pregnancy tested better for autonomic stability and reflex behavior. Researchers concluded that aspects related to school attendance and home environment were more predictive of child outcomes than Cannabis exposure during pregnancy.[651]

In Reproduction and Cannabinoids: Ups and Downs, Ins and Outs, the writers offer this sentiment:

> "Although it is not certain that smoking cannabis when pregnant harms the fetus, it is probably unwise to subject a developing nervous system to exogenous cannabinoids because it could potentially disrupt the endogenous cannabinoid system, a system that ensures proper neural development."[652]

### HOW DO MEN AND WOMEN EXPERIENCE CANNABIS DIFFERENTLY?

Unfortunately, women, people of color, and LGBTQIA+ individuals are drastically under-represented in medical research. It is very common for medical research data derived primarily from Caucasian cisgender male and/or female patient populations to be assumed to be directly applicable to all other types of people in the world – which is simply not the case. Physiology is complex, and people are complex. This issue is confounded even more by the presence of well-documented racial, gender, and social class biases among physicians which often leads to under-reporting of clinical data, misrepresentation of clinical cases, and other issues that compromise the quality of medical data being used to form conclusions.[653] [654] [655]

Despite these limitations in medical research, a fair number of investigations of the differences in endocannabinoid system expression between male and female rodents has been extensive. Because we know that the endocannabinoid system is intimately connected to the HPG axis and hormone signaling, we also know that biologically male presenting and biologically female presenting bodies will respond to Cannabis differently, due to their differing hormone profiles.

---

[650] Dreher MC, Nugent K, Hudgins R. 1994. Prenatal Marijuana Exposure and Neonatal Outcomes in Jamaica: An Ethnographic Study. Pediatrics. 93(2): 254-260. https://pubmed.ncbi.nlm.nih.gov/8121737/
[651] Hayes JS, Lampart R, Dreher MC, Morgan L. 1991. Five-year Follow-Up of Rural Jamaican Children Whose Mothers Used Marijuana During Pregnancy. West Indian Med J. 40(3): 120-123. https://pubmed.ncbi.nlm.nih.gov/1957518/
[652] Stuart, J. M., Leishman, E., & Bradshaw, H. B. (2014). Reproduction and Cannabinoids: Ups and Downs, Ins and Outs. Handbook of Cannabis, 245.
[653] Hamberg K. Gender bias in medicine. Womens Health (Lond). 2008 May;4(3):237-43. https://doi.org/10.2217/17455057.4.3.237
[654] Garb, H. N. (1997). Race bias, social class bias, and gender bias in clinical judgment. Clinical Psychology: Science and Practice, 4(2), 99–120. https://doi.org/10.1111/j.1468-2850.1997.tb00104.x
[655] Garb HN. Race bias and gender bias in the diagnosis of psychological disorders. Clin Psychol Rev. 2021 Dec;90:102087. https://doi.org/10.1016/j.cpr.2021.102087

Women feature more CB1 receptors in the cerebellum, prefrontal cortex, amygdala, and hippocampus compared to men.[656] [657] These parts of the brain are responsible for motor coordination, emotional regulation, and memory among other functions. Some research indicates that women may be more likely to experience reduced movement and sedation compared to men.

As women age, CB1 receptor density in other regions of the brain such as the basal ganglia, lateral temporal cortex and limbic regions increase, while this does not appear to be the case in men.[658]

There is some evidence that **anandamide levels peak in women during ovulation** and are at their lowest during the luteal phase of the menstrual cycle.[659] These changes in anandamide levels are correlated with changes in sex hormones in the body, indicating an interplay between the endocannabinoid system and the menstrual cycle. On a practical level, what these differences may mean, therapeutically, is that lower dosages of cannabinoid treatments may be necessary during ovulation versus other phases of the menstrual cycle.

It has also been reported that women are generally more sensitive to the effects of THC, yet also develop tolerance to THC more readily. However, there is conflicting research around this topic. Women also report experiencing more severe withdrawal symptoms after stopping their use of Cannabis compared to men - particularly mood and gastrointestinal symptoms like nausea and stomach pain.[660]

When it comes to differences between cis gender and trans gender individuals, the data is nearly non-existent. Because the endocannabinoid system is connected to the reproductive system and influenced by hormones, including gonadal hormones, this may mean that a transgender person undergoing transition therapy may experience the effects of Cannabis differently as their hormone profile changes in their body. This may present itself as increased THC sensitivity, for instance.

Anecdotally clinicians have reported that Cannabis affects people of different ethnicities uniquely as well, related to unique genetic patterns among different groups of

---

[656] Xing G, Carlton J, Jiang X, Wen J, Jia M, Li H. Differential Expression of Brain Cannabinoid Receptors between Repeatedly Stressed Males and Females may Play a Role in Age and Gender-Related Difference in Traumatic Brain Injury: Implications from Animal Studies. Front Neurol. 2014 Aug 28;5:161. https://doi.org10.3389/fneur.2014.00161

[657] Xing G, Carlton J, Zhang L, Jiang X, Fullerton C, Li H, Ursano R. Cannabinoid receptor expression and phosphorylation are differentially regulated between male and female cerebellum and brain stem after repeated stress: implication for PTSD and drug abuse. Neurosci Lett. 2011 Sep 8;502(1):5-9. https://doi.org10.1016/j.neulet.2011.05.013

[658] Van Laere K, Goffin K, Casteels C, Dupont P, Mortelmans L, de Hoon J, Bormans G. Gender-dependent increases with healthy aging of the human cerebral cannabinoid-type 1 receptor binding using [(18)F]MK-9470 PET. Neuroimage. 2008 Feb 15;39(4):1533-41. https://doi.org/10.1016/j.neuroimage.2007.10.053

[659] Cui N, Wang L, Wang W, Zhang J, Xu Y, Jiang L, Hao G. 2017. The correlation of anandamide with gonadotrophin and sex steroid hormones during the menstrual cycle. Iranian Journal of Basic Medical Sciences. 20: 1268-1274. https://doi.org/10.22038%2FIJBMS.2017.9488

[660] Herrmann ES, Weerts EM, Vandrey R. Sex differences in cannabis withdrawal symptoms among treatment-seeking cannabis users. Exp Clin Psychopharmacol. 2015 Dec;23(6):415-21. https://doi.org/10.1037/pha0000053

people around the world.[661] There are likely other ways in which Cannabis affects people differently that will continue to be understood as Cannabis is further studied in the future. It is critical that future research focuses on teasing out these differences in effects to maximize the efficacy of Cannabis or cannabinoid therapies while minimizing any potential risks in vulnerable populations.

### EFFECTS OF CANNABIS ON DRIVING ABILITY

There is also great debate over the relationship between Cannabis use and motor coordination impairment related to driving and piloting vehicles. Does Cannabis impair driving skills similarly to alcohol to warrant legal consequence? While Cannabis use does alter psychomotor coordination, there also seems to be evidence that these effects are dose related and **Cannabis users are often able to compensate for their driving impairment due to a sustained or enhanced awareness of their own impairment**.[662] In other words, a "high" driver might drive more carefully because they are conscious that they are impaired. **If Cannabis use is combined with alcohol use, however, impairment effects tend to become substantially worse than they would be with either Cannabis or alcohol used alone**. There is also some evidence that acute Cannabis users exhibit greater impairment symptoms than chronic users, further complicating the issue.

A 2022 study found that Cannabis users often subjectively feel safe to drive after approximately 1.5 hours of smoking, although their driving performance remained markedly worse than a non-user for up to 4.5 hours.[663] This finding indicates that it may be safest to wait at least 4 or 5 hours to drive after consuming Cannabis.

Determining Cannabis intoxication at the time of a traffic stop is very difficult due to the persistence of cannabinoids in the body for prolonged periods of time after initial administration. For chronic users that consume Cannabis daily for years, they could stop consuming Cannabis and be likely to fail any variety of drug tests well over a month later.

Some states in the US have instituted THC blood level limits for driving, similar in theory to the Blood Alcohol Content (BAC) used for determining legal suitability to drive after alcohol consumption. Other states rely on field sobriety tests and obvious signs of recent Cannabis use to discern Cannabis impaired drivers. Some companies are pursuing the development of roadside saliva tests that could potentially discern Cannabis use within a three or four-hour time frame.[664]

Even so, the debate remains as to whether roadside drug testing for Cannabis, due to the persistence of exogenous cannabinoids and metabolites in the body after

[661] https://cacpodcast.com/bts-19-dr-junella-chin-on-medical-uses-of-cannabis-pediatric-use-womens-health/

[662] Sewell RA, Poling J, Sofuoglu M. The effect of cannabis compared with alcohol on driving. Am J Addict. 2009 May-Jun;18(3):185-93. https://doi.org/10.1080/10550490902786934

[663] Marcotte TD, Umlauf A, Grelotti DJ, et al. Driving Performance and Cannabis Users' Perception of Safety: A Randomized Clinical Trial . JAMA Psychiatry. 2022;79(3):201–209. https://doi.org/10.1001/jamapsychiatry.2021.4037

[664] Jehanli, A., Brannan, S., Moore, L., & Spiehler, V. R. (2001). Blind trials of an onsite saliva drug test for marijuana and opiates. Journal of Forensic Science, 46(5), 1214-1220. https://pubmed.ncbi.nlm.nih.gov/11569567/

administration as well as the difficulty correlating concentrations of cannabinoids in the body with significant levels of impairment, can be used to properly identify impairment or endangerment to society at all.

> *Never drive or pilot a vehicle or operate heavy machinery after consuming THC-rich Cannabis or cannabinoid products. DUI and DWI laws in the United States are applicable to driving under the influence of Cannabis, the same as driving under the influence of alcohol.*

# Enduring Understandings

- There are variety of ways of studying medical effects and deriving medical claims, each with different levels of predictive power associated with them.
- The type of medical research of the lowest quality, meaning the least predictive power for a generalized population, is anecdotal reporting. The type of medical research of the highest quality, meaning the greatest predictive power, are placebo-controlled double-blind clinical trials.
- There is little clinical research that has been performed with herbal Cannabis or Cannabis extracts. Most Cannabis research is performed with isolated cannabinoids and mixtures of isolated cannabinoids.
- Cannabinoids exhibit exceptionally low toxicity with very high LD50s. It is considered physically impossible to lethally overdose on traditional herbal Cannabis.
- Sexual hormones affect how cannabinoids interact with the body, leading to differences in effects between people with testosterone dominant sex hormones versus estrogen dominant sex hormones.
- Some of the primary health risks of THC-rich Cannabis use are memory and attention disruptions, anxiety, paranoia, motor discoordination, increased heart rate, and increased risk of stroke and heart attack. Additional risks may incur if smoking such as chronic bronchitis or COPD. If pregnant, Cannabis use can potentially cause low birth weight and may exacerbate other pregnancy complications. Adverse neonatal, perinatal, and postnatal effects may be more primarily associated with smoking than cannabinoids themselves and more research is needed.
- Tolerance and dependence can develop with repeated Cannabis use.
- A wide variety of therapeutic uses of Cannabis and cannabinoids have been identified, and many medical experts agree that Cannabis or cannabinoids can be effective at treating chronic pain, spasticity, nausea, and other conditions.
- Most medical research on Cannabis and cannabinoids has focused on either THC or CBD dominant chemovars, which represents a very narrow window of chemical varieties of Cannabis available. Future research is likely to focus on elucidating how cannabinoids in various ratios to one another as well as how CBG, CBC, THCV, and CBDV dominant chemovars affect medical conditions uniquely compared to THC or CBD dominant chemovars.
- The ECS is bidirectionally linked with the HPG axis and influences reproduction and development through interactions with hormones like testosterone and estrogen.
- Women feature greater CB1 receptors in areas of the brain related to movement, memory and sleep.
- Anandamide levels peak during ovulation and decrease through other stages of the menstrual cycle

# Chapter 23:
## MEDICAL CANNABIS RESEARCH

*"We have now a lot of evidence, both laboratory and clinical, that better results accrue when dealing with complex mixtures from Cannabis extracts compared to pure compounds."*

Ethan Russo, MD, BTS #5 Curious About Cannabis Podcast

---

### Learning Questions

- What are the various ways that medical claims are derived?
- How toxic are cannabinoids?
- What are the health risks associated with Cannabis use?
- How does Cannabis interact with other drugs?
- What are the therapeutic potentials and limitations of Cannabis?

---

Medical claims are derived through a variety of methods. Usually these methods include anecdotal reporting, case studies, surveys, *in vitro* studies, *in vivo* non-human animal models, or human preclinical and clinical trials. When reading about the medical claims of a product, it is important to understand how a claim about a product was derived in the first place to determine if the claim is worth considering.

**Anecdotal reporting** consists of first-hand or eyewitness reports. Sometimes anecdotal reports lead to future clinical trials which verify those reports, while other times anecdotal reports end up being proven incorrect. Anecdotal data is considered to be very low-quality data, in terms of predictive power, as it only represents a sample of one person and is highly susceptible to mistaken interpretation, placebo/nocebo effects, uncontrolled variables, or erroneous recall. **Case studies** are professional reports of observation of a subject over a period of time. **Surveys** are used to collect data from a population to understand behavior and attitude trends.

***In vitro* studies** are studies performed in a sterile controlled environment like a petri dish. These are studies typically consisting of growing certain cells in a petri dish and then exposing the cells to various compounds to record any changes that are exhibited. *In vitro* actually means "in glass". *In vivo* studies are performed in live organisms. Typically, ***in vivo* studies** are performed on rodents and dogs. Human clinical trials are studies performed on humans to determine the effects of a compound. A placebo containing an inactive compound is used to determine if any exhibited effects are more profound than the psychological effect of simply taking a "medicine."

| | Type of Research | Description |
|---|---|---|
| **Less Predictive Quality** | **Anecdotal Reporting** | Eyewitness testimony, personal accounts; impossible to test or falsify |
| | **Case Studies/Observational Studies** | Professional observations; less subjective than anecdotes |
| | **Surveys** | Population behavior and attitude assessment using questionnaires; biased toward people that will answer surveys |
| | **_in vitro_ Studies** | Cell or tissue culture studies to assess how something will affect particular tissue types, chemical receptors, etc.; results can be limited in scalability or practical significance to animals |
| | **Pre-Clinical _in vivo_ Non-Human Studies** | Often rodent or monkey based to evaluate health effects and safety profile in mammals |
| | **Single Blind, Placebo Controlled Human Clinical Trials** | The participants do not know who received placebo, but administrators know; study is repeatable, but administrator may introduce bias accidentally by knowing who received placebo. |
| **Higher Predictive Quality** | **Double Blind, Placebo Controlled Human Clinical Trials** | Neither the participants nor the administrators know who received placebos; study is repeatable and highly controlled. |

When an _in vivo_ study is performed in a non-human animal, the dosages used in the study must be scaled up in a particular way to determine what the **human equivalent dose (HED)** would be. It is incorrect to assume that the dose identified as effective in an animal study will be the same dose that a human would require. Particularly, care must be taken to understand how the study animal's body surface area, which is correlated with metabolic rate, and weight are different from a human.

This method of taking these two factors into account when scaling a dose is called **allometric scaling**. However, even this method is not without its problems. This is why researchers always apply a safety correction factor to any identified HED. For instance, if the HED of a dose used in a rodent study were 20mg/kg, researchers might divide that value by 10 to start a study at 2mg/kg when first administering a drug to humans, just to be extra safe.

**Cell culture** models are performed in sterilized and controlled environments with reactions occurring in isolation of exposure to other compounds that might be present in a human body system. The behavior of rodents can sometimes be difficult to interpret. Humans are often eating a variety of foods and ingesting a variety of other medicines or drugs that will interfere or confuse the effects of cannabinoids. The cannabinoids themselves exhibit unique effects on cannabinoid receptors, leading to competing effects.

There are a variety of informational charts in circulation which detail the health effects of each individual cannabinoid and terpenoid, but these are *very* limited in their practical application and should be considered largely entertainment or speculation than education. The majority of research that has looked at how cannabinoids might influence human health has been through *in vitro* cell culture models or *in vivo* rodent models, each with their own significant limitations for scaling up result interpretations to the human biological system. Very few completed Cannabis or cannabinoid studies have yet been replicated and some studies that have been replicated ended up contradicting one another.

Despite the limited number of actual human clinical trials currently completed, there is already promising data supporting the therapeutic value of Cannabis. **Human clinical trials have been successful in determining cannabinoid compounds as effective treatments for a variety of conditions including nausea, pain, inflammation, spasticity, reduced appetite, and sleep disturbance**.[665] More human clinical trials are required to establish what other medical conditions might be effectively treated with Cannabis or cannabis compounds and what dosages and preparation methods are required to obtain desired medicinal effects in a practical way.

| STAGES OF HUMAN CLINICAL TRIALS | | |
|---|---|---|
| **Trial Phase** | **Sample Size** | **Purpose** |
| Phase 0 | Very Small | Proof of Concept; How does the drug work? |
| Phase 1 | Small | Is the drug safe? |
| Phase II | Moderate | How effective is the drug? |
| Phase III | Large | Randomized, blind testing; drugs are usually approved after Phase III |
| Phase IV | Very Large | Determine long-term safety of a drug, usually after it has been approved |

Whenever a medical claim is made about any compound or natural product, it is important for a potential consumer to do their research to see how the claim was made

[665] Whiting PF, Wolff RF, Deshpande S, Nisio MD, Duffy S, Hernandez AV, Keurentjes JC, Lang S, Misso K, Ryder S, Schmidlkofer S, Westwood M, Kleijnen J. 2015. Cannabinoids for Medical use: A Systematic Review and Meta-analysis. JAMA. 313(24):2456-2473. https://doi.org/10.1001/jama.2015.6358

and if the results of the study that made that claim can be applied to the human body in a realistic way. On the flip side, it is the responsibility of every Cannabis company to use information responsibly, cite informational sources, and avoid misleading health claims for the sake of marketing.

## HOW IS CANNABIS COMMONLY CONSUMED?

### METHODS OF ADMINISTRATION

Cannabis and its chemical constituents can be consumed, or administered, in a variety of ways commonly including pulmonary methods (through the lungs), oral (edibles), sublingual (under the tongue), and epicutaneous/topical (on the skin) administrations, however, Cannabis can also be administered in the form of nasal sprays, vaginal or rectal suppositories as well as direct injection in muscle tissue or blood, though these methods are currently uncommon.

### TYPES OF CANNABIS PRODUCTS

Some common types of Cannabis products typically available at a legal Cannabis dispensary include:

> - Dried and cured flowers (buds)
> - Concentrated resins and semi-solid extracts
> - Topical oils, creams, salves, and balms
> - Topical sprays
> - Sublingual drops or sprays
> - Infused edibles (cookies, candies, caramels, etc)
> - Food oils (olive, sunflower, coconut, etc)
> - Tinctures
> - Suppositories

Each method of administration demonstrates markedly different levels of bioavailability, which will be discussed in a following section.

### CANNABINOID DOSING

How much of any particular cannabinoid does someone need to ingest to achieve a therapeutic response? This is a tricky question to answer for many reasons. One is that cannabinoid product formulations can vary substantially, product to product. A product featuring a cannabinoid isolate, such as CBD or THC isolate, is going to behave much differently than a product featuring a wider diversity of phytochemistry from the Cannabis plant or elsewhere. Additionally, each person's biochemistry may be different, influencing how they will respond to cannabinoid treatment. To further complicate matters, the bioavailability of different cannabinoids varies.

Finally, cannabinoids tend to stick to fatty tissues in the body and release slowly overtime. This means that there is a big difference between taking a cannabinoid product once, versus taking one every day. Taking a cannabinoid product daily results in a slow buildup of cannabinoids in the body, which will continue to release into the body even when the user stops taking the product. It may be possible to find adequate effects at very low dosages if the product is taken every day. However, if acute relief is needed, a large dose may be needed.

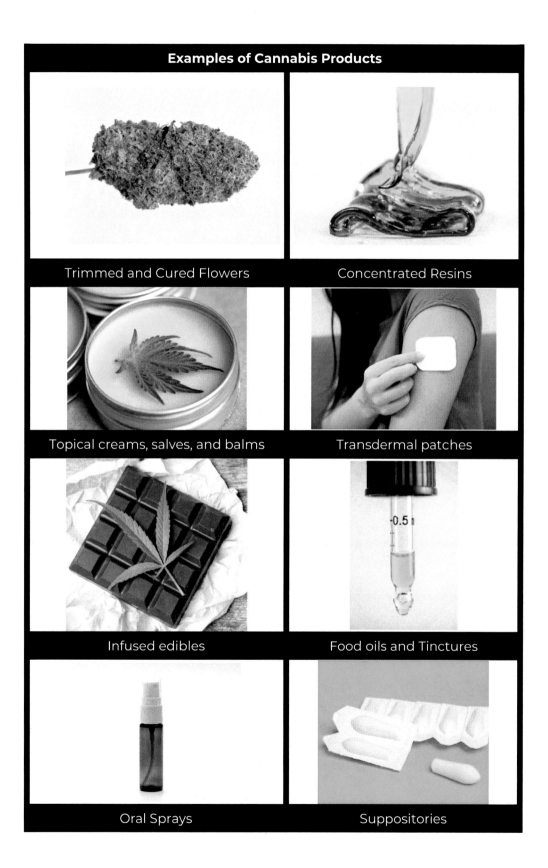

**Examples of Cannabis Products**

Trimmed and Cured Flowers

Concentrated Resins

Topical creams, salves, and balms

Transdermal patches

Infused edibles

Food oils and Tinctures

Oral Sprays

Suppositories

There is some research that has been done that shows that Cannabis extracts with a wider diversity of phytochemistry may perform better than cannabinoid isolates – but there still needs to be a lot more research done on this topic to really understand what factors influence these differences in responses.[666] [667]

A 2019 review of cannabidiol (CBD) dosing used in clinical trials revealed that, for many conditions, dosages of less than 2.5mg/kg of body weight were largely ineffective, except in the case of treating sleep or anxiety.[668] In Epidiolex trials, dosages of 5mg/kg to 20mg/kg were utilized to treat epilepsy in children, with clinicians advising not to exceed 15mg/kg to avoid adverse side effects. For the cannabinoid pharmaceutical Sativex, which features a standardized Cannabis extract consisting of equal parts THC to CBD, it is recommended to titrate up from approximately 2.5mg THC and CBD to 30mg THC and CBD per day for multiple sclerosis symptoms. The recommend dosing for the THC pharmaceutical Marinol indicates that dosing should start at 2.5mg orally twice daily for anorexia and 5mg/m$^2$ 4-6 times per day for nausea and vomiting associated with chemotherapy.

Clearly cannabinoid dosing is complex for many reasons, so what can be done in light of this complexity? In general, it is often recommended to start off with low, sub-therapeutic, doses and slowly work up to a minimum effective dose. Usually, a dose of somewhere around 1 or 2mg of THC or CBD is considered a suitable starting point, and subsequent doses can increase in 2 to 5mg increments until an optimum dose is found. It is also generally recommended to keep journals or "dose diaries" when taking Cannabis or cannabinoid-based products to determine which products and dosages are working best.

## How Does Cannabis Work?

The "high" produced from Cannabis is caused, primarily, by the stimulation of cannabinoid receptors in the brain. When the <1% of bioavailable THC makes its way to the brain, it stimulates a variety of receptors including the cannabinoid type 1 (CB1) and cannabinoid type 2 (CB2) receptors on neurons. When CB1 receptors throughout the central nervous system are agonized, or stimulated, it causes a whole cascading series of effects in the body that lead to things like altered time perception, disrupted memory formation, appetite stimulation, pain reduction, and euphoria – all the typical symptoms associated with a Cannabis "high". While THC is the primary cannabinoid in Cannabis that agonizes, or stimulates, CB1 receptors, other cannabinoids may also cause intoxicating effects such as delta-8 THC, CBN, CBND, and THCV – ultimately manipulating the effects of THC and the experience of the consumer.

---

[666] Gallily, R., Yekhtin, Z., & Hanuš, L. O. (2015). Overcoming the bell-shaped dose-response of cannabidiol by using cannabis extract enriched in cannabidiol. Pharmacology & Pharmacy, 6(02), 75. http://www.scirp.org/journal/PaperInformation.aspx?PaperID=53912&#abstract
[667] Russo, E. B. (2019). The case for the entourage effect and conventional breeding of clinical cannabis: no "strain," no gain. Frontiers in plant science, 1969. https://doi.org/10.3389/fpls.2018.01969
[668] Millar, S. A., Stone, N. L., Bellman, Z. D., Yates, A. S., England, T. J., & O'Sullivan, S. E. (2019). A systematic review of cannabidiol dosing in clinical populations. British journal of clinical pharmacology, 85(9), 1888-1900. https://doi.org/10.1111/bcp.14038

As CB1 receptors are repeatedly stimulated, they decrease in concentration in the brain, leading to a reduced psychoactive effect, often referred to as **tolerance**. After at least 48 hours of discontinued use, CB1 receptors may begin returning to their normal concentrations and tolerance will begin to decrease.

Some cannabinoids like CBD, CBDV, CBC, and CBG can block, or antagonize, CB1 receptors, potentially reducing or limiting the psychoactive effects of THC. It has been reported that some terpenoids may also limit or modulate the "high" associated with Cannabis.[669] Many companies and researchers are trying to understand these dynamics better so that drugs may be developed to interrupt uncomfortable or potentially psychologically dangerous Cannabis intoxication experiences.

### Cannabinoid Pharmacology: Absorption, Distribution, Metabolism, and Elimination

**Bioavailability** is a measurement of the amount of a compound that will readily make its way to a "site of action" in the body, like a chemical receptor. Often this is considered the same as the amount of an active substance that makes its way into the blood.

In general, cannabinoids are not very bioavailable, with the vast majority of cannabinoids consumed excreted from the body without reaching any sites of action. This is primarily because cannabinoids are very lipophilic (oily) compounds which become bound very quickly in the blood to fatty acid binding proteins, which then causes them to become bound with glucose (sugar) before being eliminated from the body.

Cannabinoids also do not dissolve very readily in gastric fluids, which makes it difficult for cannabinoids to be absorbed in the digestive system. In addition, cannabinoids "stick" to a lot of tissues within the body, restricting their ability to reach sites of action.

Bioavailability and absorption can vary for many reasons including unique body chemistry, dosage, administration method, and consumption behavior. Although up to half of the THC present in a flower or extract may be bioavailable, depending on the consumption method, very little of it ever makes it to the brain. According to one study, only 1% of THC brought into the lungs reaches the brain.[670] [671]

The most common administration route used among medical Cannabis patients is **pulmonary**, or **respiratory**, delivery through smoking or vaporizing of the Cannabis flowers or extract. This allows for effects to manifest within seconds of administration, rather than thirty minutes or more when administered orally. As the cannabinoids in the smoke or vapor pass into the lungs, they are readily absorbed and delivered directly into the blood stream where they are carried to the brain and throughout the body. The sites of

[669] Russo EB. Taming THC: potential cannabis synergy and phytocannabinoid-terpenoid entourage effects. Br J Pharmacol. 2011 Aug;163(7):1344-64. https://doi.org/10.1111%2Fj.1476-5381.2011.01238.x
[670] Adams IB, Martin BR. 1996. Cannabis: Pharmacology and toxicology in humans and animals. Addiction. 91(11):1585 - 1614. https://doi.org/10.1046/j.1360-0443.1996.911115852.x
[671] Huestis MA. 2007. Human Cannabinoid Pharmacokinetics. Chem biodivers. 4(8): 1770-1804. https://doi.org/10.1002%2Fcbdv.200790152

gas and blood exchange in the lungs are called the alveoli and are pictured on the next page.

| Administration Route | Cannabinoid Bioavailability | Approximate Time to Onset |
|---|---|---|
| Pulmonary (Inhalation) | 2 - 56% (30% average) | 30 sec. – 5 minutes |
| Oral | 10 - 20% | 20 – 90 minutes or more |
| Oromucosal - Sublingual (Under the Tongue) | 1.5 – 10% | 5 – 10 minutes |
| Oromucosal - Buccal (Inside of Cheek) | See Sublingual | See Sublingual |
| Epicutaneous (Topical) | ? | 10 – 30 minutes |
| Vaginal or Rectal Suppository | <14% | 5 – 25 minutes |

SOURCE: HUESTIS MA. 2007. HUMAN CANNABINOID PHARMACOKINETICS. CHEM BIODIVERS. 4(8): 1770-1804

FIGURE 64: CANNABIS PRODUCT ADMINISTRATION ROUTES, BIOAVAILABILITY, AND TIME TO ONSET

Although pulmonary administration is the traditional method for medical Cannabis ingestion, it is typically not a method that can be accepted clinically due to negative health effects associated with smoking. An alternative to smoking is "vaporizing", or lightly heating plant material or extracts until cannabinoids are released in a thin vapor, presumably leaving behind tars and other toxic components.

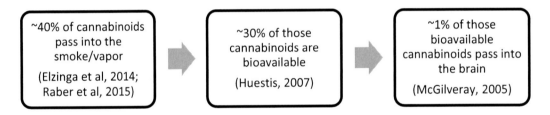

FIGURE 65: AVERAGE RECOVERY OF ADMINISTERED CANNABINOIDS IN SMOKE OR VAPOR, BLOOD, AND CEREBROSPINAL FLUID

In 1996, the California branch of the National Organization for the Reform of Marijuana Laws (NORML) and the Multidisciplinary Association for Psychedelic Studies (MAPS) funded a study that examined the differences between several pulmonary delivery methods for Cannabis including three versions of water pipes, two different vaporizers, a filtered Cannabis cigarette, and an unfiltered Cannabis cigarette.[672] The researchers examined the ratio of cannabinoids to tar to determine which administration methods presented the least risk to a user's health. They found that relative to the unfiltered cigarette, **all the devices were effective at reducing exposure to tars**. However, when the cannabinoid to tar ratio was measured, **only vaporization resulted in an enhanced cannabinoid/tar exposure ratio compared to an unfiltered cigarette**.

---

[672] https://maps.org/news-letters/v06n3/06359mj1.html

| Bioavailability Variability through Pulmonary Administration of 1g of 20% Total THC or CBD Cannabis (200mg) | | | | |
|---|---|---|---|---|
| | **Worst Case (2%)** | **Average (30%)** | **Best Case (56%)** | **Impossibly Perfect (100%)** |
| In the Smoke/Vapor | ~80mg | ~80mg | ~80mg | 200mg |
| Bioavailable | ~1.6mg | ~24mg | ~44.8mg | 200mg |
| To the Brain | ~0.016mg | ~.24mg | ~0.448mg | 2mg |

FIGURE 66: BIOAVAILABILITY VARIABILITY VIA PULMONARY ADMINISTRATION OF 200MG OF THC OR CBD

The first vaporizer that was examined, which was a "battery-powered metal hot plate inside a jar to trap the vapor, achieved a 26% improvement in the cannabinoid/tar ratio." The second vaporizer that the researchers tested featured water filtration. The researchers already saw that water pipes were the most inefficient at reducing the tar/cannabinoid ratio, so it was no surprise that this second vaporizer that featured water filtration had a statistically insignificant effect on the cannabinoid/tar ratio compared to an unfiltered cigarette. The author admits that using water filtration "seemed in retrospect to be a design flaw in the experiment." The researchers also noticed that **vaporizers produced more CBN** than other methods.

To continue studying these effects, NORML and MAPS performed a second study looking at vaporization's effects of limiting carbon monoxide exposure and toxic hydrocarbon exposure. **At 185°C, or 365°F, they found that tar was reduced by over 56%, carbon monoxide was reduced by over 33%, and three toxic hydrocarbons – benzene, toluene, and naphthalene – were reduced 100%.**[673] However, THC was also reduced by 85%. The message being that vaporization can provide less health risks, but also results in significantly less exposure to cannabinoids, potentially requiring repeated consumption and exposure to tar and carbon monoxide more frequently, but the tar and carbon monoxide exposure is likely to be less than with traditional smoking methods.

So instead of pulmonary exposure, medical clinical trials for Cannabis and cannabinoid products typically utilize sublingual (under the tongue), nasomucosal

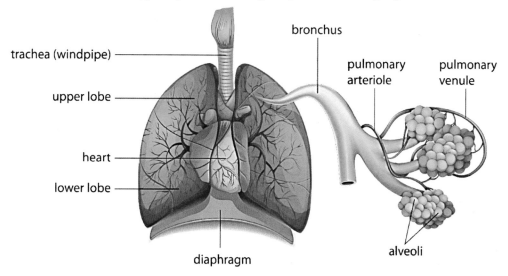

[673] https://maps.org/news-letters/v11n1/11120gie.html

(through the nose) or oral delivery systems. Other administration routes include topical (on the skin), intravenous (in the blood), and suppository delivery via the anal or vaginal mucosa.

One of the most frequently studied administration routes for phytocannabinoids is through **sublingual** delivery, typically by way of a formulated spray or liquid that is dropped under the tongue. The administered compounds then readily pass through the mucous membrane of the mouth and into capillaries beneath. This method provides effects much more quickly than oral administration, usually between five and fifteen minutes, but not as quickly as pulmonary administration.

Similar so sublingual delivery, **nasal mucosal** administration is also possible. Drugs can easily be administered into the nose through a spray which lines the mucous membranes inside the nose where cannabinoids and other compounds can easily be absorbed into capillaries beneath the mucosa.

Cannabis extracts and cannabinoids can also be delivered **orally**. Cannabis products administered orally take anywhere between thirty minutes to an hour or more to produce effects. This is because orally administered drugs are subject to the first-pass effect, where the compounds

PRE-1937 CANNABIS PREPARATION

must undergo hepatic metabolism in the liver before passing on into the blood and to the brain. This process results in an overall reduction in the number of target drug compounds reaching the vascular system to be distributed throughout the body. This can provide dosage and administration challenges for researchers, clinicians, dispensary workers, and patients.

When delta-9-tetrahydrocannabinol (THC) passes through the **hepatic metabolism** system, it is converted to 11-hydroxy-delta-9-tetrahydrocannabinol (11-OH-THC). Even though cannabinoids are subject to the **first-pass effect** and are reduced in concentration before reaching the brain, 11-OH-THC is more potent than THC and passes the blood-brain barrier more readily. This is why users of edible products often report different effects which are often very potent as opposed to ingesting Cannabis through other administration routes like smoking, vaping, or using sublingual drops or buccal sprays.

### CANNABIS AMERICANA
#### U. S. P.
*Physiologically Tested*

OUR American variety is the answer to the the question which has so long troubled manufacturers.

With our material a finished product can be turned out at a reasonable cost.

IT is no longer necessary to depend on the foreign variety which is of high cost and slightly superior. The uncertainty of further supplies of it is another factor favoring the American product.

**J. L. HOPKINS & CO.**, 100 William St. **New York**

Due to high demand and excess cost of importing cannabis, the united states began producing its own domestic varieties. Cannabis was a part of the US Pharmacoepia and a staple of pharmacies everywhere in the United States until it was omitted from the USP in 1942.

Another way Cannabis compounds might be administered is through **epicutaneous**, or **topical**, delivery through the epidermis layer of the skin. Topical administration results in very little, if any, of the drug compounds reaching the dermis and the vascular system either due to the lack of space for compounds to pass around cells to reach capillaries in the dermis, or due to the complex lipophilic-hydrophilic layering of the transcellular pathway. Terpenes, volatile compounds that make up essential oils which are present in Cannabis, have been shown to enhance epidermal permeability, allowing for more effective absorption of target drug compounds.

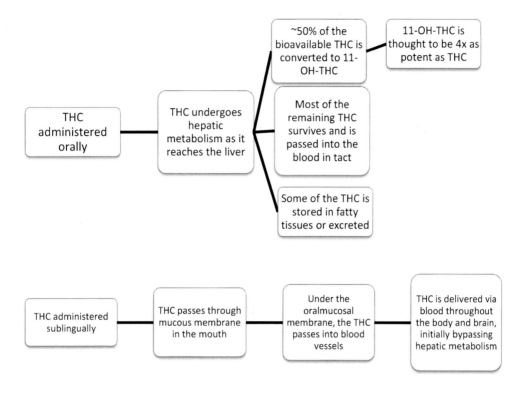

FIGURE 67: ORAL VS SUBLINGUAL ADMINISTRATION DYNAMICS

Cannabis can also be delivered as a **suppository**, resulting in the absorption of target drug compounds through rectal or vaginal wall surfaces. Drug compounds administered through rectal suppository are readily absorbed in the blood vessels throughout the rectal mucosa. Drug compounds administered through vaginal suppositories pass through the vaginal epithelium, a mucosal surface, and on to capillaries which lead to systemic circulation. Drug administration through suppository delivery systems is ideal for patients with extreme nausea or vomiting tendencies that cannot tolerate other drug delivery systems. Drug administration through suppository is relatively fast acting, usually between fifteen and thirty minutes, and avoids hepatic metabolism and the production of 11-OH-THC.

Cannabinoids can be delivered **intravenously** or **intramuscularly** as well, although there is limited research about these administration routes at varying clinically significant dosages.

## How Long Does it Take to Get Cannabinoids Out of the Body?

The **half-life** of a compound is the amount of time that it takes for approximately half of the concentration of that compound to break down or be eliminated from the body. Because cannabinoids linger in the body, stuck to fatty tissues, cannabinoids have a long half-life, especially for chronic users.

The half-life of THC and CBD is estimated to be anywhere from 1 to 6 days, depending on the frequency of consumption – although different studies that have attempted to ascertain the half-life of cannabinoids have been inconsistent.[674] This may be primarily related to the fact that different studies utilize different testing methodologies, some of which are more sensitive and can detect extremely low concentrations of cannabinoids compared to other methods. This might indicate that some studies that report lower half-lives may be mistaken because the testing methods used were simply incapable of accurately detecting extremely low concentrations of cannabinoids.

Let's put this into perspective, if we assume that for a chronic Cannabis user, the half-life of THC is 5 days, it will take approximately 100 days for the THC-COOH to reach levels below the limit for most urinary drug tests, which usually have a limit of around 50 nanograms, or 0.00005mg of THC-COOH. This seems to accurately compare to personal reports received by the author from chronic users that have had to spend up to 3 months or longer abstaining from Cannabis use to pass a workplace urinalysis.

Assuming an approximate 1-day (24 hour) half-life for an *infrequent* Cannabis user, approximately 90% or more THC would be eliminated within 5 days. Whereas, for a chronic user, it could take several weeks to achieve the same effect.

## Cannabis as a Polypharmaceutical

Because Cannabis contains hundreds of active compounds, Cannabis is considered by some to be a **polypharmaceutical**, meaning that it is a drug made of many drugs. Previous chapters explored the various compounds in Cannabis and many of these compounds were noted for demonstrating various beneficial pharmacological actions. Many researchers are now shifting their focus toward trying to understand how these compounds interact with one another in an "entourage effect" to produce unique therapeutic or psychoactive effects.

> *"CBD's ability to modulate THC's well-known intoxicating activity along with a growing body of evidence for an entourage effect among the many cannabinoids of the Cannabis plant may extend therapeutic benefit beyond the purified cannabinoid leading to greater interest in the use of Cannabis herbal extract preparations."*
>
> Alcorn et al, 2019
> Pediatric Dosing Considerations for Medical Cannabis[675]

---

[674] Huestis MA. 2007. Human Cannabinoid Pharmacokinetics. Chem biodivers. 4(8): 1770-1804. https://doi.org/10.1002%2Fcbdv.200790152
[675] Alcorn J, Vuong S, Wu F, Seifert B, Lyon A. (2019). Pediatric Dosing Considerations for Medical Cannabis. Recent Advances in Cannabinoid Research. Chapter 10:181-200 http://dx.doi.org/10.5772/intechopen.85399

| Half-Life Elimination Model for a Chronic Cannabis Consumer with a Starting Concentration of 100mg of THC-COOH in the Body (5 Day Half-Life) | | | | | |
|---|---|---|---|---|---|
| Mg of THC-COOH | Days | Mg of THC-COOH | Days | Mg of THC-COOH | Days |
| 50 | 5 | 0.390625 | 40 | 0.003051758 | 75 |
| 25 | 10 | 0.1953125 | 45 | 0.001525879 | 80 |
| 12.5 | 15 | 0.09765625 | 50 | 0.000762939 | 85 |
| 6.25 | 20 | 0.048828125 | 55 | 0.00038147 | 90 |
| 3.125 | 25 | 0.024414063 | 60 | 0.000190735 | 95 |
| 1.5625 | 30 | 0.012207031 | 65 | 0.000095 | 100 |
| 0.78125 | 35 | 0.006103516 | 70 | 0.000048 | 105 |

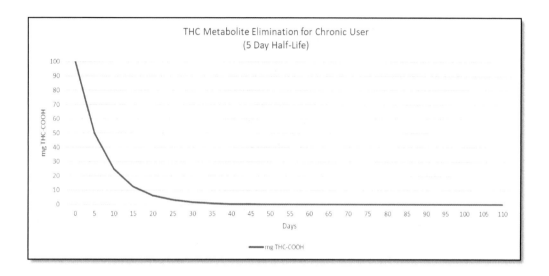

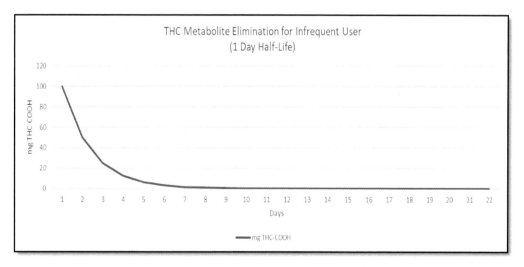

Users often report that isolated cannabinoid products do not produce the level of therapeutic action compared to consuming whole plant botanical Cannabis or broad-spectrum Cannabis extracts. There are numerous compounds present in Cannabis that work to modulate the effects of the other present compounds. For instance, numerous terpenes like pinene and numerous cannabinoids like cannabichromene may exhibit memory enhancement effects, potentially working to limit the amnesic, or memory loss, effects of THC.

A study examining the differences in levels of an inflammatory marker called TNFa demonstrated that a plateauing of therapeutic response with CBD isolate could be overcome if using a CBD-rich Cannabis extract with a wide variety of phytochemistry.[676]

> *"I think the best depiction of this idea of the entourage effect, or what we have called synergy in medicinal plants, is a symphonic effect. Think about a Mozart symphony that is so incredibly beautiful - and you have a lead violin, and then you have all these other instruments. All those other instruments support the lead violin. What's happened in pharmacology is, under the illusion that we can control the dose, we've isolated the lead violin and just used that in our pharmacology. And the rationalization for this is actually not very strong scientifically..."[677]*
>
> Kevin Spelman, PhD
> **The Curious About Cannabis Podcast**
> Behind-the-Scenes (BTS) Episode #04

## ARE CANNABINOIDS TOXIC?

The **LD50**, or median lethal dose, of a compound is used to indicate the severity of toxicity of a compound. It is measured in mg/kg and is **the amount of a compound necessary to kill half of a test population**, usually of rodents. The ratio of compound concentration to body weight is then scaled up to estimate the LD50 for a human population. Many clinicians and researchers point out that this method of scaling up results from rodent LD50 models is not a suitable way to understand how toxic a compound might be to humans. Another index is sometimes used to evaluate toxicity called the **Therapeutic Index**. It is a comparison of the therapeutic effect of a compound versus any toxic effects the compound elicits.

In 1988 administrative law judge Francis Young published *Opinion and Recommended Ruling, Findings of Fact, Conclusions of Law and Decision of Administrative Law Judge* in regard to a Cannabis rescheduling petition. In this report, Young stated:

> *"...in order to induce death a marijuana smoker would have to consume 20,000 to 40,000 times as much marijuana as is contained in one marijuana cigarette...A*

---

[676] Gallily, R., Yekhtin, Z., & Hanuš, L. O. (2015). Overcoming the bell-shaped dose-response of cannabidiol by using cannabis extract enriched in cannabidiol. Pharmacology & Pharmacy, 6(02), 75. http://www.scirp.org/journal/PaperInformation.aspx?PaperID=53912&#abstract
[677] https://cacpodcast.com/bts-04-kevin-spelman-phd-on-the-endocannabinoid-system-plant-synergies-and-dietary-supplement-research/

*smoker would theoretically have to consume nearly 1,500 pounds of marijuana within about fifteen minutes to induce a lethal response.*"[678]

The primary reason for the low lethality of Cannabis is due to the small number of cannabinoid receptors on the brainstem and the fact that THC and other cannabinoid receptor agonists found in Cannabis are only partial receptor agonists. Other drugs like alcohol and heroin can be dangerous in much less quantities because they have strong effects on the brainstem, which in turn affects the performance of all other organs like the heart and lungs. Overdosing on alcohol or heroin can stop the heart or lungs, but this is generally not the case for Cannabis.

The precise LD50 is difficult to ascertain. An often-quoted bit of research by Thompson et al. (1973) found that "...oral doses of delta-9-THC and delta-8-THC between 3000 – 9000 mg/kg were nonlethal."[679]

| LD50s of Major Phytocannabinoids | |
|---|---|
| D9-Tetrahydrocannabinol (THC) | 3000 – 9000 mg/kg (oral, dogs) |
| Cannabidiol (CBD) | 212 mg/kg (IV, rhesus monkeys)[1] |
| Cannabigerol (CBG) | 5600 mg/kg (oral, rat)[2] |
| Cannabichromene (CBC) | 270 mg/kg (IV, rhesus monkeys)[1] |

FIGURE 68: LETHAL TOXICITY OF MAJOR CANNABINOIDS

[1]Rosenkrantz et al, 1981; [2]Cayman Chemical Cannabigerol MSDS, 2014

| LD50s of Non-Cannabinoid Compounds | |
|---|---|
| Aflatoxin (produced by *Aspergillus sp.* Fungi) | 0.003 mg/kg (oral, rat) |
| Cyanide | 10 mg/kg (oral, rat) |
| Nicotine | 50 mg/kg (oral rat) |
| Caffeine | 200 mg/kg (oral, rat) |
| Ethanol | 7000 mg/kg (oral, rat) |
| Sucrose | 30,000 mg/kg (oral, rat) |

FIGURE 69: LETHAL TOXICITY OF NON-CANNABINOID COMPOUNDS

Source: Trautmann NM and The Environmental Inquiry Team. Table 1.1 Lethal Doses of Some Common Compounds. Assessing Toxic Risk: Student Edition. National Science Teachers Association

Recall the wise words of Paracelsus:
*"Alle Dinge sind Gift und nichts ist ohne Gift, allein die Dosis macht es, dass ein Ding kein Gift ist."*

"All things are poison, and nothing is without poison; only the dose makes a thing not a poison."

---

[678] http://www.druglibrary.org/schaffer/library/studies/young/index.html
[679] Thompson GR, Rosenkrantz H, Schaeppi UH, Braude MC. 1973. Comparison of acute oral toxicity of cannabinoids in rats, dogs and monkeys. Toxicol Appl Pharmacol. 25(3):363-72. https://doi.org/10.1016/0041-008x(73)90310-4

## Test Your Cannabis Related Medical Vocabulary!

Match these medical terms to their definitions!

| | | |
|---|---|---|
| ____ Acute | A | Something that provides pain relief |
| ____ Anesthesia | B | Refers to the heart and blood vessels |
| ____ Analgesia | C | Increased appetite; "munchies" |
| ____ Insulin | D | Immediate / short-term |
| ____ Xerostomia | E | Refers to the stomach and intestine |
| ____ Polyphagia | F | Something that provides nausea relief |
| ____ Chronic | G | The fluid pressure inside the eye |
| ____ Antiemetic | H | Pain relief |
| ____ Conjunctival hyperemia | I | Condition of dilated blood vessels in the eyes; red eyes |
| ____ Analgesic | J | Hormone made by the pancreas that regulates glucose in the blood. |
| ____ Gastrointestinal | K | Ongoing, long-term |
| ____ Cardiovascular | L | Use of a substance to remove sensitivity to pain |
| ____ Emesis | M | Dry mouth |
| ____ Intraocular pressure (IOP) | N | Nausea |
| ____ Nociception | O | "in tissue" |
| ____ In vitro | P | Pain perception |
| ____ In vivo | Q | "in glass" |

Answers: D, L, H, J, M, C, K, F, I, A, E, B, N, G, P, Q, O

412

## How Does Cannabis Interact with Other Drugs?

There is not a lot of information about how cannabinoids interact with other drugs currently available. One of the primary contraindications that is known is that THC will exacerbate any sedative effects initiated by another drug. Consuming alcohol prior to consuming Cannabis can enhance the bioavailability of cannabinoids and thus enhance the potency of psychoactive cannabinoids. Additionally, THC-rich Cannabis is known to decrease blood pressure in chronic users, which could present a risk to users taking blood-pressure lowering drugs.

### CBD and the Grapefruit Effect

As mentioned previously, in certain concentrations, CBD, and to a lesser extent THC, can temporarily inhibit a set of enzymes in the liver that is responsible for transforming a wide variety of compounds into hydrophilic (water-loving) compounds so that they can be absorbed readily into the kidneys.[680] [681] [682] This set of liver enzymes is called Cytochrome P450 and it is even responsible for metabolizing CBD itself, as well as THC and other cannabinoids. This means that when CBD is ingested, there is a battle between CBD and Cytochrome P450 enzymes as the CBD inhibits the enzyme activity and the enzymes work to metabolize the CBD.

Have you ever received a medication that had a label attached to the bottle stating, "Do Not Consume Grapefruit While Taking This Medication", or similar? That's because grapefruit, and various other foods, exhibit this same effect on the liver. These enzymes are responsible for metabolizing all sorts of drugs that people take, such as blood thinning or chemotherapy drugs.

If a patient is taking medications prior to beginning an intensive CBD regimen, it is possible that the levels of those medications may rise in the blood because the patient's liver will not be able to metabolize the drugs due to Cytochrome P450 inhibition – leading to recirculation of the drug back into the blood stream and throughout the body before it comes back to the liver again. This can potentially lead to dangerously elevated levels of drugs in the patient's system which could be very toxic.

On the other hand, it might be possible to titrate certain medications down in response to this inhibition so that less of a medication could then be used to achieve the same effect. In one case study, a patient was able to reduce their dose of the drug Warfarin by 30% over the course of a CBD drug trial.[683] In clinical trials that sought to identify how CBD affects the performance of the epileptic drug clobazam, researchers found that levels of clobazam increased and adverse side effects increased, which were managed once

---

[680] Devitt-Lee A. 2015. CBD-Drug Interactions: Role of Cytochrome P450. Project CBD. https://www.projectcbd.org/article/cbd-drug-interactions-role-cytochrome-p450

[681] Bornheim LM, Everhart ET, Li J, Correia MA. 1993. Characterization of cannabidiol-mediated cytochrome P450 inactivation. Biochem Pharmacol. https://doi.org/10.1016/0006-2952(93)90286-6

[682] Yamaori S, Ebisawa J, Okushima Y, Yamamoto I, Watanabe K. 2011. Potent inhibition of human cytochrome P450 3A isoforms by cannabidiol: role of phenolic hydroxyl groups in the resorcinol moiety. Life Sci. https://doi.org/10.1016/j.lfs.2011.02.017

[683] Grayson L, Vines B, Nichol K, Szaflarski JP; UAB CBD Program. An interaction between warfarin and cannabidiol, a case report. Epilepsy Behav Case Rep. 2017 Oct 12;9:10-11. https://doi.org/10.1016/j.ebcr.2017.10.001

dosages of clobazam were reduced.[684] Much more research is needed on this topic to better understand how CBD might interact with other drugs and at what dosages its effects on the liver are clinically significant.

It should be noted that much of the current research indicating that CBD inhibits these enzymes was performed using **supraphysiological** doses, meaning doses that are greater than what an average person would typically be exposed to on a regular basis. If one were to extrapolate the data from one of the most infamous studies that identified this enzyme suppression effect, it would indicate that someone would have to consume grams of CBD a day to illicit a significant inhibitory response.[685]

In animal trials, the results are a bit more confounding. Rodent studies have revealed that, while CBD may suppress liver enzymes at first, CBD and some of its metabolites might induce, or stimulate, certain metabolic enzymes with repeated exposure. One particular enzyme that CBD and its metabolites seem to induce, CYP1A1, is responsible for breaking down many cancer-causing compounds in the body, helping prevent carcinogenic substances from reaching the blood stream.

However, only human trials will give us the data we need to determine whether this effect may be appreciable at typical therapeutic doses or not. Until then, it is best to exercise caution and always work with a physician when starting a new therapeutic regimen.

As mentioned before, Cytochrome P450 is involved in the metabolism of THC. This has certain implications for oral dose administration. If CBD is administered and Cytochrome P450 is inhibited, less THC will be converted to 11-OH-THC, potentially limiting the sometimes-intense psychoactive effect elicited by infused edibles.

Diet is another crucial factor influencing drug metabolism. Many commonly consumed foods such as grapefruits, tomatoes, spinach and more also inhibit Cytochrome P450. **It is important to talk to your doctor about how Cytochrome P450 inhibition might affect your current medications if you are considering a chronic high dose CBD treatment**.

[684] Geffrey AL, Pollack SF, Bruno PL, Thiele EA. Drug-drug interaction between clobazam and cannabidiol in children with refractory epilepsy. Epilepsia. 2015 Aug;56(8):1246-51. https://doi.org/10.1111/epi.13060
[685] Iffland K and Grotenhermen F. 2017. An Update on Safety and Side Effects of Cannabidiol: A Review of Clinical Data and Relevant Animal Studies. Cannabis and Cannabinoid Research. Vol. 2.1. http://doi.org/10.1089/can.2016.0034

| Examples of Common Drugs Metabolized by Cytochrome P450 Enzymes |
|---|
| Benzodiazepines (Valium, Xanax, Versed, Doral, Dormalin, Halcion) |
| Amphetamines (Adderall, Vyvanse) |
| Caffeine |
| Other stimulants (Ritalin, Concerta) |
| Certain statins (Lipitor, Mevacor, Zocor, Simlup, Simcor, Simvacor) |
| Anti-arrhythmic drugs (Cordarone, Multaq, Qunidex, Cardioquin, Quinora, Norpace, Rythmol, Coreg) |
| Anti-migraine drugs (Cafergot, Ergomar, Elavil, Endep, Vanatrip, Nimotop) |
| Erectile dysfunction drugs (Viagra, Cialis, Levitra) |
| Acetaminophen (Tylenol) |
| Lamotrigine |
| Codeine, Methadone, Oxycodone |
| Antihistamines (Benadryl) |
| Source: https://en.wikipedia.org/wiki/Grapefruit–drug_interactions |

FIGURE 70: COMMON DRUGS METABOLIZED BY CYTOCHROME P450 ENZYMES

## CANNABINOIDS AND THE GUT MICROBIOME

Research is now showing that there is a very deep connection between gut health, the immune system and mental health. This connection is sometimes referred to as the "gut-brain axis".[686] Evidence suggests that the gut and the brain exert bi-directional effects on one another, meaning that the gut affects the brain, and the brain affects the gut. It's not a one-way street.

One way that the gut and the brain are linked is through a direct connection between the autonomic and central nervous systems. Research has demonstrated that the ecosystem of bacteria and fungi that live in the gut affect the development of the enteric nervous system (ENS) and central nervous system (CNS). The enteric nervous system is part of the autonomic nervous system and is sometimes referred to as the body's "second brain". Although the ENS communicates with the CNS to control reflexes and other bodily functions, if it loses contact with the CNS – for instance if the vagus nerve is severed – it will continue to function on its own.[687] The ENS also produces neurotransmitters like the ones found throughout the CNS, such as serotonin, acetylcholine, and dopamine.[688]

Endocannabinoids play a critical role in regulating how the vagus nerve affects gut motility and nausea responses through CB1, CB2, and TRPV1 receptors.[689] It has also been shown that endocannabinoids play a role in visceral pain responses in the gut.

---

[686] Carabotti M, Scirocco A, Maselli MA, Severi C. 2015. The gut-brain axis: interactions between enteric microbiota, central and enteric nervous systems. Ann Gastroenterol. 28(2):203-209. http://www.ncbi.nlm.nih.gov/pmc/articles/pmc4367209/
[687] Li Y, Owyang C. Musings on the wanderer: what's new in our understanding of vago-vagal reflexes? V. Remodeling of vagus and enteric neural circuitry after vagal injury. Am J Physiol Gastrointest Liver Physiol. 2003 Sep;285(3):G461-9. https://doi.org/10.1152/ajpgi.00119.2003
[688] Goyal RK, Hirano I. The enteric nervous system. N Engl J Med. 1996 Apr 25;334(17):1106-15. https://doi.org/10.1056/nejm199604253341707
[689] Storr, MA., Sharkey, KA. 2007. The endocannabinoid system and gut–brain signalling. Current Opinion in Pharmacology, 7(6), 575–582. https://doi.org/10.1016/j.coph.2007.08.008

Besides the vagus nerve and the gut-brain axis, the activity of the gut is immensely influenced by the ecosystem of bacteria that reside in the gut. There are approximately 100 trillion cells that make up the gut microbiome in each of our bodies![690] That's 100,000,000,000,000 cells! To put that into perspective, that is ten times the number of cells that make up the entire human body!

These micro-organisms perform several different functions, primarily helping our bodies digest food and metabolize compounds produced during digestion. When gut microflora communities are thrown out of whack, often through improper diet, the use of antibiotics, disease, or genetic predisposition, these microorganisms can cause things like inflammation and gut permeability. Conditions like obesity and diabetes are associated with increased gut permeability. Generally, when the abundance and diversity of microorganisms in the gut are reduced, inflammation and metabolic syndromes follow.[691]

Cannabinoids also affect the permeability of intestinal walls. When the gut's lining is too permeable, it results in a condition often called "leaky gut," where things leak out of the gut and into nearby tissues, resulting in inflammation and alterations to the types of bacteria in the surrounding area. In an *in vitro* study, THC and CBD were both found to reduce the damaging effects of inflammation on intestinal permeability.[692] In the same study, the common endocannabinoids Anandamide and 2-AG were found to promote permeability, indicating that endocannabinoids could damage the gut in certain scenarios.

The endocannabinoid system is also involved in hunger signaling, influencing the types of foods that reach the gut, ultimately influencing the community of microflora in the gut. Research into understanding how phytocannabinoids like THC or CBD affect gut microflora is still relatively new. A recent studying examining the effects of a CBD-rich Cannabis extract on gut microflora revealed that initially CBD increased the abundance of one microbe, *Akkermansia muciniphila*, but ultimately ended up decreasing the relative abundance of all species of gut flora.[693]

Another study has shown that when THC and CBD are administered together, they may prevent the accumulation of *Akkermansia muciniphila* and possibly prevent microbial imbalances that could exacerbate symptoms of multiple sclerosis.[694] This

---

[690] Cani PD, Plovier H, Van Hul M, Geurts L, Delzenne NM, Druart C, Everard A. 2015. Endocannabinoids – at the crossroads between the gut microbiota and host metabolism. Nature Reviews Endocrinology. 12(1): 133-143. https://doi.org/10.1038/nrendo.2015.211

[691] Cani PD, Plovier H, Van Hul M, Geurts L, Delzenne NM, Druart C, Everard A. 2015. Endocannabinoids – at the crossroads between the gut microbiota and host metabolism. Nature Reviews Endocrinology. 12(1): 133-143. https://doi.org/10.1038/nrendo.2015.211

[692] Alhamoruni A, Wright KL, Larvin M, O'Sullivan SE. Cannabinoids mediate opposing effects on inflammation-induced intestinal permeability. Br J Pharmacol. 2012 Apr;165(8):2598-610. https://doi.org/10.1111/j.1476-5381.2011.01589.x

[693] Skinner CM, Nookaew I, Ewing LE, Wongsurawat T, Jenjaroenpun P, Quick CM, Yee EU, Piccolo BD, ElSohly M, Walker LA, Gurley B, Koturbash I. Potential Probiotic or Trigger of Gut Inflammation - The Janus-Faced Nature of Cannabidiol-Rich Cannabis Extract. J Diet Suppl. 2020;17(5):543-560. https://doi.org/10.1080/19390211.2020.1761506

[694] Al-Ghezi ZZ, Alghetaa HF, Nagarkatti M, Nagarkatti P. 2017. Combination of cannabinoids, delta-9-tetrahydrocannabinol (THC) and cannabidiol (CBD), mitigate experimental autoimmune

indicates that CBD-rich Cannabis extracts with little to no amount of THC in them may skew the gut microbiome toward imbalance in some people. However, if someone may be experiencing an abnormal deficiency of *A. muciniphila* in the gut, cannabidiol may increase *A. muciniphila* to adequate amounts without encouraging imbalance, but more research is needed.

Diet is another important factor influencing the gut microbiome. It is generally well known that THC-rich Cannabis consumption can cause a condition of urgent hunger called "the munchies". This is because the body uses certain cannabinoid receptors and endocannabinoid signaling to trigger hunger signals in the brain. For instance, researchers have found that whenever rodents taste fatty foods, endocannabinoid levels increase in certain parts of the intestines.[695] This rise in endocannabinoid signaling includes CB1 receptor signaling, which triggers a hunger signal in the brain and causes the rodent to consume more of the high-fat food. Because diet influences the communities of micro-organisms in the gut, this effect of hunger signaling can indirectly lead to changes in the gut microbiome, which can then go on to affect things like inflammation or even mood.

While stimulating CB1 receptors may lead to a certain type of change in the gut microflora, antagonizing, or blocking, CB1 receptors can lead to totally different effects. Mehrpouya-Bahrami et al (2017) found that blocking CB1 receptors can have profound impacts to gut microflora:

> "CB1 blockade dramatically increased relative abundance of Akkermansia muciniphila and decreased Lanchnospiraceae and Erysipelotrichaceae in the gut. Together, the current study suggests that blocking of CB1 ameliorates Diet-Induced Obesity and metabolic disorder by modulating macrophage inflammatory mediators, and that this effect is associated with alterations in gut microbiota and their metabolites."[696]

| Cannabinoid | Effects on Gut Flora | Notes |
|---|---|---|
| CBD | Increases abundance of *A. muciniphila*, overall decrease in abundance of other flora | Related to CB1 antagonism |
| THC | Decreases abundance of *A. muciniphila* | Related to CB1 agonism |

encephalomyelitis (EAE) by altering the gut microbiome. J Immunology. 198(1). https://doi.org/10.1016/j.bbi.2019.07.028

[695] DiPatrizio NV, Astarita G, Schwartz G, Li X, Piomelli D. Endocannabinoid signal in the gut controls dietary fat intake. Proc Natl Acad Sci U S A. 2011 Aug 2;108(31):12904-8. https://doi.org/10.1073/pnas.1104675108

[696] Mehrpouya-Bahrami P, Chitrala KN, Ganewatta MS, Tang C, Murphy EA, Enos RT, Velazquez KT, McCellan J, Nagarkatti M, Nagarkatti P. 2017. Blockade of CB1 cannabinoid receptor alters gut microbiota and attenuates inflammation and diet-induced obesity. Scientific Reports. 7:15645. https://doi.org/10.1038/s41598-017-15154-6

# CLINICAL INDICATIONS OF CANNABIS AND CANNABINOID PRODUCTS

The research surrounding Cannabis and cannabinoids and their efficacy for the treatment of various conditions and symptoms is complicated. There is a wide range of studies that have been conducted utilizing various synthetic and plant derived cannabinoid compounds to test therapeutic efficacy for various conditions. However, **there are very few studies that have been conducted using vaporized Cannabis flower or whole plant Cannabis extracts**. Much of the cannabinoid research that has been performed to date has been through either *in vitro* cell culture models or *in vivo* rodent models, both limited in their scalability to humans, although they do provide pieces to the ongoing biological puzzle researchers are trying to solve.

A review of cannabinoid clinical trials published in 2015 in the Journal of the American Medical Association listed several conditions that cannabinoids can effectively treat, using data from 79 different clinical trials. The researchers concluded **that there was evidence that cannabinoids can be used successfully to treat chronic pain, spasticity, nausea, vomiting, sleep disorders, and Tourette syndrome with clinical significance**.[697]

Most of these studies did not utilize drug delivery methods of products that are being used by current medical Cannabis patients in states or countries where Cannabis use is permitted. **Only two of the included studies used Cannabis inflorescence (flower) in a smoked or vaporized form as the drug intervention. 23 of the 79 studies utilized THC as a drug intervention.** Many of the included research articles utilized synthetic cannabinoids which specifically target either CB1 or CB2 receptors exclusively and do not necessarily represent the effects of phytocannabinoids or the matrix of cannabinoids present in a Cannabis inflorescence.

In addition, the 2015 study did not examine efficacy for conditions other than nausea/vomiting, chronic pain, spasticity, HIV/AIDS, sleep disorders, psychosis, Tourette syndrome, anxiety disorder, glaucoma, and depression (Whiting, 2015). For instance, many patients using Cannabis as medicine report treating conditions outside of this scope including skin cancer, arthritis and other inflammatory conditions, fibromyalgia, irritable bowel syndromes including Crohn's Disease, and autism.

A report published by the National Academy of Sciences in 2017[698] indicated that there was conclusive or substantial evidence that Cannabis or cannabinoids are effective for the treatment of chronic pain, nausea, vomiting, and spasticity. They reported that there was moderate evidence that Cannabis and cannabinoids are effective for treating short-term sleep problems associated with sleep apnea, fibromyalgia, chronic pain, and multiple sclerosis. The committee reported that there was limited evidence that Cannabis

---

[697] Whiting PF, Wolff RF, Deshpande S, Nisio MD, Duffy S, Hernandez AV, Keurentjes JC, Lang S, Misso K, Ryder S, Schmidlkofer S, Westwood M, Kleijnen J. 2015. Cannabinoids for Medical use: A Systematic Review and Meta-analysis. JAMA. 313(24):2456-2473. https://doi.org/10.1001/jama.2015.6358
[698] National Academies of Sciences, Engineering, and Medicine; Health and Medicine Division; Board on Population Health and Public Health Practice; Committee on the Health Effects of Marijuana: An Evidence Review and Research Agenda. The Health Effects of Cannabis and Cannabinoids: The Current State of Evidence and Recommendations for Research. Washington (DC): National Academies Press (US); 2017 Jan 12. https://doi.org/10.17226/24625

or cannabinoids could be an effective treatment for appetite and weight loss, Tourette syndrome, anxiety, and post-traumatic stress disorder (PTSD). Finally, the committee reported that there was some limited evidence that Cannabis or cannabinoids are ineffective for dementia, glaucoma, and depression associated with chronic pain.

Interestingly enough, the National Academy of Sciences report does acknowledge that there is currently not enough information available to refute any claims that Cannabis or cannabinoids may be effective for conditions like cancers, irritable bowel syndrome, epilepsy, amyotrophic lateral sclerosis (ALS), symptoms associated with Huntington's disease, motor discoordination associated with Parkinson's disease, dystonia, reduction of use of addictive substances, or schizophrenia or schizophreniform psychosis.

There is an important caveat to mention here. Cannabis is not a single static thing. Cannabis can come in a wide variety of chemical profiles and administration methods which can affect patient outcomes differently. For instance, CBD dominant chemovars of Cannabis will likely affect conditions very differently than THC dominant chemovars. But there are also many other chemovars circulating or in development, such as CBG, CBC, THCV, and CBDV dominant chemovars. Most of the data used by both the 2015 JAMA study, and the 2017 National Academy of Sciences report are based on THC-dominant products, with a small number of CBD-dominant products represented. There is still a lot to learn, research and understand regarding how cannabinoids in different ratios and in the presence of other compounds, or co-administered with other medications, will affect patient outcomes differently.

Caution should be taken when interpreting summaries like those mentioned here that purport to have identified the clinical efficacy and inefficacy of Cannabis and care should always be taken to understand exactly how these conclusions are drawn. What Cannabis was used? Was it herbal Cannabis? Cannabis extracts? Isolated cannabinoids? What cannabinoids? In what ratios? In the presence of what other compounds? At what dosages? Through what administration method? The medical use of Cannabis is a heavily nuanced topic, and there is still a lot that we do not understand and do not have enough clinical data to draw conclusions about.

### History of Medical Cannabis Use

Oral traditions of Cannabis use for appetite stimulation and fighting the effects of old age date back to nearly 3000 years BCE.[699] That's 5000 years ago! In 1500 BCE, the Atharva Veda indicates that Indians were using Cannabis for anxiety relief.[700] [701] Cannabis is suspected to even be a component of the holy anointing oil of the Hebrews as far back as 750 BCE.[702] The juice of the leaves was noted to be a remedy for earaches in the first century.[703] In the second century Chinese records indicate Cannabis was used in wine as

[699] Shou-Zhong Y. 1997. The Divine Farmer's Materia Medica: A Translation of the Shen Nong Ben Cao Jing. Boulder, CO: Blue Poppy Press.
[700] Grierson, GA. 1894. The hemp plant in Sanskrit and Hindi literature. Indian Antiquary. 260-262.
[701] Russo EB. 2007. History of Cannabis and its preparations in saga, science and sobriquet. Chemistry and Biodiversity. 4: 2624-2648. https://doi.org/10.1002/cbdv.200790144
[702] Alter R. The Five Books of Moses: A Translation with Commentary. 2004. New York: W.W. Norton & Co.
[703] Dioscorides P and Beck LY. 2011. De Materia Medica. Hildesheim: Olms-Weidmann.

an anesthetic.[704] In the early 10th century Persian records indicate it was even used to stimulate hair growth.[705] In 1542 it was noted that the Cannabis roots could be boiled and used to treat gout and burns.[706] Throughout the 16th century records indicate Cannabis was used for sore muscles, stiff joints, burns, wounds, jaundice, colic and even tumors.[707]

In 1839 a researcher named O'Shaughnessy studied Indian use of Cannabis and performed experiments in dogs, and then later people, to determine if Cannabis was a suitable treatment for tetanus, rabies, epilepsy, and rheumatoid disease.[708] Shortly after O'Shaughnessy published his findings, Cannabis began showing up in the European and United States Pharmacopoeias.

As records become more easily obtainable, we can find records throughout the 18th and 19th centuries of Cannabis being used to treat migraines, pain, spasticity, anxiety, depression, and insomnia.[709]

Cannabis was even featured in the US Pharmacopoeia as a medicine until the 12th edition released in 1942 after marijuana prohibition had begun in 1937.[710] You can still look up old issues of the USP and look for Extractum Cannabis or Tinctura Cannabis aka Extract of Hemp or Tincture of Hemp. Upon the initial publication of Cannabis in the USP in 1851, the 9th edition of the US Dispensatory had this to say about the medical use of Cannabis:

> "It has been found to cause sleep, to allay spasm, to compose nervous disquietude, and to relieve pain...The complaints in which it has been specially recommended are neuralgia, gout, rheumatism, tetanus, hydrophobia, epidemic cholera, convulsions, chorea, mental depression delirium tremens, insanity, and uterine hemorrhage."[711]

Jump forward to 1918, the US Dispensatory revised its description of the medical uses of Cannabis based on what physicians were seeing. This 1918 update reads:

> "Cannabis is used in medicine to relieve pain, to encourage sleep, and to soothe restlessness. Its action upon the nerve centers resembles opium, although much less certain, but it does not have the deleterious effect on the secretions. As a

[704] Julien MS. Chirugie chinoise. Substance anesthétique employée en Chine, dans le commencement du III-ième siecle de notre ère, pour paralyser momentanement la sensibilité. Comptes Rendus Hebdomadaires de l'Académie des Sciences. 1849. 28:223–229.

[705] Lozano I. 2001. The therapeutic use of Cannabis sativa L. in Arabic medicine. Journal of Cannabis Therapeutics. 1: 63-70. https://doi.org/10.3989/asclepio.1997.v49.i2.373

[706] Fuchs L. The great herbal of Leonhart Fuchs: De historia stirpium commentarii insignes, 1542 (notable commentaries on the history of plants). 1999. Stanford, CA: Stanford University Press.

[707] Gerard J and Johnson T. The Herbal: or, General History of Plants. 1975. New York: Dover Publications

[708] O'Shaughnessy WB. (1838–1840). On the preparations of the Indian hemp, or gunjah (Cannabis indica); their effects on the animal system in health, and their utility in the treatment of tetanus and other convulsive diseases. Transactions of the Medical and Physical Society of Bengal, 71–102, 421–461. http://www.ncbi.nlm.nih.gov/pmc/articles/pmc5592602/

[709] Russo E. 2014. The Pharmacological History of Cannabis. Chapter 2. Handbook of Cannabis. Oxford University Press. p.23-29

[710] United States Pharmacopoeia 12th Edition. 1942

[711] Wood GB, Bache F, eds., 1851, The Dispensatory of the United States of America, 9th ed. Philadelphia: Lippincott, Grambo, 1851, pp. 310-311.

*somnifacient it is rarely sufficient by itself, but may at times aid the hypnotic effect of other drugs. For its analgesic action it is used especially in pains of neuralgic origin, such as migraine, but is occasionally of service in other types. As a general nerve sedative it is used in hysteria, mental depression, neurasthenia, and the like. It has also been used in a number of other conditions, such as tetanus and uterine hemorrhage, but with less evidence of benefit. One of the great hindrances to the wider use of this drug is its extreme variability."*[712]

After Cannabis prohibition began, Cannabis became unavailable as a medicine, and research into the plant progressively slowed down into the late 1950s. Modern medical research into Cannabis really took off in the 1960s when THC was isolated and synthesized.[713] A little-known fact – but CBD was actually isolated and characterized approximately 24 years prior to when THC was isolated.[714] But because CBD did not elicit an intoxicating effect, it was largely ignored at first.

As THC research progressed throughout the 1960s and 1970s, research confirmed that THC could reduce nausea and vomiting associated with cancer chemotherapy[715], that THC had the same analgesic activity as codeine (Noyes et al, 1975), and that THC performed as well as the anti-asthma drug salbutamol aka albuterol or Ventolin as a bronchodilator.[716]

[712] http://resource.nlm.nih.gov/101539510
[713] Gaoni Y and Mechoulam R. 1964. Isolation, Structure, and Partial Synthesis of an Active Constituent of Hashish. J. Am. Chem. Soc. 86(8): 1646-1647. https://doi.org/10.1021/ja01062a046
[714] Adams R, Hunt M, Clark JH. 1940. Structure of Cannabidiol, a Product Isolated from the Marihuana Extract of Minnesota Wild Hemp. I. J. Am. Chem. Soc. 62(1): 196-200. https://doi.org/10.1021/ja01858a058
[715] Sallan SE, Zinberg NE, Frei E 3rd. 1975. Antiemetic effect of delta-9-tetrahydrocannabinol in patients receiving cancer chemotherapy. New England Journal of Medicine. 293: 795–797. https://doi.org/10.1056/nejm197510162931603/
[716] Williams SJ, Hartley JP, Graham JD. 1976. Bronchodilator effect of delta1-tetrahydrocannabinol administered by aerosol of asthmatic patients. Thorax 31: 720–723. http://dx.doi.org/10.1136/thx.31.6.720

# THE

# PHARMACOPŒIA

## OF THE

# UNITED STATES OF AMERICA

## (THE UNITED STATES PHARMACOPŒIA)

### TWELFTH REVISION
### (U. S. P. XII)

---

BY AUTHORITY OF THE
**UNITED STATES PHARMACOPŒIAL CONVENTION**
MEETING AT WASHINGTON, D. C., MAY 14 AND 15, 1940

---

PREPARED BY THE COMMITTEE OF REVISION AND
PUBLISHED BY THE BOARD OF TRUSTEES

OFFICIAL FROM NOVEMBER 1, 1942

ELECTROTYPED, PRINTED AND DISTRIBUTED BY
MACK PRINTING COMPANY
EASTON, PA.

FIGURE 71: COVER OF THE 12TH EDITION OF THE USP

**ARTICLES OFFICIAL IN THE U. S. P. XI BUT NOT ADMITTED TO THE U. S. P. XII**

| | |
|---|---|
| Acetum Scillæ | Liquor Sodii Hypochloritis Dilutus |
| Acidum Aceticum Dilutum | Magma Ferri Hydroxidi |
| Acidum Acetyltannicum | Massa Hydrargyri |
| Acidum Sulfuricum Aromaticum | Merbaphenum |
| Aconitum | Mistura Opii et Glycyrrhizæ Composita |
| Acriflavina | Oleum Maydis |
| Acriflavinæ Hydrochloridum | Oleum Santali |
| Æthylhydrocupreinæ Hydrochloridum | Paraffinum |
| Albumini Tannas | Paraffinum Chlorinatum |
| Ammonii Benzoas | Pepsinum |
| Ammonii Bromidum | Pilulæ Aloes |
| Ammonii Salicylas | Podophyllum |
| Arseni Triiodidum | Potassii Chloras |
| Asafœtida | Pulvis Ipecacuanhæ et Opii |
| Bismuthi Subgallas | Pulvis Sennæ Compositus |
| Calcii Bromidum | Pyrogallol |
| Calcii Creosotas | Quinina |
| Cannabis | Resina Podophylli |
| Cantharis | Santoninum |

FIGURE 72: USP 12TH EDITION LIST OF ITEMS EXCLUDED FROM 11TH EDITION

The 1980s ushered in renewed interest in CBD as well as continued research on THC. In 1981 CBD was identified as an anticonvulsant.[717] A year later it would be found that CBD could help relieve the anxiety brought on by THC.[718] In 1985, the unique flavonoid Cannflavin A was discovered, breaking Cannabis research away from the cannabinoid chemical class to encompass other types of plant compounds.[719] It was also in 1985 that the pharmaceutical drug Marinol was approved by the FDA for chemotherapy related nausea.[720]

In 1988 scientists finally discovered a chemical receptor in the body that seemed to be responsible for most of THC's effects – the cannabinoid type 1 receptor, or CB1 receptor.[721] This marks the beginning of piecing together a fascinating puzzle about a physiological system that had since been ignored – the endocannabinoid system, which wouldn't be formally named for another 10 years.[722]

---

[717] Carlini EA and Cunha JM. 1981. Hypnotic and antiepileptic effects of cannabidiol. Journal of Clinical Pharmacology. 21: 417S–427S. https://doi.org/10.1002/j.1552-4604.1981.tb02622.x

[718] Zuardi AW, Shirawaka I, Finkelfarb E, Karniol IG. 1982. Action of cannabidiol on the anxiety and other effects produced by delta 9-THC in normal subjects. Psychopharmacology. 76: 245–250. https://link.springer.com/article/10.1007/BF00432554#article-info

[719] Barrett ML, Gordon D, Evans FJ. 1985. Isolation from Cannabis sativa L. of cannflavin – a novel inhibitor of prostaglandin production. Biochemical Pharmacology. 34: 2019–2024. https://doi.org/10.1016/0006-2952(85)90325-9

[720] Russo E. 2014. The Pharmacological History of Cannabis. Chapter 2. Handbook of Cannabis. Oxford University Press. p.23-29

[721] Devane WA, Dysarz FA 3rd, Johnson MR, Melvin LS, Howlett AC. 1988. Determination and characterization of a cannabinoid receptor in rat brain. Molecular Pharmacology. 34: 605–613. https://pubmed.ncbi.nlm.nih.gov/2848184/

[722] Di Marzo V. 1998. 'Endocannabinoids' and other fatty acid derivatives with cannabimimetic properties: biochemistry and possible physiopathological relevance. Biochimica et Biophysica Acta. 1392: 153–175 https://doi.org/10.1016/s0005-2760(98)00042-3

In 1993 CBD's anti-anxiety effects that had been previously noted in the 1980s was again confirmed.[723] In 1997 it was found that THC could help reduce agitation in patients with dementia.[724]

In 2003 clinical trials of the Cannabis based pharmaceutical Sativex began, investigating whether it could be effective in treating multiple sclerosis symptoms.[725] In 2005 Sativex would go on to be approved in Canada for the treatment of MS related pain. Over the years Sativex would later be approved for other types of pain such as neuropathic pain and cancer pain. Eventually Sativex would be approved in the UK and Spain for spasticity in MS patients (Novotna et al, 2011).[726] In 2010 it would be discovered that Sativex can also treat nausea related to chemotherapy treatments.[727]

In 2018, the United States Food and Drug Administration approved the cannabis derived cannabidiol (CBD) pharmaceutical, Epidiolex, currently for treatment-resistant forms of epilepsy and seizures in children.[728]

### Examples of Cannabinoid Pharmaceuticals

| Name | Components | Date | Indications | Approved in US? | Note |
|------|-----------|------|-------------|-----------------|------|
| Nabilone / Cesamet | delta-6a,10a-dimethyl heptyl tetrahydrocannabinol (DMHP) | 1985 | Cancer related nausea, pain | Yes | Synthetic |
| Marinol | Synthetic THC | 1985 | Cancer related nausea and pain | Yes | Synthetic |
| Sativex | 1:1 ratio THC:CBD Cannabis extract | 2003 | MS symptoms, cancer related nausea, pain | No | Cannabis derived |
| Epidiolex | Cannabis-derived isolated CBD | 2018 | Treatment resistant epilepsy | Yes | Cannabis derived |

[723] Zuardi AW, Cosme RA, Graeff FG, Guimarães FS. Effects of ipsapirone and cannabidiol on human experimental anxiety. J Psychopharmacol. 1993 Jan;7(1 Suppl):82-8. https://doi.org/10.1177/026988119300700112

[724] Volicer, L, Stelly M, Morris J, McLaughlin J, Volicer BJ. 1997. Effects of dronabinol on anorexia and disturbed behavior in patients with Alzheimer's disease. International Journal of Geriatric Psychiatry. 1997. 12: 913–919. https://pubmed.ncbi.nlm.nih.gov/9309469/

[725] Wade, DT, Robson P, House H, Makela P, Aram J. 2003. A preliminary controlled study to determine whether whole-plant cannabis extracts can improve intractable neurogenic symptoms. Clinical Rehabilitation. 2003. 17: 18–26. https://doi.org/10.1191/0269215503cr581oa

[726] Novotna, A., Mares, J., Ratcliffe, S., Novakova, I., Vachova, M., Zapletalova, O., ... & Sativex Spasticity Study Group. (2011). A randomized, double-blind, placebo-controlled, parallel-group, enriched-design study of nabiximols*(Sativex®), as add-on therapy, in subjects with refractory spasticity caused by multiple sclerosis. European journal of neurology, 18(9), 1122-1131. https://doi.org/10.1111/j.1468-1331.2010.03328.x

[727] Duran M, Perez E, Abanades S, Vidal X, Saura C, Majem M, Arriola E, Rabanal M, Pastor A, Farre M, Rams N, Laporte JR, Capella D. 2010. Preliminary efficacy and safety of an oromucosal standardized cannabis extract in chemotherapy-induced nausea and vomiting. British Journal of Clinical Pharmacology. 2010. 70: 656–663. https://doi.org/10.1111/j.1365-2125.2010.03743.x

[728] https://www.fda.gov/news-events/press-announcements/fda-approves-first-drug-comprised-active-ingredient-derived-marijuana-treat-rare-severe-forms

## CHRONIC PAIN AND CANNABIS

One of the primary reasons that people use Cannabis is to relieve chronic pain. Cannabis is effective at alleviating pain by manipulating pain signaling and controlling inflammation. Although our understanding of the relationship between cannabinoids, cannabinoid receptors, and pain response is relatively new, it turns out that our body's own endocannabinoids have been helping modulate our pain responses all our lives.

First, it seems that cannabinoids interact with chemical pathways in the brain which control pain signaling and excitatory responses. Cannabinoids tend to decrease glutamate activity, which is responsible for causing excitatory signals, while increasing GABA activity, which causes suppressive signaling. Cannabinoids achieve this effect by manipulating calcium channels on neurons, effectively blocking them, which has subsequent effects on various neurotransmitters and receptors. In this way, cannabinoids can "turn down the volume" of pain.[729]

In addition to affecting glutamate and GABA activity to achieve pain reduction, cannabinoids can also modulate inflammation responses via the cannabinoid type 2 (CB2) and vanilloid receptors, among other more obscure receptor types. Cannabinoids can induce a certain cascade of signaling which essentially tells the body's immune system to calm down. This causes a reduction of inflammation, which can end up resulting in less pain.[730]

Unfortunately, until recently many physical and mental health care practitioners have been dismissive of anecdotal claims that Cannabis reduces pain, often interpreting such claims as an excuse to "get high" and indulge in substance abuse. This often resulted in patients feeling withdrawn and uncomfortable to share their Cannabis use with their doctor, and at times patients have even reported feeling attacked and ridiculed by health care professionals for sharing their experience. It is critically important that the future of health care recognizes the validity of many of these anecdotal claims and takes them seriously, otherwise the doctor-patient relationship may become eroded and a distrust in the provider may be cultivated within the patient.

## CANCER AND CANNABIS

Cannabinoids have already been shown to be effective in treating many cancer-associated symptoms either caused by the cancer or by the chemotherapy treatment. **Cannabinoids have been reported to be effective at treating cancer-associated anorexia, chemo or radiotherapy induced nausea and vomiting, relief from insomnia, enhanced mood, appetite stimulation, and pain relief.**[731] Along with treating the

---

[729] Rea K, Roche M, Finn DP. Supraspinal modulation of pain by cannabinoids: the role of GABA and glutamate. Br J Pharmacol. 2007 Nov;152(5):633-48. https://doi.org/10.1038/sj.bjp.0707440
[730] Cabral GA, Raborn ES, Ferreira GA. 2015. Phytocannabinoids and the Immune System. Handbook of Cannabis. Oxford University Press. 261-279.
[731] Engels FK, de Jong FA, Mathijssen RHJ, Erkens JA, Herings RM, Verweij J. 2007. Medicinal cannabis in oncology. European Journal of Cancer. 43:2638-2644 https://doi.org/10.1016/j.ejca.2007.09.010

symptoms of cancer and cancer treatments, cannabinoids have also exhibited specific anticancer properties in animal models.[732] [733] [734] [735]

When cancer is present in the human body, CB1 and CB2 receptor expression tend to increase in the diseased tissues. This lets us know that the endocannabinoid system must play an important role in the progression and regulation of cancer. CB1 receptor expression can even be correlated with disease severity and cancer aggressiveness.[736] [737]

Both CB2 and GPR55 receptors also seem to follow this same pattern. Although cannabinoids and cannabinoid receptor expression play a critical role in cancer growth, it also plays a critical role in tumor suppression. Blocking CB1 receptor expression in animals has resulted in carcinogenesis (cancer growth) in the intestines of mice, demonstrating that CB1 receptor activity actively suppresses tumor growth.[738]

**Research has provided mixed results concerning how cannabinoids influence cancer**. Some reports show cannabinoids reducing the prevalence of cancer while some other studies report cannabinoid induced cancer growth.[739] [740] [741] [742] Nonetheless, **cannabinoid treatments have been shown to promote apoptosis (cell death) of cancer cells, impair cancer cell growth, and slow or block the spread of cancer.**[743]

The primary way that cannabinoids kill cancer cells is by preventing the growth of blood vessels in the cells and/or causing vascular endothelial cells to kill themselves.[744]

---

[732] Guzman M. 2003. Cannabinoids: potential anticancer agents. Nat Rev Cancer 3(10):745-755. https://doi.org/10.1038/nrc1188

[733] Sarfaraz S, Adhami VM, Syed DN, Afaq F, Mukhtar H. 2008. Cannabinoids for cancer treatment: progress and promise. Cancer Res. 68(2):339-342. https://doi.org/10.1158/0008-5472.can-07-2785

[734] Pisanti S, Picardi P, D'Alessandro A. Laezza C, Bifulco M. 2013. The endocannabinoid signaling system in cancer. Trend Pharmacol Sci. 34(5):273-282. https://doi.org/10.1016/j.tips.2013.03.003

[735] Velasco G, Sanchez C, Guzman M. 2012. Towards the use of cannabinoids as antitumour agents. Nat Rev Cancer. 12(6):436-444. https://doi.org/10.1038/nrc3247

[736] Malfitano AM, Ciaglia E, Gangemi G, Gazzerro P, LaezzaC, Bifulco M. 2011. Update on the endocannabinoid system as an anticancer target. Expert Opin Ther Targets. 15(3):297-308. https://doi.org/10.1517/14728222.2011.553606

[737] Velasco G, Sanchez C, Guzman M. 2012. Towards the use of cannabinoids as antitumour agents. Nat Rev Cancer. 12(6):436-444. https://doi.org/10.1038/nrc3247

[738] Wang D, Wang H, Ning W, Backlund MG, Dey SK, DuBois RN. 2008. Loss of cannabinoid receptor 1 accelerates intestinal tumor growth. Cancer Res. 68(15):6468-6476. https://doi.org/10.1158/0008-5472.can-08-0896

[739] Cudaback E, Marrs W, Moeller T, Stella N. 2010. The expression level of CB1 and CB2 receptors determines their efficacy at inducing apoptosis in astrocytomas. PLoS One 5 (1), e8702. https://doi.org/10.1371/journal.pone.0008702

[740] Hart S, Fischer OM, Ullrich A. 2004. Cannabinoids induce cancer cell proliferation via tumor necrosis factor alpha-converting enzyme (TACE/ADAM17)-mediated transactivation of the epidermal growth factor receptor. Cancer Res. 64(6):1943-1950. https://doi.org/10.1158/0008-5472.can-03-3720

[741] McKallip RJ, Nagarkatti M, Nagarkatti PS. 2005. Delta-9-tetrahydrocannabinol enhances breast cancer growth and metastasis by suppression of the antitumor immune response. J Immunol. 174(6):3281-3289. https://doi.org/10.4049/jimmunol.174.6.3281

[742] Zhu LX, Sharma S, Stolina M, Gardner B, Roth MD, Tashkin DP. 2000. Delta-9-tetrahydrocannabinol inhibits antitumor immunity by a CB2 receptor-mediated, cytokine-dependent pathway. J Immunol. 165(1):373-380. https://doi.org/10.4049/jimmunol.165.1.373

[743] Velasco G, Sánchez C, Guzmán M. Endocannabinoids and Cancer. Handb Exp Pharmacol. 2015;231:449-72. https://doi.org/10.1007/978-3-319-20825-1_16

[744] Velasco G, Sanchez C, Guzman M. 2012. Towards the use of cannabinoids as antitumour agents. Nat Rev Cancer. 12(6):436-444. https://doi.org/10.1038/nrc3247

Cannabinoids also affect autophagy, which is the process in the body by which cellular debris is broken down and eliminated from the body. When apoptosis occurs, and cell death is initiated, it is important that the body also engages in autophagy to handle the resulting cellular debris, so they do not build up in the body. If cellular debris builds up in the body, it can cause inflammatory responses. Think of autophagy as your body's way of producing a series of "pac men" that gobble up cellular debris when cells die.

Unfortunately, much of the research that has been conducted thus far concerning Cannabis, cannabinoids and cancer has largely been with synthetic cannabinoid compounds of varying dosage, quality, and administration routes used. Many of the studies performed to date have not utilized large, randomized sample populations. More research will need to be performed before appropriate data will be available that can help shine more light on how cannabinoids can best be utilized as a treatment for not only cancer symptoms, but for the treatment of cancer itself.

### EPILEPSY AND CANNABIS

Cannabis reportedly can reduce the intensity and frequency of seizures in some individuals. Numerous examples have been featured in the media lately highlighting stories of children that have regained their lives by utilizing cannabidiol rich Cannabis treatments. One famous example is that of Charlotte Figi who inspired the famous CBD rich Cannabis strain, Charlotte's Web. However, it must be noted that the epidemiological data supporting the use of Cannabis for the treatment of seizures is not very strong. According to a review performed by Szaflarski and Bebin (2014), most interviews of epilepsy patients that have used Cannabis as an alternative treatment reveal that most of the time Cannabis does not actually provide appreciable relief from seizures. In many cases, Cannabis exacerbated seizure symptoms, rather than providing relief.[745]

CBD has demonstrated antiepileptic effects in many animal research models, although it is unclear how CBD produces these effects. A series of experiments has shown that the CB1 receptor is critical in controlling seizures and that CBD exerts its anti-seizure effects through receptors other than those found in the endocannabinoid system.

It could be speculated that the relatively new appreciation of the diversity of THC/CBD ratios found among Cannabis varieties has not been well represented in previous studies. High resin yielding CBD dominant Cannabis plants are relatively new to the market and many people seeking alleviation of spasticity symptoms with Cannabis have perhaps been using THC dominant varieties. **As cannabinoid ratio data is gathered in future research, a clearer picture of how Cannabis can treat epilepsy symptoms will develop**. Ultimately at this point, there is little quality data available that can lead one to draw any conclusions, but better-quality research projects are currently being designed and implemented. As more states legalize Cannabis and allow its research, this data will become available.

### CANNABINOID ASSISTED NEUROPROTECTION

Some cannabinoids have demonstrated neuroprotective effects. For instance, cannabidiol (CBD) has demonstrated neuroprotective, anti-oxidative, and anti-apoptotic

---

[745] Szaflarski JP, Bebin EM. Cannabis, cannabidiol, and epilepsy--from receptors to clinical response. Epilepsy Behav. 2014 Dec;41:277-82. https://doi.org/10.1016/j.yebeh.2014.08.135

effects against β-amyloid peptide toxicity, a critical component of Alzheimer's disease.[746] Both THC and CBD have exhibited neuroprotective effects against glutamate toxicity in rodent cortical neuron cell culture studies.[747] In rodent models, THC as well as endocannabinoids have exhibited neuroprotective effects against **ischemia**, a condition characterized by insufficient blood flow to the brain.[748] [749]Cannabinoids have also been indicated as effective in protecting the brain during a concussion, which has gathered the attention of sports communities.

### PEDIATRIC MEDICAL CANNABIS USE

There is a limited amount of information currently available about the use of Cannabis medically in children. Most of the information that is available is in the form of case studies produced by doctors and nurses that have worked with pediatric patients to treat a medical condition with cannabinoids or herbal Cannabis. Much of this data that *is* available is difficult to interpret, because dosages, administration methods, and product formulations are not standardized. In addition, many of these reports feature very small sample sizes, sometimes as low as just one individual. The results of small sample sizes cannot be confidently extrapolated to a larger patient population.[750]

Because children are growing and changing so rapidly, dosing for children is highly dynamic, depending on the age range of the child. Traditionally, the primary age ranges considered for pediatric dosing are:

- Pre-term newborn infants born at less than 36 weeks of gestation
- Term newborn infants that are age 0 to approximately 28 days
- Infants and toddlers that are age 28 days to approximately 2 years
- Children that are age 2 to 11 years
- Adolescents that are age 12 to 18 years

Before solid Cannabis or cannabinoid dosing guidelines can be developed for pediatric patients, the safety and the efficacy of Cannabis for different medical conditions must be studied in each of these age groups. Some health care professionals and caregivers that administer medical Cannabis or cannabinoids to children rely on scaling down dosing information available for adults down to children based on body surface area and body weight.

However, this is not always appropriate, because there can be a number of changes happening within a child that will affect the way that Cannabis constituents are

[746] Iuvone T, Esposito G, Esposito R, Santamaria R, Di Rosa M, Izzo AA. 2004. Neuroprotective effect of cannabidiol, a non-psychoactive component from Cannabis sativa, on beta-amyloid-induced toxicity in PC12 cells. Journal of Neurochem. 89:134-141. https://doi.org/10.1111/j.1471-4159.2003.02327.x

[747] Hampson AJ, Grimaldi M, Axelrod J, Wink D. 1998. Cannabidiol and THC are neuroprotective antioxidants. PNAS. 95(14):8268-8273. https://doi.org/10.1073/pnas.95.14.8268

[748] Louw DR, Yang FW, Sutherland GR. 2000. The effect of THC on forebrain ischemia in rat. Brain Research. 857:183-187. https://doi.org/10.1016/s0006-8993(99)02422-1

[749] Sinor AD, Irvin SM, Greenberg DA. 2000. Endocannabinoid protect cerebral cortical neurons from in vitro ischemia in rats. Neuroscience Letters. 278:157-160. https://doi.org/10.1016/s0304-3940(99)00922-2

[750] Alcorn J, Vuong S, Wu F, Seifert B, Lyon A. (2019). Pediatric Dosing Considerations for Medical Cannabis. Recent Advances in Cannabinoid Research. Chapter 10:181-200 https://doi.org/10.1016/j.ejim.2018.01.004

processed in the body, which do not correlate directly with body surface area and body weight. For instance, one example is in metabolic rates in children. A child's metabolic rate can dramatically change at different stages of life, without being directly correlated to the child's size. One study found that scaling dosing for hydrophobic drugs, like cannabinoids, tends to work well enough based on body weight for patients between 1 month and 1 year of age, however for older children, this model was less effective, and instead dosage scaling based on body surface area was more effective.[751]

To deal with this problem of a lack of dosage recommendations, parents, caregivers, and healthcare professionals are left with the classic trial and error approach, where low dosages are initially used, and then slowly scaled up until a therapeutic or adverse response is obtained.

Research is mixed regarding whether health care professionals support pediatric use of Cannabis to treat medical conditions. In one study, physicians that were surveyed cited that the primary barriers to their support for pediatric Cannabis use are a lack of formulation, potency, or dosing standards.[752] The primary conditions currently being treated with Cannabis in children are cancer-related nausea, epilepsy, motor disorders, and autism.

One case study reports cardiac arrest and death in an 11-month-old male child following THC exposure.[753] No other risk factor could be identified other than THC metabolites in the child's body, leading the physicians to present the possibility that THC may have caused inflammation of the heart (myocarditis) which eventually led to a heart attack. While it is impossible to say whether THC was the primary factor responsible for the child's death, it at least highlights a risk factor that all parents and pediatricians should be aware of regarding pediatric Cannabis use or accidental pediatric Cannabis exposure.

## BACK INTO THE FOLD: STANDARDIZING CANNABIS MEDICINE

In 2020 researchers representing an expert panel on Cannabis for the United States Pharmacopeia (USP) published a paper entitled "Cannabis Inflorescence for Medical Purposes: USP Considerations for Quality Attributes" in which they provide a framework for bringing Cannabis back into the United States Pharmacopoeia as a standardized medicinal herb.[754] At the time of publication, this was incredibly significant news and signals a path toward reintegrating Cannabis into the medicinal plant toolbox that it had been excommunicated from nearly a hundred years prior.

The identification of standardized quality attributes for herbal Cannabis is important for integrating Cannabis into the national and global natural products industry,

---

[751] Johnson TN. (2008). The problems in scaling adult drug doses to children. Archives of Disease in Childhood. 93(3):207-211 https://doi.org/10.1136/adc.2006.114835

[752] Ananth P, Ma C, Al-Sayegh H, Kroon L, Klein V, Wharton C, Hallez E, Braun I, Michelson K, Rosenberg AR, London W, Wolfe J. 2018. Provider Perspectives on Use of Medical Marijuana in Children with Cancer. Pediatrics. 141(1):e20170559 https://doi.org/10.1542/peds.2017-0559

[753] Nappe TM, Hoyte, CO. 2017. Pediatric Death Due to Myocarditis After Exposure to Cannabis. Clin Pract Cases Emerg Med. 1(3):166-170. https://doi.org/10.5811/cpcem.2017.1.33240

[754] Sarma ND, Waye A, ElSohly MA, Brown PN, Elzinga S, Johnson HE, Marles RJ, Melanson JE, Russo E, Deyton L, Hudalla C, Vrdoljak GA, Wurzer JH, Khan IA, Kim NC, Giancaspro GI. 2020. Cannabis Inflorescence for Medical Purposes: USP Considerations for Quality Attributes. J. nat. Prod. 83: 1334-1351. https://doi.org/10.1021/acs.jnatprod.9b01200

whether as THC-rich medical or adult use Cannabis (aka "marijuana") or as CBD or CBG-rich Cannabis ("hemp"). This allows companies to use these quality attributes to assess the acceptability of Cannabis ingredients, for example. Prior to these recommendations, Cannabis infused product manufacturers had to establish their own quality guidelines or rely on the quality guidelines provided by their respective state, which may or may not be adequate. These recommendations also provide a reference point for states that have not yet legalized medical or adult-use Cannabis, or that have not adopted testing regulations yet for Cannabis products. It may also be a path toward standardizing all Cannabis testing requirements among all states in the United States, as well as across countries around the world.

It should be noted that these USP recommendations are for quality attributes associated with herbal Cannabis (Cannabis inflorescence). At the time of this writing there is still a lot of work to be done to define quality attributes for other Cannabis products, like extracts.

# Summary of Recommended USP Quality Attributes for Herbal Cannabis

| Quality | Example(s) | Description/Notes |
|---|---|---|
| **Naming** | "Cannabis Inflorescence" | Dried pistillate (female) inflorescence of the plant Cannabis sativa L., family Cannabaceae, including its subspecies, varieties and chemotypes. |
| **Identification** | Macroscopic/Microscopic HPTLC HPLC and GC | |
| **Chemical Profile** | Type I – THC Dominant Type II – THC/CBD Type III – CBD Dominant | Dominant and co-dominant terpenes should also be identified. |
| **Contaminants** | Pesticides, Elemental Contaminants, Microbial Contaminants, and Mycotoxins (See below) | |
| **Pesticides** | See USP Chapter <561> | |
| **Elemental Contaminants** | Arsenic: 0.2 ug/g Cadmium: 0.2 ug/g Lead: 0.5 ug/g Mercury: 0.1 ug/g | |
| **Microbial Contaminants** | Total Aerobic Bacteria: 100,000 CFU/g Yeast/Mold: 10,000 CFU/g Bile-Tolerant Gram-Negative Bacteria: 1,000 CFU/g Salmonella: ND E. Coli: ND | More stringent requirements recommended for sensitive or at-risk populations |
| **Mycotoxins** | Total Aflatoxins (B1, B2, G1, G2): ≤ 20 ppb B1 Aflatoxin: ≤ 5 ppb | |
| **Water Activity** | 0.6 ± 0.05 aw | |
| **Foreign Organic Matter** | ≤ 5% of stems ≤ 2% other | Stems must be 3mm or less in diameter, otherwise they are considered "other" |
| **Total Ash and Acid-Insoluble Ash** | ≤ 20% Total Ash ≤ 4% Insoluble Ash | |
| **Packaging and Storage** | 8 – 15°C ≤ 40% relative humidity | |
| **Labeling** | Cannabis Inflorescence Type I Cannabis sativa L. 250mg/g Total THC Dominant Terpenes: Myrcene, Limonene, Terpinolene | Any other cannabinoids over 10mg/g should also be labeled. |
| **Adulteration** | Presence of synthetic cannabinoids | |

**FIGURE 73: SUMMARY OF USP RECOMMENDATIONS FOR CANNABIS QUALITY**

# What Strain is Best for My Medical Condition?

Dispensary technicians, physicians, nurses, and caregivers alike are often asked this question by patients wanting to treat a specific medical condition with Cannabis. The question itself is a loaded one and assumes that a Cannabis product's efficacy is correlated with the supposed genetic lineage of the Cannabis used to produce it – or that strain names reliably correlate with genetic lineage or chemical profile. As featured in previous chapters, there are many problems associated with the taxonomy, or categorization, of Cannabis "strains".

In previous chapters we learned that a plant's chemotype, or chemical profile, is variable and influenced by both genetics *and* environment. The Cannabis plant exhibits phytochemical polymorphism, producing varying concentrations of different terpenoids and other compounds throughout the plant. In addition, plants of the same strain, grown in the same area, may exhibit different chemotypes. Even after the plant is harvested, the chemistry is changing.

In a 2016 interview, Cannabis researcher Dr. Ethan Russo commented, "Since the taxonomists cannot agree, I would strongly encourage the scientific community, the press, and the public to abandon the sativa/indica nomenclature and rather insist that accurate biochemical assays on cannabinoid and terpenoid profiles be available for Cannabis in both the medical and recreational markets. Scientific accuracy and the public health demand no less than this."[755]

While accurate tests of a plant's chemical profile are important for helping patients make better decisions when choosing a Cannabis product, recent research indicates that more often than not people tend to enjoy Cannabis that they also find aromatically pleasing.[756] And it turns out that these correlations did not hold up when focusing on terpene data alone, reminding us that aroma is about more than just terpenes. While this research relates primarily to subjective enjoyment of THC-rich Cannabis, it remains an interesting lesson for patients that sometimes there are qualities of Cannabis which may not be adequately quantified and featured on a test result, that contribute to the quality of outcome of using Cannabis. It is always important to pay attention to organoleptic qualities of Cannabis (appearance, smell, etc) along with analytical data to find Cannabis cultivars or products that are best for any individual person.

**Keeping an experience journal** that can be shared with a physician to find trends is a great start toward discovering what unique terpene profiles, cannabinoid profiles,

---

[755] Piomelli D, Russo EB. The Cannabis sativa Versus Cannabis indica Debate: An Interview with Ethan Russo, MD. Cannabis Cannabinoid Res. 2016 Jan 1;1(1):44-46. https://doi.org/10.1089/can.2015.29003.ebr

[756] Plumb, Jeremy, Shaban Demirel, Jeremy L. Sackett, Ethan B. Russo, and Adrianne R. Wilson-Poe. 2022. "The Nose Knows: Aroma, but Not THC Mediates the Subjective Effects of Smoked and Vaporized Cannabis Flower" Psychoactives 1, no. 2: 70-86. https://doi.org/10.3390/psychoactives1020008

aromas and flavors work best for you. Some of the information you should document in an experience journal include:

| Attribute | Description/Example |
|---|---|
| Product type | Flower, tincture, edible, concentrate |
| Strain name | "Blue Dream", "Jack Herer", "Granddaddy Purple" |
| CBD:THC ratio | 20:1 (high CBD), 4:1, 2:1, 1:1, 1:2, 1:4, 1:20 (high THC) |
| Potency | 15% Total THC, 6% Total CBD, 15mg THC, 20mg CBD |
| Dose amount | 1 gram, 1 cookie, 2 mL, 1 unit |
| Dominant terpenes | Myrcene, limonene, linalool |
| Notable smells | Fruity, floral, earthy, spicy, fuely |
| Distinct colors | Dark purple, pink tones |
| Administration route/Consumption method | Vaporization, sublingual, oral, topical, smoking |
| Pre-consumption pain score | 1 (no pain) – 10 (unbearable pain) |
| Pre-consumption mood description | Anxious, serene, angry, sad, bored, happy, hopeful |
| Time of administration | 5:30pm PST |
| Time of onset | 5:42pm PST |
| Post-consumption pain score | 1 (no pain) – 10 (unbearable pain) |
| Post-consumption mood description | Anxious, serene, angry, sad, bored, happy, hopeful |
| Narrative | Stream of consciousness description of experience before, during, and after consumption |

FIGURE 74: EXAMPLE CANNABIS EXPERIENCE JOURNAL ENTRY

# Chapter 24:
## VETERINARY USES OF CANNABIS AND CANNABINOIDS

SCAN ME

## Learning Questions

- Is Cannabis safe for animals to consume?
- How are the endocannabinoid systems of cats, dogs, horses, and other animals similar and different compared to a human's ECS?
- Why don't insects have endocannabinoid systems?
- What veterinary conditions can be treated with Cannabis or cannabinoids?
- What doses of cannabinoids are effective for therapeutic applications?

When we introduced the endocannabinoid system in previous chapters, you might recall that we mentioned that all vertebrate mammals seem to have endocannabinoid systems – though they can show up quite differently between animals.

In fact, at the time of this writing it is thought that, except insects and protozoa – all animals have developed endocannabinoid systems, presumably at the same time as developing central nervous systems.[757] Because other animals also have endocannabinoid systems, it should then follow that there is a place for cannabinoids in veterinary medicine.

---

[757] Silver, R. J. (2019). The endocannabinoid system of animals. Animals, 9(9), 686. doi.org/10.3390/ani9090686

# INSECTS AND ENDOCANNABINOIDS

In the late 1990s and early 2000s, Cannabis researcher John McPartland searched for cannabinoid receptors in insects and came up empty handed.[758] This was somewhat surprising on one hand because it would seem that older ancestors of insects and mammals developed endocannabinoid systems. However, on the other hand, perhaps this finding was not surprising at all.

> *"No other mammalian neuroreceptor has been found to be lacking in insects. This is the only case in comparative neurobiology that a mammalian neuroreceptor is absent in insects."*[759]

Insects do not produce substantial amounts of the chemical substrates required to build endocannabinoids to interact with cannabinoid receptors. Specifically, insects are not good at producing arachidonic acid, from which most endocannabinoids are derived. Without ligands to interact with a receptor, there is no need to produce that receptor and it can be selected out.

So, what do we know about Cannabis' effects in other animals beyond humans? The data that exists on cannabinoids and animals is a bit murky and with a lot of gaps that need to be addressed.

First off, a lot of the pre-clinical research that has been performed with cannabinoids to date has been either in mice, rats, or guinea pigs – so we technically have the most data about how Cannabis affects these animals than others. Next to rodents, we probably have the most data regarding cannabinoids in canines and horses, which will be highlighted in this chapter. As we will note again later, there is very little information available about how cannabinoids affect cats. Beyond a bit of research that has been done on cows eating Cannabis supplemented feed, there is not much else available. This highlights an incredible opportunity for future research.

Another issue worth noting is that most of the data that we have regarding Cannabis or cannabinoids in other species of animals is largely from studying cannabinoid

---

[758] McPartland, J.; Marzo, V.D.; Petrocellis, L.D.; Mercer, A.; Glass, M. Cannabinoid receptors are absent in insects. J. Comp. Neurol. 2001, 436, 423–429. doi.org/10.1002/cne.1078

[759] Silver, R. J. (2019). The endocannabinoid system of animals. Animals, 9(9), 686. doi.org/10.3390/ani9090686

poisonings and toxicology.[760] Similarly how Cannabis and cannabinoid research has traditionally focused on toxicology and safety in humans, usually trying to identify how Cannabis may cause harm, veterinary research has suffered much the same fate.

Deficiencies acknowledged, there is a lot to learn from the research that *has* been performed in non-rodent animals that we will try to unpack in the following sections.

| Cannabinoid Receptors in Invertebrates | | |
|---|---|---|
| **Species** | **CB Receptors?** | **CB Signaling?** |
| *Actinothoe albocincta* (Sea Anemone) | Yes | No |
| *Ciona intestinalis* (Sea Vase) | Yes | Yes |
| *Jasus edwardsii* (Rock Lobster) | Yes | Yes |
| *Homarus americanus* (American Lobster) | Yes | Yes |
| *Lumbricus terrestris* (Earthworm) | Yes | Yes |
| *Pangrellus redivivus* (Mat Nematode) | Yes | Yes |
| *Caenorhabditis elegans* (Common Nematode) | No | No |
| *Peripatoides novae-zealandiae* (Velvet Worms) | Yes | Yes |
| *Tethya aurantium* (Orange Puffball Sponge) | Yes | No |
| *Apis mellifera* (Western Honey Bee) | No | No |
| *Drosophila melanogaster* (Fruit Fly) | No | No |
| *Gerris marginatus* (Water Strider) | No | No |
| *Zophobas atratus* (Beetle) | No | No |

**FIGURE 75 CANNABINOID RECEPTORS IN INVERTEBRATES**

---

[760] Landa, L., SULCOVA, A., & Gbelec, P. (2016). The use of cannabinoids in animals and therapeutic implications for veterinary medicine: a review. Veterinární medicína, 61(3). doi.org/10.17221/8762-VETMED

# Cannabinoids and Canines (Dogs)

Man's best friend exhibits a few differences in the development of their endocannabinoid system compared to humans. Dogs seem to have much more CB1 receptors in structures toward the back of the brain including the cerebellum, brain stem, and medulla oblongata.[761] [762] This means that **dogs are particularly sensitive to THC compared to humans**.

In an excellent review by Silver (2019), the author points out that the density of CB1 receptors in these parts of the brain present unique symptoms for dogs when they consume THC. Namely, dogs often have trouble sitting still or exhibit uncontrollable swaying or pacing when consuming substantial doses of THC. This condition is called "static ataxia" and will typically happen to dogs when exposed to doses of THC greater than 0.5mg/kg intravenously.[763] [764] It has also been found that dogs that exhibit atopic dermatitis, or eczema, have upregulated CB1 receptors.[765]

Dogs also feature CB1 receptors in other areas of the body beyond the brain and central nervous system including salivary glands, hair follicles, skin, inner ear, eyes, thyroid

---

[761] Silver, R. J. (2019). The endocannabinoid system of animals. Animals, 9(9), 686. doi.org/10.3390/ani9090686

[762] Herkenham, M.; Lynn, A.B.; Little, M.D.; Johnson, M.R.; Melvin, L.S.; de Costa, B.R.; Rice, K.C. Cannabinoid receptor localization in brain. Proc. Natl. Acad. Sci. USA 1930, 87, 1932–1936. https://doi.org/10.1073/pnas.87.5.1932

[763] Dixon, W.E. The Pharmacology of Cannabis indica. Br. Med. J. 1899, 2, 1354–1357. doi.org/10.1136/bmj.2.2030.1517

[764] Hill, M.N.; McLaughlin, R.J.; Morrish, A.C.; Viau, V.; Floresco, S.B.; Hillard, C.J.; Gorzalka, B.B. Suppression of amygdalar endocannabinoid signaling by stress contributes to activation of the hypothalamic–pituitary–adrenal axis. Neuropsychopharmacology 2009, 34, 2733. doi.org/10.1038/npp.2009.114

[765] Campora, L.; Miragliotta, V.; Ricci, E.; Cristino, L.; Di Marzo, V.; Albanese, F.; Frederica della Valle, M.; Abramo, F. Cannabinoid receptor type 1 and 2 expression in the skin of healthy dogs and dogs with atopic dermatitis. Am. J. Vet. Res. 2012, 73, 988–995. doi.org/10.2460/ajvr.73.7.988

gland and more.[766] [767] [768] [769] CB2 receptors have been found in canine hair follicles, sweat glands, lymph nodes, sebaceous glands, and blood cells.[770]

Despite their sensitivity to THC, dogs can safely tolerate THC, CBD and presumably other phytocannabinoids in proper dosages. Dogs can develop tolerance to THC, just like humans, and can be titrated up to higher doses over prolonged periods of time safely.[771] Some withdrawal effects have been noted in canines.[772]

# CANNABINOIDS AND FELINES (CATS)

Very little research has gone into understanding the endocannabinoid system of cats. Cannabinoid receptors have been identified in feline brains, intestines[773], oral mucosa[774], and skin[775].

---

[766] Dall'Aglio, C.; Mercati, F.; Pascucci, L.; Boiti, C.; Pedini, V.; Ceccarelli, P. Immunohistochemical localization of CB1 receptor in canine salivary glands. Vet. Res. Commun. 2010, 34, 9–12. doi.org/10.1007/s11259-010-9379-0

[767] Campora, L.; Miragliotta, V.; Ricci, E.; Cristino, L.; Di Marzo, V.; Albanese, F.; Frederica della Valle, M.; Abramo, F. Cannabinoid receptor type 1 and 2 expression in the skin of healthy dogs and dogs with atopic dermatitis. Am. J. Vet. Res. 2012, 73, 988–995. doi.org/10.2460/ajvr.73.7.988

[768] Mercati, F.; Dall'Aglio, C.; Pascucci, L.; Boiti, C.; Ceccarelli, P. Identification of cannabinoid type 1 receptor in dog hair follicles. Acta Histochem. 2012, 114, 68–71. doi.org/10.1016/j.acthis.2011.01.003

[769] Pirone, A.; Lenzi, C.; Coli, A.; Giannessi, E.; Stornelli, M.R.; Miragliotta, V. Preferential epithelial expression of type-1 cannabinoid receptor (CB1R) in the canine embryo. SpringerPlus 2015, 4, 804. doi.org/10.1186/s40064-015-1616-0

[770] Silver, R. J. (2019). The endocannabinoid system of animals. Animals, 9(9), 686. doi.org/10.3390/ani9090686/

[771] Silver, R. J. (2019). The endocannabinoid system of animals. Animals, 9(9), 686. doi.org/10.3390/ani9090686/

[772] Brutlag, A.; Hommerding, H. Toxicology of Marijuana, Synthetic Cannabinoids, and Cannabidiol in Dogs and Cats. Vet. Clin. Small Anim. 2018, 48, 1087–1102. doi.org/10.1016/j.cvsm.2018.07.008

[773] Stanzani, A., Galiazzo, G., Giancola, F. et al. Localization of cannabinoid and cannabinoid related receptors in the cat gastrointestinal tract. Histochem Cell Biol 153, 339–356 (2020). doi.org/10.1007/s00418-020-01854-0

[774] Polidoro G, Galiazzo G, Giancola F, Papadimitriou S, Kouki M, Sabattini S, Rigillo A, Chiocchetti R. Expression of cannabinoid and cannabinoid-related receptors in the oral mucosa of healthy cats and cats with chronic gingivostomatitis. J Feline Med Surg. 2021 Aug;23(8):679-691. doi.org/10.1177/1098612X20970510

[775] Miragliotta, V., Ricci, P.L., Albanese, F., Pirone, A., Tognotti, D. and Abramo, F. (2018), Cannabinoid receptor types 1 and 2 and peroxisome proliferator-activated receptor-$\alpha$: distribution in the skin of clinically healthy cats and cats with hypersensitivity dermatitis. Vet Dermatol, 29: 316-e111. doi.org/10.1111/vde.12658

One study that examined how cats tolerate escalating doses of cannabinoids fed up to 11 escalating doses of CBD, THC or CBD and THC in a 1.5:1 ratio.[776] Doses maxed out at 30.5 mg/kg CBD, 41.5 mg/kg THC, and 13:8.4 mg/kg CBD:THC. All the cats handled all doses safely with only mild adverse events likely associated with the MCT oil used as a carrier for the cannabinoids.

Another study from 2019 examined how well cats would tolerate a daily 2 mg/kg dose of CBD for 84 days.[777] It took approximately 2 hours for each cat to reach peak blood concentration of CBD after eating the 2 mg/kg dose. The maximum blood concentration of CBD measured in a cat in this study was 43 ng/mL. Each of the cats tolerated the doses without significant adverse effects.

# CANNABINOIDS AND EQUINES (HORSES)

At the time of this writing, cannabinoid receptors have been identified in equine sperm[778], skin[779], neurons[780], joints[781], and intestines[782]. As researchers look for cannabinoid receptors in more equine tissues, this list will expand considerably. Most of the

[776] Kulpa JE, Paulionis LJ, Eglit GM, Vaughn DM. Safety and tolerability of escalating cannabinoid doses in healthy cats. J Feline Med Surg. 2021 Dec;23(12):1162-1175. doi.org10.1177/1098612X211004215

[777] Deabold, Kelly A., Wayne S. Schwark, Lisa Wolf, and Joseph J. Wakshlag. 2019. "Single-Dose Pharmacokinetics and Preliminary Safety Assessment with Use of CBD-Rich Hemp Nutraceutical in Healthy Dogs and Cats" Animals 9, no. 10: 832. doi.org/10.3390/ani9100832

[778] Arroyo-Salvo C., Lottero R., Gambini A., Martinez S. Perez (2021) 103 Characterization of the receptors of the endocannabinoid system in equine sperm: Possible role of anandamide in sperm function. Reproduction, Fertility and Development 33, 159-159. doi.org/10.1071/RDv33n2Ab103

[779] Kupczyk, P, Rykala, M, Serek, P, et al. The cannabinoid receptors system in horses: Tissue distribution and cellular identification in skin. J Vet Intern Med. 2022; 36( 4): 1508- 1524. doi.org/10.1111/jvim.16467

[780] Chiocchetti, R, Rinnovati, R, Tagliavia, C, et al. Localisation of cannabinoid and cannabinoid-related receptors in the equine dorsal root ganglia. Equine Vet J. 2021; 53: 549– 557. doi.org/10.1111/evj.13305

[781] Miagkoff, L., Girard, C. A., St-Jean, G., Richard, H., Beauchamp, G., & Laverty, S. Cannabinoid receptors are expressed in equine synovium and upregulated with synovitis. Equine Veterinary Journal. doi.org/10.1111/evj.13860

[782] Galiazzo G, Tagliavia C, Giancola F, Rinnovati R, Sadeghinezhad J, Bombardi C, Grandis A, Pietra M, Chiocchetti R. Localisation of Cannabinoid and Cannabinoid-Related Receptors in the Horse Ileum. J Equine Vet Sci. 2021 Sep;104:103688. doi.org/10.1016/j.jevs.2021.103688

cannabinoid research that has been performed with horses thus far has been focused on CBD.

A CBD study that examined how cannabinoids are processed by horses demonstrated that dosing between 0.35 to 2 mg/kg CBD was "well-tolerated", but the authors also noted that those doses may result in blood plasma levels of CBD too low to achieve a clinical effect.[783]

In a separate pharmacokinetics study, a group of ~555lb horses were fed a single dose of 50mg, 100mg, or 250mg CBD in a pelletized form.[784] Peak blood concentration of CBD occurred at approximately 2 hours for most horses and each dose was well-tolerated with no observable negative behaviors or effects. It was also found that a minimum dose of 250mg CBD was needed to achieve 1 ng/mL blood concentration of CBD.

A study examining the effects of CBD supplementation on equine heart rate demonstrated that horses that received 100mg of CBD daily began to exhibit less reactivity in a novel object test after 6 weeks of supplementation.[785] A novel object test is an experiment where a subject is shown a new or unfamiliar object while measuring their heart rate.

In one case report, a four-year-old mare was described as exhibited "a marked adverse response to light touch over the caudal neck and withers region." The mare was treated with a number of interventions including dexamethasone, gabapentin, magnesium, vitamin E, prednisolone and aquapuncture without any relief of symptoms. The mare was then treated with 250mg of CBD twice daily and recovered within 2 days.[786]

[783] Williams MR, Holbrook TC, Maxwell L, Croft CH, Ientile MM, Cliburn K. Pharmacokinetic Evaluation of a Cannabidiol Supplement in Horses. J Equine Vet Sci. 2022 Mar;110:103842. doi.org/10.1016/j.jevs.2021.103842

[784] Draeger, Anna L.; Hoffman, Laura K.; Godwin, Patricia R.; Davis, Amanda J.; and Porr, Shea A. (2021) "Pharmacokinetics of a Single Feeding of Pelleted Cannabidiol in Horses," Steeplechase: An ORCA Student Journal: Vol. 4: Iss. 2, Article 1. https://digitalcommons.murraystate.edu/steeplechase/vol4/iss2/1

[785] Draeger AL, Thomas EP, Jones KA, Davis AJ, Shea Porr CA. 2021. The effects of pelleted cannabidiol supplementation on heart rate and reaction scores in horses. Journal of Veterinary Behavior. Vol 46. 97-100. doi.org/10.1016/j.jveb.2021.09.003

[786] Ellis, K.L. and Contino, E.K. (2021), Treatment using cannabidiol in a horse with mechanical allodynia. Equine Vet Educ, 33: e79-e82. doi.org/10.1111/eve.13168

# Enduring Understandings

- All vertebrate mammals have endocannabinoid systems and will experience effects from exposure to cannabinoids. Insects, in general, do not have endocannabinoid systems.
- Livestock have been fed Cannabis as a dietary supplement for hundreds, if not thousands, of years.
- Dogs and cats are more sensitive to the effects of THC than humans. Dogs contain a greater concentration of CB1 receptors in their brains, theoretically leading to greater effects.
- High doses of THC in dogs will cause static ataxia, which is characterized by uncontrollable swaying and movement.
- Cats can tolerate 2mg/kg/day of CBD without significant adverse effects.
- A minimum of 250mg of CBD for a ~550lb horse is required to achieve a measurable 1ng/uL of CBD in the horse's blood. 0.35 – 2mg/kg/day are well tolerated by horses but may be too low to achieve therapeutic effects.

# PART V: REFLECTIONS ON CANNABIS RESEARCH AND THE CANNABIS INDUSTRY

## Essential Questions:

How are Cannabis regulations impacting the environment?

What obstacles are facing Cannabis researchers?

What are likely to be future Cannabis and cannabinoid research targets?

# Chapter 25:
## ENVIRONMENTAL IMPACTS OF CANNABIS REGULATIONS

## Learning Questions

- What are the environmental impacts of Cannabis cultivation?
- What are the environmental impacts of Cannabis extraction and processing?
- What are the environmental impacts of Cannabis packaging?
- How can the negative environmental impacts of the Cannabis industry be mitigated?

### ENVIRONMENTAL IMPACTS OF CANNABIS CULTIVATION

Cannabis cultivation, like all forms of large-scale crop cultivation, presents a variety of environmental concerns and challenges depending on the scale of production, style of cultivation, and inputs used. Most energy consumption for indoor production comes from fossil fuel sources. Fertilizers and other chemical inputs are often also derived from fossil fuels. Water diversion for outdoor cultivation changes the flows of streams throughout watersheds which can have adverse effects both locally at the site of diversion as well as downstream due to reduced dissolved oxygen levels and increased water temperatures.

> *"The broad array of impacts from marijuana cultivation on aquatic and terrestrial wildlife in California has only recently been documented by law enforcement, wildlife agencies, and researchers. These impacts include loss and fragmentation of sensitive habitats via illegal land clearing and logging; grading and burying of streams; delivery of sediment, nutrients, petroleum products, and pesticides into streams; surface water diversions for irrigation resulting in reduced flows and completely dewatered streams." (Bauer et al, 2015)[787]*

#### ENERGY CONSUMPTION

One thing that makes Cannabis unique is that a substantial amount of its cultivation is done indoors, requiring energy inputs to control lighting and climate. A pound of indoor Cannabis flower takes approximately 2000 kWh of energy to produce according to some estimates.[788] Because Cannabis has a relatively high value per weight, the energy costs of production can be manageable whereas in other industries the costs of production would make indoor growing cost prohibitive. Cannabis produced indoors

---

[787] Bauer, S., Olson, J., Cockrill, A., Van Hattem, M., Miller, L., Tauzer, M., & Leppig, G. (2015). Impacts of surface water diversions for marijuana cultivation on aquatic habitat in four northwestern California watersheds. PloS one, 10(3), e0120016. https://doi.org/10.1371/journal.pone.0120016
[788]
https://lcb.wa.gov/publications/Marijuana/BOTEC%20reports/5d_Environmental_Risks_and_Opportunities_in_Cannabis_Cultivation_Revised.pdf

can be more consistent, potent, and produced multiple times a year, making it an attractive cultivation option.

It is estimated that approximately 3% of California's electricity is used for indoor Cannabis cultivation.[789] The level of lighting required for indoor Cannabis cultivation is nearly the equivalent of the lighting needed for hospital operating rooms and air exchange rates six times as high as found in high-tech laboratories.[790] Energy is not only used for lighting and air exchange, but also for humidification and dehumidification of the air to control mold growth. All in all, a typical "grow house" could contain 50,000 to 100,000 W of lighting power.[791]

Another method used to cultivate Cannabis which uses much less energy than indoor growing is greenhouse cultivation. Usually most of the power for greenhouse cultivation is used to warm the greenhouse in winter, run fans, and power supplemental lighting. The shape of the greenhouse and the material used to cover it are two primary factors affecting the greenhouse's energy consumption. A greenhouse can be designed in such a way that it absorbs and stores sunlight efficiently so that the greenhouse can keep itself warm for longer periods of time without supplemental heating. Mechanical shades can be built into the greenhouse for manual control of ventilation, further reducing energy demands.

### CARBON DIOXIDE EMISSIONS

Besides the energy consumption used for indoor cultivation of Cannabis, the use of $CO_2$ generators in indoor grows contribute to carbon emissions produced by indoor Cannabis cultivation. $CO_2$ generators are used to pump $CO_2$ into the grow room to help stimulate or enhance photosynthesis in the plant. The production of $CO_2$ in this manner could be responsible for 2% of the total carbon emissions attributed to indoor Cannabis growing. Indoor $CO_2$ levels are generally raised to levels twice to four times as high as the ambient levels to boost plant growth, although this effect might be less effective when plants are grown in shorter growth cycles. The use of vehicles associated with the production and distribution of the Cannabis material is responsible for approximately 15% of total carbon dioxide emissions associated with indoor grows.[792]

[789] Mills E. 2012. The carbon footprint of indoor Cannabis production. Energy Policy. Vol. 46. pp. 58-67. https://doi.org/10.1016/j.enpol.2012.03.023

[790] Mills E. 2012. The carbon footprint of indoor Cannabis production. Energy Policy. Vol. 46. pp. 58-67. https://doi.org/10.1016/j.enpol.2012.03.023

[791] Brady, P., 2004. BC's million dollar grow shows. Cannabis Culture. http://www.cannabisculture.com/articles/3268.html

[792] Mills E. 2012. The carbon footprint of indoor Cannabis production. Energy Policy. Vol. 46. pp. 58-67. https://doi.org/10.1016/j.enpol.2012.03.023

# Sources of Carbon Emissions from Indoor Cannabis Cultivation

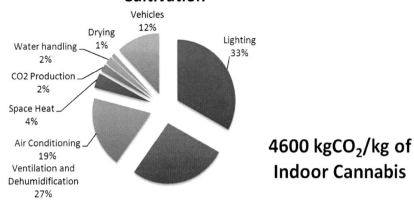

**4600 kgCO$_2$/kg of Indoor Cannabis**

FIGURE 76: CARBON EMISSIONS FROM INDOOR CANNABIS CULTIVATION

## AGROCHEMICAL INPUTS

Agrochemicals are chemicals used in agricultural production including things like pesticides, fungicides, growth hormones, and herbicides. Many of these compounds are toxic to a variety of organisms to different degrees. Some agrochemicals are very persistent and will linger in the environment for months or years before breaking down. Organisms can concentrate agrochemicals into various tissues, leading to toxic accumulations which can pass down to a predator of the contaminated organism. Cannabis is a particularly efficient hyperaccumulator with the ability to absorb compounds like heavy metals into its tissues very easily.

Many fungicides contain compounds which kill fungi by disrupting their hormone production. These compounds affect other organisms including humans. Hormone disruption can cause a variety of health conditions, including cancer. Most pesticides, whether organic or not, are toxic to soil organisms which are responsible for a variety of functions in the soil including nutrient cycling and aeration. Reduction in soil organism diversity often leads to increased demand for agrochemical inputs like fertilizers and pesticides.

Many agrochemical products are toxic to aquatic microinvertebrates and other organisms. Therefore, it is very important to keep any agricultural runoff from reaching major waterways. If microinvertebrates in the water die off, dissolved oxygen levels go down making it more difficult for larger organisms to get the oxygen needed for respiration. Aside from that, various macroinvertebrates, arthropods, and fish lose a food source when aquatic microinvertebrate populations decline. Over time, if dissolved oxygen levels are too low, other organisms will die off due to lack of oxygen. While this is all happening, the pH of the water is also changing. This leads to algal blooms which keep light from reaching other aquatic plants, diminishing the varieties of another food source for aquatic organisms. Dissolved oxygen levels continue to decline, and anaerobic bacteria populations begin to thrive, contaminating the water and potentially poisoning any organisms that then drink from the water. The water source is then contaminated and unavailable for consumption by most organisms.

Contaminated fresh water is a problem because there is relatively little of it around. Very little of the world's water is in a form that can be consumed by humans. 96.5% of water on Earth is found in the sea and cannot be consumed due to the mineral content. Sea water can be made potable, but the process is expensive and energy intensive. Approximately 2% of water on earth is bound in glaciers at the North and South Poles. Approximately 1% of water on earth is fresh water that can be used and consumed by humans. This makes any threat to fresh water a significant threat. Fresh water diversion is another threat facing water quality and the health of any organisms that are dependent on local streams.[793]

## PLASTIC SOIL MULCH

It has become commonplace in the Cannabis industry, particularly among large-scale outdoor hemp cultivators, to use plastic sheet mulch to suppress "weeds", which I prefer to call "undesirable opportunistic plants". There are various kinds of plastics that can be used, including "biodegradable" plastics, but none of them escape environmental concerns. Biodegradable plastics often contain more chemicals in them than typical plastics to expedite the breakdown process. These plastics tend to become very weak and brittle over the course of a growing season. When the plastic is removed, it often tears or breaks into smaller pieces -many of which will pollute the ground. These plastics can also leach microplastics into water, contaminating streams and water supplies.

"Compostable" plastic may be a better alternative, as "compostable" plastics are generally made of plant biomass that very quickly degrades, as opposed to "biodegradable" plastics which take a long time to break down *and* fracture more than regular plastic leading to possibly greater soil and water contamination in the short term compared to regular plastic. In general, though, it is best to avoid any type of plastic in the cultivation environment to avoid soil and water pollution. With proper spacing, timing, and the use of living ground cover, Cannabis can be cultivated in a manner that it ultimately suppresses any significant growth of undesirable opportunistic plants without the use of plastic mulches.

## WATER DIVERSIONS

Cannabis uses a lot of water during growth. A recent research study examined the changes of several watersheds in northern California due to water diversion for Cannabis cultivation.[794] It was estimated that the water demands for the cultivation of Cannabis in these areas ranged from 523,144 liters per day to 724,016 liters per day. Surface water diversions are supposed to be registered with the state, but this study found that many diversions used for Cannabis cultivation are not registered. Excessive water diversion primarily impacts organisms that live in aquatic or riparian environments. Riparian environments are the areas on the margins of a body of water.

---

[793] https://www.usgs.gov/special-topics/water-science-school/science/where-earths-water#overview United States Geological Society "Where is Earth's Water?"
[794] Bauer S, Olson J, Cockrill A, van Hattem M, Miller L, Tauzer M, et al. (2015) Impacts of Surface Water Diversions for Marijuana Cultivation on Aquatic Habitat in Four Northwestern California Watersheds. PLoS ONE 10(3): e0120016. https://doi.org/10.1371/journal.pone.0120016

As stream flows reduce, less species can survive, including fish species like salmon. Salmon require cold clean water with a lot of dissolved oxygen and particular water flow dynamics. If those conditions change, the salmon in the stream begin to struggle. As the flow reduces, the temperature of the water tends to increase.[795] As the temperature increases, dissolved oxygen levels go down. This reduces the growth rate of salmon which increases the risk that the salmon will be eaten by something else or fall susceptible to disease.[796] Reduced flows also negatively impact amphibians like salamanders and frogs. If flows are reduced in areas that already experience drought or high-water diversion for irrigation are even more susceptible to these adverse environmental effects. All in all, this leads to decreased biodiversity, compromising the ecosystem itself.

It should be noted that these water usage issues are not unique to Cannabis cultivation. All of agriculture faces the issue of how to properly acquire and use enough water to complete harvests each year. It is of greatest concern in areas that experience regular droughts. Water pollution is another ongoing major problem facing agriculture. Chemical and waste runoff can contaminate nearby waterways and groundwater. This is of extra concern in areas that experience flooding.

### CULTIVATING ENVIRONMENTAL SOLUTIONS

The key to cultivating Cannabis, or any other crop, in a manner that is more sustainable involves taking steps to tend to the ecology of the soil and the ecology of the garden or farm, which are interconnected. The ecology of the soil can be assisted using minimal soil disturbance techniques, the use of compost and compost teas, erosion control, and other soil building techniques. The ecology of the garden can be supported by using companion plants, beneficial organisms, and integrated pest management strategies.

Soil ecosystems are responsible for the efficiency of nutrient cycling, ultimately determining what nutrients are available for plant growth. A soil can be incredibly nutrient dense, and yet all those nutrients could be unavailable to a plant if the soil ecosystem, or soil microbiome, is not appropriate. The soil consists of any number of bacteria, fungi, algae, and animals that help to transform the chemical constituents of the soil and move nutrients around. All the organisms that live in the soil make up **the soil microbiome**. All the organisms that interact with the soil, above *and* below ground, such as grazing animals and birds, make up the **soil food web**.

One method of enhancing the biology of soil is to try to support diverse complex nutrient cycling pathways to, in theory, maximize the number of available nutrients in the soil that a plant can use, thus minimizing the need for external inputs like fertilizers or pesticides. Often this is done by introducing various soil bacteria as well as one or many different species of fungi to the soil. Nitrogen fixing bacteria are utilized to help capture nitrogen from the atmosphere and store it in the soil. Many plants form associations with nitrogen fixing bacteria, like legumes. Other types of bacteria interact with other bacteria and fungi to cycle nutrients in the soil.

---

[795] Moyle PB. Inland fishes of California. Berkeley: University of California Press; 2002.
[796] Marine KR, Cech JJ. Effects of High Water Temperature on Growth, Smoltification, and Predator Avoidance in Juvenile Sacramento River Chinook Salmon. North Am J Fish Manag. 2004; 24(1):198–210. https://doi.org/10.1577/M02-142

*Glomus* is a genus of fungi that includes all the **arbuscular mycorrhizal fungi (AMF)**. These fungi penetrate root cells and exchange various nutrients and water with the plant in exchange for carbon.[797] This is in contrast with **ectomycorrhizal fungi** which form sheaths around roots without penetrating the cells and are commonly found associated with bushes and trees rather than grasses or forbs (herbs and other flowering plants). Arbuscular mycorrhizal fungi produce a substance called **glomalin** which acts as a "soil glue" to hold nutrients and small soil particles together. Glomalin helps soil to stay in place and resist erosion.

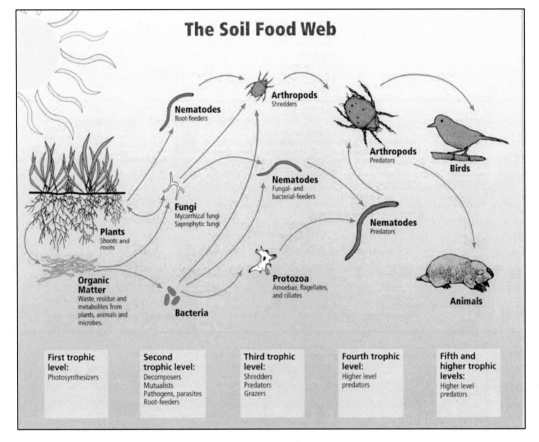

AN ILLUSTRATION OF THE SOIL FOOD WEB; IMAGE PUBLIC DOMAIN COURTESY OF USDA-NRCS

The use of fungal inoculants in Cannabis cultivation are quite common as a method of trying to enhance the biodiversity of soil microorganisms or enhance plant growth and yield. Though this concept seems straightforward, the use of mycorrhizal fungi in agriculture is not quite as simple.

**Research has shown that a plant will resist a mycorrhizal symbiont if the relationship is not needed.** One meta-analysis of field studies revealed that AMF root

---

[797] Redecker, D., R. Kodner, and L.E. Graham. 2000. Glomalean fungi from the Ordovician. Science 289:1920-1921 https://doi.org/10.1126/science.289.5486.1920

450

colonization reduces by over 30% after phosphorous fertilization.[798] So, nutrient availability, and particularly phosphorous availability, seems to be a factor influencing AMF colonization rates. If the plant is having trouble finding nutrients that are bioavailable, it might be more likely to accept a symbiosis with the AMF. If the plant is not struggling to feed itself, it might resist mycorrhizal associations. This is particularly important in the context of Cannabis, given that Cannabis is an opportunistic plant that seems to take care of itself pretty well without inputs. More research on the ecological functions and effects of Cannabis are needed to better understand how Cannabis might affect fungal populations in the soil.

Despite widely held belief, **mycorrhizal associations are not always symbiotic**.[799] As conditions change, fungi can begin to take more resources out of the relationship than the plant receives, potentially leading to a situation where the fungus is limiting plant growth and yield. AMF have been shown to counter-intuitively *restrict* root and shoot growth in some plants.[800] It has also been shown that 5%-20% of a plant's photosynthetically fixed carbon may be used *just* to maintain the fungal relationship.[801]

The point is that, although these fungi have exciting potential to expedite nutrient cycling and store water, carbon and other materials in the soil, there are yet complexities to these biological systems that are not well understood. Enhancing the biological activity of the soil does not *necessarily* mean that the plant will grow more vigorous or yield more than usual, for instance. In fact, the opposite might occur if conditions are not appropriate.

Beyond mycorrhizal fungi, sometimes microbiological inoculants for soils include the spores of **saprophytic fungi**. Saprophytic fungi are fungi that obtain energy by breaking down organic matter. These are the fungi responsible for the molds that appear on the top layer of soil that is often found in indoor Cannabis cultivation. This is *NOT* mycorrhizal fungus. This mold is usually not harmful to the plant, but it *does* indicate that conditions are ripe for the growth of other less desirable fungal species due to excess moisture content and excess organic matter in the soil. This also attracts fungus feeding insects which might also feed on plant material or roots and attract other insects that could be pests. Some pests like broad mites or russet mites travel on the backs of other insects, like ants or white flies, to find a new plant host.

Typically, a well-balanced soil microbiome will naturally limit soil pests. When soil pests are a problem, one way of handling them is by introducing predatory soil animals, like certain species of nematodes. Nematodes are a diverse group of organisms that have specialized to feed on roots, fungi, bacteria, and small insects. **When a strong soil**

---

[798] Treseder, K. K. 2004. A meta-analysis of mycorrhizal responses to nitrogen, phosphorus, and atmospheric CO2 in field studies. New Phytologist 164:347-355 https://doi.org/10.1111/j.1469-8137.2004.01159.x

[799] Kiers ET, MGA van der Heijden. 2006. Mutualistic stability in the arbuscular mycorrhizal symbiosis: exploring hypotheses of evolutionary cooperation. Ecology. 87(7):1627-1636. https://doi.org/10.1890/0012-9658(2006)87[1627:msitam]2.0.co;2

[800] Desserud PA, Naeth MA. 2012. An unexpected response of a bunch grass (rough fescue) to arbuscular mycorrhizae fungi. Ecological Restoration. 30(3):165-168. http://www.jstor.org/stable/44743650

[801] Douds, DDJ, PE Pfeffer, and Y Shachar-Hill. 2000. Carbon partitioning, cost, and metabolism of arbuscular mycorrhizas. Pages 107-129 in Y. Kapulnik and DDJ Douds, editors. Arbuscular mycorrhizas: physiology and function. Kluwer Academic Publishers, Dordrecht, The Netherlands.

**microbiome is built up through careful cultivation methods and minimal soil disturbance, the need for agrochemical inputs can be drastically reduced or eliminated.**

**No-till cultivation** helps nurture soil micro-organism communities by minimizing soil disturbance. Instead of tilling the soil, time is spent building a rich series of deep soil horizons, or layers, home to a diverse community of soil organisms. No-tillage cultivation methods tend to result in enhanced soil moisture at greater soil depths compared to conventional tillage cultivation techniques.[802] No-tillage methods have also been shown to decrease nutrient mobility in the soil, meaning that the nutrients present in the soil remain in place rather than washing away.[803] Additionally, minimizing soil disturbance also minimizes the growth of unwanted opportunistic plants (aka "weeds") by not digging up and exposing their seeds to things like water and light which will cause the seeds to germinate and grow.

> No-tillage cultivation methods tend to result in enhanced soil moisture at greater soil depths compared to conventional tillage cultivation techniques.

Conventional and no-tillage systems have unique soil ecosystems. Bacteria have an upper hand in conventional tillage methods and are the dominant type of organism breaking down the organic matter.[804] The frequent disturbance of the soil limits the ability of fungi to thrive. Nematodes, protozoa, and small worms feed on bacteria in soil. Fungi, on the other hand, are more common in no-tillage systems. Fungi are often fed on by insects, nematodes, small mammals, and worms.

To deal with environmental water concerns, some cultivators have developed methods to maximize the efficiency of water use in farming by **slowing** water down, **spreading** it throughout an area, **sinking** it deep into the ground, and keeping it in the ground using mulch and **cover crops** to minimize evaporation. **Drought tolerant varieties** of Cannabis may be chosen for cultivation to further minimize water use. Thick mulches of organic material can act as a sponge to help retain water, while also working to suppress the growth of unwanted opportunistic plants.

**Companion plants** and other crops may be planted in the garden to provide functions like soil building or attracting predatory insects, to support the ecosystem of the garden itself. Companion plants can also help fill in space in the garden or farm to reduce the presence of unwanted opportunistic plants.

---

[802] Blevins, R.L., Cook, D., Phillips, S.H. and Phillips, R.E. (1971), Influence of No-tillage on Soil Moisture1. Agron. J., 63: 593-596. https://doi.org/10.2134/agronj1971.00021962006300040024x

[803] Hendrix PF, Parmelee RW, Crossley Jr. DA, Coleman DC, Odum EP, Groffman PM. 2014. Detritus Food Webs in Conventional and No-tillage Agroecosystems. BioScience. 36 (6):374-380. https://doi.org/10.2307/1310259

[804] Hendrix PF, Parmelee RW, Crossley Jr. DA, Coleman DC, Odum EP, Groffman PM. 2014. Detritus Food Webs in Conventional and No-tillage Agroecosystems. BioScience. 36 (6):374-380. https://doi.org/10.2307/1310259

**Compost** and **compost teas** are used to boost soil nutrient availability and introduce various bacteria and fungi to the soil which help break down organic matter and release nutrients to the soil. Rather than spending resources keeping low-performing plants alive, poor performing plants are allowed to die off, leaving plants that are better adapted to their particular environment. This method of cultivation, sometimes referred to as biodynamic (or ecodynamic) no-till cultivation, can be both productive and economical while minimizing environmental impacts and in some cases enhancing the environment.

Cannabis and sunflowers serving as companion plants for one another.

Comfrey and other companion plants in the Cannabis garden

Compost tea is aerated to limit growth of anaerobic bacteria.

This cultivation site utilized mulching and companion planting to absorb and trap water, reducing watering requirements. This mulch was inoculated with edible mushroom species to build soil while also producing food for the farmer.

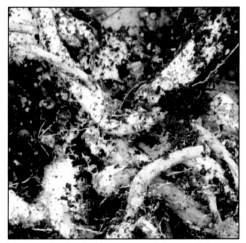

This root ball of a harvested Cannabis plant has been colonized by saprophytic fungi. Fungi break down organic matter in the soil, assisting nutrient cycling, building soil, and providing food for local wildlife, including humans.

King Stropharia mushrooms cultivate easily in mulch beds and are edible.

A broad fork can be used to turn soil, rather than using a tiller. A broad fork reduces gas or electricity costs, disturbs the biology of the soil less than rototilling and results in less overall nutrient loss from the soil.

One way of reducing water usage in cultivation is by using "hügelkultur" style raised beds. Hügelkultur beds consist of wood which is buried. The wood absorbs and slowly releases water, reducing water input requirements, while decomposing and contributing to the generation of soil.

As pathways for the hügelkultur beds are carved out, the dirt is piled on top of the wood, burying it.

As seasons pass, the wood decomposes, and the raised bed flattens out and sinks

After establishing a cultivation area, it is important for all gardeners and farmers to consider designing ways in which the area may still support the life of nearby native wildlife to minimize the negative impacts of disturbing and clearing habitat. One suggestion is to **create wildlife "corridors"** throughout the gardening or farming landscape which include interconnected areas of native plant life and habitat to support native insects, birds, and other native wildlife that are critical for the support of the ecosystems present around the cultivation area. Accommodating wildlife in the garden or farm can bring other benefits, like enhanced pest control and food crop yield.

## CANNABIS AS A BIOREMEDIATION TOOL

Although Cannabis cultivation can present environmental risks, as all forms of farming can, it can also present potential environmental remedies. Cannabis can tolerate absorbing many different compounds from the soil including potentially toxic compounds like heavy metals. Because of this, researchers have been looking at whether Cannabis could be used to extract excess levels of metals or other toxins from contaminated soils.

While there is relatively little information available about Cannabis' abilities to uptake and tolerate metals, it has been found that Cannabis accumulates nickel more than lead, and lead more than cadmium (nickel > lead > cadmium).[805] During one particular study, cultivated hemp could extract 126g of cadmium from contaminated soil within one vegetative period without sacrificing the fiber quality.[806] Metals can be distributed into every tissue in the plant, although they are most accumulated in the roots.

In one study researchers inoculated Cannabis with the arbuscular mycorrhizal fungus *Glomus mosseae* and measured the degree of metal uptake. They found that the inoculation of the fungus caused reduced plant growth and changes in the ways that metals are stored in the plant. After colonization of roots by mycorrhizal fungi, Cannabis translocated metals from the roots to the shoots.[807]

Bioremediation is a topic that is growing in popularity. Not only can plants like Cannabis be used to extract potentially toxic compounds from the environment, but other hyperaccumulating organisms like fungi, lichen, and bacteria (as well as many other types of plants) can also be utilized in a collaborative effort against soil contaminants.

---

[805] Linger P, J Mussig, H Fischer, J Kobert. (2002). Industrial hemp (Cannabis sativa L.) growing on heavy metal contaminated soil: fibre quality and phytoremediation potential. Ind Crop and Prod. 16:33-42 https://doi.org/10.1016/S0926-6690(02)00005-5
[806] Linger P, J Mussig, H Fischer, J Kobert. (2002). Industrial hemp (Cannabis sativa L.) growing on heavy metal contaminated soil: fibre quality and phytoremediation potential. Ind Crop and Prod. 16:33-42 https://doi.org/10.1016/S0926-6690(02)00005-5
[807] Citterio, S, Prato, N, Fumagalli, P, Aina, R, Massa, N, Santagostino, A, Sgorbati, S, Berta, G. 2004. The arbuscular mycorrhizal fungus Glomus mosseae induces growth and metal accumulation changes in Cannabis sativa L. Chemosphere. 59(1):21-29 https://doi.org/10.1016/j.chemosphere.2004.10.009

# Pop Quiz!

Approximately how many kilograms of $CO_2$ is released to produce one (1) kilogram, or 2.2 pounds, of indoor grown Cannabis?

What makes Cannabis a bioremediation tool candidate?

What are some techniques that can be used to reduce the environmental impact of Cannabis cultivation (or any type of cultivation, for that matter)?

What cultivation techniques can be used to better tend the ecology of the soil?

What cultivation techniques can be used to better tend the ecology of the garden?

# ENVIRONMENTAL IMPACTS OF CANNABIS PROCESSING AND EXTRACTION

The environmental impacts of Cannabis processing can be challenging to assess because there are many ways to process Cannabis. The primary issues to take note of regarding the environmental impacts of Cannabis processing are energy usage, solvent use, storage methods, and waste disposal methods.

Extracting Cannabis can sometimes require a lot of energy, depending on the method. Cannabis extractions can take place entirely without electricity, as in the case of ethanol macerations, or Cannabis extractions can use quite a bit of electricity when using large electrically controlled pumps, digital control systems, water chillers, water heaters, digital temperature and pressure gauges, and atmospheric monitors, as is common with things like CO2 or hydrocarbon extraction.

The way a laboratory handles solvent can substantially affect their environmental impact. A laboratory must first ensure that all their solvents are of a known purity, as contaminants or impurities in solvents can affect how dangerous the solvent could be to the environment. Secondly, a laboratory must ensure that solvents are always properly labeled and stored so that they do not become environmental risks. Additionally, when a lab is using a solvent, it is best to implement ways in which to keep the solvent from being exposed to the atmosphere. Systems which contain the extraction solvent throughout the entire extraction process are often referred to as "closed loop systems." It is important that extraction systems are checked for leaks on a regular basis to ensure that solvents are not being expelled into the atmosphere unnecessarily.

Cannabis extraction processes can sometimes result in increased fire risks, which can present risks to the environment in the form of wildfires. This risk is most associated with laboratories performing extraction methods that utilize flammable solvents under pressure, such as ethanol or alkane extraction (hexane, butane, pentane, etc). By contrast, supercritical fluid CO2 extraction does not present this same risk since CO2 is not flammable. Additionally, mechanical forms of extraction such as dry sift hash production or rosin pressing do not present these same fire risks.

The way a laboratory stores its chemicals is critical for minimizing environmental impact. Laboratories must take steps to ensure that chemicals will not make their way into nearby water ways or public lands where they could poison wildlife. Proper chemical storage usually involves the use of special lockable storage cabinets that are completely enclosed and fire-proof so that the cabinet can contain any spillage and prevent the spread of fire. Additionally, these cabinets are often stored in designated locations within a laboratory where they will be best shielded from accidents.

Finally, it is critical that extraction laboratories properly dispose of their waste to minimize their environmental impact. Solvents and other industrial waste are often considered "hazardous waste" and must be disposed of in a special manner to ensure that the material does not present harm to the public or the environment. Hazardous waste is typically collected in designated containers with appropriate "hazardous waste" labels present to ensure that the material will be handled with care. Waste disposal companies typically dedicate certain times of the year to pick up industrial waste for a reasonable fee, or at times even free, to ensure that the material is properly managed. Solvents and other waste should never be dumped down drains or in areas where they could be washed into storm drains.

## ENVIRONMENTAL IMPACTS OF CANNABIS PACKAGING

The stringent rules and regulations that often get passed once Cannabis becomes legal in a new state or country usually results in a significant unforeseen negative consequence – trash, and lots of it. Cannabis products are often required to feature any number of warnings, test results, and batch information on the labels of each product. Additionally, most places with legal Cannabis require that Cannabis be sold in tamper-proof, or child proof, packaging. These factors end up coming together to result in Cannabis being sold in plastic bottles, akin to traditional pill bottles, as well as thick resealable plastic and mylar bags, excess boxes, and more. In some places it is even required to then place Cannabis products into a secondary container when travelling. This has led to a major problem.

The good news is that there are companies springing up to tackle this problem head-on by providing recycling services for used Cannabis packaging, such as plastic bottles and bags. However, not all packaging can be recycled. For instance, it has been reported that smaller containers, often used to hold single Cannabis joints, or Cannabis cigarettes, are too small for recycling machines to process. Additionally, labels must be removed from packaging before it can be accepted for recycling.

In a now famous Canadian Broadcasting Company (CBC) report, one gram of Cannabis was found to be accompanied by up to 70 grams of packaging.[808] That translates into approximately 70 pounds of packaging waste for every pound of Cannabis. Another Canadian report from the company [Re] Waste, a recycling company that services the Cannabis industry among others, detailed that within the first year of the legal Cannabis market in Canada, approximately 5.8 – 6.4 million kilograms, or 12.7 – 14.1 million pounds, of plastic waste was generated.[809]

In 2018 The Washington Post reported on this issue in Washington State in an article entitled, "Garbage from Washington state's booming pot industry clogs gutters, sewers and landfills."[810] In this report, Cannabis industry participants report that even if they try to recycle or compost their waste, many businesses will not work with them due to ongoing stigma around Cannabis and the Cannabis industry. This highlights how multifaceted the environmental issues surrounding the Cannabis industry can be.

While companies are beginning to attempt to fill a niche by providing recyclable and compostable packaging solutions for the Cannabis industry, it has proven challenging for many Cannabis producers to rationalize paying the premium that it takes to invest in more ecologically friendly packaging when their margins are already very tight due to the cost of operating within a highly regulated environment.

---

[808] https://cbc.ca/news/canada/new-brunswick/cannabis-packaging-excess-1.4870682
[809] https://rewaste.ca/industries/plastic-recycling-cannabis/
[810] https://www.washingtonpost.com/national/garbage-from-booming-weed-industry-overruns-washington-gutters-sewers-and-landfills/2018/08/14/66f02384-9685-11e8-a679-b09212fb69c2_story.html

There is also another issue that is quickly becoming a major environmental concern, and that is the use of vaporizer pens, or vape pens. Many vape pens are designed in such a way that consumers cannot, with ease, refill the cartridges that hold the Cannabis extract. Additionally, the batteries to vape pens are cheap and often lost, leading to these batteries making their way into landfills. Some vape pens are even designed to be disposable, with the battery and cartridge impossible to separate.

This problem is substantially more problematic than the use of plastic bottles or bags, because the waste cannot be simply recycled. Vaporizer pen cartridges vary in their materials and are complex in their designs – making them challenging to break down and recycle. At a time when more and more Cannabis users are turning to vaporizer pens due to their convenience, it is critical that careful consideration is made regarding the environmental impacts that these devices could have. When possible, it is recommended to use refillable cartridges and avoid disposable cartridges altogether. Vape pen batteries should be disposed in special disposal bins approved for collecting batteries.

It seems like the issue of Cannabis packaging filling up landfills will continue to be a problem for years to come until creative solutions are employed to improve the designs of Cannabis products to minimize environmental impacts and regulatory environments loosen up regarding product labeling and packaging – if that ever happens. In the meantime, producers and retailers can work to find companies that provide recyclable or compostable packaging and encourage consumers to re-use packaging or deliver used packaging to designated pick-up spots so that less of these items make their way onto city streets, landfills, and water ways. Consumers can choose to support companies and retailers that demonstrate a commitment to environmental stewardship, and avoid problematic products, like disposable vape pens.

---

## Enduring Understandings

- Some of the environmental problems facing Cannabis cultivation primarily relate to energy consumption, carbon dioxide emissions, the use of agrochemical inputs, water contamination and natural waterway diversions.
- Cannabis extraction activities can result in the release of greenhouse gases into the atmosphere, contamination of water systems with hazardous materials, increased fire risk, and energy consumption.
- Cannabis laws typically require child-resistant packaging for Cannabis products, leading to excess plastic waste in the form of pill-bottle style plastic tubes, thick mylar-lined plastic bags, and other waste that is often discarded quickly after use.

# Chapter 26:
# THE FUTURE OF CANNABIS RESEARCH:
# OPPORTUNITIES AND CHALLENGES

Cannabis and cannabinoid science is an exciting and relatively new field of research with many exciting opportunities on the horizon, but due to several factors there are also many challenges facing Cannabis and cannabinoid research. Just a few of these opportunities and hurdles are outlined below.

## RESEARCH OPPORTUNITIES

### RESEARCH REPEATABILITY

One of the core principles of modern sciences is repeatability. If a study comes to a particular conclusion, the same conclusions should be reached if the study were to be duplicated by different researchers. So far there are very few Cannabis or cannabinoid research studies that have actually been replicated, which makes it very difficult to interpret the findings of the research that does exist. A major opportunity for future Cannabis and cannabinoid research lies in simply repeating past studies to determine if previous conclusions still hold up or not.

### UNDERSTANDING THE ECS'S ROLE IN IMMUNE SYSTEM FUNCTIONING

Perhaps one of the biggest discoveries about the endocannabinoid system is that it is intimately connected to the control of immune system response. Particularly, the CB2 receptor has been widely speculated and demonstrated to exert a variety of effects on the immune system. Some of these effects seem to be immunosuppressive, while others seem to stimulate the immune system. Understanding these effects could help pave the way to far more efficacious treatments for auto-immune diseases and more!

### SEARCHING FOR TERPENOID ACTIVITY IN THE ENDOCANNABINOIDOME

So far, the search for terpenoid activity in the endocannabinoidome has been relatively fruitless. Recently researchers tested five common terpenoids (myrcene, linalool, limonene, $\alpha$-pinene and nerolidol) for activity at CB1 receptors and found that none of the compounds tested showed activity at CB1. Interestingly, nerolidol, the only sesquiterpenoid tested, reduced endocannabinoid activity through unknown mechanisms unrelated to CB1.

Beta-caryophyllene has been found to exhibit effects at CB2 receptors, and perhaps in the near future we will see a study published that systematically reviews the receptor interactions between common Cannabis terpenoids and CB2 receptors.

Thinking beyond the cannabinoid receptors, there is already evidence that some terpenoids found in Cannabis interact with PPARs. One study from 2020 found that none of the common Cannabis terpenoids that they tested exhibited effects on TRPV1 or TRPA1 ion channels.[811]

It is important to be careful not to jump to conclusions based on the limited amount of information we currently have about how terpenoids may influence the endocannabinoidome. As we have learned before with endocannabinoid congeners – just because something does not exhibit activity at a given receptor does not mean that it is not influencing how other compounds interact with that receptor. Additionally, terpenoids may contribute to the effects of Cannabis through other means, such as serving as skin penetration enhancers in topical products – allowing cannabinoids and other compounds to penetrate the skin more deeply. Or as is the case with borneol[812], perhaps some of these terpenoids help compounds like cannabinoids penetrate the blood-brain-barrier more readily. There is still a lot that we do not know, which means there is a huge frontier for scientists to explore.

### TEASING OUT TERPENOID ENANTIOMERS

Throughout this book we mentioned that a persistent problem facing Cannabis terpenoid data is that most Cannabis testing laboratories are not identifying specific terpenoid enantiomers. We also mentioned that although terpenoid enantiomers may look nearly identical to one another, they can elicit vastly different effects from the body. An area of Cannabis research that desperately needs attention is this area of terpenoid enantiomer identification.

Is d-Limonene only present in Cannabis? Or is l-Limonene present as well? Which enantiomers of linalool appear in Cannabis? These are important questions to answer, especially as producers are rushing to create terpenoid blends to mimic the terpene profiles of popular Cannabis cultivars. If these terpenoid blends feature terpenes from other botanical sources, they may not feature the same enantiomers as Cannabis, even if the scents are similar. This means that ultimately the effects of those non-Cannabis terpenes could be significantly different than would be produced from the Cannabis plant. We may find that certain Cannabis cultivars or chemovars feature unique terpenoid enantiomers compared to others, which would be useful for chemotaxonomy (classifying Cannabis varieties by their chemical profile). Understanding these enantiomers would also give both consumers and clinicians better data to work with to find products that are effective.

### BETTER UNDERSTANDING THE ENTOURAGE EFFECT

Pharmacological science is currently moving away from the simplified model called "the receptor concept" which is the view that drugs elicit effects from the human body by simply binding to a receptor and causing an action. Researchers now understand

---

[811] Marika Heblinski, Marina Santiago, Charlotte Fletcher, Jordyn Stuart, Mark Connor, Iain S. McGregor, and Jonathon C. Arnold.Terpenoids Commonly Found in Cannabis sativa Do Not Modulate the Actions of Phytocannabinoids or Endocannabinoids on TRPA1 and TRPV1 Channels.Cannabis and Cannabinoid Research.Dec 2020.305-317. http://doi.org/10.1089/can.2019.0099

[812] Yu B, Ruan M, Dong X, Yu Y, Cheng H. The mechanism of the opening of the blood-brain barrier by borneol: a pharmacodynamics and pharmacokinetics combination study. J Ethnopharmacol. 2013 Dec 12;150(3):1096-108. PMID: 24432371. https://pubmed.ncbi.nlm.nih.gov/24432371/

that there is a whole symphony of activity happening when people consume food or drugs, especially polypharmaceuticals like Cannabis. Researchers also now understand that an otherwise benign compound might elicit unique, and sometimes profoundly powerful, effects when in the presence of other compounds. We refer to this action as "the entourage effect" – that certain compounds together elicit unique properties that are not attributed to any compound by itself. In essence, chemicals can act greater than the sum of their parts. However, researchers understand very little about what drives these effects or just how therapeutically significant the entourage effect is in the context of Cannabis.

Currently cannabinoid researchers are beginning to look for "allosteric effectors" of cannabinoid receptors – compounds which interact with chemical receptors in such a way as to boost the efficacy of cannabinoids when they happen to bind to the receptor. In a sense, these allosteric effectors can sometimes grab hold of a receptor and bend it or shake it in just the right way so that it is easier for ligands, like endocannabinoids or phytocannabinoids, to elicit effects. These kinds of effects on receptors are called allosteric effects, and the chemical agents that cause them are aptly named, allosteric effectors.

Future Cannabis research will undoubtedly continue to explore this concept of the "entourage effect" to lead to more effective product formulations. This type of research is likely to trickle out into other areas of pharmacological research as well.

### UNDERSTANDING THE ENDOCANNABINOIDOME
The endocannabinoid system is quickly becoming too small of a concept to represent the complexities of lipid signaling in the body. As alluded to multiple times throughout this book, the endocannabinoid system is about far more than CB1 receptors, CB2 receptors, Anandamide, 2-AG, MAGL and FAAH. But even beyond the myriad receptors, ligands and enzymes involved with cannabinoid activity, there is a greater complexity. Depending on where these receptors, ligands and enzymes are located in the body – they may do different things. In essence, our bodies have various endocannabinoid systems distributed in a complex interconnected pattern throughout the body.

To further complicate things, when endocannabinoids are broken down, other active compounds are produced that interact with all sorts of other receptor targets in the body and facilitating actions – and those actions can vary depending on where in the body they are taking place. This concept of interconnected activities and systems is called the endocannabinoidome, and we are only beginning to piece together how these connected systems influence one another and how those activities may influence health and wellness.[813] The future of endocannabinoid system research will certainly be focused on further elucidating this concept of the endocannabinoidome.

### HOW MINOR ARE THE "MINOR" CANNABINOIDS?
When Cannabis research really began inventorying the chemical components of trichomes, many trace cannabinoids were dismissed as "minor cannabinoids" (I admit I still refer to them this way...). It was implied that these cannabinoids were background players, hardly contributing to effects, if they contributed at all. However, as analytical technology improved, researchers discovered there were quite an awful lot of these "minor

---

[813] Di Marzo V, Wang J. 2014. The Endocannabinoidome: The World of Endocannabinoids and Related Mediators. Academic Press. Elsevier.

cannabinoids", and some of them, like THCP, were much more potent than THC. It was also discovered that it only takes tiny amounts of CBG to agonize A2 Adrenergic receptors in the body, affecting heart rate and blood pressure. More and more evidence is mounting that these "minor cannabinoids" are playing a greater role in the overall effects of Cannabis than we have appreciated. As this appreciation has grown, so has the research interest in cannabinoids that typically show up in trace concentrations.

### SEMI-SYNTHETIC CANNABINOIDS

The future of cannabinoid research is likely to consist of lots of tinkering with traditional cannabinoids to form what are sometimes referred to as "semi-synthetic" cannabinoids. This includes things like adding or removing functional groups from the molecule, adding carbons, taking away carbons, or hydrogenating the molecules. An example of a semi-synthetic cannabinoid is VCE-003 which is essentially a quinoid derivative of CBG. Another example of semi-synthetic cannabinoids gaining attention are the hydrogenated cannabinoids like hexahydrocannabinol (HHC) and hexahydrocannabinolic acid (HHCA) derived from THC and THCA.

### FINDING CANNABINOIDS IN OTHER ORGANISMS

Cannabis is not the only plant to contain phytocannabinoids. *Helichrysum umbraculigerum*, a flower variety grown in South Africa, contains CBG-like compounds, presumably formed from a unique biochemical pathway than that which Cannabis utilizes to produce cannabinoids.[814] It has been speculated that the plant *Leonotis leonurus*, also known as lion's tail or wild dagga (aka wild Cannabis), contains cannabinoids, including THCA, but this is yet to be confirmed in a peer-reviewed publication.[815] Truffles have been found to contain endocannabinoid-like compounds.[816] Additionally, a type of liverwort called *Radula perrottetii*, as well as related species *Radula marginata* and *Radula laxiramea*, contain a cannabinoid compound called perrottetinene, which is very similar in structure to THC and exhibits some affinity for CB1 receptors.[817]

Studying cannabinoids and terpenoids in Cannabis has begun to change the way that researchers look at other chemicals in plants. This is especially true after the discovery that a variety of non-cannabinoid compounds interact with cannabinoid receptors in the body, like the sesquiterpenoids beta-caryophyllene. *Echinacea purpurea*, or purple coneflower, contains alkylamide compounds that have been found to interact with

---

[814] Pollastro F, De Petrocellis L, Schiano-Moriello A, Chianese G, Heyman H, Appendino G, Taglialatela-Scafati O. Amorfrutin-type phytocannabinoids from Helichrysum umbraculigerum. Fitoterapia. 2017 Nov;123:13-17. https://doi.org/10.1016/j.fitote.2017.09.010

[815] Nsuala BN, Enslin G, Viljoen A. "Wild cannabis": A review of the traditional use and phytochemistry of Leonotis leonurus. J Ethnopharmacol. 2015 Nov 4;174:520-39. https://doi.org/10.1016/j.jep.2015.08.013

[816] Pacioni G, Rapino C, Zarivi O, Falconi A, Leonardi M, Battista N, Colafarina S, Sergi M, Bonfigli A, Miranda M, Barsacchi D, Maccarrone M. Truffles contain endocannabinoid metabolic enzymes and anandamide. Phytochemistry. 2015 Feb;110:104-10. https://doi.org/10.1016/j.phytochem.2014.11.012

[817] Chicca A, Schafroth MA, Reynoso-Moreno I, Erni R, Petrucci V, Carreira EM, Gertsch J. Uncovering the psychoactivity of a cannabinoid from liverworts associated with a legal high. Sci Adv. 2018 Oct 24;4(10):eaat2166. https://doi.org/10.1126/sciadv.aat2166

cannabinoid receptors.[818] In addition, alkylamides from Echinacea can also inhibit the enzyme FAAH, affecting the breakdown of the endocannabinoid anandamide.

## Examples of Non-Cannabinoid Compounds That Interact with the Endocannabinoid System

### TERPENOIDS

| | | |
|---|---|---|
| **Beta-Caryophyllene** | Sesquiterpenoid found in many plant essential oils | CB2 activity[819] |
| **Isopimaric acid** | Diterpene constituent of *Pinus roxburghii* bark | CB2 activity[820] |
| **Ursolic acid** | Triterpene constituent of *Pinus roxburghii* bark | CB1 activity[821] |

### FLAVONOIDS

| | | |
|---|---|---|
| **Cyanidin** | Anthocyanidin flavonoid found in many red berries, fruit peels, etc. | CB1 and CB2 activity[822] |
| **Delphinidin** | Anthocyanidin flavonoid responsible for blue hues in flowers and berries | CB1 and CB2 activity[823] |

### POLYSACCHARIDES

| | | |
|---|---|---|
| **Polysaccharopeptide (PSP)** | Polysaccharide extracted from turkey-tail mushrooms (*Trametes versicolor*) | CB2 activity[824] |

### ALKYLAMIDES

| | | |
|---|---|---|
| **Alkylamides from *Echinacea purpurea* and *E. angustifolia*** | Alkylamides extracted from the roots of Echinacea plants | CB2 activity (Gertsch et al, 2004)<br><br>PPAR-gamma activity (Spelman et al, 2009) |

### OTHERS

818 Raduner S, Majewska A, Chen JZ, Xie XQ, Hamon J, Faller B, Altmann KH, Gertsch J. Alkylamides from Echinacea are a new class of cannabinomimetics. Cannabinoid type 2 receptor-dependent and -independent immunomodulatory effects. J Biol Chem. 2006 May 19;281(20):14192-206. https://doi.org/10.1074/jbc.M601074200

819 Gertsch J, Leonti M, Raduner S, Racz I, Chen JZ, Xie XQ, Altmann KH, Karsak M, Zimmer A. Beta-caryophyllene is a dietary cannabinoid. Proc Natl Acad Sci U S A. 2008 Jul 1;105(26):9099-104. https://doi.org/10.1073/pnas.0803601105

820 Labib RM, Srivedavyasasri R, Youssef FS, Ross SA. Secondary metabolites isolated from Pinus roxburghii and interpretation of their cannabinoid and opioid binding properties by virtual screening and in vitro studies. Saudi Pharm J. 2018 Mar;26(3):437-444. https://doi.org/10.1016/j.jsps.2017.12.017

821 Labib RM, Srivedavyasasri R, Youssef FS, Ross SA. Secondary metabolites isolated from Pinus roxburghii and interpretation of their cannabinoid and opioid binding properties by virtual screening and in vitro studies. Saudi Pharm J. 2018 Mar;26(3):437-444. https://doi.org/10.1016/j.jsps.2017.12.017

822 Korte G, Dreiseitel A, Schreier P, Oehme A, Locher S, Hajak G, Sand PG. (2009). An examination of anthocyanins' and anthocyanidins' affinity for cannabinoid receptors. J Med Food. 12(6):1407-1410. https://doi.org/10.1089/jmf.2008.0243

823 Korte G, Dreiseitel A, Schreier P, Oehme A, Locher S, Hajak G, Sand PG. (2009). An examination of anthocyanins' and anthocyanidins' affinity for cannabinoid receptors. J Med Food. 12(6):1407-1410. https://doi.org/10.1089/jmf.2008.0243

824 Wang K, Wang Z, Cui R, Chu H. Polysaccharopeptide from Trametes versicolor blocks inflammatory osteoarthritis pain-morphine tolerance effects via activating cannabinoid type 2 receptor. Int J Biol Macromol. 2019 Apr 1;126:805-810. https://doi.org/10.1016/j.ijbiomac.2018.12.212

| Falcarinol | Commonly found in carrots (*Daucus carota*) and other members of Apiaceae | CB1 inverse agonist[825] |
|---|---|---|
| Rutamarin | Commonly found in rue (*Ruta graveolens*) | Affinity for CB2 *in silico*[826] |
| 3,3'-diindolylmethane | Commonly found in cruciferous vegetables | CB2 partial agonist[827] |

FIGURE 77: NON-CANNABINOID COMPOUNDS THAT MODULATE THE ECS

Researchers will undoubtedly continue exposing other phytochemicals to cannabinoid receptors to identify what other sorts of compounds in our foods and medicines might be manipulating our endocannabinoid systems.

In addition, it turns out that some other phytochemicals closely resemble cannabinoids. For instance, in the *Rhododendron ferrugineum* plant, a chemical can be found called Ferruginene C which is uncannily similar in chemical structure to CBD.[828] What other cannabinoid-like compounds are there in other plants that we have not uncovered yet and what therapeutic promise might they hold for treating issues related to the endocannabinoid system?

### BIOSYNTHESIZING CANNABINOIDS IN MICROBIOLOGICAL FACTORIES

It is common in other industries to utilize bacteria and fungi to reproduce organic compounds once they are isolated and identified as valuable. Sure enough, this technique is already making its way into the Cannabis industry. Known as **cellular agriculture**, this method of cultivating chemicals using bacteria will be used to provide greater amounts of minor cannabinoids like CBC, CBDV, and THCV for industrial purposes.

### THE CANNABIS RHIZOSPHERE

There has been only a very small amount of research done to date looking at the ecology of the Cannabis root zone, or rhizosphere. Rhizospheres are fascinating subjects of ecological and agricultural research. By understanding how Cannabis roots affect soil and soil organisms, and how soil organisms and micro-organisms in turn affect Cannabis roots, it may be possible to develop more efficient Cannabis cultivation techniques allowing for more efficient nutrient cycling, better inherent pest control, and better water retention. Additionally, rhizosphere dynamics influence the chemistry of plant roots, primarily by changing the components of plant root exudates which are often composed of oils rich in triterpenoids and diterpenoids. As some companies begin pursuing true "whole plant" Cannabis products which incorporate all parts of the plant including flower, leaves, and

---

[825] Leonti M, Casu L, Raduner S, Cottiglia F, Floris C, Altmann KH, Gertsch J. Falcarinol is a covalent cannabinoid CB1 receptor antagonist and induces pro-allergic effects in skin. Biochem Pharmacol. 2010 Jun 15;79(12):1815-26. https://doi.org/10.1016/j.bcp.2010.02.015

[826] Rollinger JM, Schuster D, Danzl B, Schwaiger S, Markt P, Schmidtke M, Gertsch J, Raduner S, Wolber G, Langer T, Stuppner H. In silico target fishing for rationalized ligand discovery exemplified on constituents of Ruta graveolens. Planta Med. 2009 Feb;75(3):195-204. https://doi.org/10.1055%2Fs-0028-1088397

[827] Yin H, Chu A, Li W, Wang B, Shelton F, Otero F, Nguyen DG, Caldwell JS, Chen YA. Lipid G protein-coupled receptor ligand identification using beta-arrestin PathHunter assay. J Biol Chem. 2009 May 1;284(18):12328-38. https://doi.org/10.1074/jbc.M806516200

[828] Appendino, G. 2014. The International Cannabinoid Research Society (ICRS) Annual Meeting. (by way of Ryan Lee and O's News Service, O'Shaughnessy's Winter 2015/16 Issue)

roots – understanding the dynamics that influence the chemistry of the roots will become critical. We may eventually come to a point where Cannabis roots are considered to have their own unique chemotypes as seen in the plant's resins.

### CANNABIS ENDOPHYTES

As Cannabis cultivation and breeding gets more sophisticated, and an emphasis is placed on avoiding agrochemicals and maximizing the production of target compounds like cannabinoids and terpenoids, research is beginning to examine the microbiological communities present in and around the Cannabis plant and how they affect the growth and survival of the plant. As mentioned previously, while many of the endophytes present in Cannabis have been documented, their functions have not been well explored. By understanding Cannabis endophytes and their relationship to things like phytochemical production and pest resistance, future Cannabis breeding efforts can take these relationships into account and potentially breed plants that are more naturally vigorous, phytochemically rich, and resistant to pests and disease.

### MAPPING THE CANNABIS GENOME

There is still a lot to understand about how Cannabis has evolved and how it utilizes different genes to express various phenotypical and chemotypical traits. It will be crucial that as many varieties of Cannabis as possible are genetically sequenced and cataloged for current and future research efforts. As the Cannabis plant genome is better understood, it is likely that Cannabis breeding efforts will become even more sophisticated. A better understanding of the Cannabis genome will allow taxonomists to better understand how different traits have moved through Cannabis populations over time. In addition, Cannabis breeders will be able to target their breeding efforts to upregulate various traits while downregulating others. Drug manufacturers are likely to use this information to better understand the biochemical pathways of Cannabis in the pursuit of developing novel cannabinoid medicines.

### PROTECTING GENETIC DIVERSITY

Cannabis plants have been intensely hybridized to the point that the genetic diversity of the Cannabis plant has greatly suffered. This point is made at great length in McPartland and Small's 2020 paper about endangered high-THC cultivars called "A classification of endangered high-THC cannabis domesticates and their wild relatives".[829] It is urgently important to seek out varieties of Cannabis that have not been contaminated by modern hybrids to preserve their germplasm for future research and cultivation.

### CANNABIS AS A BIOREMEDIATION TOOL?

Ecologists are still trying to make sense of some of the claims of Cannabis being an effective bioremediation tool. Although it is true that Cannabis can uptake metals, and maybe other potentially toxic materials from the soil, it is still unclear how this compares to other bioremediators, like sunflowers, for instance.

There are relatively few research papers available that examine how Cannabis uptakes metals, so more research needs to be done there to collect a dataset that is sophisticated

---

[829] McPartland JM, Small E. A classification of endangered high-THC cannabis (Cannabis sativa subsp. indica) domesticates and their wild relatives. PhytoKeys. 2020 Apr 3;144:81-112. https://doi.org/10.3897/phytokeys.144.46700

enough that restoration ecologists can use it to make decisions about whether to use Cannabis for bioremediation.

# CHALLENGES TO CANNABIS RESEARCH

## BAD DATA

There is a glaring problem facing many researchers in the face, and they might not even know it. It is their third-party analytical data. There are many doctors, nurses and other healthcare professionals that have attempted to amass databases of patient outcomes with Cannabis products, using the third-party laboratory data for information about the chemistry of products used, such as cannabinoid or terpenoid content. Generally, they are hoping to identify patterns between the chemistry of Cannabis products and the outcomes patients experience so that they may be able to better predict how different Cannabis products may affect a person and what types of products may be best suited for different medical conditions. Unfortunately, some of that chemical data is wrong.

Cannabis testing has not been around for a long time. What we think of as modern Cannabis testing really began taking off around 2010 or so. Of course, there were research labs that had been performing analytical testing on Cannabis samples for many years prior to that – but usually it was only on Cannabis flower and usually focused on only a handful of chemical compounds. Today researchers, producers and consumers alike are interested in data about dozens of cannabinoids and terpenoids (as well as flavonoids and other compounds) and as laboratories have proceeded to validate testing methods to incorporate more of these compounds, an uncomfortable problem has been revealed.

It turns out that there are a lot of terpenoids that can look like one another on a chromatogram. Many terpenoids co-elute and appear as a single peak. Some cannabinoids elute at the same retention times as certain terpenoids. Some terpenoids elute at the same or similar retention times as certain cannabinoids. This problem gets compounded when a laboratory must test a more complex product like a Cannabis infused topical or food.

Laboratories are still trying to develop standardized methods for testing many of these complex Cannabis products, but the industry is certainly not going to wait for laboratories to perfect and standardize methods. So as regulators demand that laboratories provide data to facilitate Cannabis commerce, it is inevitable that a lot of unvalidated and outright bad data is circulating and will likely continue to be circulated for some time into the future. Different labs are using different testing methods, some are accredited, some are not, some perform rigorous formal method validation, some do not. Cannabis laboratory testing is still a maturing industry, and it can be extremely difficult, if not impossible, to compare data between laboratories.

This variation in data quality can be controlled if researchers perform confirmation testing or rely on data from a single laboratory – however there would still be a burden to rigorously validate the methods used to produce the data to ensure that it is both accurate and precise. While generally the data for major cannabinoids like THC and CBD is often fairly accurate, exercise caution when reviewing data about minor cannabinoid concentrations, terpenoid concentrations or the concentrations of other minor or uncommon phytochemical constituents.

## A PROBLEM WITH LAB RATS

As mentioned previously throughout this book, there is an ongoing debate about whether the results from *in vivo* rodent research can be extrapolated to properly represent humans. When discussing mental health research, we explored some of the common behavioral experiment models used for rodents and their inherent limitations. But there is another issue facing laboratory rodents that could have profound impacts for *in vivo* rodent research.

An issue with laboratory rodents bred in captivity is that they develop unique characteristics that can affect their genotypes, and thus their physiology, substantially. To put it simply – their cells age differently. This misstep of assuming that laboratory rodents must genetically and physiologically be similar to wild-type mice was not discovered in a sophisticated way until the early 2000s.[830] [831]

This issue has many potential implications, such as that cancer drug research in rodents may be prone to underestimate toxic effects, distort or exaggerate the cancer risks of compounds, and even exaggerate potential benefits of those same compounds. Additionally, rodent derived tissues and cells are often used for preliminary *in vitro* research where the unique genetic difference of laboratory rodents, primarily in the form of lengthened chromosomal telomeres, can skew experimental findings by changing the way cells respond to stress. Ultimately this issue highlights another reason why we must be very cautious when interpreting the results of *in vivo* rodent studies and *in vitro* studies that utilize rodent derived cells or tissues, especially if those studies are examining things like tissue damage, cellular repair, lifespan, cancer dynamics, or oxidative stress.

This also highlights why it is important for researchers to focus Cannabis and cannabinoid research on human research, which will ultimately provide much greater value than *in vitro* cell or tissue culture medical research or *in vivo* rodent research that may provide results that are virtually meaningless in the context of a human.

## PLACEBO AND NOCEBO EFFECTS

As clinical research of the efficacy of Cannabis as a treatment for various medical conditions is made more accessible, a big problem that any researcher must overcome is that of measuring the efficacy of the drug against the placebo effect. The placebo effect is a phenomenon in which a measurable effect is caused simply by the anticipation of an effect. **Just being in a clinical trial can cause participants to experience some measurable improvement of conditions**, complicating efficacy research.

---

[830] Weinstein BS, Ciszek D. The reserve-capacity hypothesis: evolutionary origins and modern implications of the trade-off between tumor-suppression and tissue-repair. Exp Gerontol. 2002 May;37(5):615-27. https://doi.org/10.1016/s0531-5565(02)00012-8

[831] Hemann MT, Greider CW. Wild-derived inbred mouse strains have short telomeres. Nucleic Acids Res. 2000 Nov 15;28(22):4474-8. https://doi.org/10.1093/nar/28.22.4474

**Placebo effects can increase significantly the longer a study continues and the larger the sample size becomes.**[832] To limit the placebo effect, researchers must take great care to remain neutral and not use language or behavior that would suggest what effects a user might experience during a drug study. Another complication is that seasoned Cannabis users tend to be able to easily recognize real Cannabis from placebo and even alter their consumption behavior as a result – taking longer, deeper inhalations compared to novice users in one study.[833]

To complicate this placebo puzzle even more, is the fact that research is now indicating that some placebo effects, like placebo analgesia (aka placebo pain relief), are mediated by the endocannabinoid system! Researchers studying the placebo effects seen in pain relief clinical trials discovered that the CB1 receptor is at least partially responsible for non-opioid placebo pain relief, as might be seen with non-steroidal anti-inflammatory drugs (NSAIDs) like ibuprofen or aspirin.[834]

**Nocebo** effects, on the other hand, are negative effects on health resulting from psychological effects. Examples of this in Cannabis use include things like paranoia and anxiety. Users that worry about experiencing anxiety may facilitate experiences of anxiety when exposed to either Cannabis or a placebo. This in turn affects heart rate and breathing, potentially compounding other negative health consequences. These detrimental effects may not necessarily be due to exposure to cannabinoids but may result from the psychological state of the user prior to exposure.

### DRUG DELIVERY METHODS AND STANDARDIZED PRODUCT FORMULATION

Although pulmonary delivery of Cannabis and cannabinoid extracts is the most common drug delivery method used by Cannabis users, it is generally not an acceptable model for medical research. Smoking or vaporizing causes lung irritation and exposure to potentially harmful compounds. Pulmonary delivery also delivers psychoactive cannabinoids to the brain quickly, which increases abuse potential according to traditional pharmacological models.

Alternative drug delivery methods such as nasal mucosal, oral, and sublingual drug delivery systems are currently sought after by researchers. It is likely that future Cannabis research that involves humans will utilize inhalers and nose sprays to administer cannabinoids quickly to the blood stream without having participants potentially harm their lungs. The use of these administration methods also allows the use of standardized product formulations when conducting research, whereas using herbal Cannabis or even whole plant extracts may result in inconsistent formulations between batches, and thus inconsistent results in clinical research.

---

[832] Tuttle AH, Tohyama S, Ramsay T, Kimmelman J, Schweinhardt P, Bennett GJ, Mogil JS. 2015. Increasing placebo responses over time in US clinical trials of neuropathic pain. Pain. 156(12):2616-2626. https://doi.org/10.1097/j.pain.0000000000000333

[833] Cami J, Guerra D, Ugena B, Segura J, de la Torre R. 1991. Effect of subject expectancy on the THC intoxication and disposition from smoked hashish cigarettes. Pharmacol Biochem Behav. 40(1):115-9 https://doi.org/10.1016/0091-3057(91)90330-5

[834] Benedetti F, Amanzio M, Rosato R, Blanchard C. 2011. Nonopioid placebo analgesia is mediated by CB1 cannabinoid receptors. Nat Med. 17(10): 1228-1230. https://doi.org/10.1038/nm.2435

## MEASURING ENDOCANNABINOID SYSTEM CHARACTERISTICS

Because endocannabinoids are only produced when they are needed, rather than being stored up or routinely circulated throughout the body, it can be very difficult to assess the state, or tone, of a person's endocannabinoid system. How will doctors in the future measure someone's endocannabinoid system? While it is possible to perform a spinal tap to look for the presence of endocannabinoids, there is the possibility that there may be nothing there to measure at the moment it is being measured. Likewise, a spinal tap only provides doctors with a chemical snapshot for a single moment in time, which may not actually indicate much concerning chronic states of being. Likewise, methods to measure endocannabinoids in saliva and other fluids have been developed, but still face challenges in broad research applications.

Perhaps researchers will identify compounds which correlate with endocannabinoids or cannabinoid receptor production, helping doctors infer the state of someone's endocannabinoid system without directly measuring it. A common example of this sort of measurement in action can be seen in measurements of prostate-specific antigen, or PSA, for determining the presence and virility of prostate cancer.

It may be that soon doctors will be able to take advantage of the endocannabinoid system to treat illness, but the problem of quantifying the endocannabinoid system must first be overcome.

## LIMITATIONS OF PREVIOUS CANNABIS RESEARCH

While there have been a lot of research papers published about Cannabis, much of this research consists of small sample sizes, unique conditions, a lack of standardized Cannabis material, short durations, and near-impossible reproducibility. Researchers face the task of figuring out how to conduct research with materials that can be consistently reproduced for other research. This is another reason why smoked or vaporized Cannabis can be troublesome. Each harvest of will result in slightly different material. Preferred analytical methods for cannabinoid and terpene assaying need to be accepted and adopted to bring consistency to chemotype data produced by labs, which can then enable researchers to choose and enforce chemical criteria for clinical trials utilizing herbal Cannabis.

## LEGAL HURDLES

Cannabis research in the United States still faces significant hurdles due to its illicit status federally. Cannabis is a classified as a Schedule I drug, meaning that it is indicated as having a high abuse potential with no medicinal use. Due to this restricted classification, any research requires several approvals from different government agencies like the Drug Enforcement Agency or the National Institute of Drug Abuse. If approved, typically Cannabis material for research must be provided by the federal government and can be of questionable quality, often not representing the quality of Cannabis most consumers encounter on a regular basis.

The good news is that hemp is paving the way for Cannabis research to take place by universities, non-profit entities, and public companies that were not previously able to touch the Cannabis plant for fear of legal repercussions. Of course, the limitation to this is that this research will take place with CBD-rich Cannabis, rather than THC-rich Cannabis, and many of these institutions have a learning curve to work through regarding understanding the Cannabis plant and the various nuances affecting cultivation, harvesting, processing, extraction, and analytical testing.

# Chapter 27:
## CONCLUDING REMARKS

Cannabis is truly a fascinating plant, regardless of the controversies and stigmas that human culture may associate with it. The human species has coevolved with Cannabis for a very long time, coaxing the plant to provide for many of our needs throughout history, and it is only relatively recently that this plant has been aggressively prohibited. Beyond its many industrial applications, Cannabis is responsible for producing hundreds of chemical compounds, many of which seem to pose significant therapeutic value, paving the way for a new wave of upcoming pharmaceuticals and natural products for years to come.

The Cannabis plant has helped researchers to uncover hidden aspects of human physiology, like the endocannabinoid system and the endocannabinoidome, leading health care workers and pharmacologists to rethink treatments for many common diseases like fibromyalgia, chronic inflammation, diabetes, and others. Studying the Cannabis plant has helped shed light on how our bodies process pain, regulate immune system responses, respond to trauma, and more. While there are risks associated with Cannabis use, which would be the case with any medicinal botanical, Cannabis appears to be relatively safe on a physiological level, when used responsibly.

But perhaps bigger than Cannabis itself – the study of the science of Cannabis leads one headfirst into the realization that nearly everything that is fascinating about Cannabis is, in one way or another, applicable to other plants (as well as mushrooms). As was highlighted earlier in the book, Cannabis is NOT the only plant affecting the endocannabinoidome. We will discover that all sorts of compounds interact with cannabinoid receptors, vanilloid receptors, and other components of the endocannabinoidome. Understanding the basics of the endocannabinoidome help show us new ways in which the things we eat, the medicines we take, and the lifestyle choices we make influence both human physiology and pathology as well as our psychology, and, some would even argue, spirituality.

This book, in all its noble attempts, only barely scratches the surface of many complex topics. It is entirely likely that some of the information shared in this book may become obsolete and replaced with more refined interpretations and conclusions of the available information. Throughout my academic career I encountered several mentors that would state some variation of the phrase, "Trust, but verify." For any of the information presented in this book, please trust, but verify. I have made every attempt that I could with the limited amount of time I had available to consolidate a vast assortment of information and present it as accurately and honestly as possible.

I have had to simplify some very complex topics, which always runs the risk of inaccurately representing the state of the science. I have also had to exclude a lot of information, otherwise this book would be over double its current length (as I write this I am actively trying to shave two hundred pages from this manuscript!). I hope that through these various concessions, and despite them, that this book provides you with the resources you need to take your educational journey further to discover reliable information on your own. As research on all the topics presented within this book continues over time, I intend to publish updated revisions of this book, as I have the bandwidth, to better reflect the insights and available data of the time.

It is my hope that this book has been helpful in your quest for learning and understanding the complicated and controversial topic of Cannabis science. Throughout the rest of the book, you will find research paper citations, recommended external learning resources and more so that you can continue to take your Cannabis education further, far beyond this book. Don't forget to visit member.cacpodcast.com and become a member of our Curious About Cannabis Learning Center for free and start diving into courses related to the content found here in this book!

This book features quotes from various interviews I have had with researchers, doctors, nurses, cultivators, etc. on the Curious About Cannabis Podcast. Another way you can take your Cannabis education further is by listening to episodes of the Curious About Cannabis Podcast and hearing these guests share their insights, experience, and knowledge. You can discover the Curious About Cannabis Podcast at www.CACPodcast.com.

Good luck on your continued quest for learning and **stay curious**!

# PART VI: APPENDICES

# APPENDIX A: GAMES

## Cannabis Science Crossword Puzzle

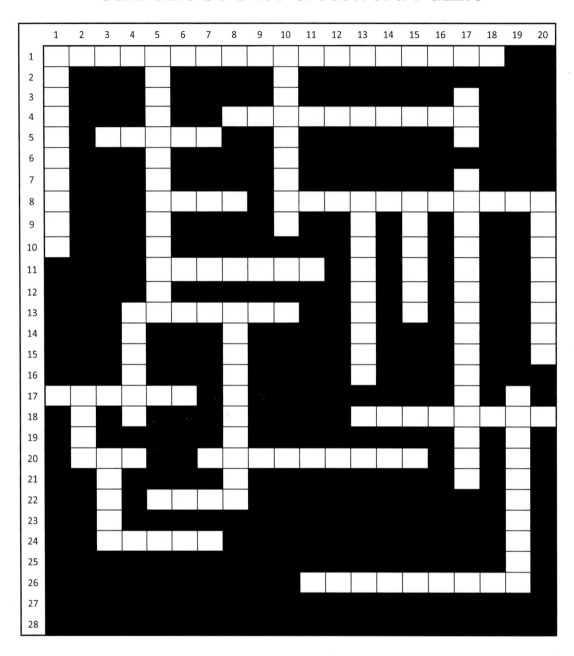

## ACROSS

1  The Expanded Endocannabinoid System

4  The first endogenous cannabinoid discovered

5  Small green leaf-like tissues found subtending branches and at the lowest part of the flower; sometimes referred to as calyx

8  Primary enzyme responsible for breaking down 2-AG

8  THC binds an _____ site on the CB1 receptor

11  Terpene associated with the characteristic sweet aroma of the "Strawberry Cough" Cannabis cultivar

13  Peptide cannabinoids

17  These small slender insects have translucent bodies when young, but become opaque and grow wings as adults

18  Cannabinoids and terpenoids are found primarily in _____ stalked and _____ sessile trichomes

20  Home of cannabinoids and terpenoids in the plant

20  Analytical method often used in microbiology for identifying organisms based on DNA

22  Common analytical method used for cannabinoid potency; preferred because it does not decarboxylate cannabinoid acids

24  Solventless extract produced by applying heat and pressure to hash or Cannabis flower

26  Polar compounds often responsible for colors in plants; several have only been found in Cannabis so far

## DOWN

1  These micro-organisms live on and within a plant, often in a mutualistic relationship

2  Cannabis cultivars that feature only trace amounts of THC

3  Chromatography literally means "_____ writing"

4  The botanical term for the entire female flower including the stigma, style, and ovary.

5  A polar cannabinoid discovered in hemp in 2010 with little affinity for CB1 or CB2, but mild affinity for TRPV1 and PPARγ

8  CBD weakly binds an _____ site on the CB1 receptor

10  terpenoid commonly exploited for its ability to help things cross the blood brain barrier

13  Building material made from Cannabis stalks, water, and lime

15  Often referred to as "hairs", the fused _____ and style help guide pollen into the ovary to begin the process of seed production

17  The process of removing a carboxylic acid functional group from a molecule, typically through exposure to heat

17  Endocannabinoid congener commonly available as a dietary supplement; Exhibits activity via PPARa, TRPV1, GPR55

19  Compound class often associated with pest resistance; canniprene is one

20  Unique variety of Cannabis that can be propagated and maintain distinguishing characteristics

# Cannabis Science Word Search

| Y | H | P | A | R | G | O | T | A | M | O | R | H | C |
|---|---|---|---|---|---|---|---|---|---|---|---|---|---|
| N | T | C | A | N | N | A | B | I | N | O | I | D | P |
| N | N | N | M | Y | C | O | T | O | X | I | N | S | T |
| T | E | S | T | I | N | G | C | E | D | P | N | R | R |
| V | A | T | P | I | C | A | R | I | E | M | I | L | I |
| A | O | G | S | B | P | U | O | D | E | E | S | A | C |
| P | T | O | R | I | T | N | A | N | N | H | E | C | H |
| E | R | A | T | C | E | R | E | E | I | O | R | O | O |
| C | C | A | N | P | G | N | N | S | N | K | I | N | M |
| T | T | I | R | O | O | I | H | A | S | H | I | G | E |
| E | T | E | R | M | P | R | O | T | P | E | C | E | R |
| R | T | T | I | O | F | L | O | W | E | R | O | N | F |
| I | E | L | A | S | I | B | A | N | N | A | C | E | S |
| R | E | T | A | R | T | N | E | C | N | O | C | R | S |

MYCOTOXINS
VAPE
KIEF
CONGENER
BRACT
CANNABINOID
PINENE
ROSIN
FLOWER
CONCENTRATE
RETROGRADE
TRICHOME
CANNABIS
HEMP
CHROMATOGRAPHY
TERPENOID
RECEPTOR
TINCTURE
CAPITATE
LIMONENE
TESTING
HASH
RESIN

Play this puzzle online at : https://thewordsearch.com/puzzle/4178650/

Scan the QR code below to play this game on your phone!

For more Cannabis science activities, games, lesson plans, and quizzes,
check out the Curious About Cannabis Educator and Student Workbooks
available at **store.cacpodcast.com**

# Appendix B: Citations List

A Preliminary FET Headspace GC-FID Method for Comprehensive Terpene Profiling in Cannabis. Aboulaghras S, Sahib N, Bakrim S, Benali T, Charfi S, Guaouguaou FE, Omari NE, Gallo M, Montesano D, Zengin G, Taghzouti K, Bouyahya A. Health Benefits and Pharmacological Aspects of Chrysoeriol. Pharmaceuticals (Basel). 2022 Aug 7;15(8):973. https://doi.org/10.3390/ph15080973

Abrahamov, A., and R. Mechoulam. 1995. An efficient new cannabinoid antiemetic in pediatric oncology. Life Sci 56(23-24):2097-102. https://doi.org/10.1016/0024-3205(95)00194-b

Abrams DI, Hilton JF, Leiser RJ, et al. 2003. Short-term effects of cannabinoids in patients with HIV-1 infection: a randomized, placebo-controlled clinical trial. Annals of Internal Medicine. 139:258-266. https://doi.org/10.7326/0003-4819-139-4-200308190-00008

Abrams DI, Vizoso HP, Shade SB, Jay C, Kelly ME, Benowitz NL. Vaporization as a smokeless cannabis delivery system: a pilot study. Clin Pharmacol Ther. 2007 Nov;82(5):572-8. https://doi.org/10.1038/sj.clpt.6100200

Adams IB, Martin BR. 1996. Cannabis: Pharmacology and toxicology in humans and animals. Addiction. 91(11):1585 - 1614. https://doi.org/10.1046/j.1360-0443.1996.911115852.x

Adams R, Hunt M, Clark JH. 1940. Structure of Cannabidiol, a Product Isolated from the Marihuana Extract of Minnesota Wild Hemp. I. J. Am. Chem. Soc. 62(1): 196-200. https://doi.org/10.1021/ja01858a058

Adams, T. C., & Jones, L. A. (1975). Phytosterols of cannabis smoke. Journal of Agricultural and Food Chemistry, 23(2), 352-353. https://doi.org/10.1021/jf60198a007

Agrawal A, Nurnberger Jr, JI, Lynskey, MT, The Bipolar Genome Study. 2011. Cannabis involvement in individuals with bipolar disorder. Psychiatry Research. 185:459-461. https://doi.org/10.1016/j.psychres.2010.07.007

Ahmed SA, Ross SA, Slade D, Radwan MM, Zulfiqar F, Matsumoto RR, Xu YT, Viard E, Speth RC, Karamyan VT, ElSohly MA. Cannabinoid ester constituents from high-potency Cannabis sativa. J Nat Prod. 2008 Apr;71(4):536-42. https://doi.org/10.1021/np070454a

Alavanja MCR, Hoppin J, Kamel F. 2004. Health Effects of Chronic Pesticide Exposure: Cancer and Neurotoxicity. Annu. Rev. Public Health. 25:155-97 https://doi.org/10.1146/annurev.publhealth.25.101802.123020

Alavanja MCR, Samanic C, Dosemeci M, Lubin J, Tarone R, et al. 2003. Use of agricultural pesticides and prostate cancer risk in the Agricultural Health Study Cohort. Am. J. Epidemiol. 157:1-13 https://doi.org/10.1093/aje/kwg040

Albucher RC, Liberzon I. Psychopharmacological treatment in PTSD: a critical review. J Psychiatr Res. 2002 Nov-Dec;36(6):355-67. https://doi.org/10.1016/s0022-3956(02)00058-4

Alcorn J, Vuong S, Wu F, Seifert B, Lyon A. (2019). Pediatric Dosing Considerations for Medical Cannabis. Recent Advances in Cannabinoid Research. Chapter 10:181-200 https://doi.org/10.1016/j.ejim.2018.01.004

Al-Ghezi ZZ, Alghetaa HF, Nagarkatti M, Nagarkatti P. 2017. Combination of cannabinoids, delta-9-tetrahydrocannabinol (THC) and cannabidiol (CBD), mitigate experimental autoimmune encephalomyelitis (EAE) by altering the gut microbiome. J Immunology. 198(1). https://doi.org/10.1016/j.bbi.2019.07.028

Alhamoruni A, Wright KL, Larvin M, O'Sullivan SE. Cannabinoids mediate opposing effects on inflammation-induced intestinal permeability. Br J Pharmacol. 2012 Apr;165(8):2598-610. https://doi.org/10.1111/j.1476-5381.2011.01589.x

Allegrone G, Pollastro F, Magagnini G, Taglialatela-Scafati O, Seegers J, Koeberle A, Werz O, Appendino G. The Bibenzyl Canniprene Inhibits the Production of Pro-Inflammatory Eicosanoids and Selectively Accumulates in Some Cannabis sativa Strains. J Nat Prod. 2017 Mar 24;80(3):731-734. https://doi.org/10.1021/acs.jnatprod.6b01126

Allegrone, G., Razzano, F., Pollastro, F. et al. Determination of melatonin content of different varieties of hemp (Cannabis sativa L.) by liquid chromatography tandem mass spectrometry. SN Appl. Sci. 1, 720 (2019). https://doi.org/10.1007/s42452-019-0759-y

Alshaarawy O, Anthony JC. Cannabis Smoking and Diabetes Mellitus: Results from Meta-analysis with Eight Independent Replication Samples. Epidemiology. 2015 Jul;26(4):597-600. https://doi.org/10.1097/ede.0000000000000314

Alter R. The Five Books of Moses: A Translation with Commentary. 2004. New York: W.W. Norton & Co.

Álvaro, L.C., Iriondo, I. and Villaverde, F.J. (2002), Sexual Headache and Stroke in a Heavy Cannabis Smoker. Headache: The Journal of Head and Face Pain, 42: 224-226. https://doi.org/10.1046/j.1526-4610.2002.02056.x

Alvheim AR, Malde MK, Osei-Hyiaman D, Lin YH, Pawlosky RJ, Madsen L, Kristiansen K, Frøyland L, Hibbeln JR. Dietary linoleic acid elevates endogenous 2-AG and anandamide and induces obesity. Obesity (Silver Spring). 2012 Oct;20(10):1984-94. https://doi.org/10.1038/oby.2012.38

Amada N, Yamasaki Y, Williams CM, Whalley BJ. 2013. Cannabidivarin (CBDV) suppresses pentylenetetrazole (PTZ)-induced increases in epilepsy-related gene expression. PeerJ. 1:e214. https://doi.org/10.7717/peerj.214 eCollection 2013.

Ananth P, Ma C, Al-Sayegh H, Kroon L, Klein V, Wharton C, Hallez E, Braun I, Michelson K, Rosenberg AR, London W, Wolfe J. 2018. Provider Perspectives on Use of Medical Marijuana in Children with Cancer. Pediatrics. 141(1):e20170559 https://doi.org/10.1542/peds.2017-0559

Anderson, L. C. (1980). LEAF VARIATION AMONG CANNABIS SPECIES FROM A CONTROLLED GARDEN. Botanical Museum Leaflets, Harvard University, 28(1), 61–69. http://www.jstor.org/stable/41762825

Andre CM, Hausman J-F and Guerriero G (2016) Cannabis sativa: The Plant of the Thousand and One Molecules. Front. Plant Sci. 7:19. doi: 10.3389/fpls.2016.00019 (Creative Commons Attribution License CC-BY)

Andre CM, Hausman JF, Guerriero G. Cannabis sativa: The Plant of the Thousand and One Molecules. Front Plant Sci. 2016 Feb 4;7:19. https://doi.org/10.3389/fpls.2016.00019

Antonisamy P, Duraipandiyan V, Ignacimuthu S. 2011. Anti-inflammatory, analgesic, and antipyretic effects of friedelin isolated from Azima tetracantha Lam. In mouse and rat models. Journal of Pharmacy and Pharmacology. Vol. 63, Issue 8. https://doi.org/10.1111/j.2042-7158.2011.01300.x

Appendino G, Gibbons S, Giana A, Pagani A, Grassi G, Stavri M, Smith E, Rahman MM. Antibacterial cannabinoids from Cannabis sativa: a structure-activity study. J Nat Prod. 2008 Aug;71(8):1427-30. https://doi.org/10.1021/np8002673

Appendino, G. 2014. The International Cannabinoid Research Society (ICRS) Annual Meeting. (by way of Ryan Lee and O's News Service, O'Shaughnessy's Winter 2015/16 Issue)

Aqil M, Ahad A, Sultana Y, Ali A. 2007. Status of terpenes as skin penetration enhancers. Drug Disc Today. 12:1061-1067. https://doi.org/10.1016/j.drudis.2007.09.001

Aqil M, Ahad A, Sultana Y, Ali A. Status of terpenes as skin penetration enhancers. Drug Disc Today. 12:1061-1067 https://doi.org/10.1016/j.drudis.2007.09.001

Armbruster DA, T Pry. 2008. Limit of Blank, Limit of Detection and Limit of Quantitation. Clin Biochem Rev. 29:49-52 https://pubmed.ncbi.nlm.nih.gov/18852857

Arroyo-Salvo C., Lottero R., Gambini A., Martinez S. Perez (2021) 103 Characterization of the receptors of the endocannabinoid system in equine sperm: Possible role of anandamide in sperm function. Reproduction, Fertility and Development 33, 159-159. doi.org/10.1071/RDv33n2Ab103

Aryal, N., Orellana, D.F. & Bouie, J. Distribution of cannabinoid synthase genes in non-Cannabis organisms. J Cannabis Res 1, 8 (2019). https://doi.org/10.1186/s42238-019-0008-7

Ashton, HC. 2001. Pharmacology and effects of cannabis: a brief review. The British Journal of Psychiatry. 178(2):101-106. https://doi.org/10.1192/bjp.178.2.101

Assmann, G., Cullen, P., Erbey, J., Ramey, D. R., Kannenberg, F., & Schulte, H. (2006). Plasma sitosterol elevations are associated with an increased incidence of coronary events in men: results of a nested case-control analysis of the Prospective Cardiovascular Münster (PROCAM) study. Nutrition, Metabolism and Cardiovascular Diseases, 16(1), 13-21. https://doi.org/10.1016/j.numecd.2005.04.001

Atsak P, Roozendaal B, Campolongo P. Role of the endocannabinoid system in regulating glucocorticoid effects on memory for emotional experiences. Neuroscience. 2012 Mar 1;204:104-16. https://doi.org/10.1016/j.neuroscience.2011.08.047

Atwood, B.K. et al. (2010). JWH018, a common constituent of 'Spice' herbal blends, is a potent and efficacious cannabinoid CB1 receptor agonist. British Journal of Pharmacology 160 (3): 585–593. https://doi.org/10.1111/j.1476-5381.2009.00582.x

Ballinger MD, Saito A, Abazyan B, Taniguchi Y, Huang CH, Ito K, Zhu X, Segal H, Jaaro-Peled H, Sawa A, Mackie K, Pletnikov MV, Kamiya A. Adolescent cannabis exposure interacts with mutant DISC1 to produce impaired adult emotional memory. Neurobiol Dis. 2015 Oct;82:176-184. https://doi.org/10.1016/j.nbd.2015.06.006

Bang MH, Choi SY, Jang TO, Kim SK, Kwon OS, Kang TC et al. 2002. Phytol, SSADH inhibitory diterpenoid of Lactuca sativa. Arch Pharm Res 25: 643–646. https://doi.org/10.1007/bf02976937

Barrett ML, Gordon D, Evans FJ. 1985. Isolation from Cannabis sativa L. of cannflavin – a novel inhibitor of prostaglandin production. Biochemical Pharmacology. 34: 2019–2024. https://doi.org/10.1016/0006-2952(85)90325-9

Barwick, V. J., & Ellison, S. L. (1999). Measurement uncertainty: approaches to the evaluation of uncertainties associated with recovery. Analyst, 124(7), 981-990. https://doi.org/10.1039/A901845J

Basile AC, Sertie JA, Freitas PC, Zanini AC. 1988. Anti-inflammatory activity of oleoresin from Brazilian Copaifera. J Ethnopharmacol 22: 101–109. https://doi.org/10.1016/0378-8741(88)90235-8

Bauer S, Olson J, Cockrill A, van Hattem M, Miller L, Tauzer M, et al. (2015) Impacts of Surface Water Diversions for Marijuana Cultivation on Aquatic Habitat in Four Northwestern California Watersheds. PLoS ONE 10(3): e0120016. https://doi.org/10.1371/journal.pone.0120016

Bauer, S., Olson, J., Cockrill, A., Van Hattem, M., Miller, L., Tauzer, M., & Leppig, G. (2015). Impacts of surface water diversions for marijuana cultivation on aquatic habitat in four northwestern California watersheds. PloS one, 10(3), e0120016. https://doi.org/10.1371/journal.pone.0120016

482

Bazaka, K., Destefani, R. & Jacob, M. Plant-derived cis-β-ocimene as a precursor for biocompatible, transparent, thermally-stable dielectric and encapsulating layers for organic electronics. Sci Rep 6, 38571 (2016). https://doi.org/10.1038/srep38571

Bechtold J, Hipwell A, Lewis DA, Loeber R, Pardini D. Concurrent and Sustained Cumulative Effects of Adolescent Marijuana Use on Subclinical Psychotic Symptoms. Am J Psychiatry. 2016 Aug 1;173(8):781-9. https://doi.org/10.1176/appi.ajp.2016.15070878

Bektas A, Hardwick KM, Waterman K, Kristof J. 2019. The occurrence of hop latent viroid in Cannabis sativa with symptoms of Cannabis stunting disease in California. Plant Disease. https://doi.org/10.1094/PDIS-03-19-0459-PDN

Bellocchio, L., Cervino, C., Pasquali, R., Pagotto, U., 2008. The endocannabinoid system and energy metabolism. J. Neuroendocrinol. 20, 850–857. https://doi.org/10.1111/j.1365-2826.2008.01728.x

Benedetti F, Amanzio M, Rosato R, Blanchard C. 2011. Nonopioid placebo analgesia is mediated by CB1 cannabinoid receptors. Nat Med. 17(10): 1228-1230. https://doi.org/10.1038/nm.2435

Benowitz NL, Jones RT. 1981. Cardiovascular effects of prolonged delta-9-tetrahydrocannbinol ingestion. Clinical Pharmacology and Therapeutics. 18-287-297. https://doi.org/10.1002/cpt1975183287

Bercht, C.L., Lousberg, R.J.C., Küppers, F.J. and Salemink, C.A., 1974. Cannabicitran: A new naturally occurring tetracyclic diether from lebanese Cannabis sativa. Phytochemistry, 13(3), pp.619-621.

Berdyshev AG, Kosiakova HV, Onopchenko OV, Panchuk RR, Stoika RS, Hula NM. N-Stearoylethanolamine suppresses the pro-inflammatory cytokines production by inhibition of NF-κB translocation. Prostaglandins Other Lipid Mediat. 2015 Sep;121(Pt A):91-6. https://doi.org/10.1016/j.prostaglandins.2015.05.001 Epub 2015 May 18. PMID: 25997585.

Bergamaschi MM, Queiroz RH, Zuardi AW, Crippa JA. Safety and side effects of cannabidiol, a Cannabis sativa constituent. Curr Drug Saf. 2011 Sep 1;6(4):237-49. https://doi.org/10.2174/157488611798280924

Bettarini F, Borgonovi GE, Fiorani T, Gagliardi I, Caprioli V, Massardo P et al. 1993. Antiparasitic compounds from East African plants: isolation and biological activtiry of anonaine, matricarianol, canthin-6-one, and caryophyllene oxide. Insect Sci Appl 14: 93–99. https://doi.org/10.1017/S174275840001345X

Bhatnagar-Mathur P, Sunkara S, Bhatnagar-Panwar M, Waliyar F, Sharma KK. Biotechnological advances for combating Aspergillus flavus and aflatoxin contamination in crops. Plant Sci. 2015 May;234:119-32. https://doi.org/10.1016/j.plantsci.2015.02.009 Epub 2015 Feb 25. PMID: 25804815.

Białoń M, Krzyśko-Łupicka T, Nowakowska-Bogdan E, Wieczorek PP. Chemical Composition of Two Different Lavender Essential Oils and Their Effect on Facial Skin Microbiota. Molecules. 2019 Sep 8;24(18):3270. https://doi.org/10.3390/molecules24183270

Biro T, Olah A, Toth BI, Czifra G, Zouboulis CC, Paus R. 2009. Cannabidiol as a novel anti-acne agent? Cannabidiol inhibits lipid synthesis and induces cell death in human sebaceous gland-derived sebocytes. Proceedings 19th Annual Conference on the Cannabinoids. International Cannabinoid Research Society: Pheasant Run, St. Charles, IL, p. 28.

Bisogno T, Hanus L, De Petrocellis L, Tchilibon S, Ponde DE, Brandi I, Moriello AS, Davis JB, Mechoulam R, Di Marzo V. Molecular targets for cannabidiol and its synthetic analogues: effect on vanilloid VR1 receptors and on the cellular uptake and enzymatic hydrolysis of anandamide. Br J Pharmacol. 2001 Oct;134(4):845-52. https://doi.org/10.1038/sj.bjp.0704327

Bisogno T, Melck D, Bobrov MY, Gretskaya NM, Bezuglov VV, De Petrocellis L, Di Marzo V. 2000. N-acyl-dopamines: novel synthetic CB(1) cannabinoid-receptor ligands and inhibitors of anandamide inactivation with cannabimimetic activity in vitro and in vivo. Biochem. J. 351:817-824. http://www.ncbi.nlm.nih.gov/pmc/articles/pmc1221424/

Bisset NG, Wichtl M 2004. Herbal Drugs and Phytopharmaceuticals: A Handbook for Practice on A Scientific Basis, 3rd edn. Medpharm Scientific Publishers: Stuttgart; CRC

Blair A, Zahm SH. 1991. Cancer among farmers. Occup. Med. 3:335-54 https://doi.org/10.5271/sjweh.2208

Blair A, Zahm SH. 1995. Agricultural exposures and cancer. Environ. Health Perspect. 103:205-8

Blake, J. (1988). MITES AND THRIPS AS BACTERIAL AND FUNGAL VECTORS BETWEEN PLANT TISSUE CULTURES. Acta Hortic. 225, 163-166 DOI: 10.17660/ActaHortic.1988.225.17

Blevins, R.L., Cook, D., Phillips, S.H. and Phillips, R.E. (1971), Influence of No-tillage on Soil Moisture1. Agron. J., 63: 593-596. https://doi.org/10.2134/agronj1971.00021962006300040024x

Bolognini D, Rock EM, Cluny NL, Cascio MG, Limebeer CL, Duncan M, Stott CG, Javid FA, Parker LA, Pertwee RG. 2013. Cannabidiolic acid prevents vomiting in Suncus murinus and nausea-induced behavior in rats by enhancing 5-HT1A receptor activation. Br J Phar. 168(6):1456-1470. https://doi.org/10.1111/bph.12043

Bonn-Miller, MO, Babson, KA, Vandrey, R. 2014. Using cannabis to help you sleep: Heightened frequency of medical cannabis use among those with PTSD. Drug and Alcohol Dependence. 136:162-165. https://doi.org/10.1016/j.drugalcdep.2013.12.008

Booth JK, Yuen MMS, Jancsik S, Madilao L, Page J, Bohlmann J. 2020. Terpene synthases and terpene variation in Cannabis sativa. Plant Physiology. doi: 10.1104/pp.20.00593

Bornheim LM, Everhart ET, Li J, Correia MA. 1993. Characterization of cannabidiol-mediated cytochrome P450 inactivation. Biochem Pharmacol. https://doi.org/10.1016/0006-2952(93)90286-6

Borrelli F, Fasolino I, Romano B, Capasso R, Maiello F, Coppola D, Orlando P, Battista G, Pagano E, Di Marzo V, et al. (2013) Beneficial effect of the nonpsychotropic plant cannabinoid cannabigerol on experimental inflammatory bowel disease. Biochem Pharmacol 85:1306–1316 https://doi.org/10.1016/j.bcp.2013.01.017

Brady, P., 2004. BC's million dollar grow shows. Cannabis Culture. http://www.cannabisculture.com/articles/3268.html

Brenneisen R. 2007. Chemistry and analysis of phytocannabinoids and other Cannabis constituents. In: Elsohly M (ed.). Marijuana and the Cannabinoids. Humana Press: Totowa, NY, pp. 17–49.

Brodie MJ, Czapinski P, Pazdera L, Sander JW, Toledo M, Napoles M, Sahebkar F, Schreiber A; GWEP1330 Study Group. A Phase 2 Randomized Controlled Trial of the Efficacy and Safety of Cannabidivarin as Add-on Therapy in Participants with Inadequately Controlled Focal Seizures. Cannabis Cannabinoid Res. 2021 Dec;6(6):528-536. https://doi.org/10.1089/can.2020.0075

Brutlag, A.; Hommerding, H. Toxicology of Marijuana, Synthetic Cannabinoids, and Cannabidiol in Dogs and Cats. Vet. Clin. Small Anim. 2018, 48, 1087–1102. doi.org/10.1016/j.cvsm.2018.07.008

Buchbauer G, Jirovetz L, Jager W, Dietrich H, Plank C. 1991. Aromatherapy: evidence for sedative effects of the essential oil of lavender after inhalation. Z Naturforsch [C] 46: 1067–1072. https://doi.org/10.1515/znc-1991-11-1223

Buchbauer G, Jirovetz L, Jäger W, Plank C, Dietrich H. Fragrance compounds and essential oils with sedative effects upon inhalation. J Pharm Sci. 1993 Jun;82(6):660-4. https://doi.org/10.1002/jps.2600820623

Burstein SH, Hull K, Hunter SA, Latham V. 1988. Cannabinoids and pain responses: a possible role for prostaglandins. FASEB J. 2(14):3022-3026. https://doi.org/10.1096/fasebj.2.14.2846397

Burstein SH, Hunter SA, Latham V, Renzulli L. 1986. Prostaglandins and cannabis. XVI. Antagonism of delta-1-tetrahydrocannabinol action by its metabolites. Biochem Pharmacol.35(15):2553-2558. https://doi.org/10.1016/0006-2952(86)90053-5

Burstein SH, McQuain CA, Ross AH, Salmonsen RA, Zurier RE. Resolution of inflammation by N-arachidonoylglycine. J Cell Biochem. 2011 Nov;112(11):3227-33. https://doi.org/10.1002/jcb.23245  PMID: 21732409; PMCID: PMC3196844.

Bush DM, Woodwell DA. Update: Drug-Related Emergency Department Visits Involving Synthetic Cannabinoids. 2014 Oct 16. In: The CBHSQ Report. Rockville (MD): Substance Abuse and Mental Health Services Administration (US); 2013: https://www.ncbi.nlm.nih.gov/books/NBK350768/

Cabral GA, Raborn ES, Ferreira GA. 2015. Phytocannabinoids and the Immune System. Handbook of Cannabis. Oxford University Press. 261-279.

Calderón-Montaño JM, Burgos-Morón E, Pérez-Guerrero C, López-Lázaro M. A review on the dietary flavonoid kaempferol. Mini Rev Med Chem. 2011 Apr;11(4):298-344. https://doi.org/10.2174/138955711795305335

Cami J, Guerra D, Ugena B, Segura J, de la Torre R. 1991. Effect of subject expectancy on the THC intoxication and disposition from smoked hashish cigarettes. Pharmacol Biochem Behav. 40(1):115-9 https://doi.org/10.1016/0091-3057(91)90330-5

Campolongo, P., Trezza, V., Palmery, M., Trabace, L., & Cuomo, V. (2009). Developmental exposure to cannabinoids causes subtle and enduring neurofunctional alterations. International review of neurobiology, 85, 117-133. https://www.nature.com/articles/npp2017162#article-info

Campora, L.; Miragliotta, V.; Ricci, E.; Cristino, L.; Di Marzo, V.; Albanese, F.; Frederica della Valle, M.; Abramo, F. Cannabinoid receptor type 1 and 2 expression in the skin of healthy dogs and dogs with atopic dermatitis. Am. J. Vet. Res. 2012, 73, 988–995. doi.org/10.2460/ajvr.73.7.988

Cani PD, Plovier H, Van Hul M, Geurts L, Delzenne NM, Druart C, Everard A. 2015. Endocannabinoids – at the crossroads between the gut microbiota and host metabolism. Nature Reviews Endocrinology. 12(1): 133-143. https://doi.org/10.1038/nrendo.2015.211

Cannabis Inflorescence Cannabis spp. Monograph. American Herbal Pharmacopoeia. 2013.

Caprioglio D, Mattoteia D, Pollastro F, Negri R, Lopatriello A, Chianese G, Minassi A, Collado JA, Munoz E, Taglialatela-Scafati O, Appendino G. 2020. The Oxidation of Phytocannabinoids to Cannabinoquinoids. J. Nat. Prod. Pre-Print. Published April 21, 2020. https://doi.org/10.1021/acs.jnatprod.9b01284

Carabotti M, Scirocco A, Maselli MA, Severi C. 2015. The gut-brain axis: interactions between enteric microbiota, central and enteric nervous systems. Ann Gastroenterol. 28(2):203-209. http://www.ncbi.nlm.nih.gov/pmc/articles/pmc4367209/

Carlini EA and Cunha JM. 1981. Hypnotic and antiepileptic effects of cannabidiol. Journal of Clinical Pharmacology. 21: 417S–427S. https://doi.org/10.1002/j.1552-4604.1981.tb02622.x

Carmona-Hidalgo B, González-Mariscal I, García-Martín A, Prados ME, Ruiz-Pino F, Appendino G, Tena-Sempere M, Muñoz E. Δ9-Tetrahydrocannabinolic Acid markedly alleviates liver fibrosis and inflammation in mice. Phytomedicine. 2021 Jan;81:153426. https://doi.org/10.1016/j.phymed.2020.153426 Epub 2020 Nov 30. PMID: 33341026.

Carrier EJ, Auchampach JA, Hillard CJ. Inhibition of an equilibrative nucleoside transporter by cannabidiol: a mechanism of cannabinoid immunosuppression. Proc Natl Acad Sci U S A. 2006 May 16;103(20):7895-900. https://doi.org/10.1073/pnas.0511232103

Carvalho-Freitas MI, Costa M (2002). Anxiolytic and sedative effects of extracts and essential oil from Citrus aurantium L. Biol Pharm Bull 25: 1629–1633. https://doi.org/10.1248/bpb.25.1629

Casano, S., Grassi, G., Martini, V., & Michelozzi, M. (2011). VARIATIONS IN TERPENE PROFILES OF DIFFERENT STRAINS OF CANNABIS SATIVA L. Acta Horticulturae, (925), 115–121. https://doi.org/10.17660/actahortic.2011.925.15

Cascio MG, Gauson LA, Stevenson LA, Ross RA, and Pertwee RG (2010) Evidence that the plant cannabinoid cannabigerol is a highly potent alpha2-adrenoceptor agonist and moderately potent 5HT1A receptor antagonist. Br J Pharmacol 159:129–141. https://doi.org/10.1111/j.1476-5381.2009.00515.x

Cascio MG, Gauson LA, Stevenson LA, Ross RA, Pertwee RG. Evidence that the plant cannabinoid cannabigerol is a highly potent alpha2-adrenoceptor agonist and moderately potent 5HT1A receptor antagonist. Br J Pharmacol. 2010 Jan;159(1):129-41. https://doi.org/10.1111/j.1476-5381.2009.00515.x

Castelli MP, Fadda P, Casu A, Spano MS, Casti A, Fratta W, Fattore L. Male and female rats differ in brain cannabinoid CB1 receptor density and function and in behavioural traits predisposing to drug addiction: effect of ovarian hormones. Curr Pharm Des. 2014;20(13):2100-13. https://doi.org/10.2174/13816128113199990430

Castillo PE, Younts TJ, Chávez AE, Hashimotodani Y. Endocannabinoid signaling and synaptic function. Neuron. 2012 Oct 4;76(1):70-81. https://doi.org/10.1016/j.neuron.2012.09.020

Cavalieri E, Mariotto S, Fabrizi C, de Prati AC, Gottardo R, Leone S, Berra LV, Lauro GM, Ciampa AR, Suzuki H. alpha-Bisabolol, a nontoxic natural compound, strongly induces apoptosis in glioma cells. Biochem Biophys Res Commun. 2004 Mar 12;315(3):589-94. https://doi.org/10.1016/j.bbrc.2004.01.088 PMID: 14975741.

Chandra, Suman; Lata, Hemant; Khan, Ikhlas A.; ElSohly, Mahmoud A. Photosynthetic response of Cannabis sativa L., an important medicinal plant, to elevated levels of CO2. Physiology and Molecular Biology of Plants. Vol. 17 (3). JUL 2011. 291-295 https://doi.org/10.1007%2Fs12298-011-0066-6

Chicca A, Schafroth MA, Reynoso-Moreno I, Erni R, Petrucci V, Carreira EM, Gertsch J. Uncovering the psychoactivity of a cannabinoid from liverworts associated with a legal high. Sci Adv. 2018 Oct 24;4(10):eaat2166. https://doi.org/10.1126/sciadv.aat2166

Chiocchetti, R, Rinnovati, R, Tagliavia, C, et al. Localisation of cannabinoid and cannabinoid-related receptors in the equine dorsal root ganglia. Equine Vet J. 2021; 53: 549– 557. doi.org/10.1111/evj.13305

Choi HS, Song HS, Ukeda H, Sawamura M (2000). Radical-scavenging activities of citrus essential oils and their components: detection using 1,1-diphenyl-2-picrylhydrazyl. J Agric Food Chem 48: 4156–4161. https://doi.org/10.1021/jf000227d

Chong Y, Shimoda S, Yakushiji H, Ito Y, Miyamoto T, Shimono N, Kamimura T, Akashi K. 2012. Fatal candidemia caused by azole-resistant Candida tropicalis in patients with hematological malignancies. J Infect Chemother. 18(5):741-746. https://doi.org/10.1007/s10156-012-0412-9

Christison A (1851). On the natural history, action, and uses of Indian hemp. Monthly J Med Sci Edinburgh, Scotland 13: 26–45. 117-121. https://www.ncbi.nlm.nih.gov/pmc/articles/PMC5891280/

Chu ZL, Carroll C, Chen R, Alfonso J, Gutierrez V, He H, Lucman A, Xing C, Sebring K, Zhou J, Wagner B, Unett D, Jones RM, Behan DP, Leonard J. N-oleoyldopamine enhances glucose homeostasis through the activation of GPR119. Mol Endocrinol. 2010 Jan;24(1):161-70. https://doi.org/10.1210/me.2009-0239 Epub 2009 Nov 9. PMID: 19901198; PMCID: PMC5428146.

Ciolino, L.A. (2015), Quantitation of Synthetic Cannabinoids in Plant Materials Using High Performance Liquid Chromatography with UV Detection (Validated Method). J Forensic Sci, 60: 1171-1181. https://doi.org/10.1111/1556-4029.12795

Citterio, S, Prato, N, Fumagalli, P, Aina, R, Massa, N, Santagostino, A, Sgorbati, S, Berta, G. 2004. The arbuscular mycorrhizal fungus Glomus mosseae induces growth and metal accumulation changes in Cannabis sativa L. Chemosphere. 59(1):21-29 https://doi.org/10.1016/j.chemosphere.2004.10.009

Citti C, Linciano P, Panseri S, Vezzalini F, Forni F, Vandelli MA, Cannazza G. Cannabinoid Profiling of Hemp Seed Oil by Liquid Chromatography Coupled to High-Resolution Mass Spectrometry. Front Plant Sci. 2019 Feb 13;10:120. https://doi.org/10.3389/fpls.2019.00120 PMID: 30815007; PMCID: PMC6381057.

Citti, C., Linciano, P., Russo, F. et al. A novel phytocannabinoid isolated from Cannabis sativa L. with an in vivo cannabimimetic activity higher than Δ9-tetrahydrocannabinol: Δ9-Tetrahydrocannabiphorol. Sci Rep 9, 20335 (2019). https://doi.org/10.1038/s41598-019-56785-1

Clarke, R. C., & Merlin, M. D. (2013). Cannabis: Evolution and Ethnobotany (1st ed.). University of California Press. http://www.jstor.org/stable/10.1525/j.ctt3fh2f8

Composition of olivetol and method of use to reduce or inhibit the effects of tetrahydrocannabinol in the human body https://patents.google.com/patent/EP3380092B1/

Cornwell PA, Barry BW (1994). Sesquiterpene components of volatile oils as skin penetration enhancers for the hydrophilic permeant 5-fluorouracil. J Pharm Pharmacol 46: 261–269. https://doi.org/10.1111/j.2042-7158.1994.tb03791.x

Craft, R. M., & Leitl, M. D. (2008). Gonadal hormone modulation of the behavioral effects of Δ9-tetrahydrocannabinol in male and female rats. European journal of pharmacology, 578(1), 37-42. https://doi.org/10.1016/j.ejphar.2007.09.004

Crippa, JA, Zuardi, AW, Martin-Santos, R, Bhattacharyya, S, Atakan, Z, McGuire, P, Fusar-Poli, P. 2009. Cannabis and anxiety: a critical review of the evidence. Hum. Psychopharmacol Clin Exp. 24(7):515-523. https://doi.org/10.1002/hup.1048

Crombie L, Ponsford R, Shani A, Yagnitinsky B, Mechoulam R. Hashish components. Photochemical production of cannabicyclol from cannabichromene. Tetrahedron Lett. 1968 Nov;(55):5771-2. https://doi.org/10.1016/s0040-4039(00)76346-5

Cudaback E, Marrs W, Moeller T, Stella N. 2010. The expression level of CB1 and CB2 receptors determines their efficacy at inducing apoptosis in astrocytomas. PLoS One 5 (1), e8702. https://doi.org/10.1371/journal.pone.0008702

Cui N, Wang L, Wang W, Zhang J, Xu Y, Jiang L, Hao G. 2017. The correlation of anandamide with gonadotrophin and sex steroid hormones during the menstrual cycle. Iranian Journal of Basic Medical Sciences. 20: 1268-1274. https://doi.org/10.22038%2FIJBMS.2017.9488

Dalir, S., Hajiqanbar, H., Fathipour, Y. and Khanamani, M. (2021), A comprehensive picture of foraging strategies of Neoseiulus cucumeris and Amblyseius swirskii on western flower thrips. Pest

Dall'Aglio, C.; Mercati, F.; Pascucci, L.; Boiti, C.; Pedini, V.; Ceccarelli, P. Immunohistochemical localization of CB1 receptor in canine salivary glands. Vet. Res. Commun. 2010, 34, 9–12. doi.org/10.1007/s11259-010-9379-0

Daniele Piomelli and Ethan B. Russo.Cannabis and Cannabinoid Research.Dec 2016.44-46. http://doi.org/10.1089/can.2015.29003.ebr

Darling MR, Arendorf TM, Coldrey NA. 1990. Effect of cannabis use on oral candidal carriage. J Oral Pathol Med. 19(7):319-321. https://doi.org/10.1111/j.1600-0714.1990.tb00852.x

Darling MR, Arendorf TM. 1992. Review of the effects of Cannabis smoking on oral health. Int Dent J. 42:19-22. https://pubmed.ncbi.nlm.nih.gov/1563817/

Davalos SD, Fournier G, Boucher F, Paris M (1977). [Contribution to the study of Mexican marihuana. Preliminary studies: cannabinoids and essential oil (author's transl)]. J Pharm Belg 32:89–99.

Davis WM, Hatoum NS (1983). Neurobehavioral actions of cannabichromene and interactions with delta 9-tetrahydrocannabinol. Gen Pharmacol 14: 247–252. https://doi.org/10.1016/0306-3623(83)90004-6

de Graaf R, Radovanovic M, van Laar M, Fairman B, Degenhardt L, Aguilar-Gaxiola S, Bruffaerts R, de Girolamo G, Fayyad J, Gureje O, Haro JM, Huang Y, Kostychenko S, Lépine JP, Matschinger H, Mora ME, Neumark Y, Ormel J, Posada-Villa J, Stein DJ, Tachimori H, Wells JE, Anthony JC. Early cannabis use and estimated risk of later onset of depression spells: Epidemiologic evidence from the population-based World Health Organization World Mental Health Survey Initiative. Am J Epidemiol. 2010 Jul 15;172(2):149-59. https://doi.org/10.1093/aje/kwq096

de Meijer E. 2015. The Chemical Phenotypes (Chemotypes) of Cannabis. Chapter Five. Handbook of Cannabis. Oxford University Press. 89-110

de Meijer, E.P.M., Hammond, K.M. The inheritance of chemical phenotype in Cannabis sativa L. (II): Cannabigerol predominant plants. Euphytica 145, 189–198 (2005). https://doi.org/10.1007/s10681-005-1164-8

De Oliveira AC, Ribeiro-Pinto LF, Paumgartten JR (1997). In vitro inhibition of CYP2B1 monooxygenase by beta-myrcene and other monoterpenoid compounds. Toxicol Lett 92: 39–46. https://doi.org/10.1016/s0378-4274(97)00034-9

De Petrocellis L, Ligresti A, Moriello AS, Allarà M, Bisogno T, Petrosino S, Stott CG, Di Marzo V. Effects of cannabinoids and cannabinoid-enriched Cannabis extracts on TRP channels and endocannabinoid metabolic enzymes. Br J Pharmacol. 2011 Aug;163(7):1479-94. https://doi.org/10.1111/j.1476-5381.2010.01166.x

De Petrocellis L, Ligresti A., Moriello A.S., Iappelli M., Verde R., Stott C.G., Cristino L., Orlando P., and Di Marzo V. 2013. Non-THC cannabinoids inhibit prostate carcinoma growth in vitro and in vivo: pro-apoptotic effects and underlying mechanisms. British Journal of Pharmacology 168 (1): 79–10 https://doi.org/10.1111/j.1476-5381.2012.02027.x

De Petrocellis L, Orlando P, Moriello AS, Aviello G, Stott C, Izzo AA, Di Marzo V. Cannabinoid actions at TRPV channels: effects on TRPV3 and TRPV4 and their potential relevance to gastrointestinal inflammation. Acta Physiol (Oxf). 2012 Feb;204(2):255-66. https://doi.org/10.1111/j.1748-1716.2011.02338.x

Deabold, Kelly A., Wayne S. Schwark, Lisa Wolf, and Joseph J. Wakshlag. 2019. "Single-Dose Pharmacokinetics and Preliminary Safety Assessment with Use of CBD-Rich Hemp Nutraceutical in Healthy Dogs and Cats" Animals 9, no. 10: 832. doi.org/10.3390/ani9100832

Deiana S. 2017. Potential Medical Uses of Cannabigerol: A Brief Overview. Handbook of Cannabis and Related Pathologies. Chapter 99. Academic Press. Pages 958-967. https://doi.org/10.1016/B978-0-12-800756-3.00115-0

486

Desai S, Borg B, Cuttler C, Crombie KM, Rabinak CA, Hill MN, Marusak HA. A Systematic Review and Meta-Analysis on the Effects of Exercise on the Endocannabinoid System. Cannabis Cannabinoid Res. 2022 Aug;7(4):388-408. https://doi.org/10.1089/can.2021.0113

Desserud PA, Naeth MA. 2012. An unexpected response of a bunch grass (rough fescue) to arbuscular mycorrhizae fungi. Ecological Restoration. 30(3):165-168. http://www.jstor.org/stable/44743650

Devane WA, Breuer A, Sheskin T, Jarbe TU, Eisen MS, Mechoulam R. 1992. A novel probe for the cannabinoid receptor. J Med Chem. 35(11):2065-2069. https://doi.org/10.1021/jm00089a018

Devane WA, Dysarz FA 3rd, Johnson MR, Melvin LS, Howlett AC. 1988. Determination and characterization of a cannabinoid receptor in rat brain. Molecular Pharmacology. 34: 605–613. https://pubmed.ncbi.nlm.nih.gov/2848184/

Devitt-Lee A. 2015. CBD-Drug Interactions: Role of Cytochrome P450. Project CBD. https://www.projectcbd.org/article/cbd-drug-interactions-role-cytochrome-p450

DeVuono MV, Parker LA. Cannabinoid Hyperemesis Syndrome: A Review of Potential Mechanisms. Cannabis Cannabinoid Res. 2020 Jun 5;5(2):132-144. https://doi.org/10.1089/can.2019.0059

Deyo R, Musty R (2003). A cannabichromene (CBC) extract alters behavioral despair on the mouse tail suspension test of depression. Proceedings 2003 Symposium on the Cannabinoids. International Cannabinoid Research Society: Cornwall, ON, p. 146.

Di Marzo V, DePetrocellis L, Bisogno T. 2005. The biosynthesis, fate and pharmacological properties of endocannabinoids. Handb. Exp.Pharmacol. 168, 147–185. https://doi.org/10.1007/3-540-26573-2_5

Di Marzo V, Melck D, Bisogno T, De Petrocellis L. Endocannabinoids: endogenous cannabinoid receptor ligands with neuromodulatory action. Trends Neurosci. 1998 Dec;21(12):521-8. https://doi.org/10.1016/s0166-2236(98)01283-1

Di Marzo V, Wang J. 2014. The Endocannabinoidome: The World of Endocannabinoids and Related Mediators. Academic Press. Elsevier.

Di Marzo V. 1998. 'Endocannabinoids' and other fatty acid derivatives with cannabimimetic properties: biochemistry and possible physiopathological relevance. Biochimica et Biophysica Acta. 1392: 153–175 https://doi.org/10.1016/s0005-2760(98)00042-3

Ding F, Li X. Apigenin Mitigates Intervertebral Disc Degeneration through the Amelioration of Tumor Necrosis Factor α (TNF-α) Signaling Pathway. Med Sci Monit. 2020 Sep 19;26:e924587. https://doi.org/10.12659/msm.924587

Dioscorides P and Beck LY. 2011. De Materia Medica. Hildesheim: Olms-Weidmann.

DiPatrizio NV, Astarita G, Schwartz G, Li X, Piomelli D. Endocannabinoid signal in the gut controls dietary fat intake. Proc Natl Acad Sci U S A. 2011 Aug 2;108(31):12904-8. https://doi.org/10.1073/pnas.1104675108

Dixon, W.E. The Pharmacology of Cannabis indica. Br. Med. J. 1899, 2, 1354–1357. doi.org/10.1136/bmj.2.2030.1517

Dorard G, Berthoz S, Phan O, Corcos M, Bungener C. Affect dysregulation in cannabis abusers: a study in adolescents and young adults. Eur Child Adolesc Psychiatry. 2008 Aug;17(5):274-82. https://doi.org/10.1007/s00787-007-0663-7

Douds, DDJ, PE Pfeffer, and Y Shachar-Hill. 2000. Carbon partitioning, cost, and metabolism of arbuscular mycorrhizas. Pages 107-129 in Y. Kapulnik and DDJ Douds, editors. Arbuscular mycorrhizas: physiology and function. Kluwer Academic Publishers, Dordrecht, The Netherlands.

Draeger AL, Thomas EP, Jones KA, Davis AJ, Shea Porr CA. 2021. The effects of pelleted cannabidiol supplementation on heart rate and reaction scores in horses. Journal of Veterinary Behavior. Vol 46. 97-100. doi.org/10.1016/j.jveb.2021.09.003

Draeger, Anna L.; Hoffman, Laura K.; Godwin, Patricia R.; Davis, Amanda J.; and Porr, Shea A. (2021) "Pharmacokinetics of a Single Feeding of Pelleted Cannabidiol in Horses," Steeplechase: An ORCA Student Journal: Vol. 4: Iss. 2, Article 1. https://digitalcommons.murraystate.edu/steeplechase/vol4/iss2/1

Dreher MC, Nugent K, Hudgins R. 1994. Prenatal Marijuana Exposure and Neonatal Outcomes in Jamaica: An Ethnographic Study. Pediatrics. 93(2): 254-260. https://pubmed.ncbi.nlm.nih.gov/8121737/

Dubertret C, Bidard I, Ades J, Gorwood P. 2006. Lifetime positive symptoms in patients with schizophrenia and cannabis abuse are partially explained by co-morbid addiction. Schizophrenia Research. 86:284-290. https://doi.org/10.1016/j.schres.2006.05.006

Duffy B, Li L, Lu S, Durocher L, Dittmar M, Delaney-Baldwin E, Panawennage D, LeMaster D, Navarette K, Spink D. 2020. Analysis of cannabinoid-containing fluids in illicit vaping cartridges recovered from pulmonary injury patients: identification of vitamin E acetate as a major diluent. Toxics. 8(1):8. https://doi.org/10.3390/toxics8010008

Duncan, M., & Izzo, A. A. (2015). Phytocannabinoids and the gastrointestinal system. Handbook of Cannabis, 227-244.

Duran M, Perez E, Abanades S, Vidal X, Saura C, Majem M, Arriola E, Rabanal M, Pastor A, Farre M, Rams N, Laporte JR, Capella D. 2010. Preliminary efficacy and safety of an oromucosal standardized cannabis extract in chemotherapy-induced nausea and vomiting. British Journal of Clinical Pharmacology. 2010. 70: 656–663. https://doi.org/10.1111/j.1365-2125.2010.03743.x

Ebersbach, P., Stehle, F., Kayser, O. et al. Chemical fingerprinting of single glandular trichomes of Cannabis sativa by Coherent anti-Stokes Raman scattering (CARS) microscopy. BMC Plant Biol 18, 275 (2018). https://doi.org/10.1186/s12870-018-1481-4 (Fig. 3)

Echeverry C, Prunell G, Narbondo C, de Medina VS, Nadal X, Reyes-Parada M, and Scorza C (2020) A Comparative in vitro study of the neuroprotective effect induced by cannabidiol, cannabigerol, and their respective acid forms: relevance of the 5-HT. Neurotox Res. https://doi.org10.1007/s12640-020-00277-y

Ed Rosenthal's Marijuana Grower's Handbook website; http://mjgrowers.com/book_what_light.htm

Ellis, K.L. and Contino, E.K. (2021), Treatment using cannabidiol in a horse with mechanical allodynia. Equine Vet Educ, 33: e79-e82. doi.org/10.1111/eve.13168

Elmes, M. W., Kaczocha, M., Berger, W. T., Leung, K., Ralph, B. P., Wang, L. et al. (2015). Fatty Acid-binding Proteins (FABPs) Are Intracellular Carriers for Δ9-Tetrahydrocannabinol (THC) and Cannabidiol (CBD). The Journal of Biological Chemistry, 290(14), 8711–8721. http://doi.org/10.1074/jbc.M114.618447

Elphick, M. R.; Egertova, M. (2001). "The neurobiology and evolution of cannabinoid signalling". Philosophical Transactions of the Royal Society B: Biological Sciences 356 (1407): 381–408. https://doi.org/10.1098/rstb.2000.0787

ElSohly HN, Turner CE, Clark AM, ElSohly MA (1982). Synthesis and antimicrobial activities of certain cannabichromene and cannabigerol related compounds. J Pharm Sci 71: 1319–1323. https://doi.org/10.1002/jps.2600711204

ElSohly MA, Slade D. 2005. Chemical constituents of marijuana: the complex mixture of natural cannabinoids. Life Sciences. 78:539-548.

Elzinga, Sytze, Jorge Dominguez-Alonzo, Raquel Keledjian, Brad Douglass, and Jeffrey C. Raber. 2022. "Acetone as Artifact of Analysis in Terpene Samples by HS-GC/MS" Molecules 27, no. 18: 6037. https://doi.org/10.3390/molecules27186037

Emboden, W.A., 1981. The genus Cannabis and the correct use of taxonomic categories. J. Psychoactive Drugs 13, 15–21.

Engels FK, de Jong FA, Mathijssen RHJ, Erkens JA, Herings RM, Verweij J. 2007. Medicinal cannabis in oncology. European Journal of Cancer. 43:2638-2644 https://doi.org/10.1016/j.ejca.2007.09.010

European Monitoring Centre for Drugs Drug Addiction (2009). Understanding the 'Spice' phenomenon. European Monitoring Centre for Drugs and Drug Addiction. doi:10.2810/27063. ISBN 9789291684113. ISSN 1725-5767.

Evans FJ (1991). Cannabinoids: the separation of central from peripheral effects on a structural basis. Planta Med 57: S60–S67. https://pubmed.ncbi.nlm.nih.gov/1659702/

Ewing LE, Skinner CM, Quick CM, Kennon-McGill S, McGill MR, Walker LA, ElSohly MA, Gurley BJ, Koturbash I. Hepatotoxicity of a Cannabidiol-Rich Cannabis Extract in the Mouse Model. Molecules. 2019 Apr 30;24(9):1694. https://doi.org/10.3390/molecules24091694

Eyal AM, Berneman Zeitouni D, Tal D, Schlesinger D, Davidson EM, Raz N. Vapor Pressure, Vaping, and Corrections to Misconceptions Related to Medical Cannabis' Active Pharmaceutical Ingredients' Physical Properties and Compositions. Cannabis Cannabinoid Res. 2022 Apr 18. https://doi.org/10.1089/can.2021.0173

Fabrizio Calapai, Luigi Cardia, Emanuela Esposito, Ilaria Ammendolia, Cristina Mondello, Roberto Lo Giudice, Sebastiano Gangemi, Gioacchino Calapai, Carmen Mannucci, "Pharmacological Aspects and Biological Effects of Cannabigerol and Its Synthetic Derivatives", Evidence-Based Complementary and Alternative Medicine, vol. 2022, Article ID 3336516, 14 pages, 2022. https://doi.org/10.1155/2022/3336516

Falk AA, Hagberg MT, Lof AE, Wigaeus-Hjelm EM, Wang ZP (1990). Uptake, distribution and elimination of alpha-pinene in man after exposure by inhalation. Scand J Work Environ Health 16: 372–378. https://doi.org/10.5271/sjweh.1771

Farag RS, Shalaby AS, El-Baroty GA, Ibrahim NA, Ali MA, Hassan EM (2004). Chemical and biological evaluation of the essential oils of different Melaleuca species. Phytother Res 18: 30–35. https://doi.org/10.1002/ptr.1348

Farha MA, El-Halfawy OM, Gale RT, MacNair CR, Carfrae LA, Zhang X, Jentsch NG, Magolan J, and Brown ED (2020) Uncovering the hidden antibiotic potential of cannabis. ACS Infect Dis 6:338–346. https://doi.org/10.1021/acsinfecdis.9b00419

Fattore L, Fratta W. 2011. Beyond THC: the new generation of cannabinoid designer drugs. Frontiers in Behavioral Neuroscience. 5(60): 1-12 https://doi.org/10.3389/fnbeh.2011.00060

Fellermeier M, Eisenreich W, Bacher A, Zenk MH. Biosynthesis of cannabinoids. Incorporation experiments with (13)C-labeled glucoses. Eur J Biochem. 2001;268:1596–1604. https://doi.org/10.1046/j.1432-1033.2001.02030.x

Fenselau, C., & Hermann, G. (1972). Identification of phytosterols in red oil extract of cannabis. Journal of Forensic Science, 17(2), 309-312. https://doi.org/10.1520/JFS10682J

Fernandes ES, Passos GF, Medeiros R, da Cunha FM, Ferreira J, Campos MM, Pianowski LF, Calixto JB. (2007) Anti-inflammatory effects of compounds alpha-humulene and (-)-trans-caryophyllene isolated from the essential oil of Cordia verbenacea. Eur J Pharmacol. 569(3):228-236. https://doi.org/10.1016/j.ejphar.2007.04.059

Fezza F, Bari M, Florio R, Talamonti E, Feole M, Maccarrone M. 2014. Endocannabinoids, Related Compounds and Their Metabolic Routes. Molecules. 19:17078-17106. https://doi.org/10.3390/molecules191117078

Fischedick JT. 2017. Identification of Terpenoid Chemotypes Among High (-)-trans-Δ9- Tetrahydrocannabinol-Producing Cannabis sativa L. Cultivars.Cannabis and Cannabinoid Research.Dec 2017.34-47. https://doi.org/10.1089/can.2016.0040

Foster JR, Ueno S, Chen MX, Harvey J, Dowell SJ, Irving AJ, Brown AJ. N-Palmitoylglycine and other N-acylamides activate the lipid receptor G2A/GPR132. Pharmacol Res Perspect. 2019 Nov 21;7(6):e00542. https://doi.org/10.1002/prp2.542 PMID: 31768260; PMCID: PMC6868653.

Franz C, Novak J. Sources of essential oils. In: Baser KHC, Buchbauer G, editors. Handbook of Essential Oils: Science, Technology, and Applications. Boca Raton, FL: CRC Press; 2010. pp. 39–82.

Fried, P. A., & Smith, A. M. (2001). A literature review of the consequences of prenatal marihuana exposure: an emerging theme of a deficiency in aspects of executive function. Neurotoxicology and teratology, 23(1), 1-11. https://doi.org/10.1016/S0892-0362(00)00119-7

Fuchs L. The great herbal of Leonhart Fuchs: De historia stirpium commentarii insignes, 1542 (notable commentaries on the history of plants). 1999. Stanford, CA: Stanford University Press.

Fuss J, Steinle J, Bindila L, Auer MK, Kirchherr H, Lutz B, Gass P. A runner's high depends on cannabinoid receptors in mice. Proc Natl Acad Sci U S A. 2015 Oct 20;112(42):13105-8. https://doi.org/10.1073/pnas.1514996112

Gadotti, V.M., Huang, S. & Zamponi, G.W. The terpenes camphene and alpha-bisabolol inhibit inflammatory and neuropathic pain via Cav3.2 T-type calcium channels. Mol Brain 14, 166 (2021). https://doi.org/10.1186/s13041-021-00876-6

Galiazzo G, Tagliavia C, Giancola F, Rinnovati R, Sadeghinezhad J, Bombardi C, Grandis A, Pietra M, Chiocchetti R. Localisation of Cannabinoid and Cannabinoid-Related Receptors in the Horse Ileum. J Equine Vet Sci. 2021 Sep;104:103688. doi.org/10.1016/j.jevs.2021.103688

Galic M, Percin A, Zgorelec Z, Kisic I. 2019. Evaluation of heavy metals accumulation potential of hemp (Cannabis sativa L.). Journal of Central European Agriculture. 20(2): 700 – 711. https://doi.org/10.5513/JCEA01/20.2.2201

Galiègue S, Mary S, Marchand J, Dussossoy D, Carrière D, Carayon P, Bouaboula M, Shire D, Le Fur G, Casellas P. Expression of central and peripheral cannabinoid receptors in human immune tissues and leukocyte subpopulations. Eur J Biochem. 1995 Aug 15;232(1):54-61. https://doi.org/10.1111/j.1432-1033.1995.tb20780.x

Galindo, L., Moreno, E., López-Armenta, F. et al. Cannabis Users Show Enhanced Expression of CB1-5HT2A Receptor Heteromers in Olfactory Neuroepithelium Cells. Mol Neurobiol 55, 6347–6361 (2018). https://doi.org/10.1007/s12035-017-0833-7

Galli JA, Sawaya RA, Friedenberg FK. 2011. Cannabinoid Hyperemesis Syndrome. Curr Drug Abuse. 4(4): 241-249. https://doi.org/10.2174/1874473711104040241

Gallily, R., Yekhtin, Z., & Hanuš, L. O. (2015). Overcoming the bell-shaped dose-response of cannabidiol by using cannabis extract enriched in cannabidiol. Pharmacology & Pharmacy, 6(02), 75. http://www.scirp.org/journal/PaperInformation.aspx?PaperID=53912&#abstract

Ganon-Elazar E, Akirav I. Cannabinoid receptor activation in the basolateral amygdala blocks the effects of stress on the conditioning and extinction of inhibitory avoidance. J Neurosci. 2009 Sep 9;29(36):11078-88. https://doi.org/10.1523/jneurosci.1223-09.2009

Ganon-Elazar E, Akirav I. Cannabinoids and traumatic stress modulation of contextual fear extinction and GR expression in the amygdala-hippocampal-prefrontal circuit. Psychoneuroendocrinology. 2013 Sep;38(9):1675-87. https://doi.org/10.1016/j.psyneuen.2013.01.014

Ganon-Elazar E, Akirav I. Cannabinoids prevent the development of behavioral and endocrine alterations in a rat model of intense stress. Neuropsychopharmacology. 2012 Jan;37(2):456-66. https://doi.org/10.1038/npp.2011.204

Gaoni Y and Mechoulam R. 1964. Isolation, Structure, and Partial Synthesis of an Active Constituent of Hashish. J. Am. Chem. Soc. 86(8): 1646-1647. https://doi.org/10.1021/ja01062a046

Garb HN. Race bias and gender bias in the diagnosis of psychological disorders. Clin Psychol Rev. 2021 Dec;90:102087. https://doi.org/10.1016/j.cpr.2021.102087

Garb, H. N. (1997). Race bias, social class bias, and gender bias in clinical judgment. Clinical Psychology: Science and Practice, 4(2), 99–120. https://doi.org/10.1111/j.1468-2850.1997.tb00104.x

Gattefosse R-M (1993). Gatefosse's Aromatherapy. C.W. Daniel: Essex, MD.

Geci M, Scialdone M, Tishler J. The Dark Side of Cannabidiol: The Unanticipated Social and Clinical Implications of Synthetic Δ8-THC. Cannabis Cannabinoid Res. 2022 Oct 19. https://doi.org/10.1089/can.2022.0126

Geffrey AL, Pollack SF, Bruno PL, Thiele EA. Drug-drug interaction between clobazam and cannabidiol in children with refractory epilepsy. Epilepsia. 2015 Aug;56(8):1246-51. https://doi.org/10.1111/epi.13060

Gerard J and Johnson T. The Herbal: or, General History of Plants. 1975. New York: Dover Publications

Gertsch J, Leonti M, Raduner S, Racz I, Chen JZ, Xie XQ, Altmann KH, Karsak M, Zimmer A. Beta-caryophyllene is a dietary cannabinoid. Proc Natl Acad Sci U S A. 2008 Jul 1;105(26):9099-104. https://doi.org/10.1073/pnas.0803601105 Epub 2008 Jun 23. PMID: 18574142; PMCID: PMC2449371.

Ghelardini C, Galeotti N, Salvatore G, Mazzanti G (1999). Local anaesthetic activity of the essential oil of Lavandula angustifolia. Planta Med 65: 700–703. https://doi.org/10.1055/s-1999-14045

Gieringer, D. 1996. Marijuana waterpipe and vaporizer study, MAPS Bull 6(3):59-66. Multidisciplinary Association for Psychedelic Studies, www.maps.org/news-letters/v06n3/06359mj1.html

Gil ML, Jimenez J, Ocete MA, Zarzuelo A, Cabo MM (1989). Comparative study of different essential oils of Bupleurum gibraltaricum Lamarck. Pharmazie 44: 284–287. https://pubmed.ncbi.nlm.nih.gov/2772005/

Giladi Y, Hadad L, Luria N, Cranshaw W, Lachman O. 2019. First Report of Beet Curly Top Virus Infecting Cannabis sativa L., in Western Colorado. Plant Disease. American Phytopathological Society. https://doi.org/10.1094/PDIS-08-19-1656-PDN

Gill EW, Paton WD, Pertwee RG. Preliminary experiments on the chemistry and pharmacology of cannabis. Nature. 1970 Oct 10;228(5267):134-6. https://doi.org/10.1038/228134a0

Gobira PH, Lima IV, Batista LA, de Oliveira AC, Resstel LB, Wotjak CT, Aguiar DC, Moreira FA. N-arachidonoyl-serotonin, a dual FAAH and TRPV1 blocker, inhibits the retrieval of contextual fear memory: Role of the cannabinoid CB1 receptor in the dorsal hippocampus. J Psychopharmacol. 2017 Jun;31(6):750-756. https://doi.org/10.1177/0269881117691567 Epub 2017 Feb 21. PMID: 28583049.

Goldschmidt, L., Day, N. L., & Richardson, G. A. (2000). Effects of prenatal marijuana exposure on child behavior problems at age 10. Neurotoxicology and teratology, 22(3), 325-336. https://doi.org/10.1016/S0892-0362(00)00066-0

Gorzalczany S, Moscatelli V, Ferraro G. Artemisia copa aqueous extract as vasorelaxant and hypotensive agent. J Ethnopharmacol. 2013 Jun 21;148(1):56-61. https://doi.org/10.1016/j.jep.2013.03.061

Gorzalka, B. B., Hill, M. N., & Chang, S. C. (2010). Male–female differences in the effects of cannabinoids on sexual behavior and gonadal hormone function. Hormones and behavior, 58(1), 91-99. https://doi.org/10.1016/j.yhbeh.2009.08.009

Goyal RK, Hirano I. The enteric nervous system. N Engl J Med. 1996 Apr 25;334(17):1106-15. https://doi.org/10.1056/nejm199604253341707

Granja AG, Carrillo-Salinas F, Pagani A, Gomez-Canas M, Negri R, Navarrete C, Mecha M, Mestre L, Fiebich BL, Cantarero I, Calzado MA, Bellido ML, Fernandez-Ruiz J, Appendino G, Guaza C, Munoz E. 2012. A Cannabigerol Quinone Alleviates Neuroinflammation in a Chronic Model of Multiple Sclerosis. J Neuroimmune Pharmacol. 7: 1002-1016. https://doi.org/10.1007/s11481-012-9399-3

Grayson L, Vines B, Nichol K, Szaflarski JP; UAB CBD Program. An interaction between warfarin and cannabidiol, a case report. Epilepsy Behav Case Rep. 2017 Oct 12;9:10-11. https://doi.org/10.1016/j.ebcr.2017.10.001

Grazia Cascio M, Minassi A, Ligresti A, Appendino G, Burstein S, Di Marzo V. A structure-activity relationship study on N-arachidonoyl-amino acids as possible endogenous inhibitors of fatty acid amide hydrolase. Biochem Biophys Res Commun. 2004 Jan 30;314(1):192-6. https://doi.org/10.1016/j.bbrc.2003.12.075 PMID: 14715265.

Grierson, GA. 1894. The hemp plant in Sanskrit and Hindi literature. Indian Antiquary. 260-262.

Groce JW, Jones LA. Carbohydrate and cyclitol content of cannabis. J Agric Food Chem. 1973 Mar-Apr;21(2):211-4. https://doi/10.1021/jf60186a003

Guo T , Liu Q , Hou P , Li F , Guo S , Song W , Zhang H , Liu X , Zhang S , Zhang J , Ho CT , Bai N . Stilbenoids and cannabinoids from the leaves of Cannabis sativa f. sativa with potential reverse cholesterol transport activity. Food Funct. 2018 Dec 13;9(12):6608-6617. https://doi.org/10.1039/c8fo01896k

Guzman M. 2003. Cannabinoids: potential anticancer agents. Nat Rev Cancer 3(10):745-755. https://doi.org/10.1038/nrc1188

Hall, W, Degenhardt, L. 2009. Adverse health effects of non-medical cannabis use. Lancet. 374:1383-91. https://doi.org/10.1016/s0140-6736(09)61037-0

Hamadeh, R, Adehali, A, Locsley, RM, York MK. 1988. Fatal Aspergillosis associated with smoking contaminated marijuana, in a marrow transplant recipient. Chest. 94(2):432-433 https://doi.org/10.1378/chest.94.2.432

Hamberg K. Gender bias in medicine. Womens Health (Lond). 2008 May;4(3):237-43. https://doi.org/10.2217/17455057.4.3.237

Hampson AJ, Grimaldi M, Axelrod J, Wink D. 1998. Cannabidiol and THC are neuroprotective antioxidants. PNAS. 95(14):8268-8273. https://doi.org/10.1073/pnas.95.14.8268

Hanus L, Abu-Lafi S, Fride E, Breuer A, Vogel Z, Shalev DE, Kustanovich I, Mechoulam R. 2-arachidonyl glyceryl ether, an endogenous agonist of the cannabinoid CB1 receptor. Proc Natl Acad Sci U S A. 2001 Mar 27;98(7):3662-5. https://doi.org/10.1073/pnas.061029898

Hanuš LO, Meyer SM, Muñoz E, Taglialatela-Scafati O, Appendino G. Phytocannabinoids: a unified critical inventory. Nat Prod Rep. 2016 Nov 23;33(12):1357-1392. https://doi.org10.1039/c6np00074f  PMID: 27722705.

Harris B (2010). Phytotherapeutic uses of essential oils. In: Baser KHC, Buchbauer G (eds). Handbook of Essential Oils: Science, Technology, and Applications. CRC Press: Boca Raton, FL, pp. 315–352.

Hart S, Fischer OM, Ullrich A. 2004. Cannabinoids induce cancer cell proliferation via tumor necrosis factor alpha-converting enzyme (TACE/ADAM17)-mediated transactivation of the epidermal growth factor receptor. Cancer Res. 64(6):1943-1950. https://doi.org/10.1158/0008-5472.can-03-3720

Hashibe M, Ford DE, Zhang ZF. 2002. Marijuana smoking and head and neck cancer. J Clin Pharmacol. 42:103S-107S https://doi.org/10.1002/j.1552-4604.2002.tb06010.x

Hatoum NS, Davis WM, Elsohly MA, Turner CE. 1981. Cannabichromene and delta-9-tetrahydrocannabinol: Interactions relative to lethality, hypothermia and hexobarbital hypnosis. Gen Pharmacol. 12(5):357-362. https://doi.org/10.1016/0306-3623(81)90090-2

Hauer D, Ratano P, Morena M, Scaccianoce S, Briegel I, Palmery M, Cuomo V, Roozendaal B, Schelling G, Campolongo P. Propofol enhances memory formation via an interaction with the endocannabinoid system. Anesthesiology. 2011 Jun;114(6):1380-8. https://doi.org/10.1097/aln.0b013e31821c120e

Hauer D, Schelling G, Gola H, Campolongo P, Morath J, Roozendaal B, Hamuni G, Karabatsiakis A, Atsak P, Vogeser M, Kolassa IT. Plasma concentrations of endocannabinoids and related primary fatty acid amides in patients with post-traumatic stress disorder. PLoS One. 2013 May 7;8(5):e62741. https://doi.org/10.1371/journal.pone.0062741  PMID: 23667516; PMCID: PMC3647054.

Haustveit G, Wold JK. Some carbohydrates of low molecular weight present in Cannabis sativa L. Carbohydr Res. 1973 Aug;29(2):325-9. https://doi/10.1016/s0008-6215(00)83018-9

Hayes JS, Lampart R, Dreher MC, Morgan L. 1991. Five-year Follow-Up of Rural Jamaican Children Whose Mothers Used Marijuana During Pregnancy. West Indian Med J. 40(3): 120-123. https://pubmed.ncbi.nlm.nih.gov/1957518/

He M, Min JW, Kong WL, He XH, Li JX, Peng BW. A review on the pharmacological effects of vitexin and isovitexin. Fitoterapia. 2016 Dec;115:74-85. https://doi.org/10.1016/j.fitote.2016.09.011

Hemann MT, Greider CW. Wild-derived inbred mouse strains have short telomeres. Nucleic Acids Res. 2000 Nov 15;28(22):4474-8. https://doi.org/10.1093/nar/28.22.4474

Hendriks H, Malingré TM, Batterman S, Bos R (1975). Mono- and sesqui-terpene hydrocarbons of the eseential oil of Cannabis sativa. Phytochem 14: 814–815. https://doi.org/10.1016/0031-9422%2875%2983045-7

Hendriks H, Malingré TM, Batterman S, Bos R (1977). Alkanes of the essential oil of Cannabis sativa. Phytochem 16: 719–721. https://doi.org/10.1016/S0031-9422(00)89239-0

Hendrix PF, Parmelee RW, Crossley Jr. DA, Coleman DC, Odum EP, Groffman PM. 2014. Detritus Food Webs in Conventional and No-tillage Agroecosystems. BioScience. 36 (6):374-380. https://doi.org/10.2307/1310259

Herkenham, M.; Lynn, A.B.; Little, M.D.; Johnson, M.R.; Melvin, L.S.; de Costa, B.R.; Rice, K.C. Cannabinoid receptor localization in brain. Proc. Natl. Acad. Sci. USA 1930, 87, 1932–1936. https://doi.org/10.1073/pnas.87.5.1932

Herrmann ES, Weerts EM, Vandrey R. Sex differences in cannabis withdrawal symptoms among treatment-seeking cannabis users. Exp Clin Psychopharmacol. 2015 Dec;23(6):415-21. https://doi.org/10.1037/pha0000053

Hetterscheid, W. L. A., & Brandenburg, W. A. (1995). Culton versus Taxon: Conceptual Issues in Cultivated Plant Systematics. Taxon, 44(2), 161–175. https://doi.org/10.2307/1222439

Hill AJ, Weston SE, Jones NA, Smith I, Bevan SA, Williamson EM, Stephens GJ, Williams CM, Whalley BJ. Δ⁹-Tetrahydrocannabivarin suppresses in vitro epileptiform and in vivo seizure activity in adult rats. Epilepsia. 2010 Aug;51(8):1522-32. https://doi.org/10.1111/j.1528-1167.2010.02523.x

Hill M, Miller G, Ho W, Gorzalka B, Hillard C. 2008. Serum endocannabinoid content is altered in females with depressive disorders: a preliminary report. Pharmacopsychiatry. 41(2):48–53.

Hill MN, Gorzalka BB. Is there a role for the endocannabinoid system in the etiology and treatment of melancholic depression? Behav Pharmacol. 2005 Sep;16(5-6):333-52. https://doi.org/10.1097/00008877-200509000-00006

Hill TDM, Cascio M-G, Romano B, Duncan M, Pertwee RG, Williams CM, Whalley BJ, Hill AJ. 2013. Cannabidivarin-rich cannabis extracts are anticonvulsant in mouse and rat via a CB1 receptor-independent mechanism. Br J Phar. 170:679-692. https://doi.org/10.1111/bph.12321

Hill, M.N.; McLaughlin, R.J.; Morrish, A.C.; Viau, V.; Floresco, S.B.; Hillard, C.J.; Gorzalka, B.B. Suppression of amygdalar endocannabinoid signaling by stress contributes to activation of the hypothalamic–pituitary–adrenal axis. Neuropsychopharmacology 2009, 34, 2733. doi.org/10.1038/npp.2009.114

Hillestad A, Wold JK, Paulsen BS. Structural studies of water-soluble glycoproteins from Cannabis sativa L. Carbohydr Res. 1977 Aug;57:135-44. https://doi.org/10.1016/s0008-6215(00)81926-6

Hillig K. 2004. A chemotaxonomic analysis of terpenoid variation in Cannabis. Biochemical Systematics and Ecology. 32(10): 875-891. https://doi.org/10.1016/j.bse.2004.04.004

Hillig, K.W. Genetic evidence for speciation in Cannabis (Cannabaceae). Genet Resour Crop Evol 52, 161–180 (2005). https://doi.org/10.1007/s10722-003-4452-y

Hoferl M, Krist S, Buchbauer G. 2006. Chirality influences the effects of linalool on physiological parameters of stress. Planta Med. 72(13): 1188-1192. https://doi.org/10.1055/s-2006-947202

Hollister LE. Structure-activity relationships in man of cannabis constituents, and homologs and metabolites of delta9-tetrahydrocannabinol. Pharmacology. 1974;11(1):3-11. https://doi.org/10.1159/000136462

Holt AK, Poklis JL, Peace MR. Δ8-THC, THC-O Acetates and CBD-di-O Acetate: Emerging Synthetic Cannabinoids Found in Commercially Sold Plant Material and Gummy Edibles. J Anal Toxicol. 2022 Jun 8:bkac036. https://doi.org/10.1093/jat/bkac036

Huestis MA. 2007. Human Cannabinoid Pharmacokinetics. Chem biodivers. 4(8): 1770-1804. https://doi.org/10.1002%2Fcbdv.200790152

Iannotti FA, De Maio F, Panza E, Appendino G, Taglialatela-Scafati O, De Petrocellis L, Amodeo P, Vitale RM. Identification and Characterization of Cannabimovone, a Cannabinoid from Cannabis sativa, as a Novel PPARγ Agonist via a Combined Computational and Functional Study. Molecules. 2020 Mar 3;25(5):1119. https://doi.org/10.3390/molecules25051119

Iffland K and Grotenhermen F. 2017. An Update on Safety and Side Effects of Cannabidiol: A Review of Clinical Data and Relevant Animal Studies. Cannabis and Cannabinoid Research. Vol. 2.1. http://doi.org/10.1089/can.2016.0034

Imran M, Rauf A, Abu-Izneid T, Nadeem M, Shariati MA, Khan IA, Imran A, Orhan IE, Rizwan M, Atif M, Gondal TA, Mubarak MS. Luteolin, a flavonoid, as an anticancer agent: A review. Biomed Pharmacother. 2019 Apr;112:108612. https://doi.org/10.1016/j.biopha.2019.108612

International Code of Nomenclature for Cultivated Plants – Eighth Edition. Page 154

Ipser J, Seedat S, Stein DJ. Pharmacotherapy for post-traumatic stress disorder - a systematic review and meta-analysis. S Afr Med J. 2006 Oct;96(10):1088-96. https://pubmed.ncbi.nlm.nih.gov/17164942/

Ismail M (2006). Central properties and chemcial composition of Ocimum basilicum essential oil. Pharm Biol 44: 619–626. https://doi.org/10.1080/13880200600897544

Ito K, Ito M. The sedative effect of inhaled terpinolene in mice and its structure-activity relationships. J Nat Med. 2013 Oct;67(4):833-7. https://doi.org/10.1007/s11418-012-0732-1

Iuvone T, Esposito G, Esposito R, Santamaria R, Di Rosa M, Izzo AA. 2004. Neuroprotective effect of cannabidiol, a non-psychoactive component from Cannabis sativa, on beta-amyloid-induced toxicity in PC12 cells. Journal of Neurochem. 89:134-141. https://doi.org/10.1111/j.1471-4159.2003.02327.x

Izzo AA, Sharkey KA. Cannabinoids and the gut: new developments and emerging concepts. Pharmacol Ther. 2010 Apr;126(1):21-38. https://doi.org/10.1016/j.pharmthera.2009.12.005

Jehanli, A., Brannan, S., Moore, L., & Spiehler, V. R. (2001). Blind trials of an onsite saliva drug test for marijuana and opiates. Journal of Forensic Science, 46(5), 1214-1220. https://pubmed.ncbi.nlm.nih.gov/11569567/

Jiang, W., Zhang, Y., Xiao, L., Van Cleemput, J., Ji, S. P., Bai, G., & Zhang, X. (2005). Cannabinoids promote embryonic and adult hippocampus neurogenesis and produce anxiolytic-and antidepressant-like effects. The Journal of clinical investigation, 115(11), 3104-3116. https://doi.org/10.1172/JCI25509

Jikomes N, Zoorob M. The Cannabinoid Content of Legal Cannabis in Washington State Varies Systematically Across Testing Facilities and Popular Consumer Products. Sci Rep. 2018 Mar 14;8(1):4519. https://doi.org/10.1038/s41598-018-22755-2 Erratum in: Sci Rep. 2020 Aug 27;10(1):14406.

Jirovetz L, Buchbauer G, Jager W, Woidich A, Nikiforov A (1992). Analysis of fragrance compounds in blood samples of mice by gas chromatography, mass spectrometry, GC/FTIR and GC/AES after inhalation of sandalwood oil. Biomed Chromatogr 6: 133–134. https://doi.org/10.1002/bmc.1130060307

Joffre J, Wong E, Lawton S, Lloyd E, Nguyen N, Xu F, Sempio C, Kobzik L, Zlatanova I, Schumacher M, Klawitter J, Su H, Rabl K, Wilhelmsen K, Yeh CC, Hellman J. N-Oleoyl dopamine induces IL-10 via central nervous system TRPV1 and improves endotoxemia and sepsis outcomes. J Neuroinflammation. 2022 May 24;19(1):118. https://doi.org/10.1186/s12974-022-02485-z PMID: 35610647; PMCID: PMC9131699.

Johnson JR, Jennison TA, Peat MA, Foltz RL (1984). "Stability of delta 9-tetrahydrocannabinol (THC), 11-hydroxy-THC, and 11-nor-9-carboxy-THC in blood and plasma". Journal of analytical toxicology 8 (5): 202–4. https://doi.org/10.1093/jat/8.5.202

Johnson TN. (2008). The problems in scaling adult drug doses to children. Archives of Disease in Childhood. 93(3):207-211 https://doi.org/10.1136/adc.2006.114835

Jones NA, Hill AJ, Smith I, Bevan SA, Williams CM, Whalley BJ, Stephens GJ. Cannabidiol displays antiepileptiform and antiseizure properties in vitro and in vivo. J Pharmacol Exp Ther. 2010 Feb;332(2):569-77. https://doi.org/10.1124/jpet.109.159145 Epub 2009 Nov 11. PMID: 19906779; PMCID: PMC2819831.

Jones, D.R. Plant Viruses Transmitted by Thrips. Eur J Plant Pathol 113, 119–157 (2005). https://doi.org/10.1007/s10658-005-2334-1

Juergens UR, Dethlefsen U, Steinkamp G, Gillissen A, Repges R, Vetter H. 2003. Anti-Inflammatory activity of 1.8-cineol (Eucalyptol) in bronchial asthma: a double-blind placebo-controlled trial. Respir Med. 97(3):250-256. https://doi.org/10.1053/rmed.2003.1432

Julien MS. Chirugie chinoise. Substance anesthétique employée en Chine, dans le commencement du III-ième siecle de notre ère, pour paralyser momentanement la sensibilité. Comptes Rendus Hebdomadaires de l'Académie des Sciences. 1849. 28:223–229.

Kamatou, G.P.P., Viljoen, A.M. A Review of the Application and Pharmacological Properties of α-Bisabolol and α-Bisabolol-Rich Oils. J Am Oil Chem Soc 87, 1–7 (2010). https://doi.org/10.1007/s11746-009-1483-3

Kametani, T., & Furuyama, H. (1987). Synthesis of vitamin D3 and related compounds. Medicinal research reviews, 7(2), 147-171. https://doi.org/10.1002/med.2610070202

Kano, M., Ohno-Shosaku, T., Hashimotodani, Y., Uchigashima, M., Watanabe, M., 2009. Endocannabinoid-mediated control of synaptic transmission. Physiol. Rev. 89, 309–380. https://doi.org/10.1152/physrev.00019.2008

Karniol IG, Carlini EA. Pharmacological interaction between cannabidiol and delta 9-tetrahydrocannabinol. Psychopharmacologia. 1973 Oct 23;33(1):53-70. https://doi.org/10.1007/bf00428793

Karschner, E., Darwin, W., McMahon, R., Liu, F., Wright, S., Goodwin, R. and Huestis, M. (2011), Subjective and Physiological Effects After Controlled Sativex and Oral THC Administration. Clinical Pharmacology & Therapeutics, 89: 400-407. https://doi.org/10.1038/clpt.2010.318

Kaur R, Sidhu P, Singh S. What failed BIA 10-2474 Phase I clinical trial? Global speculations and recommendations for future Phase I trials. J Pharmacol Pharmacother. 2016 Jul-Sep;7(3):120-6. https://doi.org/10.4103%2F0976-500X.189661

Keifer M, Mahurin R. 1997. Chronic neurologic effects of pesticide overexposure. Occup. Med. 12:291-304 https://doi.org/10.1289/ehp.95103s8205

Kessler RC, Sonnega A, Bromet E, Hughes M, Nelson CB. Posttraumatic stress disorder in the National Comorbidity Survey. Arch Gen Psychiatry. 1995 Dec;52(12):1048-60. https://doi.org/10.1001/archpsyc.1995.03950240066012

Khan AU, Gilani AH. Selective bronchodilatory effect of Rooibos tea (Aspalathus linearis) and its flavonoid, chrysoeriol. Eur J Nutr. 2006 Dec;45(8):463-9. https://doi.org/10.1007/s00394-006-0620-0

Kiers ET, MGA van der Heijden. 2006. Mutualistic stability in the arbuscular mycorrhizal symbiosis: exploring hypotheses of evolutionary cooperation. Ecology. 87(7):1627-1636. https://doi.org/10.1890/0012-9658(2006)87[1627:msitam]2.0.co;2

Killestein J, ELJ H, M Reif, B Blauw, M Smits, BMJ Uitdehaag, L Nagelkerken, CH Polman. (2003). Immunomodulatory effects of orally administered cannabinoids in multiple sclerosis. Journal of Neuroimmunology. 137:140-143 https://doi.org/10.1016/s0165-5728(03)00045-6

Kim HY, Spector AA. N-Docosahexaenoylethanolamine: A neurotrophic and neuroprotective metabolite of docosahexaenoic acid. Mol Aspects Med. 2018 Dec;64:34-44. https://doi.org/10.1016/j.mam.2018.03.004

Kinsey SG, Nomura DK, O'Neal ST, Long JZ, Mahadevan A, Cravatt BF, Grider JR, Lichtman AH. 2011. Inhibition of monoacylglycerol lipase attenuates nonsteroidal anti-inflammatory drug-induced gastric hemorrhages in mice. J Pharmacol Exp Ther. 338(3):795-802. https://doi.org/10.1124/jpet.110.175778

Knut Erik Berge (2003) Sitosterolemia: a gateway to new knowledge about cholesterol metabolism, Annals of Medicine, 35:7, 502-511, https://doi.org/10.1080/07853890310014588

Köllner TG, Held M, Lenk C, Hiltpold I, Turlings TC, Gershenzon J, Degenhardt J. A maize (E)-beta-caryophyllene synthase implicated in indirect defense responses against herbivores is not expressed in most American maize varieties. Plant Cell. 2008 Feb;20(2):482-94. https://doi.org/10.1105/tpc.107.051672 Epub 2008 Feb 22. PMID: 18296628; PMCID: PMC2276456.

Kong, Lu, Meng Tang, Ting Zhang, Dayong Wang, Ke Hu, Weiqi Lu, Chao Wei, Geyu Liang, and Yuepu Pu. 2014. "Nickel Nanoparticles Exposure and Reproductive Toxicity in Healthy Adult Rats" International Journal of Molecular Sciences 15, no. 11: 21253-21269. https://doi.org/10.3390/ijms151121253

Korte G, Dreiseitel A, Schreier P, Oehme A, Locher S, Hajak G, Sand PG. An examination of anthocyanins' and anthocyanidins' affinity for cannabinoid receptors. J Med Food. 2009 Dec;12(6):1407-10. https://doi.org/10.1089/jmf.2008.0243

Koskinen J, Löhönen J, Koponen H, Isohanni M, Miettunen J. Rate of cannabis use disorders in clinical samples of patients with schizophrenia: a meta-analysis. Schizophr Bull. 2010 Nov;36(6):1115-30. https://doi.org/10.1093/schbul/sbp031

Kulpa JE, Paulionis LJ, Eglit GM, Vaughn DM. Safety and tolerability of escalating cannabinoid doses in healthy cats. J Feline Med Surg. 2021 Dec;23(12):1162-1175. doi.org10.1177/1098612X211004215

Kupczyk, P, Rykala, M, Serek, P, et al. The cannabinoid receptors system in horses: Tissue distribution and cellular identification in skin. J Vet Intern Med. 2022; 36( 4): 1508- 1524. doi.org/10.1111/jvim.16467

Labib RM, Srivedavyasasri R, Youssef FS, Ross SA. Secondary metabolites isolated from Pinus roxburghii and interpretation of their cannabinoid and opioid binding properties by virtual screening and in vitro studies. Saudi Pharm J. 2018 Mar;26(3):437-444. https://doi.org/10.1016/j.jsps.2017.12.017

Lagos-Kutz, D., Potter, B., DiFonzo, C., Russell, H. and Hartman, G.L. (2018), Two Aphid Species, Phorodon cannabis and Rhopalosiphum rufiabdominale, Identified as Potential Pests on Industrial Hemp, Cannabis sativa L., in the US Midwest. Crop, Forage & Turfgrass Management, 4: 1-3 180032. https://doi.org/10.2134/cftm2018.04.0032

Lah TT, Novak M, Pena Almidon MA, Marinelli O, Žvar Baškovič B, Majc B, Mlinar M, Bošnjak R, Breznik B, Zomer R, Nabissi M. Cannabigerol Is a Potential Therapeutic Agent in a Novel Combined Therapy for Glioblastoma. Cells. 2021 Feb 5;10(2):340. https://doi.org/10.3390/cells10020340/

Lahdimawan, A., 2013. Effect of Ramadan fasting on endorphin and endocannabinoid level in serum, PBMC and macrophage. https://repo-dosen.ulm.ac.id/handle/123456789/17325

Lamarck, J.B. de., 1785. Encyclope´die me´thodique. Botanique. 1 part 2, Panckoucke, Paris, pp. 694–695.

Landa, L., SULCOVA, A., & Gbelec, P. (2016). The use of cannabinoids in animals and therapeutic implications for veterinary medicine: a review. Veterinární medicína, 61(3). doi.org/10.17221/8762-VETMED

Langenheim JH (1994). Higher plant terpenoids: a phytocentric overview of their ecological roles. J Chem Ecol 20: 1223–1279. https://doi.org/10.1007/bf02059809

Lanzarotta, A., Falconer, T. M., Flurer, R., & Wilson, R. A. (2020). Hydrogen bonding between tetrahydrocannabinol and vitamin E acetate in unvaped, aerosolized, and condensed aerosol e-liquids. Analytical chemistry, 92(3), 2374-2378. https://doi.org/10.1021/acs.analchem.9b05536

Lata H, S Chandra, IA Khan, MA ElSohly. 2010b. High Frequency Plant Regeneration from Leaf Derived Callus of High delta-9-Tetrahydrocannabinol Yielding Cannabis sativa L. Planta Med 76:1629-1633 https://doi.org/10.1055/s-0030-1249773

Legault J, A Pichette. (2010) Potentiating effect of B-caryophyllene on anticancer activity of a-humulene, isocaryophyllene and paclitaxel. J Parm and Pharmacol. 59:1643-1647 https://doi.org/10.1211/jpp.59.12.0005

Lemberger L, Dalton B, Martz R, Rodda B, Forney R. Clinical studies on the interaction of psychopharmacologic agents with marihuana. Ann N Y Acad Sci. 1976;281:219-28. https://doi.org/10.1111/j.1749-6632.1976.tb27933.x

Lena Normén, Paresh Dutta, Ågot Lia, Henrik Andersson, Soy sterol esters and β-sitostanol ester as inhibitors of cholesterol absorption in human small bowel , The American Journal of Clinical Nutrition, Volume 71, Issue 4, April 2000, Pages 908–913, https://doi.org/10.1093/ajcn/71.4.908

Leonti M, Casu L, Raduner S, Cottiglia F, Floris C, Altmann KH, Gertsch J. Falcarinol is a covalent cannabinoid CB1 receptor antagonist and induces pro-allergic effects in skin. Biochem Pharmacol. 2010 Jun 15;79(12):1815-26. https://doi.org/10.1016/j.bcp.2010.02.015

Leweke FM, Piomelli D, Pahlisch F, Muhl D, Gerth CW, Hoyer C, Klosterkötter J, Hellmich M, Koethe D. Cannabidiol enhances anandamide signaling and alleviates psychotic symptoms of schizophrenia. Transl Psychiatry. 2012 Mar 20;2(3):e94. https://doi.org/10.1038/tp.2012.15

Leweke, F.M., Koethe, D., 2008. Cannabis and psychiatric disorders: it is not only addiction. Addiction Biology 13, 264–275. https://doi.org/10.1111/j.1369-1600.2008.00106.x

Li J, Daughters RS, Bullis C, Bengiamin R, Stucky MW, Brennan J, et al. The cannabinoid receptor agonist WIN 55,212-2 mesylate blocks the development of hyperalgesia produced by capsaicin in rats. Pain 1999; 81:25–33. https://doi.org/10.1016/s0304-3959(98)00263-2

Li Y, Owyang C. Musings on the wanderer: what's new in our understanding of vago-vagal reflexes? V. Remodeling of vagus and enteric neural circuitry after vagal injury. Am J Physiol Gastrointest Liver Physiol. 2003 Sep;285(3):G461-9. https://doi.org/10.1152/ajpgi.00119.2003

Li Y, Yao J, Han C, Yang J, Chaudhry MT, Wang S, Liu H, Yin Y. Quercetin, Inflammation and Immunity. Nutrients. 2016 Mar 15;8(3):167. https://doi.org/10.3390/nu8030167

Ligresti A, Moriello AS, Starowicz K, Matias I, Pisanti S, De Petrocellis L, Laezza C, Portella G, Bifulco M, Di Marzo V. Antitumor activity of plant cannabinoids with emphasis on the effect of cannabidiol on human breast carcinoma. J Pharmacol Exp Ther. 2006 Sep;318(3):1375-87. https://doi.org/10.1124/jpet.106.105247

Linciano P, Citti C, Luongo L, Belardo C, Maione S, Vandelli MA, Forni F, Gigli G, Laganà A, Montone CM, Cannazza G. Isolation of a High-Affinity Cannabinoid for the Human CB1 Receptor from a Medicinal Cannabis sativa Variety: Δ9-Tetrahydrocannabutol, the Butyl Homologue of Δ9-Tetrahydrocannabinol. J Nat Prod. 2020 Jan 24;83(1):88-98. https://doi.org/10.1021/acs.jnatprod.9b00876

Linger P, J Mussig, H Fischer, J Kobert. (2002). Industrial hemp (Cannabis sativa L.) growing on heavy metal contaminated soil: fibre quality and phytoremediation potential. Ind Crop and Prod. 16:33-42 https://doi.org/10.1016/S0926-6690(02)00005-5

Linnaeus, C. 1753. Species Plantarum 2: 1027. Salvius, Stockholm. [Facsimile edition, 1957–1959. Ray Society, London, U.K.]

Loewe S. 1944. Studies on the pharmacology of marihuana The Marihuana Problems in the City of New Yorked. The Mayor's Committee on Marihuana. pp. 149–212.Lancaster, PA: The Jaques Cattell Press

Lopes NP, Kato MJ, Andrade EH, Maia JG, Yoshida M, Planchart AR et al. (1999). Antimalarial use of volatile oil from leaves of Virola surinamensis (Rol.) Warb. by Waiapi Amazon Indians. J Ethnopharmacol 67: 313–319. https://doi.org/10.1016/s0378-8741(99)00072-0

Lorenzetti BB, Souza GE, Sarti SJ, Santos Filho D, Ferreira SH (1991). Myrcene mimics the peripheral analgesic activity of lemongrass tea. J Ethnopharmacol 34: 43–48. https://doi.org/10.1016/0378-8741(91)90187-i

Louw DR, Yang FW, Sutherland GR. 2000. The effect of THC on forebrain ischemia in rat. Brain Research. 857:183-187. https://doi.org/10.1016/s0006-8993(99)02422-1

Lozano I. 2001. The therapeutic use of Cannabis sativa L. in Arabic medicine. Journal of Cannabis Therapeutics. 1: 63-70. https://doi.org/10.3989/asclepio.1997.v49.i2.373

Lutz B. The endoc annabinoid system and extinction learning. Mol Neurobiol. 2007 Aug;36(1):92-101. https://doi.org/10.1007/s12035-007-8004-x

Lykhmus O, Uspenska K, Koval L, Lytovchenko D, Voytenko L, Horid'ko T, Kosiakova H, Gula N, Komisarenko S, Skok M. N-Stearoylethanolamine protects the brain and improves memory of mice treated with lipopolysaccharide or immunized with the extracellular domain of α7 nicotinic acetylcholine receptor. Int Immunopharmacol. 2017 Nov;52:290-296. https://doi.org/10.1016/j.intimp.2017.09.023  Epub 2017 Sep 28. PMID: 28963942.

Ma EL, Li YC, Tsuneki H, Xiao JF, Xia MY, Wang MW, Kimura I. 2008. B-Eudesmol suppresses tumour growth through inhibition of tumour neovascularisation and tumour cell proliferation. Journal of Asian Natural Products Research. 10(2):159-167. https://doi.org/10.1080/10286020701394332

Machado Bergamaschi, M., Helena Costa Queiroz, R., Waldo Zuardi, A., & Crippa, A. S. (2011). Safety and side effects of cannabidiol, a Cannabis sativa constituent. Current drug safety, 6(4), 237-249. https://doi.org/10.2174/157488611798280924

Maguire W, et al. 2018. Survey of mycotoxin residues in Oregon cannabis crops by LC-MS/MS [Conference Poster]. Cannabis Science Conference, Portland, OR, 2018.

Malfitano AM, Ciaglia E, Gangemi G, Gazzerro P, LaezzaC, Bifulco M. 2011. Update on the endocannabinoid system as an anticancer target. Expert Opin Ther Targets. 15(3):297-308. https://doi.org/10.1517/14728222.2011.553606

Malingre T, Hendriks H, Batterman S, Bos R, Visser J (1975). The essential oil of Cannabis sativa. Planta Med 28: 56–61. https://doi.org/10.1055/s-0028-1097829

Marcotte TD, Umlauf A, Grelotti DJ, et al. Driving Performance and Cannabis Users' Perception of Safety: A Randomized Clinical Trial . JAMA Psychiatry. 2022;79(3):201–209. https://doi.org/10.1001/jamapsychiatry.2021.4037

Marika Heblinski, Marina Santiago, Charlotte Fletcher, Jordyn Stuart, Mark Connor, Iain S. McGregor, and Jonathon C. Arnold.Terpenoids Commonly Found in Cannabis sativa Do Not Modulate the Actions of Phytocannabinoids or Endocannabinoids on TRPA1 and TRPV1 Channels.Cannabis and Cannabinoid Research.Dec 2020.305-317. http://doi.org/10.1089/can.2019.0099

Marine KR, Cech JJ. Effects of High Water Temperature on Growth, Smoltification, and Predator Avoidance in Juvenile Sacramento River Chinook Salmon. North Am J Fish Manag. 2004; 24(1):198–210. https://doi.org/10.1577/M02-142

Marinelli S, Di Marzo V, Florenzano F, Fezza F, Viscomi MT, van der Stelt M, Bernardi G, Molinari M, Maccarrone M, Mercuri NB. 2007. N-Arachidonoyl-Dopamine Tunes Synaptic Transmission onto Dopaminergic Neurons by Activating both Cannabinoid and Vallinoid Receptors. Neuropsychopharmacology. 32:298-308. https://doi.org/10.1038/sj.npp.1301118

Marsicano G, Lafenêtre P. Roles of the endocannabinoid system in learning and memory. Curr Top Behav Neurosci. 2009;1:201-30. https://doi.org/10.1007/978-3-540-88955-7_8

Martin BR, Jefferson R, Winckler R, Wiley JL, Huffman JW, Crocker PJ, Saha B, Razdan RK. Manipulation of the tetrahydrocannabinol side chain delineates agonists, partial agonists, and antagonists. J Pharmacol Exp Ther. 1999 Sep;290(3):1065-79. PMID: 10454479.

McDaniel C, Mallampati SR, Wise A. Metals in Cannabis Vaporizer Aerosols: Sources, Possible Mechanisms, and Exposure Profiles. Chem Res Toxicol. 2021 Nov 15;34(11):2331-2342. https://doi.org/10.1021/acs.chemrestox.1c00230

McDougle DR, Watson JE, et al. 2017. Anti-inflammatory omega-3 endocannabinoid epoxides. Proceedings of the National Academy of Sciences Jul 2017, 114 (30) E6034-E6043; https://doi.org/10.1073/pnas.1610325114

McGinty D, Letizia CS, Api AM (2010). Fragrance material review on phytol. Food Chem Toxicol 48 (Suppl. 3): S59–S63. https://doi.org/10.1016/j.fct.2009.11.012

McKallip RJ, Nagarkatti M, Nagarkatti PS. 2005. Delta-9-tetrahydrocannabinol enhances breast cancer growth and metastasis by suppression of the antitumor immune response. J Immunol. 174(6):3281-3289. https://doi.org/10.4049/jimmunol.174.6.3281

McKernan KJ, Helbert Y, Kane LT, Ebling H, Zhang L, Liu B, Eaton Z, McLaughlin S, Kingan S, Baybayan P, Concepcion G, Jordan M, Riva A, Barbazuk W, Harkins T. 2020. Sequence and Annotation of 42 Cannabis Genomes Reveals Extensive Copy Number Variation in Cannabinoid Synthesis and Pathogen Resistance Genes. bioRxiv. Pre-print. Published January 05, 2020.

McLoughlin BC, Pushpa-Rajah JA, Gillies D, Rathbone J, Variend H, Kalakouti E, Kyprianou K. Cannabis and schizophrenia. Cochrane Database Syst Rev. 2014 Oct 14;(10):CD004837. https://doi.org/10.1002/14651858.cd004837.pub3

McPartland J. 2018. Cannabis Systematics at the Levels of Family, Genus, and Species. Cannabis and Cannabinoid Research. Dec 2018. 203-212. https://doi.org/10.1089/can.2018.0039

McPartland JM, Guy GW, Di Marzo V. Care and feeding of the endocannabinoid system: a systematic review of potential clinical interventions that upregulate the endocannabinoid system. PLoS One. 2014 Mar 12;9(3):e89566. https://doi.org/10.1371/journal.pone.0089566

McPartland JM, Pruitt PL. Medical marijuana and its use by the immunocompromised. Altern Ther Health Med. 1997 May;3(3):39-45. https://pubmed.ncbi.nlm.nih.gov/9141290/

McPartland JM, Russo EB. 2001b. Cannabis and Cannabis extracts: greater than the sum of their parts? J Cannabis Therap 1: 103–132.

McPartland JM, Small E. A classification of endangered high-THC cannabis (Cannabis sativa subsp. indica) domesticates and their wild relatives. PhytoKeys. 2020 Apr 3;144:81-112. https://doi.org/10.3897/phytokeys.144.46700

McPartland, J. Cannabis: the plant, its evolution, and its genetics—with an emphasis on Italy. Rend. Fis. Acc. Lincei 31, 939–948 (2020). https://doi.org/10.1007/s12210-020-00962-2

McPartland, J. M., 1996. A review of Cannabis diseases. Journal of the International Hemp Association 3(1): 19-23. https://druglibrary.org/olsen/hemp/iha/iha03111.html

McPartland, J.; Marzo, V.D.; Petrocellis, L.D.; Mercer, A.; Glass, M. Cannabinoid receptors are absent in insects. J. Comp. Neurol. 2001, 436, 423–429. doi.org/10.1002/cne.1078

McPartland, J.M. 1996. Cannabis pests. Journal of the International Hemp Association 3(2): 49, 52-55. http://www.internationalhempassociation.org/jiha/iha03201.html

McPartland, J.M., Guy, G.W. & Hegman, W. Cannabis is indigenous to Europe and cultivation began during the Copper or Bronze age: a probabilistic synthesis of fossil pollen studies. Veget Hist Archaeobot 27, 635–648 (2018). https://doi.org/10.1007/s00334-018-0678-7

McPartland, J.M., Hegman, W. & Long, T. Cannabis in Asia: its center of origin and early cultivation, based on a synthesis of subfossil pollen and archaeobotanical studies. Veget Hist Archaeobot 28, 691–702 (2019). https://doi.org/10.1007/s00334-019-00731-8

Mechoulam R, Shvo Y. Hashish. I. The structure of cannabidiol. Tetrahedron. 1963 Dec;19(12):2073-8. https://doi.org/10.1016/0040-4020(63)85022-x

Mediavilla V, Steinemann S. 1997. Essential oil of Cannabis sativa L. strains. J Intl Hemp Assoc 4: 82–84. http://www.internationalhempassociation.org/jiha/jiha4208.html

Meehan-Atrash J, Luo W, Strongin RM. 2017. Toxicant formation in dabbing: the terpene story. ACS Omega 2017: 6112-6117 https://doi.org/10.1021/acsomega.7b01130

Meehan-Atrash J, Strongin RM. 2020. Pine rosin identified as a toxic cannabis extract adulterant. Forensic Science International. 312: 110301. https://doi.org/10.1016/j.forsciint.2020.110301

Meehan-Atrash, J., 2021. Chemical Characterization of Toxicologically Relevant Molecules in Cannabis Concentrates and Vaporizer Aerosols (Doctoral dissertation, Portland State University).

Mehmedic Z, Radwan MM, Wanas AS, Khan IA, Cutler SJ, ElSohly MA. 2014. In vitro binding affinity to human cb1 and cb2 receptors and antimicrobial activity of volatile oil from high potency Cannabis sativa. Planta medica. 80(10) https://doi.org/10.1055/s-0034-1382491

Mehrpouya-Bahrami P, Chitrala KN, Ganewatta MS, Tang C, Murphy EA, Enos RT, Velazquez KT, McCellan J, Nagarkatti M, Nagarkatti P. 2017. Blockade of CB1 cannabinoid receptor alters gut microbiota and attenuates inflammation and diet-induced obesity. Scientific Reports. 7:15645. https://doi.org/10.1038/s41598-017-15154-6

Mercati, F.; Dall'Aglio, C.; Pascucci, L.; Boiti, C.; Ceccarelli, P. Identification of cannabinoid type 1 receptor in dog hair follicles. Acta Histochem. 2012, 114, 68–71. doi.org/10.1016/j.acthis.2011.01.003

Merkus FW. Cannabivarin and tetrahydrocannabivarin, two new constituents of hashish. Nature. 1971 Aug 20;232(5312):579-80. https://doi.org/10.1038/232579a0

Merzouki A, Mesa JM. 2002. Concerning kif, a Cannabis sativa L. preparation smoked in the Rif mountains of northern Morocco. J Ethnopharmacol 81: 403–406. https://doi.org/10.1016/s0378-8741(02)00119-8

Miagkoff, L., Girard, C. A., St-Jean, G., Richard, H., Beauchamp, G., & Laverty, S. Cannabinoid receptors are expressed in equine synovium and upregulated with synovitis. Equine Veterinary Journal. doi.org/10.1111/evj.13860

Millar, S. A., Stone, N. L., Bellman, Z. D., Yates, A. S., England, T. J., & O'Sullivan, S. E. (2019). A systematic review of cannabidiol dosing in clinical populations. British journal of clinical pharmacology, 85(9), 1888-1900. https://doi.org/10.1111/bcp.14038

Milligan G. Orthologue selectivity and ligand bias: translating the pharmacology of GPR35. Trends Pharmacol Sci 2011;32:317–25. https://doi.org/10.1016/j.tips.2011.02.002

Mills E. 2012. The carbon footprint of indoor Cannabis production. Energy Policy. Vol. 46. pp. 58-67. https://doi.org/10.1016/j.enpol.2012.03.023

Milman G, Maor Y, Abu-Lafi S, Horowitz M, Gallily R, Batkai S, Mo FM, Offertaler L, Pacher P, Kunos G, Mechoulam R. N-arachidonoyl L-serine, an endocannabinoid-like brain constituent with vasodilatory properties. Proc Natl Acad Sci U S A. 2006 Feb 14;103(7):2428-33. https://doi.org/10.1073/pnas.0510676103 Epub 2006 Feb 7. PMID: 16467152; PMCID: PMC1413724.

Miragliotta, V., Ricci, P.L., Albanese, F., Pirone, A., Tognotti, D. and Abramo, F. (2018), Cannabinoid receptor types 1 and 2 and peroxisome proliferator-activated receptor-α: distribution in the skin of clinically healthy cats and cats with hypersensitivity dermatitis. Vet Dermatol, 29: 316-e111. doi.org/10.1111/vde.12658

Mishra B, Priyadarsini KI, Kumar MS, Unnikrishnan MK, Mohan H. Effect of O-glycosilation on the antioxidant activity and free radical reactions of a plant flavonoid, chrysoeriol. Bioorg Med Chem. 2003 Jul 3;11(13):2677-85. https://doi.org/10.1016/s0968-0896(03)00232-3

Mlcek J, Jurikova T, Skrovankova S, Sochor J. Quercetin and Its Anti-Allergic Immune Response. Molecules. 2016 May 12;21(5):623. https://doi.org/10.3390/molecules21050623

Mokrysz C, Shaban N, Freeman TP, Curran HV. 2017. Acute effects of cannabis on the experience of speech illusion: a placebo-controlled study in adolescents and adults. European Neuropsychopharmacology. 27(1):S73

Moldzio R, Pacher T, Krewenka C, Kranner B, Novak J, Duvigneau JC, Rausch WD. 2012. Effects of cannabinoids Δ(9)-tetrahydrocannabinol, Δ(9)-tetrahydrocannabinolic acid and cannabidiol in MPP(+) affected murine mesencephalic cultures. Phytomedicine 19(8-9): 819–24 https://doi.org/10.1016/j.phymed.2012.04.002

Morales P, Reggio PH. An Update on Non-CB1, Non-CB2 Cannabinoid Related G-Protein-Coupled Receptors. Cannabis Cannabinoid Res. 2017 Oct 1;2(1):265-273. https://doi.org/10.1089/can.2017.0036

Moreau M, Ibeh U, Decosmo K, Bih N, Yasmin-Karim S, Toyang N, Lowe H, Ngwa W. Flavonoid Derivative of Cannabis Demonstrates Therapeutic Potential in Preclinical Models of Metastatic Pancreatic Cancer. Front Oncol. 2019 Jul 23;9:660. https://doi.org/10.3389/fonc.2019.00660

Mortazavi, N., Fathipour, Y., & Talebi, A. (2019). The efficiency of Amblyseius swirskii in control of Tetranychus urticae and Trialeurodes vaporariorum is affected by various factors. Bulletin of Entomological Research, 109(3), 365-375. https://doi.org/0.1017/S0007485318000640

Mothana RAA, Hasson SS, Schultze W, Mowitz A, Lindequist U. 2011. Phytochemical composition and in vitro antimicrobial and antioxidant activities of essential oils of three endemic Soqotraen Boswellia species. Food Chemistry. 126(3): 1149-1154. https://doi.org/10.1016/j.foodchem.2012.07.084

Moyle PB. Inland fishes of California. Berkeley: University of California Press; 2002.

Musty R, Deyo R (2006). A cannabigerol extract alters behavioral despair in an animal model of depression. Proceedings June 26; Symposium on the Cannabinoids. International Cannabinoid Research Society: Tihany, p. 32.

Musty RE, Karniol IG, Shirikawa I, Takahashi RN, Knobel E (1976). Interactions of delta-9-tetrahydrocannabinol and cannabinol in man. In: Braude

Nabavi SF, Braidy N, Gortzi O, Sobarzo-Sanchez E, Daglia M, Skalicka-Woźniak K, Nabavi SM. Luteolin as an anti-inflammatory and neuroprotective agent: A brief review. Brain Res Bull. 2015 Oct;119(Pt A):1-11. https://doi.org/10.1016/j.brainresbull.2015.09.002

Nachnani R, Raup-Konsavage WM, Vrana KE. The Pharmacological Case for Cannabigerol. J Pharmacol Exp Ther. 2021 Feb;376(2):204-212. https://doi.org10.1124/jpet.120.000340

Nachnani R, Raup-Konsavage WM, Vrana KE. The Pharmacological Case for Cannabigerol. J Pharmacol Exp Ther. 2021 Feb;376(2):204-212. https://doi.org10.1124/jpet.120.000340

Nanjwade BK, Patel DJ, Udhani RA, Manvi FV. Functions of lipids for enhancement of oral bioavailability of poorly water-soluble drugs. Sci Pharm. 2011 Oct-Dec;79(4):705-27. https://doi.org/10.3797/scipharm.1105-09

Nanni O, Amadori D, Lugaresi C, Falcini F, Scarpi E, et al. 1996. Chronic lymphoctic leukemias and non-Hodgkin's lymphoma by histological type in farming animal breeding workers: a population case-control study based on a priori exposure matrices. Occup. Environ. Med. 53:652-57

Nappe TM, Hoyte, CO. 2017. Pediatric Death Due to Myocarditis After Exposure to Cannabis. Clin Pract Cases Emerg Med. 1(3):166-170. https://doi.org/10.5811/cpcem.2017.1.33240

National Academies of Sciences, Engineering, and Medicine; Health and Medicine Division; Board on Population Health and Public Health Practice; Committee on the Health Effects of Marijuana: An Evidence Review and Research Agenda. The Health Effects of Cannabis and Cannabinoids: The Current State of Evidence and Recommendations for Research. Washington (DC): National Academies Press (US); 2017 Jan 12.

Nerio LS, Olivero-Verbel J, Stashenko E. Repellent activity of essential oils: a review. Bioresour Technol. 2010;101:372–378. https://doi.org/10.1016/j.biortech.2009.07.048

Nesic K, Ivanovic S, Nesic V. Fusarial toxins: secondary metabolites of Fusarium fungi. Rev Environ Contam Toxicol. 2014;228:101-20. https://doi.org/10.1007/978-3-319-01619-1_5

Neumeister A, Seidel J, Ragen BJ, Pietrzak RH. Translational evidence for a role of endocannabinoids in the etiology and treatment of posttraumatic stress disorder. Psychoneuroendocrinology. 2015 Jan;51:577-84. https://doi.org/10.1016/j.psyneuen.2014.10.012

Ngo ST, Quynh Anh Pham N, Thi Le L, Pham DH, Vu VV. Computational Determination of Potential Inhibitors of SARS-CoV-2 Main Protease. J Chem Inf Model. 2020 Dec 28;60(12):5771-5780. https://doi.org/10.1021/acs.jcim.0c00491

Nicholson AN, Turner C, Stone BM, Robson PJ. Effect of Delta-9-tetrahydrocannabinol and cannabidiol on nocturnal sleep and early-morning behavior in young adults. J Clin Psychopharmacol. 2004 Jun;24(3):305-13. https://doi.org/10.1097/01.jcp.0000125688.05091.8f

Nissen L, Zatta A, Stefanini I, Grandi S, Sgorbati B, Biavati B et al. (2010). Characterization and antimicrobial activity of essential oils of industrial hemp varieties (Cannabis sativa L.). Fitoterapia 81: 413–419. https://doi.org/10.1016/j.fitote.2009.11.010

Niyuhire F, Varvel SA, Martin BR, Lichtman AH. Exposure to marijuana smoke impairs memory retrieval in mice. J Pharmacol Exp Ther. 2007 Sep;322(3):1067-75. https://doi.org/10.1124/jpet.107.119594

Noma Y, Asakawa Y (2010). Biotransformation of monoterpenoids by microorganisms, insects, and mammals. In: Baser KHC, Buchbauer G (eds). Handbook of Essential Oils: Science, Technology, and Applications. CRC Press: Boca Raton, FL, pp. 585–736.

Notarnicola M, Tutino V, Tafaro A, Bianco G, Guglielmi E, Caruso MG. 2016. Dietary olive oil induces cannabinoid CB2 receptor expression in adipose tissue of ApcMin/+ transgenic mice. Nutrition and Healthy Aging. 4(1): 73–80. https://doi.org/10.3233/nha-160008

Novak J, Zitterl-Eglseer K, Deans SG, Franz CM. 2001. Essential oils of different cultivars of Cannabis sativa L. and their microbioal activity. Flavour and Fragrance Journal. 16(4):259-262. https://doi.org/10.3390/molecules25204631

Novotna, A., Mares, J., Ratcliffe, S., Novakova, I., Vachova, M., Zapletalova, O., ... & Sativex Spasticity Study Group. (2011). A randomized, double-blind, placebo-controlled, parallel-group, enriched-design study of nabiximols*(Sativex®), as add-on therapy, in subjects with refractory spasticity caused by multiple sclerosis. European journal of neurology, 18(9), 1122-1131. https://doi.org/10.1111/j.1468-1331.2010.03328.x

Nsuala BN, Enslin G, Viljoen A. "Wild cannabis": A review of the traditional use and phytochemistry of Leonotis leonurus. J Ethnopharmacol. 2015 Nov 4;174:520-39. https://doi.org/10.1016/j.jep.2015.08.013

O'Shaughnessy WB. (1838–1840). On the preparations of the Indian hemp, or gunjah (Cannabis indica); their effects on the animal system in health, and their utility in the treatment of tetanus and other convulsive diseases. Transactions of the Medical and Physical Society of Bengal, 71–102, 421–461. http://www.ncbi.nlm.nih.gov/pmc/articles/pmc5592602/

O'Shaughnessy's Online. 2014. McPartland's Correct(ed) Vernacular Nomenclature. http://www.beyondthc.com/mcpartlands-corrected-vernacular-nomenclature/

O'Sullivan SE, Kendall DA, Randall MD. 2004. Characterisation of the vasorelaxant properties of the novel endocannabinoid N-arachidonoyl-dopamine (NADA). Bri J of Pharm. 141:803-812. https://doi.org/10.1038/sj.bjp.0705643

O'Sullivan, S. E. (2015). Endocannabinoids and the cardiovascular system in health and disease. Endocannabinoids, 393-422.

Offertáler L, Mo FM, Bátkai S, Liu J, Begg M, Razdan RK, Martin BR, Bukoski RD, Kunos G. Selective ligands and cellular effectors of a G protein-coupled endothelial cannabinoid receptor. Mol Pharmacol. 2003 Mar;63(3):699-705. https://doi.org/10.1124/mol.63.3.699 PMID: 12606780.

Ogbe, R. J., Ochalefu, D. O., Mafulul, S. G., & Olaniru, O. B. (2015). A review on dietary phytosterols: Their occurrence, metabolism and health benefits. Asian J. Plant Sci. Res, 5(4), 10-21. https://hal.archives-ouvertes.fr/hal-03690226

Oka S, Nakajima K, Yamashita A, Kishimoto S, Sugiura T. Identification of GPR55 as a lysophosphatidylinositol receptor. Biochem Biophys Res Commun. 2007 Nov 3;362(4):928-34. https://doi.org/10.1016/j.bbrc.2007.08.078

Oláh A, Tóth BI, Borbíró I, Sugawara K, Szöllõsi AG, Czifra G, Pál B, Ambrus L, Kloepper J, Camera E, Ludovici M, Picardo M, Voets T, Zouboulis CC, Paus R, Bíró T. Cannabidiol exerts sebostatic and antiinflammatory effects on human sebocytes. J Clin Invest. 2014 Sep;124(9):3713-24. https://doi.org/10.1172/JCI64628

Onaivi ES, Ishiguro H, Gu S, Liu QR. 2012. CNS effects of CB2 caannabinoid receptors: beyond neuro-immuno-cannabinoid activity. J Psychopharmacol. 26(1): 92-103. https://doi.org/10.1177/0269881111400652

Oswald et al. Identification of a New Family of Prenylated Volatile Sulfur Compounds in Cannabis Revealed by Comprehensive Two-Dimensional Gas Chromatography. ACS Omega 2021, 6, 47, 31667–31676 Publication Date: November 12, 2021 https://doi.org/10.1021/acsomega.1c04196

Oz M. Receptor-independent effects of endocannabinoids on ion channels. Curr Pharm Des. 2006;12(2):227-39. https://doi.org/10.2174/138161206775193073

Pacher P, Batkai S, Kunos G (2006). The endocannabinoid system as an emerging target of pharmacotherapy. Pharmacol Rev 58: 389–462.

Pacher P, Mechoulam R. 2011. Is lipid signaling through cannabinoid 2 receptors part of a protective system? Prog Lipid Res. 50(2):193-211. https://doi.org/10.1016/j.plipres.2011.01.001

Pacioni G, Rapino C, Zarivi O, Falconi A, Leonardi M, Battista N, Colafarina S, Sergi M, Bonfigli A, Miranda M, Barsacchi D, Maccarrone M. Truffles contain endocannabinoid metabolic enzymes and anandamide. Phytochemistry. 2015 Feb;110:104-10. https://doi.org/10.1016/j.phytochem.2014.11.012

Pagano E, Iannotti FA, Piscitelli F, Romano B, Lucariello G, Venneri T, Di Marzo V, Izzo AA, and Borrelli F (2020) Efficacy of combined therapy with fish oil and phytocannabinoids in murine intestinal inflammation. Phytother Res. https://doi.org10.1002/ptr.6831

Pagotto U, Vicennati V, Pasquali R (2205). The endocannabinoid system and the treatment of obesity. Ann Med 37(4):270-275. https://doi.org/10.1080/07853890510037419

Paris, R.R., E. Henri, and M. Paris. 1976. Sur les c-flavonoïdes du Cannabis sativa L. Plantes Médicinales et Phytothérapie 10:144-54.

Parker LA, Mechoulam R, Schlievert C. Cannabidiol, a non-psychoactive component of cannabis and its synthetic dimethylheptyl homolog suppress nausea in an experimental model with rats. Neuroreport. 2002 Apr 16;13(5):567-70. https://doi.org/10.1097/00001756-200204160-00006

Paton WD, Pertwee RG. Effect of cannabis and certain of its constituents on pentobarbitone sleeping time and phenazone metabolism. Br J Pharmacol. 1972 Feb;44(2):250-61. https://pubmed.ncbi.nlm.nih.gov/4668592/

Pedersen W. 2008. Does cannabis use lead to depression and suicidal behaviours? A population-based longitudinal study. Acta Psychiatrica Scandinavica. 118(5):395-403. https://doi.org/10.1111/j.1600-0447.2008.01259.x

Penner EA, Buettner H, Mittleman MA. The impact of marijuana use on glucose, insulin, and insulin resistance among US adults. Am J Med. 2013 Jul;126(7):583-9. https://doi.org/10.1016/j.amjmed.2013.03.002

Penumarti A, Abdel AR. (2014) The novel endocannabinoid receptor gpr18 is expressed in the rostral ventrolateral medulla and exerts tonic restraining influence on blood pressure. J Pharmacol Exp Ther. 349:29-38 https://doi.org/10.1124/jpet.113.209213

Perry NS, Houghton PJ, Theobald A, Jenner P, Perry EK (2000). In-vitro inhibition of human erythrocyte acetylcholinesterase by salvia lavandulaefolia essential oil and constituent terpenes. J Pharm Pharmacol 52: 895–902. https://doi.org/10.1211/0022357001774598

Pertwee RG, Ross RA. 2002. Cannabinoid receptors and their ligands. Protaglandins, Leukotrienes, and Essential Fatty Acids (PLEFA). 66(2-3):101-121. https://doi.org/10.1054/plef.2001.0341

Pertwee RG. 2015. Handbook of Cannabis. Oxford University Press.

Peters M, Kogan NM. HU-331: a cannabinoid quinone, with uncommon cytotoxic properties and low toxicity. Expert Opin Investig Drugs. 2007 Sep;16(9):1405-13. https://doi.org/10.1517/13543784.16.9.1405

Pindborg JJ, Barmes D, Roed-Petersen B. 1968. Epidemiology and histology of oral leukoplakia and leukoedema among Papuans and New Guineans. Cancer. 22:379-384. https://doi.org/10.1002/1097-0142(196808)22:2%3C379::aid-cncr2820220215%3E3.0.co;2-a

Pinto L, Capasso R, Di Carlo G, Izzo AA. 2002. Endocannabinoids and the gut. Prostaglandins, Leukotrienes and Essential Fatty Acids. 66:333-341. https://doi.org/10.1054/plef.2001.0345

Pinzi L, Lherbet C, Baltas M, Pellati F, and Rastelli G (2019) In silico repositioning of cannabigerol as a novel inhibitor of the enoyl Acyl Carrier Protein (ACP) reductase (InhA). Molecules 24:2567. https://doi.org/10.3390/molecules24142567

Piomelli D, Russo EB. The Cannabis sativa Versus Cannabis indica Debate: An Interview with Ethan Russo, MD. Cannabis Cannabinoid Res. 2016 Jan 1;1(1):44-46. https://doi.org/10.1089/can.2015.29003.ebr

Piomelli D. The molecular logic of endocannabinoid signalling. Nat Rev Neurosci. 2003 Nov;4(11):873-84. https://doi.org/10.1038/nrn1247

Piomelli Daniele and Russo Ethan B. Cannabis and Cannabinoid Research. January 2016, 1(1): 44-46. doi:10.1089/can.2015.29003.ebr.

Pirone, A.; Lenzi, C.; Coli, A.; Giannessi, E.; Stornelli, M.R.; Miragliotta, V. Preferential epithelial expression of type-1 cannabinoid receptor (CB1R) in the developing canine embryo. SpringerPlus 2015, 4, 804. doi.org/10.1186/s40064-015-1616-0

Pisanti S, Picardi P, D'Alessandro A. Laezza C, Bifulco M. 2013. The endocannabinoid signaling system in cancer. Trend Pharmacol Sci. 34(5):273-282. https://doi.org/10.1016/j.tips.2013.03.003

Plumb, J., Demirel, S., Sackett, J.L., Russo, E.B. and Wilson-Poe, A.R., 2022. The Nose Knows: Aroma, but Not THC Mediates the Subjective Effects of Smoked and Vaporized Cannabis Flower. Psychoactives, 1(2), pp.70-86. https://doi.org/10.3390/psychoactives1020008

Polidoro G, Galiazzo G, Giancola F, Papadimitriou S, Kouki M, Sabattini S, Rigillo A, Chiocchetti R. Expression of cannabinoid and cannabinoid-related receptors in the oral mucosa of healthy cats and cats with chronic gingivostomatitis. J Feline Med Surg. 2021 Aug;23(8):679-691. doi.org/10.1177/1098612X20970510

Pollastro F, De Petrocellis L, Schiano-Moriello A, Chianese G, Heyman H, Appendino G, Taglialatela-Scafati O. Amorfrutin-type phytocannabinoids from Helichrysum umbraculigerum. Fitoterapia. 2017 Nov;123:13-17. https://doi.org/10.1016/j.fitote.2017.09.010

Ponomarenko A, Tyrtyshnaia A, Ivashkevich D, Ermolenko E, Dyuizen I, Manzhulo I. Synaptamide Modulates Astroglial Activity in Mild Traumatic Brain Injury. Mar Drugs. 2022 Aug 21;20(8):538. https://doi.org/10.3390/md20080538

Porter AC, Sauer JM, Knierman MD, Becker GW, Berna MJ, Bao J, Nomikos GG, Carter P, Bymaster FP, Leese AB, Felder CC. 2002. Characterization of a novel endocannabinoid, Virodhamine, with antagonist activity at the CB1 receptor. JPET. 301:1020-1024. https://doi.org/10.1124/jpet.301.3.1020

Potter D. Growth and morphology of medicinal cannabis. In: Guy GW, Whittle BA, Robson P, editors. Medicinal Uses of Cannabis and Cannabinoids. London: Pharmaceutical Press; 2004. pp. 17–54.

Power RA, Verweij KJ, Zuhair M, Montgomery GW, Henders AK, Heath AC, Madden PA, Medland SE, Wray NR, Martin NG. Genetic predisposition to schizophrenia associated with increased use of cannabis. Mol Psychiatry. 2014 Nov;19(11):1201-4. https://doi.org/10.1038/mp.2014.51

Pultrini Ade M, Galindo LA, Costa M (2006). Effects of the essential oil from Citrus aurantium L. in experimental anxiety models in mice. Life Sci 78: 1720–1725. https://doi.org/10.1016/j.lfs.2005.08.004

Puopolo T, Liu C, Ma H, Seeram NP. Inhibitory Effects of Cannabinoids on Acetylcholinesterase and Butyrylcholinesterase Enzyme Activities. Med Cannabis Cannabinoids. 2022 Apr 19;5(1):85-94. https://doi.org/10.1159/000524086  PMID: 35702400; PMCID: PMC9149358.

Raduner S, Majewska A, Chen JZ, Xie XQ, Hamon J, Faller B, Altmann KH, Gertsch J. Alkylamides from Echinacea are a new class of cannabinomimetics. Cannabinoid type 2 receptor-dependent and -independent immunomodulatory effects. J Biol Chem. 2006 May 19;281(20):14192-206. https://doi.org/10.1074/jbc.M601074200

Ramírez, B. G., Blázquez, C., del Pulgar, T. G., Guzmán, M., & de Ceballos, M. L. (2005). Prevention of Alzheimer's disease pathology by cannabinoids: neuroprotection mediated by blockade of microglial activation. Journal of Neuroscience, 25(8), 1904-1913. https://doi.org/10.1523/JNEUROSCI.4540-04.2005

Rea K, Roche M, Finn DP. Supraspinal modulation of pain by cannabinoids: the role of GABA and glutamate. Br J Pharmacol. 2007 Nov;152(5):633-48. https://doi.org/10.1038/sj.bjp.0707440

Redecker, D., R. Kodner, and L.E. Graham. 2000. Glomalean fungi from the Ordovician. Science 289:1920-1921 https://doi.org/10.1126/science.289.5486.1920

Reilly D, Didcott P, Swift W, Hall W. Long-term cannabis use: characteristics of users in an Australian rural area. Addiction. 1998 Jun;93(6):837-46. https://doi.org/10.1046/j.1360-0443.1998.9368375.x

Rice S, Koziel JA. 2015. Characterizing the smell of marijuana by odor impact of volatile compounds: an application of simultaneous chemical and sensory analysis. PLOS ONE 10(12): e0144160. https://doi.org/10.1371/journal.pone.0144160

Richardson JD, Aanonsen L, Hargreaves KM. SR 141716A, a cannabinoid receptor antagonist, produces hyperalgesia in untreated mice. Eur J Pharmacol 1997; 319:R3–4. https://doi.org/10.1016/s0014-2999(96)00952-1

Riedel G, Fadda P, McKillop-Smith S, Pertwee RG, Platt B, Robinson L. Synthetic and plant-derived cannabinoid receptor antagonists show hypophagic properties in fasted and non-fasted mice. Br J Pharmacol. 2009 Apr;156(7):1154-66. https://doi.org/10.1111/j.1476-5381.2008.00107.x

Rock EM, Goodwin JM, Limebeer CL, Breuer A, Pertwee RG, Mechoulam R, and Parker LA (2011) Interaction between non-psychotropic cannabinoids in marihuana: effect of cannabigerol (CBG) on the anti-nausea or anti-emetic effects of cannabidiol (CBD) in rats and shrews. Psychopharmacology (Berl) 215:505–512. https://doi.org/10.1007/s00213-010-2157-4

Rock EM, Kopstick RL, Limebeer CL, Parker LA. 2013. Tetrahydrocannabinolic acid reduces nausea-induced conditioned gaping in rats and vomiting in Suncus murinus. Br J Pharmacol. 170(3):641-648 https://doi.org/10.1111/bph.12316

Rodrigues Goulart H, Kimura EA, Peres VJ, Couto AS, Aquino Duarte FA, Katzin AM (2004). Terpenes arrest parasite development and inhibit biosynthesis of isoprenoids in Plasmodium falciparum. Antimicrobial Agents Chemother 48: 2502–2509. Press: Boca Raton, FL. https://doi.org/10.1128/aac.48.7.2502-2509.2004

Rollinger JM, Schuster D, Danzl B, Schwaiger S, Markt P, Schmidtke M, Gertsch J, Raduner S, Wolber G, Langer T, Stuppner H. In silico target fishing for rationalized ligand discovery exemplified on constituents of Ruta graveolens. Planta Med. 2009 Feb;75(3):195-204. https://doi.org/10.1055%2Fs-0028-1088397

Rosenblatt KA, Darling JR, Chen C, Sherman KJ, Schwartz SM. 2004. Marijuana use and risk of oral squamous cell carcinoma. Cancer Research. 64:4049-4054. https://doi.org/10.1158/0008-5472.can-03-3425

Ross SA, ElSohly MA. 1996. The volatile oil composition of fresh and air-dried buds of Cannabis sativa. J Nat Prod 59: 49–51. https://doi.org/10.1021/np960004a

Ross, S., ElSohly, H., ElKashoury, E., and ElSohly, M. (1996) Fatty acids of Cannabis seeds. Phytochem. Anal. 7, 279–283.

Rothschild M, Bergstrom G, Wangberg S-A. 2005. Cannabis sativa: volatile compounds from pollen and entire male and female plants of two variants, Northern Lights and Hawaian Indica. Bot J Linn Soc 147: 387–397. https://doi.org/10.1111/j.1095-8339.2005.00417.x

Roy P, Dennis DG, Eschbach MD, Anand SD, Xu F, Maturano J, Hellman J, Sarlah D, Das A. Metabolites of Cannabigerol Generated by Human Cytochrome P450s Are Bioactive. Biochemistry. 2022 Nov 1;61(21):2398-2408. https://doi.org/0.1021/acs.biochem.2c00383

Ruchlemer R, Amit-Kohn M, Raveh D, Hanuš L. Inhaled medicinal cannabis and the immunocompromised patient. Support Care Cancer. 2015 Mar;23(3):819-22. https://doi.org/10.1007/s00520-014-2429-3 Epub 2014 Sep 13. PMID: 25216851.

Ruhaak LR, Felth J, Karlsson PC, Rafter JJ, Verpoorte R, Bohlin L. 2011. Evaluation of the cyclooxygenase inhibiting effects of six major cannabinoids isolated from Cannabis sativa. Biological and Pharmaceutical Bulletin 34 (5): 774–778 https://doi.org/10.1248/bpb.34.774

Russo E. 2002. Cannabis treatments in obstetrics and gynecology: a historical review. Journal of Cannabis Therapeutics. 2:5-35. https://doi.org/10.1300/J175v02n03_02

Russo E. 2004. Clinical Endocannabinoid Deficiency (CECD): Can this concept explain therapeutic benefits of cannabis in migraine, fibromyalgia, irritable bowel syndrome and other treatment-resistant conditions?. Neuroendocrinology Letters. 25:31-39 https://pubmed.ncbi.nlm.nih.gov/15159679/

Russo E. 2014. The Pharmacological History of Cannabis. Chapter 2. Handbook of Cannabis. Oxford University Press. p.23-29

Russo EB, Burnett A, Hall B, Parker KK. 2005. Agonistic properties of cannabidiol at 5-HT-1a receptors. Neurochem Res 30: 1037–1043. https://doi.org/10.1007/s11064-005-6978-1

Russo EB, Marcu J. 2017. Cannabis Pharmacology: The Usual Suspects and a Few Promising Leads. Adv. Pharmacol. 80:67-134. https://doi.org/10.1016/bs.apha.2017.03.004

Russo EB, Spooner C, May L, Leslie R, Whiteley VL. Cannabinoid Hyperemesis Syndrome Survey and Genomic Investigation. Cannabis Cannabinoid Res. 2022 Jun;7(3):336-344. https://doi.org/10.1089/can.2021.0046

Russo EB. 2007. History of Cannabis and its preparations in saga, science and sobriquet. Chemistry and Biodiversity. 4: 2624-2648. https://doi.org/10.1002/cbdv.200790144

Russo EB. 2011. Taming THC: potential Cannabis synergy and phytocannabinoid-terpenoid entourage effects. Br J of Pharmacol 163:1344-1364. https://doi.org/10.1111/j.1476-5381.2011.01238.x

Russo F, Tolomeo F, Vandelli MA, Biagini G, Paris R, Fulvio F, Laganà A, Capriotti AL, Carbone L, Gigli G, Cannazza G, Citti C. Kynurenine and kynurenic acid: Two plant neuromodulators found in Cannabis sativa L. J Pharm Biomed Anal. 2022 Mar 20;211:114636. https://doi.org/10.1016/j.jpba.2022.114636 Epub 2022 Jan 31. PMID: 35124451.

Russo, E. B. (2019). The case for the entourage effect and conventional breeding of clinical cannabis: no "strain," no gain. Frontiers in plant science, 1969. https://doi.org/10.3389/fpls.2018.01969

Ryberg E, Larsson N, Sjö¨gren S, Hjorth S, Hermansson N-O, Leonova J et al. 2007. The orphan receptor GPR55 is a novel cannabinoid receptor. Br J Pharmacol 152: 1092–1101. https://doi.org/10.1038/sj.bjp.0707460

Sadhasivam S, Alankar S, Maturi R, Vishnubhotla RV, Mudigonda M, Pawale D, Narayanan S, Hariri S, Ram C, Chang T, Renschler J, Eckert G, Subramaniam B. Inner Engineering Practices and Advanced 4-day Isha Yoga Retreat Are Associated with Cannabimimetic Effects with Increased Endocannabinoids and Short-Term and Sustained Improvement in Mental Health: A Prospective Observational Study of Meditators. Evid Based Complement Alternat Med. 2020 Jun 5;2020:8438272. https://doi.org/10.1155/2020/8438272

Sagar, D.R., Gaw, A.G., Okine, B.N., Wong, A., Woodhams, S.G., Kendall, D.A., Chapman, V., 2009. Dynamic regulation of the endocannabinoid system: implications for analgesia. Mol. Pain 8, 5–59. https://doi.org/10.1186/1744-8069-5-59

Sakakibara I, Ikeya Y, Hayashi K, Okada M, Maruno M. Three acyclic bis-phenylpropane lignanamides from fruits of Cannabis sativa. Phytochemistry. 1995 Mar;38(4):1003-7. https://doi.org/10.1016/0031-9422(94)00773-m

Salamone, Stefano, Lorenz Waltl, Anna Pompignan, Gianpaolo Grassi, Giuseppina Chianese, Andreas Koeberle, and Federica Pollastro. 2022. "Phytochemical Characterization of Cannabis sativa L. Chemotype V Reveals Three New Dihydrophenanthrenoids That Favorably Reprogram Lipid Mediator Biosynthesis in Macrophages" Plants 11, no. 16: 2130. https://doi.org/10.3390/plants11162130

Salbini M, Quarta A, Russo F, Giudetti AM, Citti C, Cannazza G, Gigli G, Vergara D, Gaballo A. Oxidative Stress and Multi-Organel Damage Induced by Two Novel Phytocannabinoids, CBDB and CBDP, in Breast Cancer Cells. Molecules. 2021 Sep 14;26(18):5576. https://doi.org/10.3390/molecules26185576

Salehi B, Venditti A, Sharifi-Rad M, Kręgiel D, Sharifi-Rad J, Durazzo A, Lucarini M, Santini A, Souto EB, Novellino E, Antolak H, Azzini E, Setzer WN, Martins N. The Therapeutic Potential of Apigenin. Int J Mol Sci. 2019 Mar 15;20(6):1305. https://doi.org/10.3390/ijms20061305

Salen, G., Patel, S. and Batta, A.K. (2002), Sitosterolemia. Cardiovascular Drug Reviews, 20: 255-270. https://doi.org/10.1111/j.1527-3466.2002.tb00096.x

Sallan SE, Zinberg NE, Frei E 3rd. 1975. Antiemetic effect of delta-9-tetrahydrocannabinol in patients receiving cancer chemotherapy. New England Journal of Medicine. 293: 795–797. https://doi.org/10.1056/nejm197510162931603/

Sánchez-Duffhues G, Calzado MA, de Vinuesa AG, Appendino G, Fiebich BL, Loock U, Lefarth-Risse A, Krohn K, Muñoz E. Denbinobin inhibits nuclear factor-kappaB and induces apoptosis via reactive oxygen species generation in human leukemic cells. Biochem Pharmacol. 2009 Apr 15;77(8):1401-9. https://doi.org/10.1016/j.bcp.2009.01.004

Sarfaraz S, Adhami VM, Syed DN, Afaq F, Mukhtar H. 2008. Cannabinoids for cancer treatment: progress and promise. Cancer Res. 68(2):339-342. https://doi.org/10.1158/0008-5472.can-07-2785

Sarma ND, Waye A, ElSohly MA, Brown PN, Elzinga S, Johnson HE, Marles RJ, Melanson JE, Russo E, Deyton L, Hudalla C, Vrdoljak GA, Wurzer JH, Khan IA, Kim NC, Giancaspro GI. 2020. Cannabis Inflorescence for Medical Purposes: USP Considerations for Quality Attributes. J. nat. Prod. 83: 1334-1351. https://doi.org/10.1021/acs.jnatprod.9b01200

Sartory, D.P., Grobbelaar, J.U. Extraction of chlorophyll a from freshwater phytoplankton for spectrophotometric analysis. Hydrobiologia 114, 177–187 (1984). https://doi.org/10.1007/BF00031869

Sauer, M.A., S.M. Rifka, R.L. Hawks, G.B. Cutler, and D.L. Loriaux. 1983. Marijuana: interaction with the estrogen receptor. J Pharm Exper Therap 224:404-7.

Sawler J, Stout JM, Gardner KM, Hudson D, Vidmar J, et al. (2015) The Genetic Structure of Marijuana and Hemp. PLOS ONE 10(8): e0133292. https://doi.org/10.1371/journal.pone.0133292

Sawzdargo M, Nguyen T, Lee DK, Lynch KR, Cheng R, Heng HH, George SR, O'Dowd BF. Identification and cloning of three novel human G protein-coupled receptor genes GPR52, PsiGPR53 and GPR55: GPR55 is extensively expressed in human brain. Brain Res Mol Brain Res. 1999 Feb 5;64(2):193-8. https://doi.org/10.1016/s0169-328x(98)00277-0

Schultes, R. E., Klein, W. M., Plowman, T., & Lockwood, T. E. (1974). CANNABIS: AN EXAMPLE OF TAXONOMIC NEGLECT. Botanical Museum Leaflets, Harvard University, 23(9), 337–367. http://www.jstor.org/stable/41762285

Seidler A, Hellenbrand W, Robra BP, Vieregge P, Nischan P, et al. 1996. Possible environmental, occupational, and other etiologic factors for Parkinson's disease: a case-control study in Germany. Neurology 46: 1257-84 https://doi.org/10.1212/wnl.46.5.1275

Sewell RA, Poling J, Sofuoglu M. The effect of cannabis compared with alcohol on driving. Am J Addict. 2009 May-Jun;18(3):185-93. https://doi.org/10.1080/10550490902786934

Shamloul, R., & Bella, A. J. (2011). Impact of cannabis use on male sexual health. The journal of sexual medicine, 8(4), 971-975. https://doi.org/10.1111/j.1743-6109.2010.02198.x

Shearman LP, Rosko KM, Fleischer R, Wang J, Xu S, Tong XS, Rocha BA. Antidepressant-like and anorectic effects of the cannabinoid CB1 receptor inverse agonist AM251 in mice. Behav Pharmacol. 2003 Dec;14(8):573-82. https://doi.org/10.1097/00008877-200312000-00001

Shoemaker JL, Joseph BK, Ruckle MB, Mayeux PR, Prather PL. The endocannabinoid noladin ether acts as a full agonist at human CB2 cannabinoid receptors. J Pharmacol Exp Ther. 2005 Aug;314(2):868-75. https://doi.org/10.1124/jpet.105.085282

Shou-Zhong Y. 1997. The Divine Farmer's Materia Medica: A Translation of the Shen Nong Ben Cao Jing. Boulder, CO: Blue Poppy Press.

Shrader SH, Song ZH. Discovery of endogenous inverse agonists for G protein-coupled receptor 6. Biochem Biophys Res Commun. 2020 Feb 19;522(4):1041-1045. https://doi.org/10.1016/j.bbrc.2019.12.004 Epub 2019 Dec 7. PMID: 31818461; PMCID: PMC7218748.

Si D, Wang Y, Zhou YH, Guo Y, Wang J, Zhou H, Li ZS, Fawcett JP. Mechanism of CYP2C9 inhibition by flavones and flavonols. Drug Metab Dispos. 2009 Mar;37(3):629-34. https://doi.org/10.1124/dmd.108.023416

Siddiqui MZ. 2011. Boswellia Serrata, a Potential Antiinflammatory Agent: An Overview. Indian J Pharm Sci. 73(3): 255-261. https://doi.org/10.4103/0250-474x.93507

Silver, R. J. (2019). The endocannabinoid system of animals. Animals, 9(9), 686. doi.org/10.3390/ani9090686

Silverstein SJ, Noel D, Heilbron D. 1978. Social drug use/abuse and dental disease. J calif Dent Assoc. 6:32-37. https://pubmed.ncbi.nlm.nih.gov/284013/

Silvey B, Seto E, Gipe A, Ghodsian N, Simpson CD. Occupational Exposure to Particulate Matter and Volatile Organic Compounds in Two Indoor Cannabis Production Facilities. Ann Work Expo Health. 2020 Aug 6;64(7):715-727. https://doi.org10.1093/annweh/wxaa067

Simopoulos AP. An Increase in the Omega-6/Omega-3 Fatty Acid Ratio Increases the Risk for Obesity. Nutrients. 2016 Mar 2;8(3):128. https://doi.org/10.3390/nu8030128

Sinor AD, Irvin SM, Greenberg DA. 2000. Endocannabinoid protect cerebral cortical neurons from in vitro ischemia in rats. Neuroscience Letters. 278:157-160. https://doi.org/10.1016/s0304-3940(99)00922-2

Skinner CM, Nookaew I, Ewing LE, Wongsurawat T, Jenjaroenpun P, Quick CM, Yee EU, Piccolo BD, ElSohly M, Walker LA, Gurley B, Koturbash I. Potential Probiotic or Trigger of Gut Inflammation - The Janus-Faced Nature of Cannabidiol-Rich Cannabis Extract. J Diet Suppl. 2020;17(5):543-560. https://doi.org/10.1080/19390211.2020.1761506

Small, E., Beckstead, H.D., 1973a. Common cannabinoid phenotypes in 350 stocks of Cannabis. Lloydia 36, 144–165.

Small, E., Beckstead, H.D., 1973b. Cannabinoid phenotypes in Cannabis sativa. Nature 245, 147–148.

Small, E., Cronquist, A., 1976. A practical and natural taxonomy for Cannabis. Taxon 25, 405–435.

Small, E., H. D. Beckstead, & Chan, A. (1975). The Evolution of Cannabinoid Phenotypes in Cannabis. Economic Botany, 29(3), 219–232. http://www.jstor.org/stable/4253607

Small, E., Marcus, D., Janick, J., & Whipkey, A. (2002). Hemp: a new crop with new uses for North America.

Smith SC, Wagner MS. 2014. Clinical endocannabinoid deficiency (CECD) revisited: can this concept explain the therapeutic benefits of cannabis in migraine, fibromyalgia, irritable bowel syndrome, and other treatment-resistant conditions?. Neuro Endocrinol Lett. 35(3):198-201. https://pubmed.ncbi.nlm.nih.gov/24977967/

Smith WE, Shivaji R, Williams WP, Luthe DS, Sandoya GV, Smith CL, Sparks DL, Brown AE. A maize line resistant to herbivory constitutively releases (E) -beta-caryophyllene. J Econ Entomol. 2012 Feb;105(1):120-8. https://doi.org/10.1603/ec11107

Stahl E, Kunde R 1973. Die Leitsubstanzen der Haschisch-Suchhunde. Kriminalistik: Z Gesamte Kriminal Wiss Prax 27: 385–389.

Stanzani, A., Galiazzo, G., Giancola, F. et al. Localization of cannabinoid and cannabinoid related receptors in the cat gastrointestinal tract. Histochem Cell Biol 153, 339–356 (2020). doi.org/10.1007/s00418-020-01854-0

Starks, Michael (1990). Marijuana Chemistry: Genetics, Processing, Potency. Ronin Publishing

Staudt R, Nitzsche J, Harting P. 2003. Supercritical Fluid Extraction Using Microwave Heating. Proceedings 6th International Symposium on Supercritical Fluids, Versailles, France, April 2003.

Stone T, Henkle J, Prakash V. 2019. Pulmonary mucormycosis associated with medical marijuana use. Respiratory Medicine Case Reports 26:176–179. https://doi.org/10.1016/j. rmcr.2019.01.008

Storr, MA., Sharkey, KA. 2007. The endocannabinoid system and gut–brain signalling. Current Opinion in Pharmacology, 7(6), 575–582. https://doi.org/10.1016/j.coph.2007.08.008

Stuart, J. M., Leishman, E., & Bradshaw, H. B. (2014). Reproduction and Cannabinoids: Ups and Downs, Ins and Outs. Handbook of Cannabis, 245.

Stumpf JL, Williams LD. 2020. Management of Cannabinoid Hyperemesis Syndrome: Focus on Capsaicin. Journal of Pharmacy Practice. Jul 2. 897190020934289. https://doi.org/10.1177/0897190020934289

Sugiura T, Kondo S, Sukagawa A, Nakane S, Shinoda A, Itoh K, Yamashita A, Waku K. 2-Arachidonoylglycerol: a possible endogenous cannabinoid receptor ligand in brain. Biochem Biophys Res Commun. 1995 Oct 4;215(1):89-97. https://doi.org/10.1006/bbrc.1995.2437

Sullivan N, Sytze E, Raber JC. 2013. Determination of Pesticide Residues in Cannabis Smoke. Journal of Toxicology. Vol 2013. Article ID 378168 https://doi.org/10.1155/2013/378168

Sundararaman, P., & Djerassi, C. (1977). A convenient synthesis of progesterone from stigmasterol. The Journal of organic chemistry, 42(22), 3633-3634. https://doi.org/10.1021/jo00442a044

Szaflarski JP, Bebin EM. Cannabis, cannabidiol, and epilepsy--from receptors to clinical response. Epilepsy Behav. 2014 Dec;41:277-82. https://doi.org/10.1016/j.yebeh.2014.08.135

Taghinasab M, Jabaji S. 2020. Cannabis microbiome and the role of endophytes in modulating the production of secondary metabolites: an overview. Microorganisms. 8: 355 https://doi.org/10.3390/microorganisms8030355

Taglialatela-Scafati, O., Pagani, A., Scala, F., De Petrocellis, L., Di Marzo, V., Grassi, G. and Appendino, G. (2010), Cannabimovone, a Cannabinoid with a Rearranged Terpenoid Skeleton from Hemp. Eur. J. Org. Chem., 2010: 2067-2072. https://doi.org/10.1002/ejoc.200901464

Tambe Y, Tsujiuchi H, Honda G, Ikeshiro Y, Tanaka S (1996). Gastric cytoprotection of the non-steroidal anti-inflammatory sesquiterpene, beta-caryophyllene. Planta Med 62: 469–470. https://doi.org/10.1055/s-2006-957942

Tanney CAS, Backer R, Geitmann A and Smith DL (2021) Cannabis Glandular Trichomes: A Cellular Metabolite Factory. Front. Plant Sci. 12:721986. doi: 10.3389/fpls.2021.721986 "Figure 1"

Thakre, A. , Mulange, S. , Kodgire, S. , Zore, G. and Karuppayil, S. (2016) Effects of Cinnamaldehyde, Ocimene, Camphene, Curcumin and Farnesene on Candida albicans. Advances in Microbiology, 6, 627-643. https://doi.org/10.4236/aim.2016.69062

Thapa, D., Lee, J. S., Heo, S. W., Lee, Y. R., Kang, K. W., Kwak, M. K., ... & Kim, J. A. (2011). Novel hexahydrocannabinol analogs as potential anti-cancer agents inhibit cell proliferation and tumor angiogenesis. European journal of pharmacology, 650(1), 64-71. https://doi.org/10.1016/j.ejphar.2010.09.073

Thomas A, Baillie GL, Phillips AM, Razdan RK, Ross RA, Pertwee RG (2007). Cannabidiol displays unexpectedly high potency as an antagonist of CB1 and CB2 receptor agonists in vitro. Br J Pharmacol 150: 613–623.

Thompson GR, Rosenkrantz H, Schaeppi UH, Braude MC. 1973. Comparison of acute oral toxicity of cannabinoids in rats, dogs and monkeys. Toxicol Appl Pharmacol. 25(3):363-72. https://doi.org/10.1016/0041-008x(73)90310-4

Thors L, Belghiti M, Fowler CJ. Inhibition of fatty acid amide hydrolase by kaempferol and related naturally occurring flavonoids. Br J Pharmacol. 2008 Sep;155(2):244-52. https://doi.org/10.1038/bjp.2008.237

Tian-Tian Guo, Jian-Chun Zhang, Hai Zhang, Qing-Chao Liu, Yong Zhao, Yu-Fei Hou, Lu Bai, Li Zhang, Xue-Qiang Liu, Xue-Ying Liu, Sheng-Yong Zhang & Nai-Sheng Bai (2016): Bioactive spirans and other constituents from the leaves of Cannabis sativa f. sativa, Journal of Asian Natural Products Research, https://doi.org/10.1080/10286020.2016.1248947

Tinto F, Villano R, Kostrzewa M, Ligresti A, Straker H, Manzo E. Synthesis of the Major Mammalian Metabolites of THCV. J Nat Prod. 2020 Jul 24;83(7):2060-2065. https://doi.org/10.1021/acs.jnatprod.9b00831

Tomaso ED, Beltramo M, Piomelli D. 1996. Brain cannabinoids in chocolate. Nature. 382:677-678. https://doi.org/10.1038/382677a0

Treseder, K. K. 2004. A meta-analysis of mycorrhizal responses to nitrogen, phosphorus, and atmospheric CO2 in field studies. New Phytologist 164:347-355 https://doi.org/10.1111/j.1469-8137.2004.01159.x

Trezza V, Campolongo P. The endocannabinoid system as a possible target to treat both the cognitive and emotional features of post-traumatic stress disorder (PTSD). Front Behav Neurosci. 2013 Aug 9;7:100. https://doi.org/10.3389/fnbeh.2013.00100

Trezza V, Patrizia C. 2013. The endocannabinoid system as a possible target to treat both the cognitive and emotional features of post-traumatic stress disorder (PTSD). Frontiers in Behavioral Neuroscience. 100(7):1-6 https://doi.org/10.3389/fnbeh.2013.00100

Tsuneki H, Ma EL, Kobayashi S, Sekizaki N, Maekawa K, Sasaoka T, Wang MW, Kimura I. 2005. Antiangiogenic activity of B-eudesmol in vitro and in vivo. European Journal of Pharmacology. 512(2-3):105-115. https://doi.org/10.1016/j.ejphar.2005.02.035

Turkez H, Aydın E, Geyikoglu F, Cetin D. Genotoxic and oxidative damage potentials in human lymphocytes after exposure to terpinolene in vitro. Cytotechnology. 2015 May;67(3):409-18. https://doi.org/10.1007/s10616-014-9698-z

Turner CE, Elsohly MA, Boeren EG. Constituents of Cannabis sativa L. XVII. A review of the natural constituents. J Nat Prod. 1980 Mar-Apr;43(2):169-234. https://doi.org/10.1021/np50008a001

Turner CE, Hsu MH, Knapp JE, Schiff PL Jr, Slatkin DJ. Isolation of cannabisativine, an alkaloid, from Cannabis sativa L. root. J Pharm Sci. 1976 Jul;65(7):1084-5. https://doi.org/10.1002/jps.2600650736

Tuttle AH, Tohyama S, Ramsay T, Kimmelman J, Schweinhardt P, Bennett GJ, Mogil JS. 2015. Increasing placebo responses over time in US clinical trials of neuropathic pain. Pain. 156(12):2616-2626. https://doi.org/10.1097/j.pain.0000000000000333

Tyrtyshnaia A, Bondar A, Konovalova S, Manzhulo I. Synaptamide Improves Cognitive Functions and Neuronal Plasticity in Neuropathic Pain. Int J Mol Sci. 2021 Nov 26;22(23):12779 https://doi.org/10.3390/ijms222312779

Ujvary I, Grotenhermen F. 2014. 11-nor-9-carboxy-delta-9-tetrahydrocannbinol – a ubiquitous yet underresearched cannabinoid. A review of the literature. Cannabinoids. 9(1):1-8.

Ujváry I, Hanuš L. Human Metabolites of Cannabidiol: A Review on Their Formation, Biological Activity, and Relevance in Therapy. Cannabis Cannabinoid Res. 2016 Mar 1;1(1):90-101. https://doi.org/10.1089/can.2015.0012

United States Pharmacopoeia 12th Edition. 1942

Valdeolivas S, Navarrete C, Cantarero I, Bellido ML, Muñoz E, and Sagredo O (2015) Neuroprotective properties of cannabigerol in Huntington's disease: studies in R6/2 mice and 3-nitropropionate-lesioned mice. Neurotherapeutics 12:185–199. https://doi.org/10.1007/s13311-014-0304-z

Van Laere K, Goffin K, Casteels C, Dupont P, Mortelmans L, de Hoon J, Bormans G. Gender-dependent increases with healthy aging of the human cerebral cannabinoid-type 1 receptor binding using [(18)F]MK-9470 PET. Neuroimage. 2008 Feb 15;39(4):1533-41. https://doi.org/10.1016/j.neuroimage.2007.10.053

Van Wyk CW, Breytenbach HS, Dreyer WP. 1979. The epidemiology of preventable oral mucosal lesions in the Cape Peninsula. J Dent Assoc 34:672-676.

Vavilov, N.I., Bukinich, D.D., 1929. Zemledel'cheskii Afghanistan. Trudy po Prikl. Bot. Gen. Sel. Suppl. 33, 380–382, ([Reissued 1959, Izdatel'stuo Akademii Nauk SSSR, Moskva-Leningrad]).

Velasco G, Sanchez C, Guzman M. 2012. Towards the use of cannabinoids as antitumour agents. Nat Rev Cancer. 12(6):436-444. https://doi.org/10.1038/nrc3247

Velasco G, Sánchez C, Guzmán M. Endocannabinoids and Cancer. Handb Exp Pharmacol. 2015;231:449-72. https://doi.org/10.1007/978-3-319-20825-1_16

Venn-Watson, S., Reiner, J. & Jensen, E.D. Pentadecanoylcarnitine is a newly discovered endocannabinoid with pleiotropic activities relevant to supporting physical and mental health. Sci Rep 12, 13717 (2022). https://doi.org/10.1038/s41598-022-18266-w

Versteeg PA, Slot DE, Velden U, Weijden GAvander. 2008. Effect of cannabis usage on the oral environment: a review. Int J Dent Hygiene. 6:315-320. https://doi.org/10.1111/j.1601-5037.2008.00301.x

Voelker R, Holmes M. 2014. Pesticide Use on Cannabis. Cannabis Safety Institute white paper publication. https://cdn.technologynetworks.com/tn/Resources/pdf/pesticide-use-on-cannabis.pdf

Volicer, L, Stelly M, Morris J, McLaughlin J, Volicer BJ. 1997. Effects of dronabinol on anorexia and disturbed behavior in patients with Alzheimer's disease. International Journal of Geriatric Psychiatry. 1997. 12: 913–919. https://pubmed.ncbi.nlm.nih.gov/9309469/

Volkow, ND, Baler, RD, Compton, WM, Weiss, SRB. 2014. Adverse Health Effects of Marijuana Use. The N Engl J Med 370:2219-2227. https://doi.org/10.1056%2FNEJMra1402309

Wade, DT, Robson P, House H, Makela P, Aram J. 2003. A preliminary controlled study to determine whether whole-plant cannabis extracts can improve intractable neurogenic symptoms. Clinical Rehabilitation. 2003. 17: 18–26. https://doi.org/10.1191/0269215503cr581oa

Wang D, Wang H, Ning W, Backlund MG, Dey SK, DuBois RN. 2008. Loss of cannabinoid receptor 1 accelerates intestinal tumor growth. Cancer Res. 68(15):6468-6476. https://doi.org/10.1158/0008-5472.can-08-0896

Wang F, Wang L, Qu C, Chen L, Geng Y, Cheng C, Yu S, Wang D, Yang L, Meng Z, Chen Z. Kaempferol induces ROS-dependent apoptosis in pancreatic cancer cells via TGM2-mediated Akt/mTOR signaling. BMC Cancer. 2021 Apr 12;21(1):396. https://doi.org/10.1186/s12885-021-08158-z

Wang K, Wang Z, Cui R, Chu H. Polysaccharopeptide from Trametes versicolor blocks inflammatory osteoarthritis pain-morphine tolerance effects via activating cannabinoid type 2 receptor. Int J Biol Macromol. 2019 Apr 1;126:805-810. https://doi.org/10.1016/j.ijbiomac.2018.12.212

Ware MA. 2015. Synthetic Psychoactive Cannabinoids Licensed as Medicines. Handbook of Cannabis. Oxford University Press. Chapter 21. pp. 393-414.

Wargent, E., Zaibi, M., Silvestri, C. et al. The cannabinoid Δ9-tetrahydrocannabivarin (THCV) ameliorates insulin sensitivity in two mouse models of obesity. Nutr & Diabetes 3, e68 (2013). https://doi.org/10.1038/nutd.2013.9

Watanabe, K., Yamaori, S., Funahashi, T. et al. 8-Hydroxycannabinol: a new metabolite of cannabinol formed by human hepatic microsomes. Forensic Toxicol 24, 80–82 (2006). https://doi.org/10.1007/s11419-006-0016-0

Weinstein BS, Ciszek D. The reserve-capacity hypothesis: evolutionary origins and modern implications of the trade-off between tumor-suppression and tissue-repair. Exp Gerontol. 2002 May;37(5):615-27. https://doi.org/10.1016/s0531-5565(02)00012-8

Whiting PF, Wolff RF, Deshpande S, Nisio MD, Duffy S, Hernandez AV, Keurentjes JC, Lang S, Misso K, Ryder S, Schmidlkofer S, Westwood M, Kleijnen J. 2015. Cannabinoids for Medical use: A Systematic Review and Meta-analysis. JAMA. 313(24):2456-2473. https://doi.org/10.1001/jama.2015.6358

Williams MR, Holbrook TC, Maxwell L, Croft CH, Ientile MM, Cliburn K. Pharmacokinetic Evaluation of a Cannabidiol Supplement in Horses. J Equine Vet Sci. 2022 Mar;110:103842. doi.org/10.1016/j.jevs.2021.103842

Williams SJ, Hartley JP, Graham JD. 1976. Bronchodilator effect of delta1-tetrahydrocannabinol administered by aerosol of asthmatic patients. Thorax 31: 720–723. http://dx.doi.org/10.1136/thx.31.6.720

Wirth PW, Watson ES, ElSohly M, Turner CE, Murphy JC (1980). Anti-inflammatory properties of cannabichromene. Life Sci 26: 1991–1995. https://doi.org/10.1016/0024-3205(80)90631-1

Witkin JM, Tzavara ET, Nomikos GG. A role for cannabinoid CB1 receptors in mood and anxiety disorders. Behav Pharmacol. 2005 Sep;16(5-6):315-31. https://doi.org/10.1097/00008877-200509000-00005

Wong SK, Chin KY, Ima-Nirwana S. Quercetin as an Agent for Protecting the Bone: A Review of the Current Evidence. Int J Mol Sci. 2020 Sep 3;21(17):6448. https://doi.org/10.3390/ijms21176448

Wood GB, Bache F, eds., 1851, The Dispensatory of the United States of America, 9th ed. Philadelphia: Lippincott, Grambo, 1851, pp. 310-311.

Xing G, Carlton J, Jiang X, Wen J, Jia M, Li H. Differential Expression of Brain Cannabinoid Receptors between Repeatedly Stressed Males and Females may Play a Role in Age and Gender-Related Difference in Traumatic Brain Injury: Implications from Animal Studies. Front Neurol. 2014 Aug 28;5:161. https://doi.org10.3389/fneur.2014.00161

Xing G, Carlton J, Zhang L, Jiang X, Fullerton C, Li H, Ursano R. Cannabinoid receptor expression and phosphorylation are differentially regulated between male and female cerebellum and brain stem after repeated stress: implication for PTSD and drug abuse. Neurosci Lett. 2011 Sep 8;502(1):5-9. https://doi.org10.1016/j.neulet.2011.05.013

Xu D, Hu MJ, Wang YQ, Cui YL. Antioxidant Activities of Quercetin and Its Complexes for Medicinal Application. Molecules. 2019 Mar 21;24(6):1123. https://doi.org/10.3390/molecules24061123

Yamamoto I, Gohda H, Narimatsu S, Watanabe K, Yoshimura H. 1991. Cannabielsoin as a new metabolite of cannabidiol in mammals. Pharmacol Biochem Behav. 40(3):541-546. https://doi.org/10.1016/0091-3057(91)90360-e

Yamaori S, Ebisawa J, Okushima Y, Yamamoto I, Watanabe K. 2011. Potent inhibition of human cytochrome P450 3A isoforms by cannabidiol: role of phenolic hydroxyl groups in the resorcinol moiety. Life Sci. https://doi.org/10.1016/j.lfs.2011.02.017

Yang Y, Wei MC. 2016. A combine procedure of ultrasound-assisted and supercritical carbon dioxide for extraction and quantitation of oleanolic and ursolic acids from Hedyotis corymbosa. Industrial Crops and Products. 79: 7-17. https://doi.org/10.1016/j.indcrop.2015.10.038

Yang, M., van Velzen, R., Bakker, F.T., Sattarian, A., Li, D. and Yi, T. (2013), Molecular phylogenetics and character evolution of Cannabaceae. Taxon, 62: 473-485. doi.org/10.12705/623.9

Yao B, Mackie K. 2009. Endocannabinoid Receptor Pharmacology. Current Topics in Behavioral Neurosciences. 37-63

Ye L, Cao Z, Wang W, Zhou N. New Insights in Cannabinoid Receptor Structure and Signaling. Curr Mol Pharmacol. 2019;12(3):239-248. https://doi.org/10.2174%2F1874467212666190215112036

Yin H, Chu A, Li W, Wang B, Shelton F, Otero F, Nguyen DG, Caldwell JS, Chen YA. Lipid G protein-coupled receptor ligand identification using beta-arrestin PathHunter assay. J Biol Chem. 2009 May 1;284(18):12328-38. https://doi.org/10.1074/jbc.M806516200

Yin HY, Hadjokas N, Mirchia K, Swan R, Alpert S. Commercial Cannabinoid Oil-Induced Stevens-Johnson Syndrome. Case Rep Ophthalmol Med. 2020 Feb 19;2020:6760272. https://doi.org/10.1155/2020/6760272

Yu B, Ruan M, Dong X, Yu Y, Cheng H. The mechanism of the opening of the blood-brain barrier by borneol: a pharmacodynamics and pharmacokinetics combination study. J Ethnopharmacol. 2013 Dec 12;150(3):1096-108. https://pubmed.ncbi.nlm.nih.gov/24432371/

Yücel M, Bora E, Lubman DI, Solowij N, Brewer WJ, Cotton SM, Conus P, Takagi MJ, Fornito A, Wood SJ, McGorry PD, Pantelis C. The impact of cannabis use on cognitive functioning in patients with schizophrenia: a meta-analysis of existing findings and new data in a first-episode sample. Schizophr Bull. 2012 Mar;38(2):316-30. https://doi.org/10.1093/schbul/sbq079

Zajac D, Spolnik G, Roszkowski P, Danikiewicz W, Czarnocki Z, Pokorski M. Metabolism of N-acylated-dopamine. PLoS One. 2014 Jan 22;9(1):e85259. https://doi.org/10.1371/journal.pone.0085259  PMID: 24465516; PMCID: PMC3899008.

Zhao P, Abood ME. GPR55 and GPR35 and their relationship to cannabinoid and lysophospholipid receptors. Life Sci. 2013 Mar 19;92(8-9):453-7. https://doi.org/10.1016/j.lfs.2012.06.039

Zhu L, Xue L. Kaempferol Suppresses Proliferation and Induces Cell Cycle Arrest, Apoptosis, and DNA Damage in Breast Cancer Cells. Oncol Res. 2019 Jun 21;27(6):629-634. https://doi.org/10.3727/096504018x15228018559434

Zhu LX, Sharma S, Stolina M, Gardner B, Roth MD, Tashkin DP. 2000. Delta-9-tetrahydrocannabinol inhibits antitumor immunity by a CB2 receptor-mediated, cytokine-dependent pathway. J Immunol. 165(1):373-380. https://doi.org/10.4049/jimmunol.165.1.373

Zuardi A, Crippa J, Dursun S, Morais S, Vilela J, Sanches R, Hallak J. 2010. Cannabidiol was ineffective for manic episode of bipolar affective disorder. J Psychopharmacol. 24(1):135-137. https://doi.org/10.1177/0269881108096521

Zuardi AW, Cosme RA, Graeff FG, Guimaraes FS. 1993. Effects of ipsapirone and cannabidiol on human experimental anxiety. Journal of Psychopharmacology. 7: 82–88. https://doi.org/10.1177/026988119300700112

Zuardi AW, Morais SL, Guimarães FS, Mechoulam R. Antipsychotic effect of cannabidiol. J Clin Psychiatry. 1995 Oct;56(10):485-6.

Zuardi AW, Shirawaka I, Finkelfarb E, Karniol IG. 1982. Action of cannabidiol on the anxiety and other effects produced by delta 9-THC in normal subjects. Psychopharmacology. 76: 245–250. https://doi.org/10.1007/bf00432554

Zweifel C, Stephan R. 2011. Spices and herbs as source of Salmonella-related foodborne diseases. Food Research International. 45:765-769.

# APPENDIX C: GLOSSARY

**Actinomycetes** – also Actinobacteria; group of generally bacteria present in soils and water that give soil its characteristic smell. Actinomycetes produce a number of metabolites used in medicine.

**Alkane** – hydrocarbon compound with only single bonds

**Alkene** – hydrocarbon compound with one or more double bonds

**Alkyne** – hydrocarbon compound with one or more triple bonds

**Allele** – a form of a gene that is responsible for hereditary variation.

**Allosteric Modulator** – a compound that does not bind to the orthosteric site of a receptor, but instead binds to other sites and manipulates the shape and function of the receptor when a compound later binds to the orthosteric site.

**Amnesia** – deficit in memory

**Analgesia** – inability to feel pain

**Analgesic** – pain reliever

**Angiosperm** – flowering plant

**Anther** – the part of the stamen that holds pollen

**Antiemetic** – anti-nausea compound

**AOI (Area of Interest)** – when using the online Web Soil Survey program, this term refers to the area of which the user would like to find soil survey data

**Apical Bud** – also known as the terminal bud; the region of active growth at the top of the main stem of a plant

**Apical Meristem** – meristem region of active growth in the apical bud

**Arbuscular Mycorrhizal Fungus** – fungi of the phylum Glomeromycota; these fungi form symbiotic relationships with plant roots, exchanging phosphorous and other nutrients with the plant in exchange for carbon. Arbuscular mycorrhizae penetrate certain cells of the roots of the plant and then produce structures called arbuscules which are the sites where nutrients are exchanged with the plant.

**Available Nitrogen** - amount of Nitrogen present in molecular forms that are possible for the plant to process.

**Available Phosphorous** – amount of Phosphorous present in molecular forms that are possible for the plant to process.

**Available Potassium** - amount of Potassium present in molecular forms that are possible for the plant to process

**Available Water** – amount of water in soil that is available for a plant's roots to use

**Bioremediation** – remediation of contaminated landscapes using organisms such as plants and fungi to breakdown, absorb, or transform present contaminants.

**Bipolar spectrum** – spectrum of psychological dysfunction characterized by shifting mood states between depressed, manic, and hypomanic states

**Bronchodilation** - a bronchodilator is a substance that dilates the bronchi and bronchioles, decreasing resistance in the respiratory airway and increasing airflow to the lungs

**Bryophyte** – nonvascular plants (i.e., mosses)

**Callus** – a mass of undifferentiated cells produced by a plant in response to a wound or some other stimulus.

**Calyx** – collective term for the sepals of a flower

**Cannabinoid** – class of compounds that interact with cannabinoid receptors

**Cannabis use disorder** – spectrum disorder characterized by compulsive drug seeking and use behavior despite negative consequences in life responsibilities or relationships

**Capitate** – forming a head

**Carbamates** – a group of compounds derived from carbamic acid, commonly used as insecticides

**Certificate of Analysis** – an official laboratory document displaying the results of an ordered service signed by an appropriate laboratory representative

**Chemical Weathering –** the breakdown of rock through the changing of the chemical composition of the rock, usually through interaction with water and oxygen

**Chemotaxonomy** – method of categorizing something based on its chemical profile

**Chemotype** – the chemical profile of a living thing; the chemotype of Cannabis typically includes the cannabinoid and terpenoid content, and sometimes the flavonoid content

**Chirality** – a property of asymmetry; enantiomers are examples of chemical chirality

**Colloidal Particles** – in soil science, colloidal particles refer to the smallest particles in the soil that will suspend in solution, such as the clay and humus particles. These particles act as nutrient buffers and can cling tightly to positively charged ions.

**Column** – the part of a chromatograph that contains the stationary phase

**Comorbidity** – the co-occurrence of two or more illness, diseases, or conditions

**Conjunctival hyperemia** – red eyes

**Cotyledons** – the first leaves to sprout from a seed; the cotyledons are pre-formed in the seed before sprouting; also known as "seed leaves"

**Cytokine** – proteins important for cell signaling, especially for the immune system

**Decarboxylation Conversion Factor** – a correction factor applied to a carboxylic acid to calculate its potential decarboxylated content. For cannabinoids, this decarboxylation factor is approximately 0.88.

**Deoxyxylulose Pathway** – the chemical synthetic pathway responsible for the production of phytocannabinoids and terpenoids

**Depression** – a state of low mood and aversion to activity

**Diabetes or Diabetes mellitus** – a group of metabolic diseases characterized by high blood sugar levels over a prolonged period of time

**Dimethylallyl pyrophosphate (DMAPP)** – DMAPP joined with IPP forms GPP which is the precursor to CBGA, which goes on to form THCA, CBDA, and CBCA.

**Dissolution** – the separation of crystalline structures into their component ions in solution

**Ectomycorrhizal fungus** – mycorrhizal fungus that surrounds plant roots in a sheath and exchanges water and nutrients for carbon. Ectomycorrhizal often produce large fruiting bodies (mushrooms) and are associated with shrubs and trees.

**Egg** – the organic container of the zygote of a living thing

**Embryo** – the earliest stage of development of a plant in seed form. The embryo produces the premature cotyledons before sprouting.

**Embryo Sac** – ovule; produces an egg cell for fertilization with a sperm for reproduction

**Enantiomer** – in chemistry, two molecules with the same structure that cannot be superposed on one another ("left hand" vs. "right hand" analogy)

**Endocannabinoid** – compounds produced by the human body that act on cannabinoid receptors including anandamide and 2-Arachidonoylglycerol

**Endocannabinoidome** – complex interconnected series of physiological components associated with the functioning of the endocannabinoid system including non-cannabinoid receptors, pharmacologically active degradation products of cannabinoids, cannabinoid and non-cannabinoid receptor complexes, etc.

**Endocannabinoid System** – a lipid signaling system consisting of endogenous cannabinoid compounds, cannabinoid receptors and enzymes; the ECS is involved in various physiological processes such as appetite, pain modulation, mood, and memory.

**Endosperm** – nutrient storage unit in a seed that helps to provide nutrition for the developing embryo

**Evaporation** – conversion of a liquid to a gas at a temperature below the compound's boiling point

**External Reference Standard** – reference standards obtained from outside of the laboratory to ensure the accuracy of internal standards and results

**Fasting Insulin** – insulin level prior to the first meal of the day

**Fatty Acid** – a class of compounds that have a long hydrocarbon chain that ends in a carbon-oxygen group bonded to a glycerol; for Cannabis, fatty acids are found primarily in the seed oil.

**Fertilization** – the moment when the egg and the sperm meet, and the production of the seed contents begins

**Flavonoid** – a member of a group of polyphenolic plant pigment compounds that are water-soluble

**Forced Swim Test** - an experiment used to assay mood levels in rodents in scientific research

**Free Radical** – an atom or molecule that is very reactive due to an unpaired electron. Free radicals can cause rapid chain reactions that can destabilize other compounds, leading to more free radicals

**Functional Group** – a group of bonded atoms that give molecules particular characteristics (i.e., the carboxylic acid functional group is removed from THCA to produce THC)

**Gas Chromatograph (GC)** – instrument used in analytical chemistry to separate and measure the concentration of compounds in a solution. The solution is vaporized and steadily heated as it passes through a column, where the compounds pass across the stationary phase. A detector reports data about the separated compounds as they pass through.

**Gene** – a sequence of nucleotides on a segment of DNA that provides instructions for the production of proteins

**Gene Pool** – the genetic information among a population of individuals

**Genotype** – the genetic makeup of an organism

**Geranyl-pyrophosphate** – synthesized from the combination of DMAPP and IPP, GPP is the precursor to CBGA

**Germination** – the beginning of seedling growth when the embryo has received water and initiated growth

**Germplasm** – the living genetic material of an organism that is used for reproduction, like seeds or tissue

**Glandular Trichome** – a trichome possessing a spherical glandular secretion at the end. In Cannabis this is where the majority of common cannabinoids are produced

**Glaucoma** – group of eye diseases which can result in damage to the optic nerves and vision

**Glomalin** – a substance produced by fungi that are members of the glomeromycota that acts as a glue for various soil particles, essentially acting as a buffer for nutrients

**GMP** – good manufacturing practice

**G-Protein Coupled Receptor** – group of receptors that are a part of a large family of proteins that sense molecules outside of cells and control cell signaling and responses. Cannabinoid receptors are g-protein coupled receptors

**Grafting** – a method of propagation where a shoot is fused to another plant's rootstock so that a plant will grow that exhibits traits of both plants.

**Gymnosperm** – vascular plant that does not produce flowers (i.e., conifers)

**High Pressure (Performance) Liquid Chromatography (HPLC)** – an instrument used in analytical chemistry for the separation and identification of concentrations of compounds. HPLC is a cold method of analysis allowing for the identification of carboxylic acids and other compounds.

**Hippocampus** – area of the brain in the temporal lobe responsible for memory formation and storage among other things; the hippocampus is densely populated with CB1 receptors.

**Hippocampus** – part of the brain that belongs to the limbic system and is involved in memory and spatial navigation

**Humus** – the fraction of organic matter in soil which the organic matter is no longer recognizable

**Hydrolysis** – the breaking of a chemical bond through the addition of water

**Hydrophilic** – have an affinity for water

**Hydrophobic** – having no attraction for water

**Hyperaccumulator** – an organism that has the ability to accumulate and tolerate relatively high levels of metals in its tissues

**Hyperalgesia** – increased sensitivity to painful stimuli

**Hyperemesis** – excess nausea

**Hypomania** – mild state of mania

**Immunomodulator** – a compound that influences immune system response

**In vitro** – "in glass"; procedures performed in a petri dish or test tube are considered *in vitro*

**In vivo** – "in the living"; procedures performed on a living organism, typically a rodent

**Inflammation** - protective response that involves immune cells, blood vessels, and molecular mediators which causes pain, heat, redness, swelling, and loss of function.

**Inflammation** – response of the body to harmful stimuli characterized by pain, heat, redness and swelling

**Inflorescence** – a group of flowers on a main stem

**Insulin** – hormone used by the body to store sugar from the blood in various tissue types

**Internal Standard** – reference standard developed in-house and used to calibrate results and test instrument performance

**Internode** – space between nodes

**Intraocular pressure** – pressure within the eye

**Isomer** – molecule with the same formula as another molecule but with a different structure

**Isopentenyl-pyrophosphate (IPP)** – compound that when combined with DMAPP produces GPP, and consequently CBGA.

**Isoprene** –molecule with the formula CH2=CCH=CH2; base unit for terpenoids, aka isoprenoids

**Killer T Cell** – cells produced by the body that kill cancer cells as well as other damaged cells

**Lateral Meristem** – meristem region responsible for increasing the girth of the plant

**Leaflet** – Each individual leaflike structure that makes up an entire compound leaf

**Leukoedema** – blue, grey, or white appearance of mucosae; smoking can cause Leukoedema of the oral mucosa

**Limit of Detection** – the lowest analyte concentration that can be distinguished from a blank with at least 50% confidence

**Limit of Quantification –** the lowest concentration at which the analyte can be reliably detected at a confidence level that meets predefined quality assurance standards

**Lipid** – group of molecules including fats, waxes, sterols, fat soluble vitamins, monoglycerides, diglycerides, triglycerides, and phospholipids among other things. Lipids are used to store energy, contribute to the structure of cell membranes, and conduct signaling. The endocannabinoid system is a lipid signaling system.

**Lipophilic** – having an affinity for lipids

**Lipophobic** – not having an affinity for lipids

**Macronutrient** –nutrients required in great quantities for an organism to survive including Nitrogen, Phosphorous, and Potassium

**Mania** – state of great excitement, euphoria, delusions, and/or overactivity; one of the key components of bipolar spectrum disorder

**Mass Spectrometer (Mass Spec or MS)** – instrument used in analytical chemistry to detect the molecular weights of compounds that have passed through another instrument like a gas or liquid chromatograph

**Mechanical Weathering** – process of breaking down rock through physical processes like the expanding and condensing of water and ice in the cracks of rocks

**Meristem** – regions of active growth of a plant

**Meroterpenoid** – a compound containing a partial terpene structure

**Micronutrient** – nutrients required in small quantities for an organism to survive including iron, cobalt, chromium, copper, iodine, manganese, selenium, zinc, and molybdenum.

**Micropropagation** – methods of propagation in which plants are cloned from meristem tissue in sterile environments. Plants are grown in a nutritive solution in test tubes. This allows for the propagation of high quantities of clones in a small amount of space

**Mildew** – a type of fungus that commonly grows on plants and produces a powdery appearance

**Mobile Phase** – in chromatography, the phase that moves and passes across the stationary phase

**Mold** – a type of fungus that commonly grows on plants and soil in humid environments and produces a fluffy stringy appearance in a variety of colors. Some molds are highly toxic and produce harmful mycotoxins.

**Monoterpenoid** – class of terpenes that have two isoprene units and a molecular formula of $C_{10}H_{16}$

**Monotype** – In taxonomy, having only one species, or type.

**Morbidity –** the presence of an illness or disease

**NELAP –** National Environmental Laboratory Accreditation Program

**Non-Glandular Trichome** – trichome lacking a spherical head and having a hair like appearance

**Nonpolar** – a compound with equal sharing of electrons

**ORELAP** – Oregon Environmental Laboratory Accreditation Program

**Organochlorides** – also known as Organochlorines, chlorocarbons, or chlorinated hydrocarbon; an organic compound with at least one covalently bonded chlorine. Organochlorides are a class of pesticides

**Organophosphates** – an organic compound with a phosphate group; a class of pesticides

**Orthosteric Site** – the primary site of action on a chemical receptor

**Palmate** – shaped like a hand or palm with appendages extending from a central location

**Papillae** – small, usually round, protrusions; the stigmas of a Cannabis flower are covered with papillae that help guide pollen toward the style and into the ovary.

**Perianth** – a term referring to a flower's corolla and calyx together

**Permanent Wilting Point** – the point when water in the soil becomes unavailable for a plant's roots due to the tension the soil is exerting on the water.

**Petiole** – stalk of a leaf

**pH** – a measure of the positively charged hydrogen ions in a solution

**Phenol** – molecule consisting of an aromatic ring with a bonded –OH group; aromatic alcohol

**Phenotype** – the physical characteristics of an organism

**Phloem** – the part of the vascular system of a plant responsible for moving nutrients throughout the plant

**Phytocannabinoid** – cannabinoid produced by a plant

**Polar** – a compound with an unequal sharing of electrons

**Polymerase Chain Reaction (PCR)** – technique used in analytical chemistry to replicate a piece of DNA many times to measure

**Polyphenol** – a class of organic chemicals consisting of multiple phenol units. Phenol units are aromatic organic compounds with the molecular formula $C_6H_5OH$.

**Polytype** – in taxonomy, having more than one species, or type

**Posttraumatic Stress Disorder (PTSD)** – a psychological disorder typically following one or more traumatic events such as sexual assault, warfare, traffic accidents, terrorism, abuse, etc that is characterized by heightened states of fear, anxiety, antisocial behavior, flashbacks, and difficulty sleeping.

**Protean Agonism** – a state when a compound may agonize, or stimulate, a chemical receptor when the receptor is largely inactive, but may later change its activity to antagonize or inversely agonize the same receptor if the receptor is already active; derived from the Greek god Proteus who could change form depending on who was observing him.

**Pyrethroids** – a class of pesticides.

**Reference Standard** – a sample containing a known amount of a compound for the use of instrument calibration and result correction

**Ring Test** – the process of multiple analytical laboratories analyzing one sample with a known concentration of compounds and then sharing the results

**Saprophytic Fungus** – fungus that gains energy by breaking down dead organic matter. These fungi are responsible for the common mold seen on wet soils with heavy microbiological amendments

**Schizophrenia** – psychological disorder characterized by a variety of positive and negative symptoms including antisocial tendencies, hallucinations, delusions, false beliefs, confused thinking, catatonia, and mood swings

**Secondary Mineral** – a mineral that has been chemically weathered to become a different compound than the parent rock

**Seed Coat** – a protective layer of tissue around the seed

**Serration** – having notched edges like the teeth of a saw

**Sesquiterpenoid** – class of terpenes with three isoprene units and a formula of $C_{15}H_{24}$. Sesquiterpenes are usually the primary terpenes left in dried and cured Cannabis as the more volatile monoterpenes volatize during drying.

**Sessile** – lacking a stalk; attached at a base

**Soil Adsorption Coefficient** – a number used to represent a compound's mobility in the soil

**Solvent** – a chemical used to dissolve other compounds to form a solution

**Spinosyns** – a class of pesticides generally approved for use in organic agriculture

**Stamen** – the pollen producing part of the reproductive system of a flower

**Standard Deviation** – a measure used to show the amount of variation in a data set

**Standard Operating Procedure** – detailed instructions for various procedures to achieve repeatability and assist quality assurance

**Stationary Phase** – the phase in chromatography which compounds pass across and separate

**Stigma** – part of the flower that receives pollen and passes it to the ovary

**Style** – the connection between the stigma and the ovary

**Supercritical Fluid** – a substance at a temperature and pressure at which the substance can pass through solids like a gas but dissolve compounds like a liquid. Supercritical fluid can be used to extract essential oils from plants.

**Synthetic Seed** – germplasm or callus from tissue surrounded in a nutritive gel

**Supraphysiological** – usually used in reference to a dose; a dose greater than would be typically found in a body

**Tail Suspension Test** – an experiment used to assay mood levels in rodents in scientific research

**Taxonomy** – branch of science dealing with the description and classification of organisms

**Terminal Bud** – also known as the apical bud; region of active growth at the tip of the main stem of a plant.

**Ternary Diagram** – a diagram for calculating soil texture type based on sand, silt, and clay percentages

**Terpenoid** – also known as isoprenoids; organic chemicals synthesized by plants that are responsible for the aromas and tastes of the plant

**Terpenophenolic Compounds** – compounds consisting of both isoprene and phenol units; cannabinoids are terpenophenolic compounds.

**Thin Layer Chromatography** – a method of compound separation and quantitation involving the exposure of a sample to a plate which is later exposed to a solvent which rises up the plate through capillary action. A dye is then applied to the plate to visualize the compound separations.

**Tissue Culture** – a method of growing tissue from an organism in a sterile environment like a petri dish or test tube.

**Trichome** – glandular or non-glandular growth from the skin of a plant.

**Vasodilation** – dilation of blood vessels

**Venation** – the shapes and patterns of the veins of a leaf

**Volatilization** – to make volatile; to vaporize

**Winterization** – process of precipitating heavy lipids from an oil by bathing the oil in alcohol and exposing the mixture to cold temperatures for an extended period of time

**Xerostomia** – dry mouth

**Xylem** – the part of the plant vascular system responsible for pumping water throughout the plant

**Yeast** – a type of fungus that is unicellular and reproduces through budding

# Appendix D: Resources for Further Learning

**Disclaimer:** Resource listings are not an indication of endorsement of this book or the author by any listed associated authors, publishers, or affiliated organizations of entities listed in this appendix.

## Suggested Books/Literature

**The American Herbal Pharmacopoeia** monograph for Cannabis inflorescence covers many aspects of the Cannabis plant from the botany and biochemistry of the plant to the analysis of the plant. Visit http://www.herbal-ahp.org to order a copy.

**Handbook of Cannabis** edited by Roger Pertwee

**Cannabinoids** by Vincenzo di Marzo

**The Endocannabinoidome** by Vincenzo di Marzo and Jenny Wang

**The Pot Book: A Complete Guide to Cannabis – It's Role in Medicine, Politics, Science, and Culture** by Julie Holland

**Cannabis: Evolution and Ethnobotany** by Robert Clarke and Mark Merlin

**The Emperor Wears No Clothes** by Jack Herer

**Marijuana Horticulture: The Indoor/Outdoor Medical Grower's Bible** by Jorge Cervantes

**Hemp Diseases and Pests – Management and Biological Control** by JM McPartland, RC Clarke, and DP Watson

**Marijuana Botany** by Robert Clarke

**Cannabis: A Complete Guide** by Ernest Small

**Marijuana Chemistry: Genetics, Processing and Potency** by Michael Starks

**The Botany of Desire** by Michael Pollan

**Teaming with Microbes** by Jeff Lowenfels

**Teaming with Nutrients** by Jeff Lowenfels

**Teaming with Fungi** by Jeff Lowenfels

**Teaming with Bacteria** by Jeff Lowenfels

# Suggested Web Resources

**American Association for Laboratory Accreditation**: http://www.a2la.org
A2LA provides ISO accreditation programs and NELAP proficiency testing for analytical laboratories. They offer accreditation for medical Cannabis laboratories.

**Americans for Safe Access**: http://www.safeaccessnow.org/
Americans for Safe Access is a Cannabis education and advocacy group. Their website provides medical Cannabis related information on a variety of topics including health, law, and activism.

**American Herbal Products Association (AHPA):** http://www.ahpa.org/

**Cannabinoid Hyperemesis Syndrome Resource**: http://www.cannabinoid-hyperemesis.com/
Compiled information about CHS managed by CHS survivor and Cannabis advocate, Alice Moon, including information about symptoms, diagnosis, treatment, and ongoing research.

**Cannabis Chemistry Subdivision of the American Chemical Society**: https://dchas.org/cann/

**Cannify**: http://www.cannify.us/
Cannify is an online quiz that helps connect users, researchers, and health care professionals with relevant information about Cannabis in connection with a particular medical condition. Using results from hundreds of scientific studies, the Cannify Quiz uses a complex algorithm to generate personalized reports.

**Connect** by Confident Cannabis: http://connect.confidentcannabis.com/
Connect is a tool that allows users to evaluate the differences in chemotype between products that have passed through the Confident Cannabis software platform, used by Cannabis testing laboratories, producers, and retailers to share traceable information about Cannabis products.

**Curious About Cannabis Podcast:** http://www.CACPodcast.com/
The Curious About Cannabis Podcast is a spin-off resource from the Curious About Cannabis Book where author and science educator Jason Wilson interviews researchers, clinicians, chemists, cultivators, and others to critically explore essential questions about Cannabis. Find the Curious About Cannabis Podcast wherever you listen to podcasts.

**Future 4200 Forum**: http://www.future4200.com
The Future 4200 forum is an online forum primarily focused on sharing information about Cannabis processing technologies and techniques, however it does cover a wide variety of other Cannabis related topics as well. The forum has attracted the attention of a number of knowledgeable chemists, engineers, and other technical experts. While the forum is a repository of a lot of good information, as with any forum, it is important to be cautious when evaluating information. Trust, but verify.

**The Good Scents Company Information System**:
http://www.thegoodscentscompany.com/
The Good Scents Company provides information about odor and flavor compounds found in fragrances, foods, essential oils, and more. This resource can be utilized to find

information about smells and particular terpenes found in various products, like Cannabis. Their odor index can be found at: www.thegoodscentscompany.com/allodor.html You can find information about specific terpenes by visiting the "Found in Nature" section of the odor index.

**Integrated Taxonomic Information System (ITIS)**: http://www.itis.gov/

**International Cannabis Research Society (ICRS):** http://www.icrs.co

**International Institute for Cannabinoids (ICANNA):** http://www.institut-icanna.com/en/

**Isn't Life Curious? Podcast:** https://www.isntlifecurious.com/
Another podcast brought to you by Natural Learning Enterprises and Curious About Cannabis host/producer Jason Wilson, MS – Isn't Life Curious? explores topics that are at the intersections of philosophy, art, and science.

**Kannapedia by Medicinal Genomics:** http://www.kannapedia.net/
Kannapedia is a Cannabis strain genetics database which demonstrates the genetic relationships between different samples. The site features a massive phylogenetic tree representing their database that can make your head spin.

**List of Cannabis Sativa diseases by McPartland (2003)**:
http://www.apsnet.org/publications/commonnames/Pages/Hemp.aspx

**National Environmental Laboratory Accreditation Conference (NELAC) Institute**: http://www.nelac-institute.org/
The NELAC Institute handles environmental laboratory accreditations and more.

**Natural Resource Conservation Service Web Soil Survey:**
http://websoilsurvey.sc.egov.usda.gov/App/HomePage.htm

**O'Shaughnessy's**: http://www.beyondthc.com
O'Shaughnessy's is an excellent source for Cannabis science and research news and editorials.

**Oregon CBD:** http://www.oregoncbdseeds.com/
Cannabis research and development company that produces federally legal CBD-rich, CBG-rich, and cannabinoid varin-rich hemp seeds in the United States.

**Oregon State University Soil Testing Guide**:
http://smallfarms.oregonstate.edu/soil-testing
OSU provides great information about environmental laboratories that serve Oregon. Use their list of labs to find a lab that can test soil and water for pesticides and heavy metals. They also have a resource for interpreting soil test results and a guide to collecting soil samples.

**Pesticide Database**: http://www.pesticideinfo.org

**Pesticide Properties Database:** http://sitem.herts.ac.uk/aeru/ppdb/en/atoz.htm
This is a great website for obtaining detailed information about synthetic and naturally derived pesticides including data on mobility, persistence, toxicity, environmental impact, and more.

**BioPesticide Properties Database:** http://sitem.herts.ac.uk/aeru/bpdb/index.htm

**Phylos Galaxy by Phylos Bioscience**: http://phylos.bio/galaxy/
Phylos Bioscience provides genetic services for Cannabis cultivators and hosts an online Cannabis strain "galaxy" which maps the genetic relationships between samples that they have tested.

**Phytecs LLC:** http://www.phytecs.com/
Phytecs develops and derives products from natural plant compounds that can support and restore optimal endocannabinoid system function. Check out their educational resources and recommended reading list.

**Phytochemical Glossary**: http://www.phytopia.com/cookbook/glossary.htm

**Project CBD**: http://www.projectcbd.org

**PubChem:** http://pubchem.ncbi.nlm.nih.gov/
Find chemical information from authoritative sources including information on over 103 million compounds and 264 million substances.

**PubMed:** http://pubmed.ncbi.nlm.nih.gov/
Find more than 30 million citations for biomedical literature from various medical and life science research journals and books.

**ResTek ChromaBlogRaphy**: http://blog.restek.com/
Restek provides laboratory instrumentation and supplies as well as training and education about analytical methods and technology. Their chromatography blog provides news and updates about chromatography instrumentation and methods.

**Separation Science**: http://www.sepscience.com/
Separation Science provides online learning and training opportunities surrounding all aspects of chromatography.

**Society of Cannabis Clinicians**: https://www.cannabisclinicians.org/
"The SCC is a nonprofit educational and scientific society of healthcare professionals an dallies dedicated to advancing research and disseminating knowledge about medical cannabis."

**TLC Lab Supply:** http://www.thctestkits.com/
TLC Lab Supply is a company providing thin layer chromatography kits and supplies to the public for testing products for cannabinoids.

**Toxipedia**: www.toxipedia.org
Find information about various toxins including pesticides and chemical contaminants.

**World Health Organization Guidelines for Assessing Quality of Herbal Medicines with Reference to Contaminants and Residues**:
http://apps.who.int/medicinedocs/en/d/Js14878e/
This is an excellent overview of contaminants that can be found in herbal products, the common sources of those contaminations, and how to reduce the risk of contamination during growing, processing, and storage of herbal products.

## Zenthanol Consulting

Excellent collection of evidence-based integrated pest management information.

Web: https://www.zenthanol.com/

YouTube: https://www.youtube.com/zenthanol

# APPENDIX E: INDEX OF TABLES AND FIGURES

# APPENDIX F: CUMULATIVE EXAMINATION

1. How many species of Cannabis are there?
2. Approximately how many cannabinoids are produced by the Cannabis plant?
3. Approximately how many terpenoids are produced by the Cannabis plant?
4. In what type of trichome(s) produced by the Cannabis plant are cannabinoids primarily found?
5. What soil pH does Cannabis typically prefer?
6. Under what length of photoperiod, or light exposure, does a Cannabis plant need to remain in a vegetative state?
7. Under what length of photoperiod, or light exposure, does a Cannabis plant need to begin flowering?
8. What is a Cannabis plant that flowers regardless of light exposure?
9. What is an alternative term for "strain"?
10. What is the difference between a chemovar and a cultivar?

11. What is the chemical precursor to THCA, CBDA, and CBCA?
12. What is decarboxylation?

13. At what temperature does decarboxylation typically occur for THCA?
14. True or False: Cannabinoids are hydrophilic.
15. True or False: Terpenoids are lipophilic.
16. Which of the following is not a solventless form of Cannabis extraction?
    a. Dry Sift
    b. Bubble Hash
    c. Rosin
    d. Supercritical CO2

17. Which of the following Cannabis extraction techniques do not typically require "winterization"?
    a. Ethanol
    b. Hydrocarbon/Alkane
    c. Supercritical CO2
    d. None of the above

18. What phrase does the word "chromatography" translate to?
19. What are the basic components of a chromatography system?

20. What are the most common methods used to test Cannabis products for potency?

21. What is the primary way in which gas and liquid chromatography differ?

22. True or False: Mycotoxins are present in a product even if the source fungus has been killed or eliminated.

23. True or False: The act of concentrating Cannabis resins will also concentrate many pesticides.

24. What are the three primary components of the endocannabinoid system?

25. How does the endocannabinoidome differ from the endocannabinoid system?

26. What is the process called that converts orally consumed THC into the more potent 11-OH-THC?

27. True or False: Cannabis strain names are reliable plant names that strongly correlate with a particular chemical profile and genetic lineage.

28. Which of the following is not a common degradation product of THC?
    a. CBN
    b. Delta-8-THC
    c. CBD
    d. All of the above

29. Which of the following alcohol terpenes is produced from the true terpene, myrcene?
    a. Geraniol
    b. Linalool
    c. Menthol
    d. All of the above

30. What happens to Cannabis terpenes as the Cannabis flower dries and cures?

31. What is the most common terpenoid found in nature?
32. Why do cannabinoids have trouble penetrating the epidermis layer of the skin?

33. What are the health conditions that Cannabis users most commonly report treating with Cannabis?

34. The United States once held a patent on cannabinoids. What was it for?
35. How is hemp different than "marijuana"?

36. In what year was THC discovered to be the intoxicating element of Cannabis?
37. True or False: CBD is psychoactive.
38. In what year was CBD first discovered?
39. True or False: All vertebrate animals and many invertebrate animals contain endocannabinoid systems to some degree.
40. True or False: Terpenes account for only half of the odors detected from Cannabis by the human nose.
41. Which of the following is not a compound that contributes substantially to the colors of Cannabis?
    a. Anthocyanins
    b. Anthocyanidins
    c. Carotenoids
    d. Chlorophyll
    e. None of the above
42. List two endocannabinoids.

43. List at least two chemical receptors other than CB1 and CB2 that cannabinoids often interact with.

44. What is the most dominant enzyme responsible for breaking down fatty acids like anandamide?
45. What is the most dominant enzyme responsible for breaking down glycerol compounds like 2-AG?
46. How are divarinic cannabinoids different than traditional phytocannabinoids like THCA, CBDA, etc?
47. List two flavonoids that are thought to be unique to Cannabis.

48. What is the chemical class of compounds formed from the degradation of cannabinoids that results in a red color in Cannabis extracts?

49. What are some steps Cannabis cultivators can take to limit their environmental impact of cultivation?

50. List and briefly describe the four genetic loci that are thought to determine phytocannabinoid production.

51. Describe how cannabinoid receptor expression in the body changes in response to chronic Cannabis use.

52. What part of the brain is responsible for the memory loss effects of THC?

53. Generally, chronic Cannabis consumption leads to (increased/decreased) blood pressure and heart rate.

54. Cannabinoid receptor agonism in the gastrointestinal tract is associated with _____ (increased/decreased) motility.

55. Describe what current research has found concerning Cannabis use and driving. What challenges exist in measuring and determining driving impairment caused by Cannabis consumption?

56. What is the secondary metabolite of THC that is detected in most drug tests?

57. Explain one reason why patients with PTSD often use Cannabis as a self-medication.

58. List three ways to minimize anxiety symptoms and risk of panic when consuming Cannabis.

59. Describe the mechanisms by which cannabinoids affect cancer growth.

60. Describe the hypothesis of Clinical Endocannabinoid Deficiency. Be sure to include information about cannabinoid receptors and pain sensitivity.

61. What health conditions are associated with **excessive** endocannabinoid production?

62. What is the difference between statistical significance and clinical significance? Why is it important to distinguish the two concepts when reviewing research?

63. Describe at least three hurdles facing Cannabis research today.

64. List two endocannabinoids that are NOT Anandamide (AEA) or 2-arachidonoyl glycerol (2-AG).

65. This terpene is an aphid repellant and is correlated with narrow leaflet drug type varieties of Cannabis. Name the terpene.

66. This terpene is correlated with wide leaflet drug type varieties of Afghani origin and is often found in high ratios with Eudesmol. Name the terpene.

67. What are two primary characteristics that affect a terpene's effectiveness as a skin penetration enhancer?

68. Define the concept "phytochemical polymorphism".

69. How can cannabinoids help fight acne?

70. What is the set of liver enzymes that are temporarily inhibited by CBD?
71. THC is a _____ (partial, full, super) _____ (agonist, inverse agonist, antagonist) of CB1 receptors.
72. CBD is a _____ (partial, full, super) _____ (agonist, inverse agonist, antagonist) of CB2 receptors.
73. CBG is thought to be a protean agonist of cannabinoid receptors. Describe what it means to be a protean agonist.

74. List two FDA approved cannabinoid pharmaceutical drugs.

75. Why do the eyes turn red after consuming Cannabis?

76. True or False: Xerostomia, or dry mouth, is caused by smoking, not the ingestion of cannabinoids themselves
77. Briefly describe how cannabinoids may act as neuroprotective agents. What conditions might this affect?

78. What is apoptosis?

79. What is autophagy, and how is this process associated with apoptosis?

80. Endocannabinoids are autacoids. Describe the three primary characteristics of an autacoid.

81. Some researchers recommend CB1 antagonism and CB2 agonism as a way of treating _____.
    a. Addiction     b. Anorexia     c. PTSD     d. All of the above
82. Why are synthetic cannabinoids often more dangerous than phytocannabinoids?



83. What is the name of the Cannabis pharmaceutical containing a standardized Cannabis extract featuring a 1:1 ratio of THC to CBD, which is currently not approved for use in the United States?
84. What does it mean to "saturate" a cannabinoid?



85. List an example of a saturated semi-synthetic cannabinoid.

# APPENDIX G: EXAM ANSWER KEY

1. 1
2. >450
3. >200
4. Glandular capitate-stalked; capitate-sessile
5. 6.5-7
6. 18 hours of light; 6 hours of darkness
7. 12 hours of light; 12 hours of darkness
8. Autoflower
9. Cultivar; Chemovar
10. Cultivars are plants that can be propagated and retain desired traits like chemical profile, color, growth habit, etc; chemovars are plants of varying cultivars organized into groups based on their chemical profile alone
11. CBGA
12. Decarboxylation is the removal of a carboxylic acid functional group from a molecule, usually through the introduction of heat
13. Variable depending on atmospheric pressure and time exposed; Generally, 215°F at 15 minutes at average atmospheric pressure at 0 – 1000 ft elevation
14. False
15. True
16. Supercritical $CO_2$, though technically the water utilized in bubble hash production acts as a solvent for hydrophilic compounds in Cannabis
17. Hydrocarbon/Alkane
18. "Color writing"
19. Mobile Phase, Stationary Phase, Column, Detector
20. HPLC and GC
21. Gas chromatography is a hot process that decarboxylates the sample whereas liquid chromatography generally keeps the sample intact so that detection of cannabinoid acids is simpler
22. True
23. True
24. Endocannabinoids, Cannabinoid Receptors, Enzymes
25. The endocannabinoid system focuses on endocannabinoids and their primary receptor targets. The endocannabinoidome includes endocannabinoid congeners and ECS modulators with little to no activity at cannabinoid receptors that affect the activity of endocannabinoids.
26. First pass metabolism
27. False
28. CBD
29. All of the above
30. Monoterpenes quickly volatize away, driving up the concentration of sesquiterpenoids and other greater molecular weight terpenoids
31. Alpha-pinene
32. The epidermis features a series of hydrophobic and hydrophilic layers
33. Chronic pain is most common; Also spasticity, nausea, inflammation very common
34. The patent was "Cannabinoids for Antioxidants and Neuroprotectants"; US6630507B1

35. Hemp is legally defined as containing trace amounts of THC, with the limit varying between countries around the world, but usually between 0.2 – 1% THC; Both marijuana and hemp are Cannabis sativa
36. 1964
37. True
38. 1940
39. True
40. True
41. None of the above
42. N-arachidonoyl ethanolamine (Anandamide), 2-arachidonoyl glycerol (2-AG), Noladin ether; Virodhamine; n-arachidonoyl dopamine (NADA)
43. TRPV1, PPARy, 5HT1A, GPR55
44. Fatty acid amide hydrolase (FAAH)
45. Monoacylglycerol lipase (MAGL)
46. Divarinic cannabinoids are propyl chain cannabinoids featuring only 3 carbons in the carbon tail of the molecule
47. Cannflavin A, Cannflavin B, Cannflavin C
48. Cannabinoquinoids
49. Enhance soil quality, soil mulch, targeted drip irrigation, gravity fed irrigation, companion plants, beneficial predatory insects
50. O, A, B, C
51. CB1 receptor expression decreases with chronic stimulation
52. Hippocampus
53. Decreased
54. Decreased
55. Acute or occasional users demonstrate significant impairment; chronic users exhibit much less impairment; THC blood concentration does not correlate with impairment severity
56. Nor-9-carboxy-THC
57. Memory extinction, sleep, anxiety relief, depression relief
58. Low dose, familiar environment, eat food prior, drink water, don't mix with other substances
59. Antiangiogenesis (reduce the growth of blood vessels from cancer cells); Apoptosis (triggering cell death in cancer cells themselves)
60. Many disease states are characterized by low endocannabinoid levels and increased cannabinoid receptor expression
61. Obesity, insulin resistance, metabolic syndrome, spasticity
62. Statistical significance is how likely something is to happen compared to pure chance; clinical significance is how likely something is to be clinically relevant; some things that may be statistically significant may not be clinically significant.
63. See Chapter 26
64. Noladin ether, Virodhamine, n-arachidonoyl dopamine (NADA)
65. Trans-beta-farnesene
66. See Chapter 14
67. Boiling point, polarity, size
68. The cannabis plant produces slightly different chemistry throughout different parts of the plant – the top of the plant does not have the exact same cannabinoid and terpenoid profile as the middle or bottom of the plant.
69. Modulate sebum production, reduce acne promoting bacteria

70. Cytochrome P450 enzymes
71. Partial agonist
72. Partial agonist
73. CBG's activity at cannabinoid receptors, primarily CB1, varies depending on the prior activity at that receptor
74. Marinol, Nabilone, Epidiolex
75. As the blood vessels in the eyes contract, they become visible in the vitreous jelly of the eye.
76. False, xerostomia from Cannabis is thought to be related to cannabinoid receptor activity separate from smoking, though smoking may exacerbate dry mouth
77. Antioxidant activity via free radical scavenging, reduction of inflammation, triggering of apoptosis in unhealthy cells
78. Programmed cell death
79. Autophagy is the process by which the body cleans out cellular debris after a cell has destroyed itself via apoptosis
80. Autacoids are produced locally, on demand, where they are needed, when they are needed, and then broken down quickly
81. Addiction
82. They are often super agonists of CB1 receptors leading to severe reactions like vomiting, difficulty breathing, and loss of consciousness
83. Sativex / Nabiximols
84. Saturated cannabinoids do not contain any double bonds in a particular ring or throughout the entire molecule
85. HHC, Hexahydrocannabinol

A complete set of activities, lessons, quizzes, and assessments for educators and students are available at **store.cacpodcast.com**

# APPENDIX H: INDEX BY TERM

# NOTES

# NOTES

# Thanks for Buying This Book!
# Download the Digital Copy for Free!

Scan the QR code below to fill out a form where you can claim a free digital collectible that unlocks the digital version of the 3rd edition of the Curious About Cannabis book that you can view in browser or download for offline viewing.

**Get Your Token Now**

Once you reach the online form, simply tell us who you are, let us know where to send your digital collectible, and upload a photo of yourself with the physical copy of the book.

Note: To receive this digital collectible you will need to have a digital wallet capable of sending and receiving tokens on the Polygon blockchain. We recommend using MetaMask available at www.metamask.io

# The Curious About Cannabis Podcast

Featuring educational episodes on critical topics about Cannabis as well as exclusive interviews with Cannabis researchers, clinicians, producers, patients, and consumers – the Curious About Cannabis™ Podcast takes learners on an educational journey to critically explore essential questions about the world's most controversial plant.

Check out the Curious About Cannabis™ Podcast by visiting **www.CACPodcast.com** or search for the Curious About Cannabis™ Podcast wherever you listen to podcasts! You can also subscribe to the Curious About Cannabis™ channel on YouTube!

Join the Curious About Cannabis Learning Platform and dive into self-paced courses, expanded podcast episodes, educational videos, and more!

Scan the QR code to get started or visit member.cacpodcast.com

# The Curious About Cannabis Ecosystem

Curious About Cannabis is a learning initiative by Natural Learning Enterprises that provides a unique and robust platform for learning about Cannabis and cannabinoid science while connecting directly with experienced scientists, clinicians and industry professionals.

The Curious About Cannabis Ecosystem consists of several primary elements. Use this road map to discover all that Curious About Cannabis has to offer!

## Curious About Cannabis

**App** — Stay Connected

**Connect** — Communicate with the CAC Community on Discord

**Digital Collectibles** — Receive rewards for learning about cannabis science

**Book** — Learn Cannabis Science Basics

**Podcast** — Listen to Conversations with Curious Minds

**Learning Center** — Take Your Education to the next level

Available on Android
iOS Coming Soon

Connect with other learners and educators, participate in giveaways, discover new research and more!

Unlock digital collectables embedded with secret rewards as you learn about Cannabis science.

"...The Cannabis Science Bible..."

Dive into intensive courses, workshops, and trainings to become a certified Cannabis Science Master!

Explore critical questions about Cannabis and cannabinoids with scientists, clinicians, industry professionals and other curious minds!

# Visit Our Virtual Campus!

**The CAC Virtual Campus** provides an explorable 3D venue for curious minds to explore Cannabis and cannabinoid science topics, host educational events, meet up for study sessions, complete educational challenges to unlock rewards, or just hang out in one of the many available lounges.

The **Learning Center** provides educational resources and content about Cannabis and cannabinoid science including 3D displays and exhibits, learning challenges, virtual study/meeting rooms, self-paced courses and more.

While taking a break, head over to the **Exhibition Hall** to meet other curious minds and learn about the many contributors and sponsors that have helped support the Curious About Cannabis platform.

Throughout the Virtual Campus are "easter eggs" which unlock digital rewards and collectibles.

 **Scan this QR code with your phone's camera to hop into the Curious About Cannabis metaverse right now!**

# About the Author

Jason Wilson is a natural products researcher and passionate science communicator with work featured in science publications like *Frontiers of Pharmacology*, pop culture publications like *The Cannigma*, *Cured* and *Terpenes and Testing*, as well as local and national herbaria across the United States, including the US National Herbarium at the Smithsonian Institute. He has been featured on numerous podcasts including *Narcotica*, *Brave New Weed*, *Own Your Harvest*, *The Metagenics Podcast,* and more.

His exposure to Cannabis science began early at the University of Mississippi where he spent time fixing instruments for researchers at the NIDA Cannabis research and development laboratory. After learning about the work happening at the NIDA Cannabis labs on campus, Jason decided to go back to school to study upper-level biology and chemistry with an eye toward moving his career into natural products research.

After studying science education in graduate school, he helped build one of the first accredited Cannabis testing laboratories in Oregon. Jason went on to help build and manage a number of Cannabis testing and research facilities throughout Oregon and California before transitioning to focus on Cannabis product research and development in the late 2010s.

While working with Cannabis product manufacturers, Jason helped design and execute Cannabis research projects and implement quality systems that led to the development of more effective and consistent products ranging from Cannabis flower to extracts and formulated products.

Today Jason provides scientific and educational consulting while regularly providing guest lectures, seminars, classes and workshops on Cannabis and cannabinoid science topics for diverse audiences of all skill and knowledge bases.

Beyond his interests in Cannabis science and pharmacognosy, Jason is a certified permaculture designer, Audubon naturalist, musician and ordained dudist priest. When not in the lab or behind a computer, he prefers to be exploring the natural world while spending time with family and friends.

Learn more about Jason at JasonWilsonMS.com

# Other Projects from Natural Learning Enterprises

**Toadstool's Treasures** presents fun and educational content exploring the world of fungi - introducing children and parents alike to the critical roles that fungi play in our environments. Find our children's book, **A Toadstool's Treasures**, as well as lessons, games, and more at **Toadstool's Treasures**!

www.ToadstoolsTreasures.com

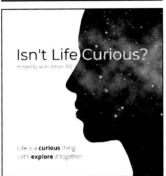

We all have a natural curiosity about life. **Isn't Life Curious?** is a podcast hosted by Jason Wilson, MS that confronts listeners and viewers with critical questions and conversations about science, philosophy, and our place within the natural world.

www.IsntLifeCurious.com

**Natural Learning Laboratories** is a natural products laboratory focused on studying the chemistry and pharmacognosy of native plants and recognized ethnobotanicals with an emphasis on research that can help improve the quality of life of everyday people.

www.NaturalLearningLabs.com

**Magnolia Botanicals** is an herbal product company focused on providing unique, safe, and effective herbal products while connecting people with the science of medicinal plants and fungi.

Magnolia Botanicals products generally result from research and development performed in collaboration with Natural Learning Laboratories and associated partners.

www.MagnoliaBotanicals.com

# Don't Forget These Other
# *Curious About Cannabis*® Titles!

## Curious About Cannabis® EDUCATOR WORKBOOK

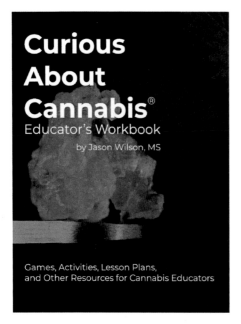

The Curious About Cannabis **Educator Workbook** is designed to accompany the Curious About Cannabis textbook to provide educators with resources and ideas for engaging students and assessing their comprehension of critical concepts related to Cannabis and cannabinoid science. The workbook itself is a great assessment tool for Cannabis science related college classes, training courses, and labs**. Student Workbooks** without answer keys are also available.

### What's Inside
Guide for Navigating Hard or Controversial Topics
Vocabulary Games
Quizzes by Topic
Worksheets, Activities and Lessons
Exam Questions
Answer Keys
Recommended Resources

## Curious About Cannabis® CURIOSITY JOURNAL

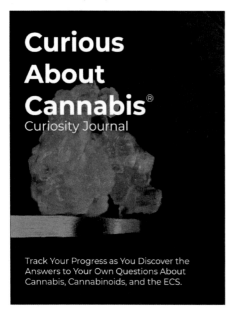

**Are You Curious About Cannabis?**
The Curious About Cannabis Curiosity Journal is a tool designed to accompany *Curious About Cannabis: A Scientific Introduction to a Controversial Plant* - also known as the "Cannabis Science Bible".

The Curious About Cannabis **Curiosity Journal** provides space for documenting your own questions about Cannabis, cannabinoids and the endocannabinoid system. As you learn, you can keep your notes organized with each question. As you come to some core understandings about a topic, jot down your takeaways. And as your progress on your educational journey, log the most valuable resources that you come across so you can share them with others! By the end of your journal, you will be able to create your own personalized Cannabis profile.

## Available at store.cacpodcast.com

Made in the USA
Columbia, SC
04 April 2023

b9686a36-ff1a-475c-9a9e-5e099343ce5dR02